THE MUSIC

OF

THE METHODIST HYMN-BOOK

being the story of each tune with
biographical notices of the composers

BY

JAMES T. LIGHTWOOD

Author of

Hymn-Tunes and Their Story,
Charles Dickens and Music,
Music and Literature,
&c.

LONDON:

THE EPWORTH PRESS

(EDGAR C. BARTON)

25-35 CITY ROAD, E.C.1

First Edition, 1935

Made and Printed in Great Britain by
Rush & Warwick (Bedford) Ltd., Harpur Printing Works, Bedford.

CONTENTS

CONTENTS

FOREWORD

'HAPPY are the chorales of whose origin nothing is known,' wrote Schweitzer in his *J. S. Bach,* and if this is so, then there will be few happy chorales and kindred compositions in the *Methodist Hymn-Book.* But it is not easy to follow out Schweitzer's line of thought, and at the present day most people like to know something of the hymn they are singing, or of the tune they are using for it. The story of the hymns in the new *Methodist Hymn-Book* has been carefully related by my good friend, the Rev. John Telford, B.A., and now I venture to submit the history of each tune, as far as it is known, with some account of the composer.

I have naturally given more space to composers of whom the world knows little. Particulars about Bach, Handel, Haydn and other great composers, are easily available, and there is nothing new to be said about them. My care has been to bring to light some particulars of composers, often humble local musicians, whose names are not to be found in the dictionaries, but whose compositions, simple though they may be, have been valuable contributions to the advancement of church worship.

The work has, of course, involved a good deal of research, and I have to express my indebtedness to those who have so willingly given their help. The exhaustive notes in the *Handbook to the Church Hymnary* have proved invaluable, especially in locating the provenance of certain tunes. The 'Historic Edition' of *Hymns Ancient and Modern* has similarly been of great assistance, and to the scholars responsible for these two works I readily acknowledge my indebtedness. The Rev. Carey Bonner has responded with willing assistance, and Miss

Gilchrist has put her unrivalled knowledge of folk-songs very readily at my disposal. The Rev. E. Ebrard Rees has furnished useful information about Welsh composers, and Mr. F. J. Metcalf, of Washington, D.C., has helped me in solving some of the mysteries of American psalmody. Thanks are due to those composers who have promptly responded to my request for biographical details. The valuable information gleaned from various volumes of *The Musical Times* has been very useful. I also acknowledge with gratitude much valuable advice from the Revs. Dr. Millar Patrick and William Cairns, M.A., both of Edinburgh.

In a book containing such a miscellaneous amount of detail, a certain number of errors are unavoidable. Any correction will be gratefully received and duly acknowledged.

Occasional discrepancies between the dates, &c., here given and those in the music edition of *The Methodist Hymn-Book* are due to fresh facts having come to light since the publication of the latter.

JAMES T. LIGHTWOOD.

14, *West Beach,*
Lytham.
January, 1935.

INTRODUCTION

SOME SOURCES OF METHODIST PSALMODY

THE story of Methodist music may be said to date
from that day in 1742 when John Wesley published his
'Foundery' Tune-Book. He was an earnest editor, but
not a great one, and the very title he adopted suggests
the amateur, for he called his little book 'A Collection
of Tunes, set to Music,' and throughout the book he dis-
regards clefs and pitch and rhythm in a strangely uncon-
cerned manner. But the value of the book consists in
the selection of tunes rather than in the form they are
printed, for his choice of forty-two tunes is representative of nearly every available source—German chorales,
French psalter-tunes, English psalm-tunes, adaptations,
early eighteenth-century tunes, are all included, with one
or two that look suspiciously like folk-songs or
traditional melodies, though they cannot be verified.

But though the 'Foundery' book makes a convenient
starting point, the sources of our present Methodist songs
extend back through the ages till we arrive at the eighth
century, whence we probably derive such plain-song
melodies as VEXILLA REGIS (No. 184), ADORO TE (691),
and VENI CREATOR (779), whilst these themselves bear
traces of Christian song of still earlier times, reaching
back in all probability to the very melodies sung by our
Lord and His apostles.

Not so far-reaching in age, but of highly respectable
antiquity, are certain pre-Reformation melodies, examples
of which will be found in RAVENSHAW (308) and ST.
AUGUSTINE (638). The latter was credited to Peter
Abelard in the *W.T.B.* (1876), but though it may
belong to his period (1079-1142) there is no record of

his association with music. Its present interest consists largely in the fact that J. S. Bach introduced it into one of his works. Another ancient melody of unknown date is CHRIST LAG IN TODESBANDEN (210), which is based on phrases from a twelfth-century Easter melody known as ' Christ ist erstanden '; this was used in early Passion plays, and in later years by Goethe in his *Faust*. Of uncertain date, but probably belonging to the fourteenth century is the Weihnachtslied, or Christmas song, IN DULCI JUBILO (143), a tune that has been arranged and harmonized by some of the master musicians of every age. Its first appearance in print in this country was in *Lyra Davidica* (1708) (referred to under No. 204). The tune CORDE NATUS (83) must also be included amongst pre-Reformation melodies. It is said to be taken from *Piae Cantiones* (1582), which is quite true, but it is of much earlier date, and Dr. Frere places it at the end of the thirteenth century.

The chief impulse to hymn-singing prior to the Reformation was given by John Huss. By a true instinct of spiritual life he was led to introduce the singing of vernacular hymns into public worship, and he insisted upon the people taking their share in the service of song. The Hussite movement was followed by the coming of the Unitas Fratrum, or the Bohemian Brethren, known in Wesley's time as the Moravians. In the early years of this Church the congregations were well provided with hymns, but as there were no tune-books one naturally wonders what melodies were used. The answer is found in an instructive passage from a letter written on October 12, 1574, by two Bishops of the Brethren, Stefan and Kalef, to the Emperor Frederic III :

> Our ancestors, living amongst the Papists, as we also do at this day, adopted as an attraction for persons of that description the practice still continued by us of singing many of our hymns to the old Gregorian tunes. And as others have borrowed our tunes, so

have we borrowed many from others, especially the Germans, some of which we hear are in other languages sung to worldly songs, which not unnaturally gives offence to those who happen to recognize them.

Some such profane melodies, as we may call them, have also been knowingly introduced by recent musicians in hopes that the common people would be the more easily drawn on to learn the truth by means of tunes to which they were but too much accustomed; and since this was done with a good intention we were unwilling to oppose it, more especially as we learned that the Germans had done the same. Still, it would be better if the authors of the hymns likewise composed the tune without borrowing from others, as was the case amongst the ancients, the same persons being both musicians and poets. But these faculties are not possessed by all. We will therefore pay attention to this matter hereafter, God permitting. Yet the measures and tunes are in themselves innocent and free from blame, and become ennobled or degraded only by the language and the sentiments of which they are the channels.

There is no tune in the present *Methodist Hymn-Book* derived direct from early Bohemian sources, but the earliest appearance in print of the medieval RAVENSHAW (308) was in a ' Gesangbuch ' published for the use of the Brethren in 1581 by one of their members, Michael Weisse. ' It pleases me well,' wrote Luther of the book, ' and is the work of a good poet '; but elsewhere he modified his opinion by declaring that Weisse had erroneous views on the Sacrament.

GERMAN CHORALES.

Luther, in his ' Table-talk ' gives ample proof of his devotion to music, and of his faith in it as a regenerative power. ' I have always loved music,' he wrote; ' whoso has skill in this art is of goodly disposition, and fitted for anything.' He was by training and instinct a musician, well fitted in every way to carry out the wish he expressed to his friend Spalatin ' to make German hymns for the people, that the word of God may dwell in their hearts by means of song also.' In order to carry out his purpose he summoned his friends, Conrad Rupff and Johann Walther, to his assistance, and in 1524 the first Lutheran hymn and chorale book appeared, the *Etlich Cristliche Lyeder*, in which we find DETTINGEN (694). A copy of this historic work is preserved in the British Museum. Five years later appeared a *Gesangbuch* edited by Joseph Klug, in which the music and words of EIN' FESTE BURG (494) first appeared, the first and by general agreement the greatest, of German chorales. No copy of this book is now known, but in 1530 Walther presented to Luther a set of MS. part-books, one of which, the tenor part, embodying the tune, still exists. Thus it is the earliest authority for both hymn and tune. A photographic reproduction of this rarity will be found on page lxxi. of the Historical Edition of *Hymns Ancient and Modern*.

The origin of some of the early melodies of the Reformation is obscure, and Schweitzer sums up the matter thus definitely in his *J. S. Bach* :

> Since we rarely know the history of a melody before it became attached to a hymn, the name of which it henceforth bears, it is difficult to decide which melodies were adapted and which composed by the musicians of the Reformation. . . . The number of musicians who wrote melodies for the Church was not large, not because at that time there were no musicians capable of the work, but rather because their services were not called for. . . . It was much more natural to impress existing melodies into the service of the Church, sacred melodies at first, and then, when these did not suffice, secular ones.

Two early examples of adaptations will be found in the melodies now known as the PASSION CHORALE (202) and

INNSBRÜCK (946). Of the latter Spitta says, 'There is no other melody that Bach used so frequently, or more thoroughly exhausted its harmonic possibilities for every variety of purpose.' Thus it forms a landmark in the story of the chorale, as being a secular melody adapted to sacred use. Although attributed to a definite source the melody is regarded by many authorities as a wayside song of itinerant workmen.

Numerous collections of chorales were issued during the seventeenth century, the more important being those edited or containing contributions by Ahle, Clauder, Corner, Crüger, Joseph (*Heilige Seelenlust*), and Vulpius, all of whom are represented in the *Methodist Hymn-Book*. The stream terminated with the publishing of two collections edited by Freylinghausen in 1704 and 1714. The earlier edition is of special importance in our story, for it was in the possession of John Wesley, whose copy is now preserved in Richmond College. He made good use of it when he was preparing his 'Foundery' tune-book, and of those that he adopted from Freylinghausen examples will be found at Nos. 233 and 357.

PSALTER TUNES.

The use of secular melodies forms a connecting link between the Lutheran chorale and the Huguenot (or Genevan) psalm-tune. But the link is soon broken, for whereas the composers of the chorales are most of them well known, it is difficult to assign definitely the composition of any Psalter tune (except two or three) to an individual source; in fact many of them are based upon popular secular tunes of the period.

When Calvin was at Strasburg in 1539 he compiled a volume of metrical psalms with tunes, and thus began the series of Genevan Psalters. Of these, various editions, each with additions, were issued up to 1562. Calvin superintended their production till 1551, when his friend Beza took up the work and continued the supervision of the succeeding issues, being assisted in the music by

Louis Bourgeois, who was undoubtedly a man of considerable musical importance in his day. Only one tune in the *Methodist Hymn-Book* (667) bears his name, and there is no certain proof that it is his own composition. In discussing the tunes of the French or Genevan psalters the word ' composing ' must be taken in a literal sense, and frequently signifies a skilful ' composing ' or putting together of various selected phrases already existing. But whether Bourgeois contributed new tunes or only adapted existing matter is of little importance, and the fact stands out that he was a musician of remarkable skill, who occupies a prominent place in the ranks of tune-book editors.

The Strasburg, Genevan and French Psalters are all represented in the *Methodist Hymn-Book,* and each is noted in its proper place. They form an important link between the German chorale and the more modern English psalm-tune, and it is interesting to note that the two forms overlap. J. S. Bach was well acquainted with the psalter tunes, and two of them (one being the OLD 100TH in triple time) occur in his choral cantatas. Several of the psalter tunes are included in *The Chorale Book for England* (1862), with the suggestion that some of them may be of secular origin.

THE ENGLISH PSALTERS.

But, regardless of the actual composers, the fact remains that we are indebted to the Genevan Psalters for many of our psalm-tunes, for we may now transfer the story to our own country, taking it up in the tunes of the late Tudor period. The practice of psalm-singing began during the reign of Henry VIII, and early in 1549 Thomas Sternhold published his metrical version of some of the psalms, but without any music. In the same year Robert Crowley (afterwards archdeacon of Hereford) brought out a metrical translation by himself of the whole of the psalms, each in common metre, for which he provided one tune only. The work begun by Sternhold was continued after his death by John Hopkins till 1553, when the coming of Queen Mary caused the English reformers to take refuge in Geneva, where their psalters came under the influence of Louis Bourgeois, the result being the issue, in 1556, of a new English psalter bearing the title *One and Fiftie Psalmes of David in English Metre.* This also contained a metrical version of the Ten Commandments, set to a tune which thus made its first appearance. It is now known as COMMANDMENTS, or LES COMMANDEMENS DE DIEU (667). The *One and Fiftie Psalmes* possesses further interest from the fact that it contains the earliest examples of verses which are in what is now known as 'Long Metre.' In the same book also appear for the first time two more new metres, the D.S.M. and the 7.6.7.6. D. A second edition of the *One and Fiftie Psalmes* (of which only one copy is now known to exist) was published in 1558 at Geneva for the use of the English Protestant refugees. A survival from this book is the OLD 44TH (785).

Psalm-singing, which had been in abeyance in England during Mary's reign, came to life again on the accession of Elizabeth, and in 1561 a new publication called *Four Score and Seven Psalmes* introduced into English use some tunes that have become famous by long usage, the OLD 100TH (2), OLD 113TH (584), OLD 134TH or ST. MICHAEL (377). A German chorale, VATER UNSER or OLD 112TH (683), dating from the days of Luther, was also introduced into English worship. In 1562 the complete Psalter of 150 psalms was published, frequently known as ' Day's Psalter,' from the name of the publisher. This contained sixty-five tunes, which were allotted to various psalms, and thus the principle of each psalm having its own, or 'proper' tune, was abandoned after only a brief life. The system, however, remained in use for a long time, nor is it yet finally abandoned. In this 1562 Psalter the melody only of each tune is given, but in the following year a harmonized edition was published, each of the four parts being in a separate book.

During the next few years attempts were made to supplant Day's Psalter, or at any rate to provide new tunes. The most prominent are those by Damon and Este, and tunes from these sources will be found at Nos. 237, 239 (Damon), and 461, 707 (Este). These were succeeded in later years by Ravenscroft's *Psalter* (1621), which presented some new features. The principle of giving names to tunes had been introduced by Este, who named three of his tunes—CHESHIRE (461) being one of them—but Ravenscroft extended the system to each of his tunes, thus establishing a practice which has since been nearly always observed. Ravenscroft also indicated the sources of his tunes, classifying them according to the districts and countries from which, in his opinion, they came. Four tunes (45, 82, 367, 721) in this collection come from Ravenscroft's work, and his classification of Scottish tunes may now lead us to a consideration of the tunes in the *Methodist Hymn-Book* derived from the Scottish psalters.

THE SCOTTISH PSALTERS.

Of these the most important, though not the earliest, is the psalter issued in 1615 by Andro Hart. When the Scottish exiles returned from Geneva they brought with them the tunes and psalms they had used in their exile, and these were published in 1564 in a volume which contained many of the tunes from the Genevan and French psalters, with a few of English origin. Other psalters were issued from time to time till the appearance of the edition published by Andro Hart marked an epoch in Scottish psalmody similar to that noted in Ravenscroft. It introduced a selection of four-line tunes which were designated 'Common,' and these are represented by seven tunes in the present book.

A few other tunes acquired from Scottish sources, like MARTYRDOM (201), SELMA (54), and STRACATHRO (102), belong to a much later period.

TALLIS, GIBBONS AND LAWES.

Returning to English productions we find that a few tunes in the *Methodist Hymn-Book* belong to the early psalter period. About 1560 Matthew Parker, Archbishop of Canterbury, wrote a metrical version of the psalms, and Thomas Tallis composed eight tunes for ' convoying with them,' and from these, two (304 and 943) have survived. From the seventeenth century are derived a few original tunes some of which have only recently been revived. ANGELS' SONG has long been known. It is taken from a set of tunes written by Orlando Gibbons to accompany Wither's *Hymns and Songs of the Church* (1641). Seven more from the same source have now been included, worthy examples of the great Stuart composer. Two years later George Sandys published his metrical version, and for the music he secured the aid of Henry Lawes, who wrote several tunes, each of them, like those of Gibbons, in two parts only. The tunes of Lawes and Gibbons represent the early Stuart period in the *Methodist Hymn-Book*. The remainder of the seventeenth century was unproductive as regards psalm-tunes, for unfortunately Henry Purcell did not contribute any that can be identified as his,[1] and it was not until the publication of Tate and Brady's ' New Version ' that any further important additions were made to our psalmody. Of the various editions of the New Version, the most important, musically, is that published in 1708. In this appeared Dr. Croft's three famous tunes HANOVER (8), ST. ANNE (878), and ST. MATTHEW (824). In the following year CROFT's 136TH (26) and BINCHESTER (419) appeared in Playford's *Divine Companion,* in company with Clark's ST. MAGNUS (72).

THE EIGHTEENTH CENTURY.

Thus we find that when John Wesley set to work on his ' Foundery ' tune-book he had plenty of material to

[1] The tune WESTMINSTER in *Sacred Harmony* (1780) is an adaptation of the song 'Fairest Isle' from Purcell's *King Arthur.*

select from, including German chorales from Freylinghausen, psalm-tunes from the Old and New Versions,
adaptations of popular tunes, and a few that he had
gleaned from no one knows where. But one capture he
made deserves to be noted, and that was THE RESURREC-
TION or EASTER MORN (204). Dating from 1708 the
tune introduced a new style in psalmody which was
destined to have far-reaching effects. The old syllabic
style—one syllable, one note—gave way to a freer form
which was readily taken up by eighteenth-century composers, and who were further assisted by the introduction
through Watts, C. Wesley and others, of inspiring hymns
in the place of the old, somewhat artificial, metrical
versions. Examples of the change that went on will be
found in Lampe's tunes (411, 496), in those from *Sacred
Melody,* like CHIMES (722), and a few from the 'Lock'
Collection, like MOSCOW (880).

The rapid output of hymns by Charles Wesley and
others soon rendered the 'Foundery' book obsolete, and
towards the close of George II's reign a massive oblong
volume appeared called *Harmonia Sacra,* produced under
the auspices of Thomas Butts, a friend and follower of
the Wesleys. There is no evidence that the book was
used by Methodists, nor did it meet with John Wesley's
approval, for it contained a large number of tunes and
set pieces that were of no use in a Methodist assembly.
'Tho' it is excellent in its kind,' wrote Wesley, 'it is not
the thing I want,' and he proceeded to publish his second
tune-book in 1761 with the title *Sacred Melody,* which,
he said, 'contains all the tunes which are in common use
amongst us.' This last statement is important, for it at
once establishes the fact that the real 'old Methodist
tunes' are those contained in the various editions of
Sacred Melody and its successor *Sacred Harmony,* and
not the fugal and repeating tunes which now pass under
that epithet.

It is only fitting that a volume devoted to the story
of Methodist music should reproduce John Wesley's

directions for using his tune-book. Here they are, and it is certain that each one of the seven sections would provide a text for a very suitable and appropriate sermon on congregational singing :

I. Learn these *Tunes* before you learn any others; afterwards learn as many as you please.

II. Sing them exactly as they are printed here, without altering or mending them at all; and if you have learned to sing them otherwise, unlearn it as soon as you can.

III. Sing *All*. See that you join with the congregation as frequently as you can. Let not a slight degree of weakness or weariness hinder you. If it is a cross to you, take it up, and you will find it a blessing.

IV. Sing *lustily* and with a good courage. Beware of singing as if you were half dead, or half asleep; but lift up your voice with strength. Be no more afraid of your voice now, nor more ashamed of its being heard, than when you sung the songs of *Satan*.

V. Sing *modestly*. Do not bawl, so as to be heard above or distinct from the rest of the congregation, that you may not destroy the harmony; but strive to unite your voices together, so as to make one clear melodious sound.

VI. Sing *in Time*. Whatever time is sung, be sure to keep with it. Do not run before nor stay behind it; but attend close to the leading voices, and move therewith as exactly as you can; and take care not to sing *too slow*. This drawling way naturally steals on all who are lazy; and it is high time to drive it out from among us, and sing all our tunes just as quick as we did at first.

VII. Above all sing *spiritually*. Have an eye to God in every word you sing. Aim at pleasing *Him* more than yourself, or any other creature. In order to do this attend strictly to the sense of what you sing, and see that your *Heart* is not carried away with the sound, but offered to God continually; so shall your singing be such as the *Lord* will approve of here, and reward you when He cometh in the clouds of heaven.

The series of Wesley's tune-books for Methodist use was continued in 1780 by the publication of *Sacred Harmony,* a smaller pocket edition being issued nine years later. An examination of all these books shows that Wesley cast his net wide in order to secure suitable tunes, and the system he worked on is exactly the same as the system adopted by the committees of recent Methodist tune-books, the only exception, perhaps, being the introduction of plain-song melodies, of which Wesley was entirely ignorant.

THE NINETEENTH CENTURY AND AFTER.

The chief contributors to Methodist psalmody during the first sixty or seventy years of the last century were local choirmasters, organists, and amateur musicians, who are well represented in the present book. It is sufficient to mention names like G. Davis, W. Arnold, Boggett, Burder, Campbell, T. Clark, W. Matthews, Newton, T. Phillips and S. Stanley. Their tunes are loved by those who have been brought up on them, and their strains also find ready acceptance amongst the younger generation. During this period the Wesleyan Methodist Church had no authorized tune-book, and the deficiency was made up by some famous collections of tunes such as Booth's *Wesleyan Psalmist,* Sugden and West's *Westminster Tune-Book,* Dobson's *Tunes New and Old,* and Hiles' Wesley Tune-Book. Perhaps the most highly esteemed of all was the *Companion* to the Wesleyan hymn-book, which appeared in the middle of last century, and long remained a favourite both in church and home. It was carefully explored for the purposes of the new *Methodist Hymn-Book,* and some of the tunes in it are contained in the present work. All these books were of sterling merit, and provided a wonderful variety of melodies for church worship.

But good as these collections were in themselves, their miscellaneous use was not conducive to unity of purpose in church worship. The matter was discussed by the Methodist Conference during the early seventies, with the result that 1876 saw the publication of a tune-book issued under authority. This introduced the 'fixed tune' system into Methodist worship, but the principle has not always been strictly adhered to. After doing good service for twenty-eight years this tune-book was supplanted by a fresh collection, referred to in these pages as the *Methodist Hymn-Book* (M.H.B.), 1904. This work is too well known to need more than a passing reference. It did good service till the coming of Methodist Union prepared the way for the publication of an entirely new hymn and tune-book which should serve the needs of the united Church. The music edition of the new work, under the name of the *Methodist Hymn-Book with Tunes,* was published during the last days of 1933.

PRIMITIVE METHODIST PSALMODY.

It is very difficult to identify the music used by the first members of the Primitive Methodists. It is quite likely that many of the hymns were sung to popular tunes of the day, thereby carrying on a principle which, as we have seen, had long prevailed, even from pre-Reformation times. William Chappell, in his *Popular Music,* gives the Scottish tune BONNIE LADDIE as an example, and also prints the tune as sung to the once popular Primitive Methodist hymn 'Stop, poor sinner, stop and think.' But though their early tunes cannot be definitely traced, the Primitive Methodists have been a singing people ever since the first gathering on Mow Cop on Sunday, May 31, 1807, when the 'diversity of pious exercises' included singing, and it is more than probable that many of the tunes then used were derived from the Methodist meeting-houses. The *Primitive*

Methodist Hymnal includes several tunes of apparently untraced origin, which may date back to the early days of the community. A hint to this effect is given in the Preface. ' Some tunes are inserted which a severe taste would reject, but these are wedded to the hymns and hallowed by old associations '—surely a sufficiently good reason for retaining them. In 1910 the Primitive Methodist Conference ordained that a ' Supplement' should be issued, with appropriate tunes. The result was a further addition to the musical resources of the Church, and it has done much to advance the cause of congregational singing. The names of Sir Henry Coward, Dr. G. Booth, of Chesterfield, and W. Heslop, of Darlington, deserve permanent record for their work in connexion with these books.

UNITED METHODIST PSALMODY.

The tunes in use amongst the early adherents of the United Methodist Church were probably derived from the same source as those of the Primitive Methodists. A tune-book edited by the Rev. John Rippon was in use for some years, and this was succeeded by the *Union Tune-Book*. But neither of these was the special possession of the Methodist New Connexion, as it was known for many years, and it was not until 1863 that the Conference ordered the preparation of a collection of tunes for use in their Church. This was published in 1864 as *The Methodist Tune-Book*, also defined as ' a companion to Hymns for Divine Worship, compiled for the Methodist New Connexion, Founded A.D. 1797.' This collection was edited by James Mills, of Ashton-under-Lyne.

Two more collections of tunes were subsequently issued for use by the United Methodist Free Church, and these were embodied in a permanent form in a volume issued in 1889. The tunes were of a somewhat sterner kind than those in the *Wesleyan Tune-Book* (1876), or the *Primitive Methodist Hymnal* (1887), and there was a total absence of tunes of the ' Old Methodist ' type. As the Preface stated, the tunes had been chosen 'on account of their great worth,' but the result was that the music proved to be somewhat in advance of its period.

WELSH PSALMODY.

The subject of early Welsh psalmody is a rather difficult one, and there is considerable doubt as to the sources of some of the melodies. The term 'Alaw Gymreig' (old melody) has been a tolerably safe ascription in past years, but it is no longer satisfactory. Tunes and words were not printed together until 1868, when *Lyfr Tonau ac Emynau,* edited by E. Stephen and J. D. Jones, was published. This collection, together with those compiled by Ieuan Gwyllt (515) and Ambrose Lloyd, provides the originals of many of the tunes by Welsh composers that are included in the present *Methodist Hymn-Book.*

FOLK SONGS.

A notable feature in the present collection is the introduction of what are variously known as Folk Songs, Traditional Airs, or Old Melodies. The whole subject of these tunes is so involved as regards their origin and history, and so many different opinions are prevalent, that it would be inadvisable to attempt to unravel the mystery that surrounds so many of them.

THE MUSIC
OF THE METHODIST HYMN-BOOK

1 (i)—Richmond.

RICHMOND, by Rev. Thomas Haweis, is from *Carmina Christo,* a collection of 250 hymns and tunes he compiled in 1792. This was the original form :

O Thou from Whom all good - ness flows, I lift my heart to Thee; In all my sor - rows, con - flicts, woes, Dear Lord, re - mem-ber me, re- mem-ber me, remember me, Dear Lord, re - mem - ber me.

It was reduced to its present form by Samuel Webbe, Junr. It has been used with great effect by H. A. Chambers in his anthem 'Praise to the holiest in the height.' The tune is named after the composer's friend, Legh Richmond, rector of Turvey (Bedfordshire), and author of the once famous story *The Dairyman's Daughter.*

The fact has only recently been brought to light that when the *Wesleyan Tune-Book* of 1876 was being prepared, the committee chose RICHMOND as the first tune for 'O for a thousand tongues to sing.' But when Gauntlett (see No. 7) succeeded George Cooper as musical editor he did not approve of the choice. In a letter written February 9, 1876, he said, 'Of course this tune will not go fast—and there are ten verses to sing—sing it slow, the hymn is destroyed; sing it fast, and the tune is destroyed.' So the committee gave way, and WINCHESTER OLD was substituted. Their original choice has at last been confirmed.

The Rev. Thomas Haweis was born at Redruth, Cornwall, January 1, 1734. From Truro Grammar School he passed to Oxford, but left without taking a degree. He then became curate at St. Mary Magdalene, Oxford, but his Methodist sympathies led to his dismissal, and he became assistant to Martin Madan at the Lock Hospital. In 1764 he became rector of Aldwinkle, Northamptonshire, where he remained till his death in 1820, in spite of various attempts to remove him owing to a technical offence. He was also chaplain to Selina, Countess of Huntingdon, and became her trustee and executor. His *Carmina Christo,* or 'Hymns to the Saviour,' passed through nine editions. He died at Bath in 1820. The Rev. H. R. Haweis, author of *Music and Morals* and other musical works, was his grandson.

1 (ii), 92—Lydia.

LYDIA has frequently been credited to Thomas Phillips, composer of NEW SABBATH (802). It is also ascribed to W. Cole by William Halford in his *Voce di Melodia,* and he is as a rule correct in his composers. A third composer who has been credited with it is Dr. Samuel Arnold, but it is certainly not in his style. LYDIA has been immortalized by Thomas Hardy in *The Return of the Native* :

One Sunday I can well mind—a bass viol day—
and Yedbright had brought his own. 'Twas the hundred and thirty-third to LYDIA, and when they'd come
to

> Ran down his beard and o'er his robes
> Its costly moisture shed,

neighbour Yedbright, who had just warmed to his
work, drove his bow into them strings that glorious
grand that he e'en a'most sawed the bass viol into two
pieces. Every winder in the church rattled as if 'twere
a thunderstorm. Not a soul in Kingsboro could hold a
candle to Yedbright.

It is also mentioned by George Eliot in *Scenes from
Clerical Life* :

It was at Shepperton church that 'they began to
sing the wedding psalm for a newly married couple, as
pretty a psalm and as pretty a tune as any in the
prayer book.' But the Rev. Amos Barton objected
to both words and music, so he called out silence, and
gave out a hymn himself to some 'meeting-house'
tune, which, as Mr. Barton afterwards explained, was
known as LYDIA.

2, 3—Old 100th.

The term 'old' is applied as a rule to those psalm-
tunes which were used in connexion with the Old, or
Sternhold and Hopkins metrical version of the Psalms.
There are in the present book :

OLD 44th—785.	OLD 113th—584.
OLD 100th—2, 3.	OLD 120th—707.
OLD 104th—45.	OLD 124th—912.
OLD 112th (VATER UNSER)	OLD 134th (ST. MICHAEL)
—683, 723.	—377, p. 594.

The OLD 23rd (361) is spurious, and has no claim to
the title. The history of these melodies is somewhat

involved, and the details are of little interest to the general reader, unless he has access to the various sources referred to. The most exact presentation of their history will be found in Dr. Frere's Introduction to the 'Historical Edition' of *Hymns Ancient and Modern*. The source of each of those used in the *Methodist Hymn-Book* is given briefly under their respective numbers.

The story of the OLD HUNDREDTH has been fully told in *The Choir* (1925-1926). Briefly, it is now generally agreed that the tune consists of phrases which were common property in the sixteenth century, and which were skilfully 'composed,' or in other words, put together by Louis Bourgeois, who is definitely known to have been what is now called the Musical Editor of the Genevan Psalter of 1551. An unfortunate incident happened whilst he was engaged on this work, as the Council at Geneva convicted him of altering the melody of certain psalm-tunes without leave, and sent him to prison. Modern editors, though equally guilty, have escaped that fate. W. H. Havergal, in his history of the tune, advanced the theory that some of the phrases of the OLD HUNDREDTH are founded on Gregorian melodies, and that there are grounds for this theory may be seen from this quotation from an *Evening Service* edited by Vincent Novello.

Su - a - vis Do-mi - ne Chris-to ju - ben - te vin - cla Mar - ti - ne ce - le - bri plau - di - te.

The statement given at the head of No. 2 in the Tune-Book that it is the 'original version' is only correct as regards this country, since it is the version found in Day's *Psalter* of 1563. The true original form is slightly different in the last line, as will be seen from the following, taken from the Genevan *Psalter* of 1551 :

4, 28—St. Francis.

ST. FRANCIS (LASST UNS ERFREUEN) receives its second name from the initial words of an Easter hymn beginning 'Lasst uns erfreuen herzlich sehr.' The name is misleading, as the fine translation by Dr. Draper of the hymn by St. Francis has nothing to do with Easter. The first name ST. FRANCIS has, therefore, been used as more in keeping with the hymn, and also because most people will find it easier to pronounce. The tune is from *Geistliche Kirchengesäng*, published at Cologne in 1623. The composer is unknown, but he was probably well acquainted with the Genevan psalm-tune known to us as OLD 113th (See No. 584).

5 (i)—Dallas.

DALLAS is the composition of the Rev. F. L. Wiseman, B.A. It first appeared in the *New People's Hymnary* (1922).

The Rev. F. Luke Wiseman is well known for his devotion to music, and his wide experience has been of great service to his Church. As a member of the 1904 *Methodist Hymn-Book* Committee, and as Chairman of the Committee that prepared the present Tune-Book, he has rendered invaluable service. His father, the Rev. Luke H. Wiseman, who died in 1875, was a distinguished preacher (he was President of the Methodist Conference) and also an accomplished amateur musician. His hymn-tunes figure in several collections of the mid-Victorian period, and he was a performer of considerable skill on the violoncello. His love of music was inherited by his daughter (see No. 321) and also by his two sons. John, the elder, was at one time organist of Liverpool Road Wesleyan Methodist Chapel, London, and to him belongs the credit of having been the first to introduce Bach's music to a Methodist congregation; this was in 1872.

5 (ii)—Luckington.

LUCKINGTON was composed for the hymn and first appeared in the *Oxford Hymn-Book* (1908), of which Dr. Harwood was editor.

Dr. Basil Harwood was born at Woodhouse, Glos., in 1859. After leaving Charterhouse he went to Trinity College, Oxford, and there pursued the study of music under J. L. Roeckel, G. Riseley, and Dr. Corfe. After a term at Leipzig under Reinecke and Jadassohn he was appointed organist at St. Barnabas, Pimlico. Appointments at Ely Cathedral and Christ Church, Oxford, followed. He was the first conductor of the Oxford Bach Choir. He retired from the musical profession in 1907. His compositions include choral and organ works, amongst the latter being the *Dithyramb* and *Paean,* also a concerto for organ and orchestra, which was heard at the Gloucester Festival, 1910. His church services are widely used.

6—Saul.

SAUL is adapted from the air—

> Shall I in Mamre's fertile plain
> The remnant of my days remain—

in Handel's oratorio *Joshua* (1747). The tune has a second obvious name FERTILE PLAINS, and has also been

known as MAMRE, but why it has been christened SAUL
is a mystery, as the tune does not appear in the oratorio
of that name.

George Frederick Handel was born at Halle in 1685.
His father wished him to be a lawyer, but the boy preferred music to the law, and ultimately prevailed. He
was placed under Zachau, organist of Halle cathedral,
who taught him the organ, harpsichord, and composition,
and to these young Handel added the violin and oboe,
and studied music so seriously that at the age of ten he
composed six sonatas for two oboes and bass. ' The
oboe was my favourite instrument,' he said in later years.
After visiting Hamburg, Handel went to Lübeck, intent
on becoming city organist, but as one condition of that
appointment was taking the retiring organist's daughter
in marriage, Handel returned home. After a three years'
visit to Italy he came to England in 1710, and wrote his
first opera, *Rinaldo*, working at such a rate that his
librettist complained that he had not time to compose
his verses. After a brief visit to Germany, he returned
in 1711 and finally settled in England. In 1717 he
became musical director to the Duke of Chandos at his
palace at Canons, where the composer wrote his six
Chandos anthems, and also his first oratorio *Esther*. A
long succession of operatic works followed, but in their
production Handel had endless trouble with his singers
and operatic managers, and finally with the public, with
the Prince of Wales at their head. After a visit to the
baths at Aix-la-Chapelle, Handel returned to England
with renewed vigour, and abandoning the opera, set to
work to write a series of oratorios which brought him
both prosperity and renown. In 1726 he became a
naturalized Englishman by special Act of Parliament.
His visit to Ireland in 1742 to conduct the first performance of *Messiah* was a memorable occasion. It still
remains the most popular of his works, though Handel's
own choice appears to have been *Theodora*. As he was
completing his last oratorio *Jephthah*, blindness came on,

from which he never recovered. He died in April, 1759.

7—Houghton.

HOUGHTON was written for the *Congregational Psalmist* (1861) of which Gauntlett was the editor. He was a prolific composer of hymn-tunes, most of which reach a high standard. Born at Wellington in 1805, he spent his early years at Olney, where his father was vicar. His love of music led to a desire to take it up as a profession, but his father decreed otherwise, and young Gauntlett entered a solicitor's office. From 1827 to 1837 he gained distinction in the legal world, but at last music got the upper hand and the law knew him no longer. He held several important posts as organist, notably at St. Olave's, Southwark (no longer existing), where he planned an organ on highly original lines. He did excellent work as a reformer of psalmody, and was a great advocate of congregational singing. In 1852 he produced the *Church Hymn and Tune-Book* which marked a new era in psalmody, the 'fixed tune' principal being adopted, which was subsequently firmly established in *Hymns Ancient and Modern*.

In 1846 Gauntlett was at the organ during the first performance of *Elijah* at Birmingham under Mendelssohn. He wrote to his wife on August 20, 'I am just returned from rehearsal where, as I almost expected, I had to play the oratorio from the long manuscript German copy, there being no organ part. I got through as cautiously as I could, and believe made as few mistakes as the circumstances allowed. I daresay the folks thought the organ quiet—be it so—better this than row and observation. I saw Mendelssohn, who inquired kindly after you, and desired his respects.'

Mendelssohn, writing from Berlin in 1844 said, 'I have had the good fortune of becoming thoroughly acquainted with Dr. Gauntlett's musical talents, and I know but very few of his countrymen or of mine whose masterly performance on the organ, whose skill in writing, and whose perfect knowledge of musical literature of ancient and modern times may be compared to his.'

In 1852 Dr. Allon appointed Gauntlett as his organist at Union Chapel, Islington, and he raised the church psalmody to a high degree of excellence.   Allon and Gauntlett joined forces in producing *The Congregational Tune-Book,* a notable production on which the musician firmly impressed his personality, especially in the Preface.   In 1875 Gauntlett was invited to succeed George Cooper in the editorship of the *Wesleyan Tune-Book,* but his death early in the following year prevented his finishing the work.

8—Hanover.

HANOVER.   The ' New Version ' of the Psalms, metrically rendered by Nahum Tate and Nicholas Brady, was published at the end of 1696.   They followed up this with a *Supplement,* and in the sixth edition appeared amongst others the tunes ST. ANNE'S, HANOVER and ST. MATTHEW, which still retain their place in our church song.   HANOVER originally received the cumbrous title ' A New Tune to the 149th Psalm of the New Version, and the 104th of the Old.'   John Wesley, in his ' Foundery ' Tune-Book (1742) reduced this to BROMSWICK, doubtless out of compliment to the reigning house of Brunswick. Wesley also christened it Tally's, possibly under the impression that it was by Tallis.   The present name was given the tune after George III ascended the throne.   No composers' names are given in the *Supplement,* but there is every reason to suppose that Dr. Croft deserves the credit.   Sir George Macfarren introduced HANOVER in his oratorio *St. John the Baptist,* working it into a fugue with the first line of the tune as the subject, using it afterwards in inverse movement.

William Croft was born (probably in 1678) at the

Warwickshire village of Nether Eatington. The church where he was baptized is now in ruins, but it contains a monument to the musician's memory, erected by a descendant in 1835. After serving as a chorister in the Chapel Royal, St. James's, under Dr. Blow, he was appointed organist at St. Anne's, Soho, where he remained till 1707, when he was appointed organist at the Chapel Royal, St. James's, a position which he had shared since 1704 with Jeremiah Clark (see No. 72). Croft held other lucrative appointments, including the organistship at Westminster Abbey, which he held from 1708 till his death in 1727. It certainly would seem that Croft was at the head of his profession, a position which he held with due dignity. Dr. Burney says of him :

He seems to have gone through life in one even tenor of professional activity and propriety of conduct. We hear of no illiterate traits of envy, malevolence, or insolence. He neither headed nor abetted fiddling factions; but insensibly preserving the dignity of his station, without oppressing or mortifying his inferiors by reminding them of it. The universal respect he obtained from his talents and eminence in the profession seems to have blended with personal affection.

An excellent testimonial, and one well worthy of the composer of HANOVER, ST. ANNE'S and ST. MATTHEW. But his most famous work is *Musica Sacra,* a collection of thirty anthems, containing, amongst other notable compositions, the famous Burial Services by Croft and Purcell. Croft wrote many anthems for special occasions, such as the victories of Blenheim and Oudenarde. He evidently led a very industrious life, and hence had no time for the ' fiddling factions ' that Burney referred to. There is some mystery about his appointment to St. Anne's Church, as the ' Croft ' mentioned in the church records is invariably referred to as ' Philip,' and the name is occasionally spelt ' Crofts.'

9 (i)—Woodhouse Grove.

WOODHOUSE GROVE is by Mr. George Jefferson, who succeeded Mr. Norman Strafford as master of the music at Woodhouse Grove School, Apperley Bridge. His musical experiences have been extensive—organist, conductor, official accompanist at the Sheffield Studios of the B.B.C., and in all these departments he has distinguished himself. As organist at Cross Gates Methodist Church, Leeds, he will be remembered for the work he did as organist and choirmaster. Many important choral works were given under his direction, and the hearty congregational singing was a notable testimony to his able guidance.

9 (ii)—Sanctissimus.

SANCTISSIMUS, by W. H. Cooke, appeared in the enlarged 1881 edition of *The Bristol Tune-Book*. It was subsequently purchased by the Rev. Garrett Horder for the music edition of his *Worship Song*. The composer lived the greater part of his life in Bath, and for twenty-four years he was organist at Argyle Congregational Chapel (1856-1880). After leaving here, he occasionally acted as honorary choirmaster at Bath Abbey. He died in 1912. He was a familiar figure in the streets of Bath, and was easily identified by a large plaid shawl he invariably wore.

10—Nun Danket.

NUN DANKET first appeared in *Praxis Pietatis Melica*, a collection of melodies edited by Johann Crüger, who is usually credited with the composition of this chorale. The earliest existing copy dates from 1647, consequently the tune was not composed to celebrate the peace of Westphalia, as has been stated, which took place in November, 1648. The romantic story told about both words and tune in *Hymn Tunes and their Story* is incorrect, as the dates do not agree, and Rinkart, who wrote the hymn, was no composer. Both hymn and tune have been used to celebrate many famous events in history, and Mendelssohn has appropriately introduced it in his *Lobgesang*.

Johann Crüger was born at the Prussian village of Grossbriesen in 1598. He studied at Breslau, whence he went to take a course of theology at Wittemberg, 1620. Two years later he was appointed Precentor of St. Nicholas Church, Berlin, where he was in office forty years till his death in 1662.

11—Datchet.

DATCHET was written by G. J. Elvey for Maurice's *Choral Harmony* (1854).

Born at Canterbury in 1816, Sir George Job Elvey was originally a choir boy at Canterbury Cathedral under Highmore Skeats. When his voice broke he placed himself as an organ student under his elder brother, Dr. Stephen Elvey, who for many years, until his death in 1860, was choragus at Oxford University. In 1834, while he was lay clerk at Christ Church, Oxford, he carried off the Gresham Medal for an anthem; and in the following year, on the death of the younger Highmore Skeats, he was appointed by William IV organist at St. George's Chapel, Windsor, which post he retained until 1882, when he retired into private life. It was at Windsor that Elvey's best work was done, both as composer and teacher; and among the numerous musicians who have studied under his guidance may be mentioned Sir Hubert Parry. The oratorio *Resurrection and Ascension*, which was his 'exercise' for the degree of Mus.B., was performed at the Sacred Harmonic Concerts and elsewhere, but otherwise Elvey's fame as a composer rests almost exclusively upon his part-songs and his music for the church. He wrote two full services in F and B flat, a Communion and two evening services, besides anthems, part-songs and several hymn-tunes. His anthems, with their attractive vocal phrases and ease of appreciation have deserved and received the gift of long life.

12 (i)—Praise, My Soul.

PRAISE, MY SOUL, by John Goss, was written for the third edition of R. Brown-Borthwick's *Supplemental Hymn and Tune-Book* (1869), where it is set to this hymn.

Sir John Goss was born in 1800 at Fareham, Hants, where his father was organist of the parish church. In his eleventh year the boy went to London to become one of the children of the Chapel Royal. Here he learnt singing, but instrumental music he had to teach himself. On leaving the Chapel Royal he became a pupil of Thomas Attwood, organist of St. Paul's Cathedral. In 1821 he obtained his first organ appointment, at St. Andrew's Church, Lambeth, and from there he went to St. Luke's, Chelsea, where he stayed thirteen years (1824-1837). During this period he wrote some orchestral music, and also edited a collection of hymn-tunes called *Parochial Psalmody*. He was also appointed a professor of harmony at the R.A.M., holding the position for forty-seven years. In 1838 he succeeded Attwood as organist of St. Paul's Cathedral. Here he was frequently brought into contact with the Rev. Sydney Smith, Canon of St. Paul's, whose humorous remarks must greatly have delighted the new organist. The Canon had a great dislike for music in the minor key and one day he said to the organist : ' Mr. Goss, no more minor music, if you please, while I am in residence.'

Goss had a curious organ to play on, twenty-eight stops on the three manuals, and only one pedal stop of two octaves. That he made the best of his instrument those who heard him can readily testify. He did not compose any anthems till he had passed his fortieth birthday, but from that time there came a succession of works which

put him in the front rank of English Church composers.
In 1872 he wrote his *Te Deum in D* and an anthem in
celebration of the recovery of Edward, Prince of Wales.
Shortly afterwards he resigned his position, having
received the honour of knighthood from Queen Victoria,
and also her thanks for his music. In 1880 his long and
active life came to a close. 'As a man, Goss commanded
universal respect. The chief features of his character
were humility, genuine religious feeling, and a strong
love of home' (Sir John Stainer). Of all his anthems
the one that most clearly reveals the innate religious spirit
of the composer is 'O Saviour of the World.'

12 (ii)—Regent Square.

REGENT SQUARE was written for *Psalms and Hymns
for Divine Worship* (1867). The composer, Henry
Thomas Smart, was born in 1813. He soon developed a
liking for music, but, like most boys, found the daily
practising not at all to his liking. A taste for mechanics
took the first place in his affections, and the knowledge he
gained in this direction in early life proved invaluable to
him in after years. A favourite resort of his was St.
Martin's Lane, where were situated the organ works of
Messrs. Robson & Flight, and here he gained much useful
practical knowledge of organ building. As he grew
older he availed himself more readily of the opportunities
afforded him of gaining musical experience, and his
uncle's influence enabled him to obtain a seat in the
orchestra at Covent Garden, where his attention was
divided between the musical performances of his neighbours and the mechanical devices on the stage.

After a period of school life at Highgate, he was
articled to a solicitor, a position by no means of his own
choosing. His father had died in 1823, and his mother's
relations, disregarding the boy's tastes, chose what they
considered a genteel occupation for him. However,
Smart was not destined to become a shining light in the

legal world. After four years' drudgery an opportunity occurred for him to escape from the lawyer's desk. His master suddenly disappeared, having transferred the youth's articles to another solicitor. Smart had learnt enough law to discover a flaw in the transfer, as it had not been properly witnessed. He took the matter into his own hands. ' I took up law to please my relations,' he said to his mother, ' and now I'll leave it to please myself.'

His skill in mechanics stood him in good stead on more than one occasion. Having become enamoured of Bach's *Forty-Eight,* he soon made the acquaintance of the organ fugues, and he promptly solved the difficulty of performance by making a set of organ pedals, which he attached to the drawing-room pianoforte. In company with his mother he paid several visits to Yarmouth, and on one occasion he asked for, and obtained access to, the organ in St. Nicholas Church. There were, of course, no composition pedals, and Smart offered to supply the deficiency. Having obtained the needful permission he set to work, and when he had completed the job he gave a recital, producing effects from the organ such as had never been heard before. Several years later the organ was greatly altered and enlarged by Messrs. Hill, and in 1870 the new instrument was opened by Smart.

His first permanent appointment was at Blackburn parish church, where he remained three years. It was here that he wrote his Reformation cantata containing the fine Handelian chorus ' Salvation to our God,' and also— at the request of the Methodists—the tune LANCASHIRE (see No. 245) for one of their missionary meetings, set to Heber's ' From Greenland's icy mountains.'

In 1838 Smart returned to London to become organist at St. Philip's Church, Regent Street. Six years later he competed for, and won, a similar position at St. Luke's, Old Street, the judges being Goss, Topliff (a blind organist), and Turle. It is said that when the other competitors heard that Smart was one of the number, the majority of them folded up their music and stole

silently away. He remained at St. Luke's for twenty
years, when he was offered and accepted the position of
organist at St. Pancras Church, Euston Road, which he
held till his death in 1879.

For many years he suffered from defective eyesight,
and the malady gradually became worse, till in 1865 he
became totally blind. Henceforth, all his compositions,
including most of his organ music and his oratorio *Jacob*
were transcribed to paper by means of an amanuensis,
the work being performed by his daughter, who devoted
herself heart and soul to the work. Nor did he allow his
affliction to interfere with his other duties. He retained
his post at St. Pancras, and carried out all his engagements in London and the country with unfailing perseverance and regularity. Within a month of his death
he received the news that a Civil List pension of £100 per
annum had been granted to him, but neither he nor any
member of his family ever received a penny of it.

In addition to contributing a large number of tunes to
various hymnals, Smart was invited to edit two tune-
books, one for the United Presbyterian Church of
Scotland (*The Presbyterian Hymnal*), and the other the
Choral Book which he prepared for the use of the congregation at St. Luke's. The latter is perhaps the more
important work from a musical point of view, for though
it contains only fifty old church melodies, the harmonies
which Smart has supplied are most excellent models for
less experienced editors to work from. In this work
Smart has done for the English hymn-tune what Bach
did for the German choral, and let it be added that he
has done it equally well, but with greater fidelity to the
originals. The work concludes with examples of the
varied yet interesting ways in which a hymn-tune may be
' given out.'

Though his writings for the church and for the organ
are not numerous, the same cannot be said for his secular
vocal works, which number upwards of three hundred and
fifty. He wrote one oratorio, *Jacob,* produced at the

Glasgow Musical Festival of 1873, and three cantatas, *The Bride of Dunkerron,* for the Birmingham Festival of 1864, *King René's Daughter,* and *The Fishermaidens,* the last named being for female voices.

13—Laus Deo.

LAUS DEO (or REDHEAD No. 46 or DRESDEN) was adapted by Redhead from some unknown source, possibly German. Redhead did not give names to his tunes, but called them by his own name followed by a number. The following tunes by him are in the present book :

REDHEAD No. 4—529, 675.
REDHEAD No. 47—358, 978.
REDHEAD No. 66—160, 563.
REDHEAD No. 76—498.
For ST. VICTOR see No. 567.

LAUS DEO is from the composer's *Church Hymn-Tunes* (1835).

Richard Redhead was born at Harrow in 1820 and received his musical education as a chorister at Magdalen College, Oxford, under Walter Vicary, who was also the University organist. Here Redhead came under the influence of the Rev. Frederick Oakeley (translator of ADESTE FIDELES, No. 118), who in 1839 invited him to be organist at Margaret Street Chapel, W., on the site of which All Saints' Church now stands. This Church was prominent in the Oxford Movement, and thus Redhead had ample opportunity for displaying his interest in Gregorian music. This he showed in a practical manner by setting the Canticles and Psalms to Gregorian tones, and publishing them in his *Laudes Divinae* (1843). In 1864 he went to St. Mary Magdalene, Paddington, and for thirty years he was the presiding genius over its music. He was a skilled trainer of boys' voices, whilst as an organist he was known not so much as an executant but ' as an accompanist of devotional spirit, whose extemporizing seemed inspired by his faith.'

14—Russell Place.

RUSSELL PLACE, by Sir W. S. Bennett, was contributed to Mauricês *Choral Harmony* (1854).

William Sterndale Bennett was born in Howard Street, Sheffield, in 1816. He came of a musical stock, his grandfather, John Bennett, being noted in the Derbyshire Peak district for his singing and oboe playing, while his father, Robert Bennett, was organist for many years at Sheffield parish church.

Amongst Robert Bennett's friends in Sheffield was Dr. John Sterndale, whose son William supplied the musician with some songs which he set to music. Robert felt so indebted to his friend that when in 1816 his third child and only son appeared on the scene, he decided to show his gratitude by giving the boy the name of his friend.

After the death of his father in 1819 the boy went to the house of his grandfather, John Bennett, who was a lay-clerk at King's College, Cambridge. The youngster flourished exceedingly in the musical atmosphere of his new home, and showed such aptitude that he was entered as a chorister at King's College Chapel at the age of eight. Here he remained for two years, during which period his talents attracted the notice of several influential people, and by their advice he was sent to the Royal Academy of Music, thus entering upon his London career just as he was completing his tenth year. The judgement of his Cambridge friends was confirmed by the Academy authorities, amongst whom was the principal, Dr. William Crotch, and he entered into residence at once. He was promptly taken off to the schoolroom, where he aroused much interest owing to his small stature; as Grattan Cooke afterwards said, he was ' the smallest boy,' though ' the greatest man,' with whom the Academy had to do. John Ella, a sub-professor at the time, tells a story of how he went into the schoolroom and found the boys holding an examination on their own account, which took the form of striking confused handfuls of notes on the piano, which young Bennett, dressed in a brown jacket with two rows of brass buttons on it and a white frill, was naming correctly, to the great satisfaction of all.

After being a pupil at the Royal Academy of Music for ten years, and a professor for another twenty, Bennett's connexion with his Alma Mater was temporarily interrupted; but when in 1866 Charles Lucas resigned the office of Principal, there was only one possible successor; in fact, Madame Jenny Lind Goldschmidt affirmed that Bennett was the only man in England who could raise the Institution from the state of decay into which it had fallen. Bennett took office at a time when the Academy was threatened with dissolution, but under his careful management and general influence it was promptly reestablished on a firm basis, and entered on a new life. Many well-deserved honours came to Bennett in his later life. He was Professor of Music at Cambridge from 1856 till his death, and received the degrees of Mus.D. and M.A. from the University. In 1870 Oxford recognized his work by making him a D.C.L., while in the following year he was knighted by the Queen.

Bennett's claim on posterity is emphasized by the fact that it was owing to his efforts that Bach's choral and orchestral music first began to gain a hearing in England. It was in 1849 that he first unfolded his scheme in a talk with Charles Steggall (see No. 540). This led to a meeting being held at the composer's house, at which it was decided to form a ' Bach Society.' Perhaps none showed more real devotion than Miss Helen Johnstone, who was the first candidate for election to the new Society, and whose exertions on its behalf were invaluable in results. ' Rather eccentric in appearance ' (to quote Mr. J. S. Bennett), ' with eyes beaming through large spectacles, and with her own ideas of dress, her youth was somewhat disguised. A violinist, unversed in musical chronology, attending the rehearsals for the first time, and astonished at the enthusiasm she displayed, seriously inquired of his neighbour, " Is it *Mrs.* Bach? " '

Bennett's two chief choral works were *The Woman of Samaria,* written for the Birmingham Festival, 1867, and *The May Queen,* for the opening of Leeds Town Hall, 1858. An oratorio, *Zion,* that he schemed out, never reached completion. He wrote several anthems, and amongst his piano works the *Barcarolle in F,* the *Three Musical Sketches,* and a few others, together with his songs, are still held in esteem.

15, 21—Leoni.

LEONI is from John Wesley's *Sacred Harmony* (1780), where it is set to Oliver's hymn, ' The God of Abraham praise.'

About the year 1770 Thomas Olivers was attending a conference at Wesley's Chapel in City Road, and one Friday evening he went to the Jewish synagogue in Aldgate, where he heard a version of the old Hebrew doxology, usually sung on the eve of the Jewish Sabbath. The leader of the singing at that time was Leoni, and Olivers, who was much taken with the melody he had heard, applied to him for a copy, and then wrote his celebrated hymn to it, ' The God of Abraham praise,' which is really founded on the doxology referred to. It was then published in leaflet form, and shortly after it appeared in the *Gospel Magazine* of April, 1775. The origin of this melody is quite unknown, but it is doubtful if it is much older than the eighteenth century. (See also No. 264.)

16, 228—Austria.

Whilst Haydn was staying in England in 1794 he was much impressed with the spontaneous singing of the National Anthem, and its evident effect on the people, and it was his desire that his own people should have a similar national song. He found the opportunity to hand when, on returning home after his second visit to England he noticed that the influence of the French Revolution had been countered by the Austrian poet Lorenz Hauschka, who had written a patriotic hymn at the request of the Austrian Prime Minister. Haydn was requested to write music for the hymn, and it was first sung throughout Austria on the Emperor's birthday, February 12, 1797. This *Hymn to the Emperor* soon reached this country, and its usefulness as a hymn-tune was promptly recognized, the first to publish it as such being Dr. Edward Miller, of ROCKINGHAM fame. However, his attempt to make it fit a hymn of ' eight lines sevens ' metre was not ideal, and the air was given a more suitable setting in the anonymous hymn, ' Praise the Lord, ye heavens adore Him,' which was in use at the Foundling Hospital at the beginning of last century.

Haydn's biographer, Carl F. Pohl, relates that the *Hymn to the Emperor* was the composer's favourite work, ' and he often consoled himself by playing it with great feeling.' He made use of the air as the slow movement of his Quartet in C (Op. 76, No. 5), weaving a wonderful set of variations round the melody, and these were skilfully arranged for the organ some years ago by Dr. E. J. Hopkins.

Mendelssohn made good use of this melody when he visited St. Peter's Church, Cornhill. As he entered, the congregation were singing Haydn's well-known tune. He was asked to play the out-going voluntary, and took as his theme the tune which had been sung, *The Emperor's Hymn,* and wrought it out for more than half an hour, exhausting every contrivance (so it seemed) of ' reply, rejoinder, harmonic change, and episodical embellishment.' On the following Thursday, at Christ Church, Newgate Street, he was asked to take again the same theme. A grand fantasia and fugue was the result, totally different from that on the previous Sunday, ' save in its consummate variety and skill, as if it had been the work of other organists' hands and feet ' and—may one not add?—brains. In the course of the movement

Mendelssohn held down the top A on the swell and treated it as an inverted pedal point of great length. His auditors thought that the long A was a cipher, and that the manual would become useless; but after harmonizing the note in a variety of different ways, he held it for some time alone, when the A quietly glided through G sharp to G natural, and then to F sharp. On coming down from the organ loft and rejoining his friends, he laughingly said, 'You thought it was a cipher—I know you did.'

The source of the music has proved a fruitful subject for discussion. Is it an original air, or did Haydn find the germ of it already existing?

Two suggestions in support of the latter theory have been put forward. Professor Niecks pointed out that the opening bars of the Austrian Hymn may have been suggested by the opening bars of a rondo by Telemann in his vocal and instrumental *Dergetreue Musik-Meister*, published in Hamburg in 1728.

This is probably only a coincidence, or possibly an unconscious reminiscence, for the fertile Haydn was not given to borrowing.

Far more attractive, and, indeed, much more to the point, is the argument advanced in Sir W. H. Hadow's booklet *A Croatian Composer*. In this the author maintains that Haydn founded the melody on a Croatian folksong, and he certainly makes out a good case for his theory.

Joseph Haydn has left us an autobiographical record of his early days:

'I was born on the last day of March in 1732, in the

market town of Rohrau, near Prugg on the river Leitha, in Lower Austria. The calling of my late father was that of a wheelwright (in the service of Count Harrach). He was a great lover of music by nature, and played the harp without knowing a note of music, while, as a boy of five, I sang all his short simple pieces very fairly; this induced my father to send me to the rector of the school at Haimburg, a relative of ours, in order to learn the first elements of music and other juvenile acquirements. Our Almighty Father (to whom above all I owe the most profound gratitude) had endowed me with so much facility in music that even in my sixth year I was bold enough to sing some masses in the choir, and also played a little on the piano and the violin.

' In my seventh year the late Capellmeister von Reutter, when passing through Haimburg, heard my weak but pleasing voice. He forthwith took charge of me in the Capell-Haus (in Vienna) where, in addition to my other studies, I learned singing, the piano, and the violin, from very good masters. I sang soprano both at St. Stephen's and at Court with great applause till my sixteenth year, when I finally lost my voice and was forced for eight whole years to gain a scanty livelihood by giving lessons; many a genius is ruined by this miserable mode of earning daily bread, as it leaves no time for study. This I, alas! know too well for myself from experience, and I could never have accomplished even what I did, if in my zeal for composition I had not pursued my studies through the night. I wrote diligently, though not quite correctly, till at length I had the good fortune to learn the genuine rudiments of composition from the celebrated master Porpora (who was at that time in Vienna).

' At length, by the recommendation of the late Herr von Fürnberg (from whom I received unusual kindness) I was appointed Capellmeister to his Highness Prince Esterhazy, in whose service I hope to live and die.'

During the thirty years that Haydn laboured as chief musician to the Esterhazy family he produced a vast number of original works—quartets, symphonies, and operas following each other in rich profusion. The position he held gave him unusual advantages. 'My prince,' (he declared), 'was satisfied with all my works; I received approbation; I could, as chief of the orchestra, try my works; could observe the impression they made; could add, correct, or retrench what was not good; I could be bold; I was separated from the world; nobody near me to lead me astray or distress me, and thus it was natural that I should become original.'

But at last the time came when Haydn wearied of Court life, and he therefore readily accepted an invitation from the London conductor, J. P. Salomon, to visit England in 1791, and conduct. During this visit he wrote twelve new symphonies for Salomon's concerts. He also attended many social functions and concerts and became acquainted with some of Handel's oratorios, which must have been almost new to him, and he was more than impressed by the mighty choruses he heard at the Handel Festival at Westminster Abbey in 1791. The outcome of this experience was a great desire to write a choral work on a scale larger than he had hitherto attempted, and the opportunity came when his friend Salomon gave him a libretto compiled largely from Milton's *Paradise Lost,* dealing with 'the Creation of the World,' which is said to have been originally designed for Handel's use. A German version was provided for Haydn by his friend Von Swieten, and he soon got to work. 'Never was I so pious,' he wrote, 'as when I was composing *The Creation.* I felt so endowed with religious feeling that before I sat down to the pianoforte I prayed earnestly to God that He would enable me to praise Him worthily.' By the time the original libretto had been translated into German and brought back into English for the first performance in this country in 1800, it had become so disguised as to be entirely unworthy of the music, and it is only the ever-fresh beauty of the latter that has saved the oratorio.

So successful was *The Creation* that Haydn was induced to start on another similar work, and an adaptation from Thompson's *Seasons* was provided for him. Although it has not, perhaps, attained the popularity of his first work it is in every way characteristic of the composer, and contains some of the finest music he ever wrote.

This work proved to be his swan song. The effort had been too much for him; the fount had well-nigh run dry, and his work had been worthily and nobly completed. He spent his days in quiet retirement, disturbed only by the French bombardment of Vienna in 1809. He lingered on till May, when he passed away and was laid to rest with all the honours due to a great composer and a much-loved man.

17—Amsterdam.

AMSTERDAM is from the 'Foundery' Tune-Book (1742). It is probably founded on a German chorale, but its origin is unknown.

18—Ever Faithful.

EVER FAITHFUL was written by Arthur Sullivan for *Church Hymns* (1874).

A tablet on No. 8, Bolwell Terrace, Lambeth, marks the house where Sir Arthur Sullivan was born in 1842. An interview with Sir George Smart (see No. 57) led to the music-loving boy being admitted as a Chapel Royal chorister. Whilst he was here he wrote his first anthem, ' Sing unto the Lord,' and a song, ' O Israel,' the latter strongly reminiscent of ' Hear ye, Israel ' in *Elijah*. After three years at the Chapel Royal he won the Mendelssohn scholarship, which gave him three years at Leipzig. Returning to England he acted as assistant to his old master, Rev. T. Helmore, who engaged him to

teach the young choristers not music, but the three R's!
He also took to organ playing, and after five months
under George Cooper he obtained, by competition, a post
at St. Michael's, Chester Square, where he formed a
choir of policemen who were christened 'the Harmonious
Blue Bottles.' His next appointment (and last, as an
organist) was at St. Peter's, Cranley Gardens, and at
this period he was also organist at Covent Garden Opera
House. Many of his songs were composed at this period,
providing him with a comfortable income. In 1874 he
edited *Church Hymns,* the source of many tunes in the
present *Methodist Hymn-Book.* Most of Sullivan's
anthems belong to his earlier years. His one contribution to service music is a setting in D, and he also wrote
two Festival *Te Deums,* but being composed to order
they lack that inspired touch which is one of the essential
attributes of immortality.

Sullivan's contributions to oratorio include *The Light
of the World, The Prodigal Son, The Martyr of Antioch,*
and *The Golden Legend,* all written for various festivals.
He once considered the prophecy of Isaiah as a subject,
but when he discovered that in the song of praise celebrating the recovery of King Hezekiah he would have to
find suitable music for the statement ' let them take a cake
of figs and lay it upon the boil,' Sullivan found himself
unequal to the task, and the oratorio remained unwritten.
Sullivan will long be remembered for his operas written
in association with W. S. Gilbert. He also wrote much
incidental music for the theatre, and his orchestral works
include the *In Memoriam* Overture (see No. 506), *Overture di Ballo,* and *Symphony in E.* He died, greatly
regretted, in 1900.

19—Monkland.

MONKLAND is from a Moravian collection called *Hymn
Tunes of the United Brethren.* This was published in
1824 with John Lees as editor in this form :

This book appears to have got into the hands of an organist named John Wilkes, who played at Monkland Church, near Leominster, of which Sir H. W. Baker, chairman of the first *Hymns Ancient and Modern* committee was vicar. It is suggested that Wilkes got possession of a copy of Lee's book, extracted the tune, trimmed it, and submitted it to Baker, who found a place for it in *Hymns Ancient and Modern* (1861). No hint is given as to the composer of MONKLAND, and there is no reason why the name of Mr. John Wilkes should be associated with it any longer.

20—Te Deum Laudamus.

TE DEUM LAUDAMUS, by Stainer, first appeared anonymously in *The Day School Hymn-Book* (1896).

Sir John Stainer was born in Southwark in 1840, in a house that has long since disappeared. He received early lessons from his father, and he made good use of a one-manual organ in the home. There is an amusing picture in *The Musical Times* for May, 1901, showing the boy playing this organ, balancing himself on one leg and blowing the bellows with the other. In 1849 Stainer became a full chorister in St. Paul's Cathedral under John Goss (see No. 12), and sang in the choir at the funeral service of the Duke of Wellington. His first organ appointment was at St. Benet's Church, E.C., and he also took the organ occasionally for Goss. On one occasion Ouseley heard him perform, and was so impressed that he took him off to be organist at St. Michael's College, Tenbury. Two years later, when he was only nineteen, Stainer was appointed organist at Magdalen College, Oxford, and a year later organist to the University. He entered St. Edmund Hall in order to read for his Arts degree. Whilst at Oxford he took a prominent part in all educational movements for the advancement of music, and he was also heard as organ soloist at the Crystal Palace concerts. In 1872 he became organist at St. Paul's Cathedral, a post he held for sixteen years, when failing eyesight compelled him to retire. In 1889 he became Professor of Music at Oxford, being succeeded in 1899 by Sir H. Parry (see No. 145). His numerous compositions include anthems : ' The Morning Stars sang together,' ' I saw the Lord,' ' Lo, summer comes again,' and cantatas *The Crucifixion, Gideon, The Daughter of Jairus,* also an *Organ Primer,* and *The Music of the Bible.* His last composition was a six-page unaccompanied ' Service in C ' for St. Paul's Cathedral choir. He died in 1901.

21—Leoni. See No. 15.

22—Better World.

BETTER WORLD. The composer of this has never been traced. It is from Richard Weaver's *Tune-Book* (1862). Dr. Lyth, the author of the hymn ' There is a better world, they say,' said that it was written in 1845 for the anniversary of an infant school at Randwich, near Stroud (Glos.), and sung to an air very popular at the time known as ALL IS WELL.

23—Gwalchmai.

GWALCHMAI is by J. D. Jones, who was born at Bryngrugog, Montgomeryshire, in 1827. So poor were his parents that they could only give their son a year's schooling, and his boyhood was largely spent in learning all he could about music. Before he reached his twentieth year he published a few psalm-tunes with the title *Y Perganiedydd* (the sweet singer). The financial results were so satisfactory that he found he had sufficient funds to go to a training college in London. From this time his music became very popular in Wales, and also proved remunerative. In order to help young musicians he published the original and helpful *Cydymaith y Cerddor* (the Singer's Companion), and also *Alawon y Bryniau* (Melodies of the Hills), a collection of Welsh melodies. For use in church he published, in 1868 (in association with the Rev. E. Stephen), *Llyfr Tonau ac Emynau,* which contained his tune GWALCHMAI. His cantata *Llys Arthur* (The Court of Arthur) won great favour both in England and Wales. He died in 1870. Two of J. D. Jones's sons have achieved fame, the Rev. J. D. Jones, D.D., minister of Richmond Hill Congregational Church, Bournemouth, and Mr. Haydn Jones, M.P.

24—Palatine.

PALATINE, or more correctly, SONG 67, is by Orlando Gibbons.

In his preface to *The Songs of the Old Testament* (1621), George Wither, the poet-Puritan of the Stuart period, wrote 'That to the glory of God they may be sung either in public or in private. . . . I have endeavoured to procure from some of our best musicians such notes as (being easy and proper to the matter) might the more accommodate them.' This principle he also carried out in his second contribution to sacred poetry, known as *The Hymnes and Songs of the Church* (1623). He called to his assistance Dr. Orlando Gibbons to fit them with tunes, and Wither acknowledged his help by saying that the doctor ' hath chosen to make his music agreeable to the matter, and what the common apprehension can best admit, rather than the curious fancies of the time.'

Gibbons contributed a number of tunes or ' Songs,' as he called them, to Wither's volume, eight of which appear in the present tune-book :

> SONG 1—458, 892.
> SONG 5—86.
> SONG 13 (SIMPLICITY)—178, 549.
> SONG 20—507.
> SONG 24—469.
> SONG 34 (ANGELS' SONG)—384, 388, 478.
> SONG 46—501.
> SONG 67 (PALATINE)—24.

Orlando Gibbons was born at Cambridge in 1583, where his father is said to have been one of the town ' wayts ' or watchmen. At the age of twenty-three Orlando took his Musical Bachelor's degree, and five years later became associated with his famous contemporaries Byrd and Bull in a compilation of instrumental pieces for the Virginals. His share in the work consisted of a *Fantasia* in four parts, in which he displayed a great mastery of his art. Again, in the following year, 1612, he brought out his ' First Set of Madrigals and Motetts of five parts; apt for viols and voices.' The volume contained thirteen madrigals, a species of composition which was greatly affected in the Elizabethan period, and reached its highest development in the hands of Gibbons with such works as ' The Silver Swan,' ' O that the Learned Poets!' ' Dainty, Fine Bird,' and ' What is Our Life?' The last-named is an especially good instance of the transitional character of Gibbons's work, and, as it has been well observed, his music partakes of that peculiar beauty which seems to belong to all transitional art. The degree of Doctor of Music was conferred at Oxford on Gibbons, by the request of Camden, on the occasion of his founding the professorship of History. On the same occasion the University conferred the

Doctor's degree on William Heather, who founded, some years later (in 1628), the professorship of Music. He is believed to have been incapable of composing his musical exercise for the doctorate, and it is thought that Gibbons' grand eight-part anthem, ' O clap your hands!' served for both the new doctors. In 1623 he succeeded John Parsons as organist of Westminster Abbey. He only held the post for two years, his death occurring at Canterbury, where he had been summoned to attend the nuptials of Charles I and Henrietta Maria.

25—Würzburg.

Würzburg is taken from a collection of German chorales called *Andächtige und auserlesene Gesänge,* published at Würzburg (Bavaria) in 1705. The composer is unknown.

26—Croft's 136th.

Croft's 136th was ' set by Mr. William Crofts' to Psalm 136 in *The Divine Companion,* 2nd edition, 1709 (see No. 8).

27 (i)—Lytham St. Annes.

Lytham St. Annes. This tune came to the composer whilst on a bicycle tour in the Lake District. It was first brought into use at the Drive Wesleyan Church, St. Annes-on-Sea, in 1900.

James Thomas Lightwood, the youngest son of the Rev. Edward Lightwood, was born at Leeds in 1856, and baptized in Brunswick Methodist Chapel, famous for its wonderful ' Booth' organ. He was educated at Kingswood School, Bath, passing both Oxford and Cambridge Local Examinations in every subject taken except music. One of the questions—' Write out " God Save the Queen," ' utterly floored him. After leaving school he served for three years with Mawer and Collingham, drapers in Lincoln, and then resigned the yard measure for a scholastic career. In 1879 he joined his brother Edward R. Lightwood in opening a boarding school at Lytham, long famous as Pembroke House School. In 1910 he started the *Choir* under the auspices of the Methodist Publishing House, and has since that date had charge of the music at the Headquarters of Methodism. He has written a good deal on the music of Methodism and also *The Romance of Cycling*.

27 (ii)—Seraphim.

SERAPHIM was contributed by Henry Smart (see No. 12), to *Psalms and Hymns for Divine Worship*, 1867. This work was published under the auspices of the Presbyterian Church of England. A notable feature was the large number of original tunes and new adaptations it contained, the contributors including H. Smart, J. Hullah, J. B. Dykes, G. A. Macfarren and E. F. Rimbault. The collection formed a happy hunting ground for tune-book editors for many years, and its resources are not yet exhausted.

28 —St. Francis. See No. 4.

29—Te Laudant Omnia.

TE LAUDANT OMNIA was composed by J. F. Swift about 1889 for a children's service at St. Bede's Church, Liverpool. It is taken from the 1904 edition of the *Methodist Hymn-Book*.

James Frederick Swift was born in Manchester in 1847. Three years later the family removed to Liverpool. He soon developed an aptitude for music, and obtained at Cranmer Street Wesleyan Chapel his first position as an organist at the age of fourteen. Other churches served by him were St. Andrew's, Renshaw Street, and St. Bride's, Percy Street. In 1881 he acted as deputy

for W. T. Best at St. George's Hall, and in the same
year he revived the Liverpool Musical Society, and also
directed the concerts of several other organizations. In
1892 he moved to Liscard, on the Cheshire side of the
Mersey, where he continued his musical activities. In
1898 he was appointed Provincial Grand Organist
(Masonic) for the Province of Cheshire. Under the
pen-name of ' Godfrey Marks ' he became a successful
song-writer, and his ' Sailing ' spread to nearly every
quarter of the globe. His music was tunefully robust,
healthy in tone, and characteristic of the better class
songs of his period. He died in 1931.

30—Sheen.

SHEEN, by G. Holst, was written for the hymn ' From
glory to glory advancing, we praise Thee, O Lord,' in
The English Hymnal (1906).

Gustav Theodore Holst was born at Cheltenham in
1874. His father was organist at All Saints' Church,
famous at the time for its excellent musical service. The
son was organist for a time at Little Rissington Church,
a village on the hillside above Bourton-on-the-Water.
His early acquaintance with the district doubtless
inspired the idea of the *Cotswolds Symphony* heard at
Bournemouth in 1902. Holst studied at the Royal
College of Music under Stanford and Hoyte, taking the
organ with the latter, but hand trouble led him to take up
the trombone, on which he had become an expert. The
greater part of his life was devoted to teaching, and
since 1905 he acted as professor of music at St. Paul's
Girls' School in London. He tried many forms of
composition, and has succeeded in most of them—as far
as one can succeed in music to-day. He has been heard
at the chief provincial festivals, and he has had three
operas placed on the stage. Although at one time an
organist, he has not contributed any music for the instrument. His church music, though not definitely styled so,

includes some of his best choral music. His outstanding works are the *Choral Symphony*, produced at the 1925 Leeds Festival, *The Planets* (Symphonic), *The Perfect Fool* (Opera), and *The Hymn of Jesus*. Holst died in 1934. The name is a Swedish one, formerly Von Holst, but his ancestors left the Russian Baltic provinces many years ago.

31—Compton.

COMPTON was written by Sir George Clement Martin for insertion in the *Methodist Hymn-Book* (1904). The composer was born at Lambourn, Berks, in 1844. It was not until he reached his sixteenth year that he began to entertain thoughts of taking up music as his profession, and he was then quite unable to play any instrument. After some months' study it was found that he was fully competent to take the parochial services, and he was appointed organist of Lambourn church. For more advanced study in the theory of music he put himself under Dr. Stainer, then organist of Magdalen College, Oxford, and in due course took his degree of Bachelor in Music.

In 1871 he was appointed organist to the private chapel of the Duke of Buccleuch at Dalkeith, which post he held, together with that of organist of St. John's, Edinburgh, until 1874, when he was invited by the Dean and Chapter of St. Paul's to be music master to the boys of the newly-constructed choral foundation of the cathedral.

Two years later he succeeded George Cooper as sub-organist. In this position Martin showed himself possessed to such a large degree of the many qualities necessary to a successful administrator—for the direction of such a choir as that of St. Paul's demands something more than executive ability—that, when in 1888 Sir John Stainer resigned his position as chief organist, Martin was appointed his successor. Both by his editorial work, and also by his original compositions (chiefly anthems), he did good service to the cause of English church music. He died in 1916 and was buried in the crypt of the cathedral.

32—Maryton.

MARYTON first appeared in *Church Hymns* (1874). The composer, the Rev. Henry Percy Smith, was Charles Kingsley's curate for two years at Eversley, leaving in 1851 for a curacy at Farnborough, Surrey. He then became vicar at Great Barnton from 1868 to 1882, when he accepted a chaplaincy at Cannes. He died in 1898.

33—Strasburg.

STRASBURG. There were various editions of the *Strasburg Psalters* (from which this tune is derived) from 1525 till about 1580. At Geneva, Strasburg, and in England, the church song of the Reformation took the form of the metrical psalm, as distinct from the German chorale, and hymnody was not looked upon with favour. The few tunes from the *Strasburg Psalters* still in use have undergone much alteration, and they are not now easy to identify. One of the most famous is the OLD 113th (No. 584).

34—St. Denio.

ST. DENIO (also known as JOANNA) is based on a Welsh folk-song. The *Journal* of the Welsh Folk Song Society (Volume I) suggests several sources, the nearest being a ballad of about 1810, ' Can Mlynedd i' Nawy (=' A hundred years from now'). Another form is in the collection of folk-songs made by the Rev. John Jenkins, Vicar of Keri (or Kerry), in Montgomeryshire, who died in 1829. It was exhibited by him at the Wrexham Eisteddfod in 1820, and is now in the National Library of Wales at Aberystwyth. It is printed as PALESTINA in J. Roberts' *Caniadau y Cyssegr* (1839), and in more modern times it is found in H. Bennett's *Alawon* (1896).

35—Noricum.

NORICUM was contributed to the *Methodist Hymn-Book* of 1904. The composer, Frederic James, born in 1858, spent his boyhood at Rotherham, where his father played the organ at Masboro' Wesleyan Chapel. At the age of eleven the son deputized for his father, and also at this period gained proficiency on the double bass and the violin. After acting as teacher at the Rotherham Wesleyan School, James entered the Westminster Training College in 1877. Whilst here he acted as College organist, and also as organist at Warwick Gardens Chapel. On leaving Westminster he obtained a post at Ellesmere Wesleyan School, Sheffield, where he remained nearly six years, when in 1884 Dr. Vinter engaged him as music master at Woodhouse Grove School, near Bradford. In the same year he graduated Mus.B. at Cambridge. Amongst his other engagements, he served a long period as singing master at Headingley Wesleyan College, Leeds. He died in 1922.

Mr. James took an active part in the various movements of his time for the advancement of music. He was one of the earliest members of the Incorporated Society of Musicians, and in various papers to the Society, and in his public lectures, he covered a wide scope of musical subjects, showing remarkable gifts for proclaiming and expounding his musical and musico-religious faith. He never attempted any extensive work as a composer, confining himself chiefly to part-songs, services, and hymn-tunes. He was an excellent teacher, and had a wonderful influence with boys. On coming to Woodhouse Grove he promptly dispensed with the master who was present at the singing classes ' to keep order,' and never had reason to regret his action.

36—Nicæa.

NICÆA was composed for Heber's hymn in *Hymns Ancient and Modern* (1861). It owes its name to the fact that the doctrine of the Trinity became a recognized dogma at an Ecumenical Council held at Nicæa (Asia Minor) in 325 A.D.

John Bacchus Dykes was a Yorkshireman both by birth and descent, his ancestors having been connected for many years with Hull, where he was born on March 10, 1823. That a boy who was destined to become a great musician and a true churchman should have received the name of one of the gayest and giddiest of heathen gods seems distinctly *malapropos*, but the explanation is simple. In a letter received many years ago from one of his sons, the Rev. E. N. Dykes, the mystery was thus cleared up :

' In reply to your inquiries, " Bacchus " is an old family name; a certain George (?) Bacchus, a former Mayor of Hull, married Miss Huntington, of which family my mother was a member. Her father's name was Bacchus Huntington.'

Dykes' father, a banker, was a distinguished musical amateur, and took a prominent part in the musical life of Hull. In 1834 a grand musical festival was held in Holy Trinity Church, for which there was much preliminary practising. Young John, who had a good voice, had a great reputation for reading music, and the lady sopranos smuggled him in amongst them, hoping he would not be discovered. However, Sir George Smart, who was the one and only conductor at that time, soon detected the intruder, and the lad was promptly ejected, much to his disappointment.

Dykes' musical talent seems to have shown itself quite early. He could play by ear almost anything that he heard. An aunt undertook to teach him his notes, but it was not such an easy matter, as playing by ear came so readily to him. He was also taught the violin and piano. The organ, however, was his special favourite. His grandfather was incumbent of St. John's Church in Hull, and there the little fellow used to go to practise. From his biography we learn that his younger sisters long retained a lively recollection of being made useful as organ-blowers in early times, their remuneration being at the rate of one halfpenny an hour! In this same grandfather's church he was playing the organ when he was only ten. 'It was curious to see the small, pale child— for he never was tall or robust-looking—trying to reach the pedals and bringing so much out of the organ.'

In 1841 the family removed to Wakefield, and young Dykes was presented by the congregation with a gold watch and chain in acknowledgement of his services for several years as assistant organist.

On going to Cambridge Dykes soon found that his musical skill brought him many friends. He became an active member of the Cambridge University Musical Society, and succeeded William Thompson as President. Thompson, who afterwards became famous as Lord Kelvin, highly esteemed his brother musician, whom he used to speak of as 'Incomparable John Dykes.' When in later years Lord Kelvin was evolving his sounding-machine for taking deep-sea soundings a companion asked him how he was going to make use of a coil of pianoforte wire which he saw on the table. He was told it was for sounding. This answer only increased the curiosity of his questioner, who asked 'What note?' 'The deep C' was Lord Kelvin's prompt reply.

During his undergraduate days, Dykes became acquainted with the glories of the Lake District, which subsequently became one of his favourite resorts. On one occasion he visited Keswick with a reading party, and during an expedition to Scafell they got lost for several hours. Being without refreshment of any kind it was reported that one of the party was reduced to catching and eating grasshoppers!

In 1848 Dykes took priest's orders, and he soon found that his musical gifts were to be greatly to his advantage, for in the following year he was appointed Precentor and Minor Canon of Durham Cathedral. He now devoted what time he could spare to composition, one of his earliest works being the anthem, ' These are they which came out of great tribulation.' He entered with great delight on his new sphere of labour. He had the sole management of the cathedral choir, and also superintended their religious training.

It was about 1856 that Dykes commenced writing the long succession of hymn-tunes which have made his name famous in the story of our church music. A year later he contributed thirteen tunes to Gray's Hymnal, including RIVAULX and ST. AGNES. In 1860 he commenced his long association with *Hymns Ancient and Modern.*

During the last year of his Precentorship the University of Durham conferred the Mus.D. degree on Dykes, and in the following year he resigned his cathedral appointment after fourteen years' service on being presented to the Vicarage of St. Oswald's, Durham.

Unfortunately the last years of his life were embittered by a dispute with the Bishop of Durham on questions of ritual. This disaster, coupled with the strain of work in a large and unwieldy parish, hastened his end, and he passed quietly away at St. Leonards on January 20, 1876. He was buried at St. Oswald's Church, Durham, and in later years a handsome memorial window was erected to his memory.

Dykes had little opportunity during his lifetime of making any provision for his family, and when he died they were left almost unprovided for. A memorial fund was promptly inaugurated, headed, it is pleasant to record, by the Bishop of Durham, and so highly was Dykes esteemed, and so wide was his fame as a hymntune composer, that a sum of £10,000 was subscribed, and then the fund was closed.

Writing in reference to Dr. Dykes' tunes Sir George C. Martin said, ' the world is richer for Dr. Dykes' music, and his memory deserves to be loved and honoured by all those who, like himself, strive to follow in the footsteps of the Divine Master.'

37, 139—Dunfermline.

Dunfermline. The tunes from the old Scottish psalters included in the present hymn-book are from two sources :

1.—*The CL. Psalmes of David* in Prose and Meeter with their whole usual Notes and Tunes (1615), published by Andro Hart (Nos. 37 (139), 347, 625 (749), 698).

2.—*The Psalmes of David* in Prose and Meeter, with their whole Tunes in foure or mo parts . . . (1635). (Andro Hart died in 1621, and this 1635 psalter was published by ' the Heires of Andrew Hart.) (See Nos. 224 London New, 446 Culross, 512 Wigtown.)

In the old psalters the tunes which were identified with any particular psalms were called ' Proper.' In Scottish psalters the term ' Common ' was applied to tunes not identified with one psalm, but which might be used to any psalm of the same metre.

Dunfermline first appeared in Andro Hart's *CL. Psalmes of David* (1615), whence it was transferred some years later by Ravenscroft to his *Whole Book of Psalms*, and classed amongst the Scottish tunes. It is said to have been the composition of a certain Dean John Angus, who was connected with the ' Abbacie of Dumfermling ' at the time of the Reformation, when he joined the Protestants, and was appointed to one of the livings attached to the Chapel Royal at Stirling. Nothing more seems to be known about him.

38—Rivaulx.

Rivaulx, by J. B. Dykes (see No. 36), was written for Hon. and Rev. J. Grey's *Hymnal for Use in the English Church* (1866).

39—Fairfield.

Fairfield, by Peter Latrobe, was composed in 1852 and inserted two years later in Maurice's *Choral*

Harmony. He was the eldest son of C. I. Latrobe (see 440). Born in 1795, he was educated at Fulneck, Yorks., and became Moravian Mission Secretary in 1836, retaining the position till his death in 1863. In 1854 he edited the *English Moravian Tune-Book*.

40—Croft's 136th. See No. 26.

41—Breslau.

BRESLAU is from a collection of ' spiritual and pleasing new songs' published at Leipzig in 1625. This book, *As Hymnodus Sacer,* contains twelve hymns and eight tunes, of which BRESLAU is one. No composers' names are given. The tune, which was originally in triple time, has been considerably altered by various editors. Mendelssohn uses it as a chorale in *St. Paul.*

42, 126—Vom Himmel Hoch.

VOM HIMMEL HOCH (or ERFURT), by Martin Luther, is found in *Geistliche Lieder,* published at Leipzig in 1539. It is used five times in various forms by Bach in his *Christmas Oratorio,* notably in the movement that closes the second part, with interludes between the lines.

Martin Luther was born at Eisleben, Saxony, in 1483. He went to school at Magdeburg and then at Eisenach, where he lodged with Frau Ursula Cotta, who had been charmed with his beautiful voice. Here he learnt to play the lute and the flute, preferring the former, as he could use it to accompany his song. As he grew up he became greatly interested in the national and traditional songs which the labourers sang at their work. Their simplicity and beauty charmed him, and it is on record that when hearing them he compared the strain to Gregorian chants, to the great disparagement of the latter, though reminiscences of them were destined to appear in his own melodies. Throughout his life he found solace in music, and his writings are full of testimony of his love for it. In his *Table Talk* he makes frequent reference to its influence—'Except theology, there is no art which can be placed in comparison with music,' and elsewhere he affirmed that 'singing is the best exercise there is; we have nothing else at all comparable to it.' His influence musically in his own home was great, though musical and poetical work was, of course, a subordinate element in his energetic life. Yet Coleridge did not overstate his case when he said that 'Luther did as much for the Reformation by his hymns as by his translation of the Bible.' How many of the tunes that bear his name he is really responsible for is uncertain, but the best authorities are agreed that he is probably responsible for EIN' FESTE BURG (494), VOM HIMMEL HOCH (42), AUS TIEFER NOTH and VATER UNSER (683), though the last is doubtful.

43—St. Flavian.

ST. FLAVIAN is the first half of an eight-line tune set to Psalm 132 in the *English Psalter* of 1562, sometimes known as Day's *Psalter* from the name of the printer. This edition contains the melody only of sixty-three tunes; these are harmonized in four parts in the next edition, issued in 1563. The 1562 edition was regarded as the standard book of psalm-tunes in the English Church for many years. But even in those days people were not satisfied with their new tune-book, and they certainly had some ground for complaint. It contained only sixty-five tunes, three of them being duplicates. Of the psalm-tunes more than half were double common metres, which, of course, was inevitable, as most of the metrical versions were in ballad (8. 6. 8. 6.) metre. Attempts were soon made to overcome this monotony, and private ventures, such as Damon's (see No. 237), Este's (see No. 461), and Ravenscroft's (see No. 45) Psalters were published, introducing new tunes to supplement the 1563 *Psalter*. This psalter contained, in addition to English tunes, some from the French and Genevan psalters.

John Day, one of the most noted printers of his time, was born at Dunwich, a place on the Suffolk coast that has now practically disappeared. Going to London he learnt the art of printing and set up on his own account in Aldersgate, where he also had a shop for the sale of his books. He got into trouble for printing, in 1559, a copy of the metrical psalms ' without lysense,' but he seems to have got over this, for during the next few years several editions of the Psalter, with and without music, came from his press, including one in Dutch. A famous production of his is Archbishop Parker's Psalter, containing tunes by Thomas Tallis (see No. 304). In 1572 he opened a shop in St. Paul's churchyard, and continued to produce books of great merit, including illustrated works, amongst them a fine copy of Foxe's *Book of Martyrs*. He printed forty-six metrical psalters, including forty-one of the ' Old ' or Sternhold and Hopkins version. Day died in 1584 and was buried at Little Bradley in his native county.

44—Firmament.

FIRMAMENT is one of four tunes composed by H. Walford Davies to be sung by the London Church Choir Association at their Festival in St. Paul's Cathedral in 1908.

Sir Henry Walford Davies was born at Oswestry in 1869. In his thirteenth year he became a chorister at St. George's, Windsor, under Walter Parratt. In 1890 he went to the R.C.M., and also obtained the post of organist at St. Annes', Soho. From here he went to Christ Church, Hampstead, for eight years, and then he succeeded Dr. E. J. Hopkins at the Temple Church, where for twenty years he maintained and indeed advanced the choral singing which Hopkins had already made famous.

During this period he wrote an oratorio *The Temple,* produced at Worcester in 1902, and this was followed by *Everyman* at Leeds, which at once established firmly the composer's reputation. Other important works followed, including his *Solemn Melody* for strings. His educational works, and especially his great services to the advancement of music in Wales, procured him the honour of knighthood in 1922. For some years he has done excellent service in compiling and editing collections of hymn-tunes, and his contributions to this form of the art, though few, are of a fine type.

Sir Walford Davies was, perhaps, the first prominent musician to identify himself closely with the work of the B.B.C. In the early days of broadcasting his talks on ' Music and the Ordinary Listener ' became famous. His completely natural manner in the studio helped to give him more of the elusive quality of ' microphone personality ' than is possessed by any other regular broadcaster. Impromptu vocal and piano illustrations are features of his simple, intimate style. He first began broadcasting to schools in 1925. He has recently been appointed Master of the Music to His Majesty King George V in succession to the late Sir Edward Elgar.

45, 329—Old 104th.

OLD 104TH first appeared in *The Whole Booke of Psalmes* edited by T. Ravenscroft, and published in 1621. This historic work, known briefly as Ravencroft's ' Psalter,' contained a selection of tunes from various sources, which Ravenscroft classified according to the countries with which each was identified, saying in his Preface that they are such ' as have been and are usually sung in England, Scotland, Wales, Germany, Italy, France, and the Netherlands.' He also gave names to his tunes, a custom initiated by Este in 1592, who named three tunes, whilst Ravenscroft named forty. He also gave minute directions as to singing :

> Rule 1.—Psalmes of Tribulation to be sung with a low voice and long measure.
>
> Rule 2.—Psalmes of Thanksgiving to be sung with a voice indifferent, neither too loud nor too soft, and with a measure neither too swift nor too slow.
>
> Rule 3.—Psalmes of Rejoicing to be sung with a loud voice, a swift and jocund measure.

The conclusion of his Preface or 'Address' is well worth reproducing :

> Accept kindly what I have laboured earnestly, and use it to thy comfort. Thus I end, humbly wishing to all true Christian hearts, that sweet consolation, in singing praises unto God here upon earth as may bring us hereafter to bear a part with the Quire of Angels in the Heavens.
>
>   Your well according and
>   best wishing brother,
>
>   THOS. RAVENSCROFT.

Little is known of Ravenscroft's life. Born in 1592, he was a chorister at St. Paul's Cathedral, and he may have been a master at Christ's Hospital. Besides his *Psalter,* he published three collections of vocal music. These, and his 'Brief Discourse' on the rules of music, give him a high position amongst contemporary musicians. The date of his death is uncertain (1633 or 1635).

46—St. Saviour.

F. G. Baker, the composer of ST. SAVIOUR, was born in 1840 in the Isle of Wight, where he held positions as organist at various churches. He sent his tune to the editor of the *Bristol Tune-Book,* who inserted it in the second edition, 1876.

47—Eisenach.

EISENACH, ascribed to J. H. Schein, originally appeared
in leaflet form, and in 1645 was included in a *Cantional*
edited by him. The original form, as given by Zahn
(2.3.8.3) :

is very different from that now in use. The chorale is
used by J. S. Bach in the St. John Passion music, and
also in his cantata No. 139 (' Wohl dem '), and it is in
C. P. E. Bach's *Choral gesänge*, but in none of these is
the melody or the arrangement the same as in the
Methodist Hymn-Book.

Johann Hermann Schein was born at Grünhain,
Saxony, in 1586. He studied at Leipzig, and then
became a private tutor. After a brief term as Court
Capellmeister at Saxe-Weimar, he became cantor of St.
Thomas's Church, Leipzig, a post he was well fitted for
through his early training as a chorister. As a composer
he wrote motets, instrumental suites, and a volume of
sacred pieces in the form of madrigals. He died in 1630.

48—Berkshire.

BERKSHIRE is by Charles Wesley, Junr. (see No. 366), and
is taken from *The Psalmist*, where it is called *Leicester*,
and assigned to ' C. Wesley arranged by S. Wesley.' It
was wrongly assigned to S. Wesley in the earlier issues
of the *Methodist Hymn-Book* (1933). *The Psalmist* was

an important collection of tunes that appeared in four parts, 1835—1843. It was originated by four members of the Baptist Church in Devonshire Square, Bishopsgate. Tired of the crudities of Rippon's Tune-Book, they spared no trouble or expense in getting together a collection of tunes ' that would render the work deserving of general adoption.' V. Novello was appointed editor, and he secured new tunes from S. Wesley, Horsley, T. Adam, and other composers, a notable contribution being Turle's WESTMINSTER (No. 73).

49—University.

UNIVERSITY first occurs in *A Collection of Psalm and Hymn-Tunes* (1784), edited by John Randall. He was born in 1715, and brought up as a chorister at the Chapel Royal under Bernard Gates, at whose house he took the part of Esther in a dramatic presentation of Handel's Oratorio. It was afterwards given at the King's Theatre, Haymarket, another performer being Samuel Howard, composer of ST. BRIDE (see No. 81). After graduating at Cambridge he was appointed organist at King's College, and subsequently succeeded Dr. Greene as professor of music.

50—Kilmarnock.

KILMARNOCK is by Neil Dougall, who was born at Greenock in 1776. He went to sea as a youth; engaged in buccaneering exploits; and as a result of a shooting accident on board his ship, lost both his eyesight and his right arm. But for this distressing occurrence, KILMARNOCK might never have come into being. As it was, Dougall, to amuse his weary hours, took to singing and the study of music generally. The peculiarities of the pentatonic scale (the so-called ' Scotch scale,' which omits the semitones of the modern major scale) were pointed out to him one day, and he resolved to make a

psalm-tune out of it. The result was KILMARNOCK, in
which neither the fourth nor seventh notes of the usual
scale appear. There is a fine Scottish flavour about the
tune, reminding one of R. A. Smith's short metre SELMA,
constructed in exactly the same way.

The tune has been traced to J. P. Clarke's *Parochial
Psalmody* (1831), but it is quite possible that it had been
in circulation before that.

51—St. Columba.

ST. COLUMBA is from a melody (No. 1043) in the complete Petrie collection of old Irish airs (1855), where it
is called 'An Irish Hymn sung at the dedication of a
Chapel, Co. Londonderry.'

52—Martham.

MARTHAM, by J. H. Maunder, first appeared in the
Westminster Abbey Hymn-Book, (1883; music edition,
1897). The composer was born at Chelsea in 1858, and
received his musical education at the Royal Academy of
Music. He held various organ appointments, and also
did a good deal of work as accompanist, in which
capacity he was for a time associated with Sims Reeves,
who greatly appreciated his gifts. As a composer,
Maunder was widely known, and his cantatas, anthems
and services have met with wide approval. Amongst his
best known works are his sacred cantatas *Penitence
Pardon and Peace, Olivet to Calvary,* and *A Song of
Thanksgiving.* His secular music was very popular with
the larger choirs that used to assemble at the Crystal
Palace, notably *The Song of Thor.* He died in 1920.

53 (i)—Sussex.

SUSSEX is from the *English Hymnal* (1906) where it
is said to be 'from a traditional English melody,' though
no authority is given for the statement. It appears to

belong to a group of folk-tunes associated with an old
song ' Madam, I am come to court you,' or ' Lady on the
Mountain.' It may have been one of old Henry
Burstow's songs, the famous Horsham bell-ringer and
song-singer, who had a wonderful store of old Sussex
songs of all kinds.

53 (ii)—Unser Herrscher.

UNSER HERRSCHER (or NEANDER, or MUNICH) is found
in Neander's *Glaub-und Liebes-übung,* where it is set to
his own hymn ' Unser Herrscher, unser König,' which
has not become current in England. The collection or
' Bundeslieder ' was published at Bremen in 1680.

Joachim Neander was the son of an assistant master
in the Latin School at Bremen, where he was born in
1650. After a somewhat riotous youth he was led to take
a serious view of life, and was appointed Rector of a
school at Düsseldorf. Here his independent spirit
brought him into conflict with the authorities and he was
suspended for a fortnight. His later years were occupied
in hymn-writing. Nos. 64 and 70 in the present hymn-
book are by him. Neander died in 1680.

54, 470—Selma

SELMA is from *Sacred Music,* a collection made by
R. A. Smith for use in St. George's Church, Edinburgh
(1825). It is said to be ' an ancient Scottish melody '
which Smith claimed to have heard in the Isle of Arran.

Robert Archibald Smith was born in 1780 at Reading,
where his parents had gone to live from Paisley owing to
the temporary failure of the silk-weaving trade. The
boy's musical instincts soon found an outlet, and he
became skilful in learning and noting down melodies he
heard, a practice which was to prove useful to him in
after life. He became a member of a church choir,
possibly at St. Lawrence's, where he had been baptized.

In 1800 he returned with his parents to Paisley, and shortly afterwards adopted music as a profession. In 1807 he was appointed precentor of the Paisley Abbey Church, where he raised the music of the church to a high degree of excellence. In 1821 he commenced his chief work, *The Scottish Minstrel,* a collection of Scottish melodies which extended to six volumes. In 1823 he moved to Edinburgh to accept the position of precentor at St. George's Church, under the Rev. Dr. Andrew Thomson, retaining the position till his death in 1829. He edited several other important collections of music, and also wrote an *Introduction to Singing.* He composed several songs, of which ' Jessie, the flow'r of Dunblane ' gained him lasting fame.

55—Kingston.

KINGSTON (or MAGDALEN COLLEGE) is taken from Dr. W. Hayes *Sixteen Psalms,* and has been slightly altered in the process, the original form of the first three lines being :

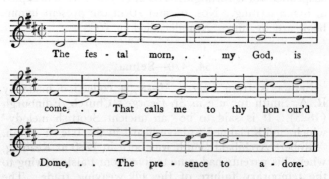

It is set to Merrick's version of Psalm cxxii. Dr. Hayes designed his tunes ' for the use of Magdalen College Chapel in Oxford,' and he kept copies of his work on sale at his home. The tunes have an organ accompaniment, with short preludes, interludes and codas.

Dr. William Hayes was born at Hanbury, Worcester-shire, in 1706. (The fact that he was baptized at St. Aldate's Church, Gloucester, has led to the erroneous statement that he was born in that city.) He became a chorister in Gloucester Cathedral, being articled to the organist, William Hine, and ' became excellent in playing church music and extempore voluntaries. Few men knew the power of that instrument better; and by a very happy facility of expressing the genius of various stops was often attended to by the admirers of that species of playing with heartfelt satisfaction.'

In 1729 Hayes was appointed organist at St. Mary's, Shrewsbury. Here he stayed four years when he went to Worcester Cathedral, and in the following year advanced to Magdalen College, Oxford, becoming Pro-fessor of Music at the University. In presenting him with the honorary degree of Mus.D., Dr. Bradley, Professor of Astronomy, described Hayes ' not only as a man eminent in his faculty, but as one whose sweetness of temper vied with that of his art.' Hayes composed a quantity of church music, most of which is now for-gotten. He was a man of culture and learning, and wrote a book defending Handel's fame against the asser-tion of Charles Avison, of Newcastle, who maintained that his own master Geminiani was far superior.

56—St. Stephen.

ST. STEPHEN. The Rev. William Jones, composer of this tune, was born in 1726. He was a lineal descendant of the Col. J. Jones who was one of the signatories of the Death Warrant of Charles I. He used regularly to observe the thirtieth of January as a day of fasting and humiliation for the sin of his ancestor. After leaving Oxford, Jones entered the Church, and held a varied succession of appointments, one of them being at Finedon, Northants. He would probably enjoy playing on and listening to the famous organ by Bernard Smith, which remains to this day to perpetuate the name and fame of this noted eighteenth-century builder. He then became perpetual curate at Nayland, a village on the borderland of Essex and Suffolk. But it is as a musician that he appeals to us, for, as he himself declared, 'music was the delight of his soul and he was master of it.' He not only wrote a treatise on the use and value of music, but he put his knowledge to practical use by publishing :

TEN CHURCH PIECES for the ORGAN, with Four Anthems in Score, composed for the Use of the Church of Nayland, in Suffolk, and Published for its benefit. By William Jones, M.A., F.R.S., author of a treatise on the Art of Music, &c. Opera II.

The hymn-tune ST. STEPHEN is on the last page of this volume, being set in open score to the old version of the twenty-third psalm by Sternhold :

> My Shepherd is the living Lord,
>   Nothing therefore I need;
> In pastures fair near pleasant sheaves
>   He setteth me to feed.

The organ pieces are tuneful, simple, and well written. The composer was very partial to suspensions, and makes free use of them. In ' Piece No. 8 ' he ventures on a three-part fugue with considerable success.

The tune ST. STEPHEN also appears at the end of his last published musical work :

A MORNING and EVENING SERVICE performed in St. George's Chapel, Windsor, before His Majesty, and in the Cathedral Churches of Canterbury, St. Paul, and Norwich.

This was issued in 1795. The tune is the same ST. STEPHEN as in the previous volume, but here it is called ' Nayland Tune.' There are two or three slight variations in the harmony.

57, 427—Wiltshire.

WILTSHIRE, by G. T. Smart, is from *Divine Amusement,* a collection formed by him for use in the chapel of St. James's Palace, probably about 1795. The tune has been much altered from what Smart wrote. This was the original form :

G. T. SMART.

The Lord, the on - ly God is great,

Let Him be e - - ver prais'd.

In Si - on, on its cho - sen mount,

His sa - cred throne was rais'd.

but the alteration to the present form seems to have met with Smart's approval, as he adopted it in a work edited by him in 1863, when he was in his eighty-seventh year.

Sir George Thomas Smart, although not usually included among the representative English Church composers, is entitled to more than a passing notice, seeing that he spent nearly the whole of his long life in the service of the Chapel Royal, of which he became a chorister in 1786, under Dr. Edmund Ayrton. He studied organ playing under Dr. Dupuis and his successor, Dr. Arnold, and soon rose to considerable eminence in his profession. In 1811 he was knighted by the Duke of Richmond, when Lord Lieutenant of Ireland, for having very successfully conducted some concerts in Dublin. In 1822 he succeeded Charles Knyvett as one of the organists of the Chapel Royal, and on the death of Attwood in 1838, was appointed composer. It is as a conductor that he is remembered, for he displayed an administrative ability that has rarely been excelled. He conducted five Musical Festivals at Liverpool, including the one held in 1836, when Mendelssohn's *St. Paul* was first performed in England; also at Norwich, Derby, Cambridge, Westminster Abbey (in 1834), and at Manchester in 1836, when Malibran died. Smart conducted for several years the oratorios which were given on the Wednesdays and Fridays in Lent at the theatres, and it was at his instance that Beethoven's *Mount of Olives* was first performed in this country in 1814. It is well known that he was long resorted to by singers desirous of acquiring the traditional manner of singing Handel's airs, having been so taught by his father, who had seen Handel conduct his oratorios. He edited Handel's *Dettingen Te Deum* for the Handel Society, and Orlando Gibbons' *Madrigals and Motets for Five Voices* for the Musical Antiquarian Society. Smart was the friend of all foreign musicians who came to London, and it was at his house, 91, Great Portland Street, that C. M. von Weber breathed his last in 1826. At a later period of his life he removed to 12, Bedford Square, where, after a laborious, useful, and honorable life he died in 1867.

This tune figures in Hardy's *The Mayor of Caster-*

bridge, when Michael Henchard, the ex-mayor, makes the church fiddlers play it to the paraphrase of Psalm 22. ' Old Wiltshire,' he said, ' is the only tune worth singing —the psalm-tune that would make my blood ebb and flow like the sea when I was a steady chap.'

58—Adoration.

ADORATION appeared anonymously in Vol. III of the *Parish Choir* (1851). It is generally ascribed to the Rev. W. H. Havergal, an earnest church musician to whom great credit is due for his efforts to arouse and sustain interest in the best forms of psalmody. Born in 1793, he entered the church in 1816, and after serving two curacies he was appointed rector of Ashley, Worcestershire, in 1829. His first published musical composition was a setting of ' From Greenland's icy mountains.' In 1836 the Gresham prize medal was awarded to him for his *Cathedral Service in A,* and five years later he was awarded another gold medal for his anthem *Give Thanks.* After this second success he devoted his attention almost entirely to the interests of metrical psalmody. In 1844 he published a reprint of Ravenscroft's *Psalter* of 1621, and followed this with his *Old Church Psalmody.* To supplement this work, J. C. Ward, a London organist, issued a collection of tunes which he intended to be a sequel to *Old Church Psalmody,* but Havergal, who had very definite ideas as to what was good and bad in church music, declined his support to the work on the ground that HELMSLEY, MARINERS, and in a less degree ABRIDGE and ROCKINGHAM were inconsistent with the title ' Church Psalmody.' He died in 1870.

59—Elevation.

ELEVATION was composed by R. Mellor for a Sunday-school anniversary, to the hymn ' Rise, my soul, and stretch thy wings.' It became widely known through being sung by 7,000 children in front of the Victoria Hall, Leeds, at their Whitsuntide gathering in 1861.

Richard Mellor was a very prominent figure in the musical life of Huddersfield and district during the greater part of last century, and although he belongs to a past generation his name is still remembered as that of a man of keen enthusiasm and striking personality. Born at Huddersfield in 1816, he became a skilful organist at an early age, and deputized at various places of worship until, at the age of eighteen, he settled at Zion Chapel, Lindley, for two years, and then a new organ attracted him to Christ Church, Linthwaite, where as a boy he had sung in the choir and also on occasion led the singing to the accompaniment of a violoncello. Hearing that an aeolophon—a sort of harmonium, locally christened 'the elephant'—was to be installed at Honley Methodist Chapel he went to hear it, and was so delighted with the novelty that he accepted an invitation to preside at the instrument. A vacancy at Halifax then attracted his attention, but his skill at the organ had also attracted the attention of Father Trappes of the Roman Catholic Church in Huddersfield, and he engaged Mellor as his organist, offering him £15 a year. Mellor bargained for £17 and got it, remaining two years at St. Patrick's.

In 1840 a new organ was opened in Ramsden Street Chapel, Huddersfield, by Thomas Parratt (father of Sir Walter Parratt), and the instrument so pleased Mellor that he applied for and obtained the position of organist. Here he remained for upwards of thirty years and made the musical service famous throughout the district. He made a special feature of the Sunday-school anniversaries. The children received a thorough drilling from him, and on one occasion the 'Hallelujah Chorus' (*Messiah*) was sung by 600 youngsters backed by a choir of the leading choralists of the district.

In spite of Mellor's efforts to maintain the dignity of church music attempts were sometimes made to introduce in the Sunday school secular melodies like ' Annie

Laurie' and 'Scots wha hae.' Mellor strenuously
resisted such innovations, and he went so far as to decline
to play such melodies in public worship.

Mellor was brought into contact with some of the
leading singers of his day. Whilst he was organist at
Zion Chapel he accompanied Miss Sykes in the first solo
she sang in public. The young lady afterwards became
the famous Mrs. Sunderland. It was at Lindley, too,
that he had as a pupil George Woodhouse, son of the
leader at Zion Chapel. The boy subsequently went to
Bolton and became famous as an architect, and also as
the first organist at Park Street Methodist Church,
where he performed wonders on an indifferent instrument.

Mellor retired from Ramsden Street Chapel in 1874,
and held no further appointment. He had an extensive
music and piano business, and earned a certain amount
of fame by responding to three summonses (at intervals)
for blocking up the public footway with piano cases.
His literary efforts were confined to two pamphlets, one
of them being *Music Defended* (1845), written in answer
to a pamphlet *Music and its Influences,* in which the
writer condemned the use of music in divine worship.
In another pamphlet Mellor described in racy style a
month's tour he had on the continent in 1866. He died
in 1882.

60—Pearsall.

PEARSALL is by R. L. Pearsall, and is from a St. Gall
Gesangbuch (1863), of which he was part editor.

Robert Lucas Pearsall was born in 1795 at Clifton.
As a boy he showed a great love of music, and composed
a cantata *Saul and the Witch of Endor* before he was
fourteen. He was educated for the legal profession, and
in 1821 was called to the Bar, but preferred writing
articles on music for a Bristol paper. An attack of illness caused him to leave England, and he remained

abroad for a few years, forming many literary and musical acquaintances. During one of his visits home he heard performances by Bristol and London Madrigal Societies, and this form of composition so delighted him that he proceeded to pay special attention to it, with the result that he has enriched English music with some fine specimens of madrigal writing. In 1842 he bought the Castle of Wartensee, on the Lake of Constance, and made it his home till his death in 1856. Towards the close of his life the Bishop of St. Gall received him into the Roman Church. His fame rests on such fine choral works as *Sir Patrick Spens* (ten parts), *Great God of Love* (eight parts), *Light of my soul* (six parts), and the four-part *In dulci jubilo*; but to very many he is best known by *O who will o'er the downs so free,* and *The Hardy Norseman* (see A.T. No. 11). Amongst his continental friends were Kaspar Ett (see No. 615), a musician who did great service in reviving the pure style of early church music, and Raphael Kieswetter, founder of the famous library that bears his name.

61—Exultation.

Exultation, by Sir A. C. Mackenzie, was composed for the *Westminster Abbey Hymn-Book* (1883; music edition, 1897).

Sir Alexander Campbell Mackenzie was born at Edinburgh in 1847. He came of a musical stock, his father being an orchestral player and song writer. The boy's first instrument was the fiddle, and at the age of ten he was sent to Germany to learn the violin and also harmony. In 1862 he came to London and entered the R.A.M., helping to maintain himself by playing in theatre orchestras. In 1865 he returned to Edinburgh, and for fourteen years led an active life of teaching and concert giving. His next move was to Florence, where he lived in retirement, devoting his time to composition. Whilst he was here he made the acquaintance of Liszt, with whom he became very friendly. In after years Sir

Alexander took an active part in inviting Liszt to visit England in 1886. Two years later Mackenzie was appointed Principal of the R.A.M., and under his powerful influence the Academy reached the highwater mark of success. He resigned the position in 1924, and has since been living in retirement. During his residence in Italy he wrote his cantatas *The Bride* and *Jason*, also his opera *Colomba* (in 1883). Since then he has produced numerous compositions of all kinds, and has delivered a large number of lectures on various subjects.

62—O Amor Quam Exstaticus.

O AMOR QUAM EXSTATICUS is taken from the *Oxford Hymn-Book* (1908). Its origin is unknown, but it is said to be derived from an old French melody. The lengthy Latin title seems to have no association whatever with the tune.

63—Ossett.

OSSETT is by Accepted Widdop, about whom little is known, though his Christian name suggests a Puritan ancestry. He was a cloth worker by trade, and an amateur musician of considerable fame in his day. His life was spent in the adjacent villages of Illingworth and Ovenden, which lie about two miles from Halifax. The date of his birth is uncertain (probably about 1749). He died in 1801 and was buried at Ovenden, where his tombstone bears this inscription :—

To the memory of Accepted Widdop, of Ovenden. Died, March 9, 1801, aged 52. A celebrated singer, author of several volumes of Anthems and many well-known Psalm-Tunes.

> Music, the noblest science known to man,
> Which angels honour'd long ere time began,
> Was his delight; his sweet seraphic lays,
> Will hand his mem'ry down to future days,
> And he, we hope, in sweeter strains above,
> Now chants the praises of redeeming Love.

64—Lobe den Herren.

LOBE DEN HERREN. The present form of this tune is taken from *The Chorale Book for England,* edited by Sterndale Bennett and Otto Goldschmidt in 1863. There it is said to be derived from the 1668 edition of *Praxis Pietatis Melica.* It has, however, a still earlier source, for it has been traced to a song-book published at Stralsund in 1665, though the melody is not quite the same.

65, 553—Tarsus.

TARSUS was written by Sir John Goss (see No. 12) for Hackett's *National Psalmist* (1840).

66—Harwich.

HARWICH, by Benjamin Milgrove, is included in his *Sixteen Hymns as they are sung at the Right Honourable the Countess of Huntingdon's Chapel in Bath.* These were published about 1769, and it is probable that Milgrove was either precentor or organist (or both) at the chapel referred to in the Vineyard. According to the Bath directories he was also a ' toyman,' or owner of a fancy shop in Bond Street. When John Wesley built New King Street Chapel in Bath he invested the financial affairs in a body of ' proprietors,' one of them being Milgrove, who held a single £100 share in the building, which he parted with in 1787. Horace Walpole visited the Countess of Huntingdon's Chapel when Milgrove had charge of the music and thus related his experiences :

I have been at an opera, Mr. Wesley's. They have boys and girls with charming voices that sing hymns, in parts, to Scotch ballad tunes. But indeed so long that one would think they were already in eternity, and knew how much time they had before them. The Chapel is very neat with true Gothic windows (yet I

am not converted); but I was glad to see that luxury
is creeping in upon them before persecution. They
have very neat mahogany for benches, and brackets of
the same in taste. At the upper end is a broad *hautpas*
of four steps, advancing in the middle; at each end of
the broadest part are two eagles with red cushions for
the parson and clerk. Behind them rise three more
steps, in the midst of which is a third eagle for pulpit,
scarlet arm-chairs to all three. On either hand a
balcony for elect ladies. The rest of the congregation
sit on forms. Behind the pulpit, in a dark niche, is
a plain table within rails.

67, 80—Dresden.

DRESDEN is by Johann Schmidlin, who compiled several
collections of *Geistliche Lieder* towards the end of the
eighteenth century. They were published at Zurich
between 1758 and 1773.

DRESDEN is No. 27 in *Schweitzerlieder mit Melodien,*
Zurich (1796). It is headed 'Lied der demotratischen
Kantone den ihrer jährlichen Landsgemeine.' It probably
occurs also in one of Schmidlin's earlier collections. The
tune is exactly as he composed it, and has undergone
no alteration, a most unusual thing with old melodies.

68—Jeshurun.

JESHURUN was composed by Dr. Gauntlett (see No. 7)
for the first edition of *Tunes New and Old.* This
collection was formed by John Dobson, a lover of
psalmody, who was born at Manchester in 1814. The
basis of his *Tunes New and Old* was a manuscript collection prepared by John Fernley in 1839 for the Wesleyan
Chapel, Oxford Road, Manchester. Dobson enlarged
this collection, confining his choice to 'syllabic tunes' as
being the 'most suitable for the united expression of
praise and prayer.' Like other editors he had to contend

with copyright difficulties in his selection, and he therefore invited new contributions from recognized musicians.
Gauntlett sent a number of tunes, as did S. Reay, J. Goss
and others. The first edition was published in 1864, and
was so successful that in 1876 a new edition was issued
to which J. F. Bridge and others contributed. Dobson
died in 1888, and his valuable library was dispersed by
auction, a large number of his tune-books going to
America, including the very scarce (and probably unique)
copy of *Hymns and Sacred Poems* (1749), containing
IRISH (No. 503).

69—Celeste.

CELESTE probably made its first appearance in *Sacred
Hymns and Harmonies,* which is said on the title page to
be ' The Musical Companion to " Lancashire Sunday
School Songs." ' This remarkably cheap shilling's worth
(bound in cloth) of children's sacred songs was edited
by the Rev. J. Compston, at that time living at Bramley,
near Leeds. He belonged to an East Lancashire family
noted for their love of and skill in music. He gathered
his tunes from all sources, including standard psalm-
tunes, and various adaptations, from the National
Anthem to the once popular ' I'd be a butterfly ' (amended
to ' I'd be a missionary '). No. 22 is CELESTE set to ' We
sing of the realms of the blest.' As the writer of this
hymn died in 1829 it is quite likely that this tune was in
existence before 1857, when the ' Lancashire Sunday
School Songs ' appeared, but it has not yet been traced to
an earlier date. No composer's name is attached to the
tune.

70—Meine Hoffnung.

MEINE HOFFNUNG is from the same ' Bundeslieder '
as UNSER HERRSCHER (No. 53). There is some uncertainty as to whether it is Neander's own composition or
an adaptation by him of an earlier melody.

71—Luther.

LUTHER.   Although Luther's name is frequently associated with this tune there is no definite proof that he composed it.   It dates from the *Gesangbuch* published by Joseph Klug in 1535.   This is the second edition of a collection of chorales published six years earlier, but as no copy is known to exist it is not certain whether LUTHER is in it.   Only one copy of the second edition (1535) is known.   The tune was brought into England towards the end of the eighteenth century, and soon became popular, chiefly through a dramatic arrangement by Baumgarten, organist of the Lutheran Chapel in London, for solo voice with trumpet obligato.   It had a wonderful popularity in country churches, and it is said that on certain occasions when this version was used the trumpeter would be concealed somewhere in the building, and the sound of the instrument coming in thus unexpectedly, and apparently from nowhere, produced a realistic effect calculated to arouse the most hardened sinner in the parish.

Stainer and Barrett have recorded in their *Dictionary* twenty-one different versions of this tune, including one in triple time.   The most remarkable specimen is the version used by Sterndale Bennett in the overture to *The Woman of Samaria,* where the composer has given the melody in common time ' driven against and in combination with a movement in triple measure.'

There is a legend to the effect that Luther was once riding along a country road when he heard a wayfaring man singing a melody which greatly attracted him. Dismounting, he induced the singer to repeat the tune, and, as he did so, Luther noted it down on a piece of paper.   Such was the origin, so it is said, of LUTHER. If this were true it would reveal the great reformer in a new sphere, namely as the first collector of folk-songs !

72, 244—St. Magnus.

St. Magnus originally appeared without a name in *The Divine Companion* (1709), compiled by Henry Playford. The composer is not given, but internal evidence suggests that it is by Jeremiah Clark, and it is now always attributed to him. It was reprinted in Gawthorne's *Harmonia Perfecta* (1730), where it is named Notingham, but it was rechristened St. Magnus by Riley in his *Parochial Psalmody* (1762), though Clark had no connexion with the London church of that name.

Little is known of Clark's early life, save that he was a chorister at the Chapel Royal with Dr. Blow for his master. After three years as organist at Winchester College he was appointed organist at St. Paul's in 1695, but the rebuilding of the Cathedral was still in progress, and Clark did not enter on his duties till the end of 1697, when he opened Father Smith's new organ. He was also joint organist with Dr. William Croft at the St. James's Chapel Royal. It is interesting to note that Clark held his position without a doctor's degree in music, which is to-day an essential qualification for a cathedral organist, who is often assisted in obtaining it through a Lambeth degree, conferred by the Archbishop of Canterbury. Clark was also music-master to Queen Anne, for whose use he composed some ' Choice Lessons ' for the harpsichord. His career was blighted by a love affair, which so demoralized him that he decided to terminate his life. Riding into the country he left his horse, and crossing a field came to a pond surrounded by trees. Uncertain whether hanging or drowning would be the better method of hastening his end, he tossed up for it, but unfortunately for him the coin stuck on its edge. He returned home and settled his fate by blowing out his brains with a ' screw pistol.' [1] This sad event

[1] A screw pistol is one in which the barrel screws off for loading and no loading rod is fitted. Such pistols were popular in the Queen Anne period, for pocket and carriage, and usually had a tapered ' cannon '-shaped barrel. They were much smaller than holster pistols.

took place at his house in St. Paul's Churchyard on December 1, 1707.

73—Westminster.

WESTMINSTER is by James Turle. It originally appeared in *The Psalmist*, Part II (1836), where it was called BIRMINGHAM.

James Turle was born at Somerton (Somerset) in 1802. He became a chorister at Wells Cathedral, where he was educated in a musical atmosphere and left his mark on the building itself by landing a stone through the nose of St. Andrew in one of the stained glass windows. In 1819 he went to London and after holding church appointments at Christ Church, Southwark, and St. James's, Bermondsey, he became assistant organist at Westminster Abbey, under Thomas Greatorex (see No. 383), after whose death in 1831 he was appointed to the full position. Here he remained till 1875, when J. Frederick Bridge was appointed his assistant, so that when Turle died in 1882 he had been officially connected with the Abbey for sixty-three years. He composed various anthems and church services, but his fame chiefly rests on his chants, many of them being published in the *Westminster Chant Book*.

He was highly esteemed as a teacher, and the number of his pupils who rose to prominence in their profession is ample testimony of his skill and ability. His *Psalm and Hymn-Tunes* were collected by his daughter, S. A. Turle, and published in 1885. Of these WESTMINSTER alone has survived. As a church organist he was a fine example of the old school, and was greatly skilled in playing from the old figured bass scores. It is said that his hands were inclined to be ' outsize.' On one occasion, when visiting at the Prussian Embassy, he met Neukomm, of organ storm fame, who proudly boasted that he could stretch an octave and three notes on the keyboard. Turle watched him with deep interest, and

then went to the pianoforte and took an octave and a
half in his huge hand, quietly remarking ' one more for
luck ' !

74—Gerontius.

GERONTIUS takes its name from Newman's poem *The
Dream of Gerontius.* The tune was written for the
Appendix to *Hymns Ancient and Modern* (1868), by
J. B. Dykes (see No. 36).

75, 927—Melcombe.

MELCOMBE was originally a setting of the Latin hymn
' O Salutaris Hostia ' in *A Collection of Motetts,* &c.,
(1792), by Samuel Webbe. It had appeared ten years
earlier in *An Essay on the Church Plain Chant,* but without any composer's name.

Samuel Webbe, the prince of English glee writers, is
a striking example of a self-made man, whose industry
and perseverance, touched with genius, overcame all
obstacles. Soon after his birth in 1740, the boy's father
was sent to Minorca in some Government capacity, and,
having secured a house, he wrote for his wife and infant
boy to join him. Before they could leave England a
further message arrived announcing the father's death
in Minorca. The property that should have come to the
widow was diverted to other purposes, and young Webbe
grew up without enjoying any of the advantages of
education beyond what his mother herself could give
him. At the age of eleven he was apprenticed to a
cabinet-maker, but the occupation was little to his taste,
and in after years he bitterly deplored the wasted seven
years that he had spent in the carpenter's shop. Unwilling to follow this line of business, he found himself
at twenty years of age without any suitable employment.
Music, however, had already an attraction for him, and
he secured work as a music copyist from a Mr. Welcher,
who kept a well-known music shop in Gerrard Street,

Soho. It is difficult to know how young Webbe found time even to live at this period, for his copying work frequently occupied him from five o'clock in the morning till midnight, yet during the next three years he took up the study of Latin and French, while the continued music-copying, so far from wearying him, aroused his interest in the art to such an extent, that he determined to make himself master of it, both in theory and practice.

Webbe's two most noted secular compositions are ' When winds breathe soft' and 'Swiftly from the mountain's brow,' which even in the lifetime of their composer were termed ' the King and Queen of glees.' It is a curious fact that the writer of the words of the first-named has never been traced, and the glee owes its existence to an accidental circumstance. Here is Webbe's own version of the story. Having sent his servant one day to the chandler's shop to purchase some article, he brought it back wrapped up in a piece of paper. Webbe happened to examine the printed matter on the paper, and found it consisted of some verses, which promptly appealed to his musical genius, and thus did ' When winds breathe soft' come into existence. Perhaps few of his glees have been sung oftener than ' Glorious Apollo,' though not one of his best.

For many years Webbe held the position of organist at the Catholic Church of St. Agatha, which, in his time, was known as the Chapel of the Sardinian Embassy, or ' The Sardinian Chapel.' It stood in a narrow street leading westward out of Lincoln's Inn Fields, and in the eighteenth century it was the principal Catholic Church in London. As such, it suffered severely in the Gordon Riots of 1780, the whole of the interior, including the organ, being destroyed. That he was not overpaid for his work is evident from a letter written by his friend Samuel Wesley to Vincent Novello, asking him to look out for a voluntary assistant for Webbe, since the latter's salary as organist was only £10 or ten guineas per annum. To provide suitable music for his choir Webbe composed

a series of easy masses and motets, which are still in
use. The music possessed three essential qualifications
—tuneful, devotional, and easy to sing.

It is to the music of these masses that the Protestant
Church is indebted for two of her most popular and
widely-used hymn-tunes, namely MELCOMBE and BENE-
VENTO (566).

The former is a setting of the hymn, ' O Salutaris
Hostia,' and the latter was written to the words ' Tantum
ergo sacramentum.'

To Webbe also we are indebted for the modern forms
of the music of ADESTE FIDELES (No. 118), and STABAT
MATER (Nos. 185, 287), both of which appear in his
book of *Easy Masses.*

76 (i)—Hardwicke.

HARDWICKE makes its first appearance in the present
Methodist Hymn-Book. The composer, Cecil T. Groves,
is a Methodist missionary at present stationed in India.

76 (ii)—Dominus Regit Me.

DOMINUS REGIT ME was composed by J. B. Dykes (see
No. 36) for the 1868 Appendix to *Hymns Ancient and
Modern.*

77, 650—Jerusalem.

JERUSALEM is from *Hymns used at St. Thomas Church,*
Dudley, where Simeon Grosvenor was organist in the
middle of the nineteenth century. Details about him are
wanting. It was also inserted (' by kind permission of
Mr. S. Grosvenor ') in Adam Wright's *Congregational
Psalmody* (1844), which he compiled for use at Carr's
Lane Chapel, Birmingham, where he was organist.

78—Soll's Sein.

SOLL'S SEIN is taken from *Songs of Praise* (1931). It
is of German origin, found in one of D. G. Corner's
collections (1631-1680).

79, 486—Justification.

Justification is by the Rev. John Eagleton. Born at Coventry in 1785, he was one of the first scholars at the Sunday school founded in that town by the Rev. George Burder (see No. 275). The boy was very fond of music, and acted as leader of the choir at his chapel till his voice broke. Then he became a Wesleyan local preacher, and on reaching his twenty-first birthday he succeeded his father in the pastorate of a meeting-house near Coventry. Later he had charge of a Congregational Church in Vicar Lane, Coventry. His musical abilities were specially directed to improving the music at his church, and for the use of his choir and congregation he published in 1816 a set of original tunes called *Sacred Harmony*, in which his Justification first appeared. Eagleton also held pastorates at Birmingham and at Ramsden Street Congregational Chapel, Huddersfield, where he died in 1832. Just before his death he published a *Manual of Hymns for Family, Social and Public Worship*, which was in use at Ramsden Street for many years.

80—Dresden. See No. 67.

81, 352—St. Bride.

St. Bride and Stafford (No. 557) both originally appeared in William Riley's *Parochial Harmony, consisting of a Collection of Psalm-Tunes in three and four parts*, &c. (1762). St. Bride is there called St. Bridget's Tune, set to Psalm cxxx. N.V. ' From lowest depths of woe.'

The composer, Dr. Samuel Howard, was an eighteenth-century church organist who learnt his music as a young chorister at the Chapel Royal under Dr. Croft. He then studied with Dr. Pepusch, and having thus rendered himself worthy, he became organist at St. Clement Danes, Strand (where Dr. Johnson, who attended that church, may have heard him) and also at St. Bride's, Fleet Street (hence the name of the tune). These two positions he held concurrently. He distinguished himself in secular works by writing music for a pantomine, and was the composer of several songs. He also assisted his old master, Dr. Boyce, when he was compiling his volumes of cathedral music.

Howard seems to have been of an amiable disposition, and his contemporaries have recorded nothing but what is good about him. Dr. Burney thus referred to him:

> The ballads of Dr. Samuel Howard, which were long the delight of natural and inexperienced lovers of music, had the merit of facility: for this honest Englishman, brought up in the Chapel Royal, preferred the style of his own country to that of any other so much that he never staggered his belief of its being the best in the world by listening to foreign artists or their productions.

It is also recorded of Howard that he was ' ever ready to relieve distress, to anticipate the demand of friendship, and to prevent the necessities of his acquaintance.' Howard was one of the singers who took part in the first performance of Handel's *Esther* in London. (See No. 49.)

82, 703—Bristol.

BRISTOL is from Ravenscroft's ' Psalter ' (1621) (see No. 45), where it is called an *English tune*.

83—Corde Natus.

CORDE NATUS. This old melody came into modern use through Part II of the *Hymnal Noted* (1854), where it is set to the hymn ' Corde natus ex parentis,' translated by Dr. Neale as ' Of the Father's love begotten.' The melody is, however, of much older date, and is found in a collection of church and school songs called *Piae Cantiones*. This work was published at Nyland in 1582 by Theodoric Petri. He formed the collection whilst he was a student at the University of Rostock, a large sea-port on the Baltic. He himself published a second edition in 1625 and during the next hundred years some of the songs were frequently reprinted.

Nothing is known of the composer of CORDE NATUS. In *Piae Cantiones* the tune is set to a different hymn: ' Divinum mysterium modo declaratur,' which does not fit the music very easily. In fact Petri, the compiler of *Piae Cantiones*, does not appear to have been well served by his musical editor or arranger, a certain Augustus Ferber, who printed the work at his office in Grieswald, not far from Rostock, where, as has been stated, Petri was a student.

84—St. Theodulph.

ST. THEODULPH is usually ascribed to Melchior Teschner, who at the beginning of the seventeenth century was precentor at a church in the Bavarian village of Fraustadt. He composed it in 1614 to a funeral hymn written by his pastor, Herberger, when over two thousand people in the district perished during a fearful pestilence. The tune is used by Bach (much elaborated) in his *St. John Passion*. The value of the tune for congregational use is somewhat discounted by two facts: (1) the melody is not standardized, and varies in different books, (2) opinions differ as to how the tune is to be fitted to the words. Some editions (as here) make a refrain of the first verse. Others treat it as an ordinary eight-line hymn, to be sung straight through. In *The Oxford Hymn-Book* is a totally different theory as to the origin of the tune. Teschner's claim is ignored altogether, and it is ascribed to ' William Byrd, 1542-1623 (adapted from *Sellinger's Round*, 1580).' This was a very popular tune of a maypole dance character in the Elizabethan and Stuart periods, and there are numerous references to it in the plays and other literature of the period. There is no proof that Byrd composed it, though he wrote a set of variations on it.

Sellinger's Round.

85, 401—Nativity.

Nativity is from Lahee's *Metrical Psalter* (1855).
Henry Lahee was born in Cheyne Walk, Chelsea, not
far from the residence of John Goss, who throughout life
remained one of his closest friends. He received pianoforte lessons from Cipriani Potter and later from
Sterndale Bennett. His early organ appointments were
at Christ Church, Chelsea, and at St. Benet's, off Queen
Victoria Street, E.C. From there he went to St.
Swithin's, opposite Cannon Street Station, and in 1847
entered upon his last and longest appointment at Holy
Trinity, Brompton, where he remained for twenty-six
years. The vicar, Dr. Irons (to whom we owe the well-
known translation of 'Dies Irae'), was desirous of
having a really musical service, but his congregation was
not prepared for it. One of his plans for arousing
interest was a series of services with choir and orchestra
which Arthur Sullivan conducted. Dr. Irons had an
eclectic choice in hymns, and as *Hymns Ancient and
Modern* did not suit his ideas he made his own selection

of a hundred hymns and for these Lahee chose a hundred tunes, printing his selection in a book at his own expense, losing heavily. One of the tunes he composed for this collection was NATIVITY, which has since proved very popular.

Lahee had a large teaching connexion chiefly amongst ladies' schools, working in close association with Sterndale Bennett. He was also associated with John Curwen, who in the early sixties was having a difficulty in getting choral works issued in Tonic Sol-fa notation. Curwen proceeded to become his own publisher, and commissioned Lahee to write a cantata, for which he chose Longfellow's 'Building of the Ship.' His other compositions include *The Sleeping Beauty* (for ladies' voices) and numerous glees and part-songs.

86—Song 5. See No. 24.

87 (i)—Orientis Partibus.

ORIENTIS PARTIBUS is the classic name of a melody known in common language as 'the Hymn of the Ass.' The story of the flight of Mary and Joseph into Egypt forms the groundwork of many traditional carols, including this one. It was the custom thus to commemorate the journey; a maiden carrying a child in her arms, and riding a richly caparisoned ass, rode at the head of a procession through the chief streets of a town. A motley crowd followed chanting some verses in a curious language made up of French and German indescriminately. Each verse finished up with the refrain :

Hail, Sir Donkey, hail !

The words and music were known as 'The Prose of the Ass,' and it was designed 'to set forth the praise of the ass in connexion with his coming to the manger at Bethlehem.' It may be well to point out that the procession was a solemn affair, and not a burlesque.

The tune is of indefinite origin, dating probably from the thirteenth century. It was revived by Richard Redhead (see No. 13) in his *Church Hymns with Tunes* (1853).

87 (ii)—Savannah.

Sᴀᴠᴀɴɴᴀʜ (or Hᴇʀʀɴʜᴜᴛ) is from the ' Foundery ' Tune-Book (1742). It is probably of German origin, but its history is not known.

88—St. Asaph.

The return of this tune to the *Methodist Hymn-Book* will be welcomed by many who remember it as a useful help in selecting a D.C.M. tune. There is a certain air of mystery both about the tune and about its composer. The correct way to spell his name appears to be Giornovichj, while his second christian name is also recorded as Maria, which seems more probable than Mane, as given by good authorities. On arriving at manhood he took a dislike to his surname, and decided in future to be known as Jarnowick, and under this name he is recorded in Grove's *Dictionary*, the editor being apparently ignorant of the fact that his real name was Giornovichj. Jarnowick is, perhaps, easier to spell, so it will serve for the present. Born at Palermo in 1745 (though this date has been questioned) he studied the violin under Lolli, who was, according to all accounts, not only a great player, but capable of all sorts of odd tricks on his instrument, anticipating, to some extent, the extraordinary performances of Paganini, though far inferior to the latter in talent.

He visited Paris in 1770 and established himself as a public favourite by his playing at the Concert Spirituel (or Sacred Concert, a standing Paris institution). His talents justified his success; his playing, full of suppleness and grace, was distinguished by remarkable correctness of intonation, great facility both of fingers and bow, and a pure taste in the choice and execution of ornaments, but a more powerful tone and a greater breadth of phrasing would have been desirable. His admirers, however, thought him perfect, especially when he played his own music. His success in other places helped his reputation in Paris, where he would probably have settled but for certain untoward incidents which made his departure from that city and from France highly desirable. He went to Berlin, where he was soon engaged in the Chapel Royal.

What the 'untoward incidents' were is uncertain, but he was sufficiently eccentric and capricious to turn his friends against him. One day he was at the house of Bailleux, a musical editor, when he accidentally broke a pane of glass. 'Who breaks pays,' said Bailleux. 'That is fair,' replied Jarnowick, 'what is the price of that square?' 'Thirty sous.' Jarnowick gave him a crown. 'I have no change,' said Bailleux. 'That is of no consequence,' answered the fiddler, and he at once smashed another pane. On one occasion he announced a concert in Lyons at six francs per seat. The figure was excessive and the house was empty, but Jarnowick determined to have his revenge, and announced a concert shortly after at three francs a head. This time the hall was full, but Jarnowick had left the city some hours before the time of the concert. It is not perhaps surprising that such a madcap found it expedient to leave the country.

Jarnowick visited both England and Scotland, living for some time at Edinburgh, but nothing is known of his career in either country. The actual source of St. Asaph is unknown. James Love examined several of the composer's works, but was quite unable to trace the melody. Its introduction as a hymn-tune appears to be due to R. A. Smith, who inserted it in his *Sacred Music* (1825).

89—Lübeck.

LÜBECK. Johann Anastasius Freylinghausen was the son of the burgomaster at Gandersheim, Brunswick, where he was born in 1670. After passing through the University of Jena he became a private tutor for a time. Later he was associated with A. H. Francke in the management of the latter's orphanage, and ultimately, after Francke's death, became sole director. He died in 1739. Freylinghausen prepared and edited an extensive selection of hymns with melodies and issued them in two parts—(1) *Geist-reiches* Gesang-Buch (1704), and (2) *Neues Geist-reiches* Gesang-Buch (1714). In 1741 these two volumes were combined, and the single volume went through various editions till 1771, in which year the complete collection was issued.

90—Theodora.

THEODORA is adapted from the air 'Angels ever bright and fair' in Handel's oratorio. Theodora is a Christian who has been required to join with her companions in offering sacrifices to Venus. She refuses and prays for deliverance in the song :

> Angels ever bright and fair
> Take, oh take me, to your care.

The oratorio, written in 1749, was a great favourite with the composer, who was much disappointed that it had not attracted the public, and he did not conceal his feelings. On hearing that a person of note had undertaken to engage all the boxes if *Theodora* was given again, Handel said, 'He is a fool, the Jews will not come to it as to *Judas Maccabaeus,* because it is a Christian story, and the ladies will not come because it is a virtuous one.' It was the last oratorio but one that Handel composed, *Jephthah* following it two years later.

91—Miles Lane.

MILES LANE, by William Shrubsole, probably made its first appearance in the *Gospel Magazine* for November, 1779, in this form :

HYMN.

All hail the Pow'r of Je-fu's Name, Let

An-gels proftrate fall ; Bring forth the Roy-al

crown him,

Di - a - dem, crown him,

To crown him,

CHORUS.

crown him Lord of all,

crown him Lord of all.

Both words and music were anonymous, and only one verse was printed. Four months later the hymn was printed in its full form of eight stanzas. ' Miles ' is a corruption of (St.) Michael's, and until 1831 a church dedicated to that saint stood in the Lane,[1] and gave its name to it. In the eighteenth century a dissenting meeting-house was added to the attractions of Miles Lane, one of its earliest pastors being Stephen Ashworth (see No. 120). Shrubsole, who is stated to have been a black-smith's son, began his musical career as a chorister in Canterbury Cathedral. On reaching man's estate he settled down for a time as a music teacher in London, and appears to have met with success, as two of his pupils, William Russell and Benjamin Jacob, both attained distinction. The former was organist of the Foundling Hospital, and also at Great Queen Street Wesleyan Chapel.

Shrubsole's career as a teacher, though apparently successful, was certainly brief, as at the age of twenty-two he was appointed organist at Bangor Cathedral, at a salary of forty guineas per annum; and it is interesting to know that he made such a favourable impression on the authorities that they thought proper to give him a further sum of eight guineas to defray the cost of the removal of his harpsichord and other effects from London. Unfortunately these good relations did not last long, for Shrubsole appears to have been in the habit of attending Nonconformist meetings. This did not find favour with the Cathedral Chapter, and he was solemnly warned of the consequences of ' attending conventicles.' These warnings, however, he cheerfully disregarded, with the consequence that he was dismissed from his position, and returned to London after a residence of nearly two years in Bangor. It would be very interesting if more details could be brought to light concerning Shrubsole's experiences in the Welsh city, but there is no chance of obtaining further information.

[1] Off Cannon Street; near London Bridge.

It is not recorded whether the Dean and Chapter paid for the carriage of his goods and chattels on the return journey, probably not. However, Shrubsole had not to wait long for an appointment, and he became organist of Spa Fields Chapel, which was at that time one of the chief places in London belonging to the Countess of of Huntingdon's Connexion. Here he remained till his death, so it is evident that his sympathies were wholly on the side of the evangelical movement of his time. The *Musical Directory* of 1794 describes him as an alto singer, and it appears that he took part in several of the festivals and great musical gatherings of the period. He died in 1806, and was buried in Bunhill Fields Cemetery.

92—Lydia. See No. 1 (ii).

93—Grafton.

GRAFTON is taken from a French collection called *Chants Ordinaires de l'Office Divin,* published in Paris in 1881.

94—All Hallows.

ALL HALLOWS, by F. Luke Wiseman (see No. 5), was written for the 1904 *Methodist Hymn-Book.*

95—Coldrey.

COLDREY was composed by Henry Smart (see No. 12) for *Psalms and Hymns for Divine Worship* (1867).

96—Southampton.

SOUTHAMPTON was contributed anonymously to *The Psalms of David for Use in Parish Churches* (1791). (See No. 465.)

97—Eccles.

ECCLES is by Richard Boggett, who was born at Kippax, near Leeds, about 1810. He was a corn miller

by trade. His taste for music brought him into notice,
and though self-taught, he became known both for his
playing and his compositions. He was choirmaster at
the Methodist Church at Kippax, and took an active part
in the various departments of church life. ECCLES was
included in his *Original Set of Psalm and Hymn-Tunes,*
where it is set to Wesley's hymn 'How weak the
thoughts, and vain.' Boggett used to say that the
proudest moment of his life was when he heard Dr. S. S.
Wesley play this tune at a festival in Brunswick Chapel,
Leeds. The composer was one day seated at his instrument when the Rev. Abraham Eccles Farrar, a well-
known minister of the time, came into his room and said,
'What are you doing, Richard?' 'Trying over a tune
I've been making.' 'Why, can you make a tune?' said
the minister, 'let's hear it.' So Boggett played the new
tune to him. 'That's a fine tune, and it will live,' said
Mr. Farrar. 'What are you going to call it?' 'I haven't
thought about that yet.' 'Well then,' was the reply, 'you
had better call it ECCLES after me.' The composer died
in 1879.

98—Warwick Gardens.

WARWICK GARDENS was contributed by T. C. Gregory
for the present edition of the *Methodist Hymn-Book.* It
was written for Wesley's hymn 'Thou hidden Source
of calm repose,' and is named after the Wesleyan
Church in Warwick Gardens, in the West of London,
built originally for the famous preacher, W. Morley
Punshon. It was ruthlessly destroyed some years ago.
In the vestry of this church the composer had his
habitation whilst studying at the Royal College of Music.

Theophilus Cyril Gregory was born at Thorne, Yorks,
in 1901, and was educated at Kingswood School, Bath.
He came from a musical home, and his natural gifts for
music were developed whilst at Kingswood by the music
master there, Mr. Alfred Beer, of whom he speaks in
terms of the highest admiration and respect. In the

school choir he sang in turn as treble, alto, tenor and bass, and so passed to the position of school organist, which he held for four years. Leaving school, he decided to enter the musical profession, influenced largely by the impressions received whilst taking part in Bach's choral works at Oxford under Sir Hugh Allen's conductorship. Entering the R.C.M. he studied under Dr. George Dyson and others, and was ' proxime accessit ' in the theory examination at the College, receiving further instruction in later years from J. A. Sowerbutts, now of Guildford Cathedral, and Dr. C. H. Kitson. From September, 1925, to the end of 1928 he was assistant master in the Royal Grammar School, Guildford, and then he was appointed master of the music at Rydal School, Colwyn Bay. In 1933 he took his M.A. degree at Oxford. In addition to hymn-tunes he has composed songs and part-songs.

99—St. Peter.

St. Peter was first published in *Psalm-Tunes for the Voice and Pianoforte,* composed by A. R. Reinagle. The date of the book is uncertain, but ranges between 1826 and 1830.

A. R. Reinagle came of a musical stock, his father, Joseph, being a famous violoncello player of the day. When he reached his twenty-second year he was appointed organist of St. Peter-in-East, Oxford, where he remained till 1853, when he retired into private life. ' He was short in stature and had thick white hair; was deliberate in his movements, quaint in conversation, and a most kindhearted man.' His salary at St. Peter's was only £20, and after he had served the parish faithfully for about forty years some pettifogging, parsimonious parishioners actually proposed that it should be reduced to £15. This was too much even for the gentle Reinagle, and he issued a circular in which he set forth his own side of the case. After describing the work expected of him, he ended up by saying, ' If you think I am overpaid, and that five pounds will be an important saving to the parish, I shall submit to the reduction.' The result of the dispute has not been put on record.

100—All Saints.

ALL SAINTS and ST. GREGORY (No. 532) are both taken from a *Gesangbuch* published at Darmstadt in 1698. ALL SAINTS is played weekly on the bells of Bath Abbey for the benefit of the citizens.

101—Theodora.

THEODORA is by Alfred Legge, who was born at Cambridge in 1843. He was a chorister at Trinity College, and also a pupil of Professor T. A. Walmisley. Later he was articled to J. L. Hopkins, whose deputy at Trinity he was. On leaving Cambridge he held various positions as organist, the last being at the parish church at Ashford, Kent. It was for the use of the choir here that he wrote THEODORA, which was inserted in the second Appendix of Allon's *Congregational Psalmist* (1875). He died in 1919.

102—Stracathro.

Charles Hutcheson, the composer of STRACATHRO, was a native of Glasgow, where he did active work as an amateur musician of considerable skill. He compiled a collection of tunes which he named *Christian Vespers* (1832), in which this tune first appeared. The following extract from St. Columba's *Church Magazine* (Edinburgh), 1933, will throw further light on the tune:

Last month we asked for some light on the origin of the name STRACATHRO given to a psalm tune which appears to have recently gained a new vogue. A member of St. Columba's sends us a most interesting letter on the subject from which it will appear that the authorship of the tune was rightly ascribed to Charles Hutcheson, born in 1792. Miss Craik writes:

'My dear Doctor Fleming,—We were interested in seeing your paragraph in the magazine about the tune STRACATHRO, and we thought you would care to know what we can remember about it. Mr. Charles Hutcheson was a friend of our father's and a member of St. George's Church, Glasgow. When STRACATHRO was published we were all interested and it was sung for the first time in St. George's Church. It took hold at once and became one of our father's favourite tunes, so it has lived in our memory.

'For the name. Just at the time it was first published Sir James Campbell—also a member of St. George's—had bought his property, Stracathro, and as the world was not quite so large as it is now, and properties did not change hands so often, it was a good deal spoken of, and the tune was called STRACATHRO as a friendly compliment to Sir James Campbell. Mr. Hutcheson, as we remember him, was an interesting and attractive personality, and one of those who carry music in their hearts. Sir James Campbell was the father of Sir Henry Campbell-Bannerman.'

103—St. Hugh.

Dr. E. J. Hopkins contributed ST. HUGH to the 1862 edition of R. R. Chope's *Congregational Hymn and Tune-Book.*

Edward John Hopkins, one of the most prominent musicians of the nineteenth century, was born in Westminster in 1818. At the age of eight he became one of the children of the Chapel Royal, St. James's, remaining there till his voice broke towards the end of 1833. As he had a remarkably fine voice young Hopkins was selected to do duty at St. Paul's Cathedral as well on Sundays, so he had a busy time of it, as there were two services at both places. The boys at the Chapel Royal wore a special and somewhat gorgeous uniform (they do so to this day), which was, of course out of place at the Cathedral, so young Hopkins had to go home and change his clothes after each service. A proper meal was impossible during the six or seven hours that the services lasted, and besides the worry of changing dress, he walked or ran some six miles or more in order to be present at them all. Rather heavy work for a youngster, though it certainly does not appear to have shortened his days, for it was after he had passed his eightieth birthday that he declared to an interviewer that he had been battling with crotchets and quavers for over seventy years !

When Hopkins's chorister days ended he decided to adopt music as a profession, his first appointment being at Mitcham Church. This provided him with more walking exercise, as he now had to travel sixteen miles each Sunday, sometimes arriving at his post wet through, with his boots waterlogged. He survived four years of this, and then went to St. Mary's, Islington, and subsequently to St. Luke's, Berwick Street, W., where he got into trouble. Having to be absent one Sunday he provided a deputy, and was pained to receive a letter from his vicar, W. H. Brookfield, a few days after, saying that the substitute provided was so inefficient that Hopkins's services would not be required any longer !

However he had not long to wait, as he had already made a name as an efficient organist. Applying, in 1843, for the vacancy at the Temple, on the death of George Warne (a blind organist), he was appointed after the honourable Benchers had made ' careful inquirie as to his antecedents.' Here he remained for fifty-four years, busily occupied with his church duties, with opening organs, and with taking an active part in the work of various musical institutions. He was one of the Founders of the (Royal) College of Organists, and his great knowledge of the instrument found an outlet in his famous work (in conjunction with E. F. Rimbault) on *The Organ, its History and Construction.* Two editions were issued and a third promised, but it was never completed.

Hopkins made many notable contributions to church music, his anthems and organ compositions proving him to have been a musician of sterling worth. On two occasions he won the Gresham gold medal, his successful efforts being ' Out of the Deep ' (1838) and ' God is gone up ' (1840). ' God, who commandest the Light to shine ' was specially written to be sung on the occasion of the recovery of the Prince of Wales in 1872. His organ works are too well known to need enumeration or description, but special mention may be made of ' Four Preludial Pieces,' one of which (that in G) though quite easy to perform, is one of the most effective little compositions ever written for the instrument.

He was a deeply interested student of the hymn-tune in all its forms, and his practical acquaintance with the subject caused him to receive several invitations to act as editor of new hymnals. One of the earliest works he undertook was the completion of the *Wesleyan Tune-Book* of 1876, the two previous editors, George Cooper and Dr. Gauntlett, having died during the progress of the work. His original hymn-tunes have also been published collectively. He died in 1901.

104—Hensbury.

HENSBURY has for many years been ascribed to Robert Bennett, and whilst there is no definite proof that he composed it, equally definite proof is wanting that he is not the composer. It was not printed during Bennett's life-time, the earliest known appearance being in R. A. Smith's *Sacred Music* (Edinburgh, 1825), where it is called EASTGATE.

Robert Bennett (father of Sir W. Sterndale Bennett) was born at Bakewell, Derbyshire, in 1788. His father was a famous local singer, who was in 1791 appointed lay clerk at King's, St. John's and Trinity Colleges,

Cambridge. Robert served as chorister at King's College, and was articled to Dr. J. Clarke-Whitfeld, for whom he acted as assistant organist at Trinity College. In 1810 he applied for the post of organist at Sheffield parish church, but the other candidate, Jonathan Blewitt, was successful. However ' Mr. Bennett's taste and execution were much admired and commended by the judges,' and in the following year he was appointed to succeed Blewitt, who resigned and left for Dublin. Bennett soon became prominent as music teacher and concert giver, but he found time to revisit Cambridge, where he married the eldest daughter of James Donn, curator of the Botanic Gardens, in 1812. Three years later a son was born, though he was not christened ' William Sterndale ' till five years later, in fact after his father's death.

Robert Bennett spent the remainder of his short life at Sheffield. In musical affairs he was associated with many people famous in their day—Samuel Mather (son of William Mather, No. 333), and Samuel Slack, the noted bass singer of Tideswell. He became an advocate of Logier's system of musical education, which involved the use of the Chiroplast, an invention to guide the hand in piano practice. It has long been discredited and Liszt even went so far as to call it the ' Asses Guide,' but Bennett and his partner, Robert Rogers, were great and successful advocates of the system. Early in 1819 Bennett's health suffered through overwork, and he died of consumption at the end of the year. His compositions were limited to *Six Melodies to Original Poetry*, an *Elegy* on the death of the Princess Charlotta (1817), and some half-dozen hymn-tunes.

105—St. Olave.

ST. OLAVE was composed by Barnby for the *Congregational Mission Hymnal* (1890).

Sir Joseph Barnby was essentially a church musician, and his experience extended from being a chorister at York Minster to the conductorship of the Royal Choral

Society. Born at York in 1838, he became a chorister at the Minster. In his sixteenth year he entered the Royal Academy of Music, and competed for the first Mendelssohn Scholarship, being beaten on the post by his fellow-student, Arthur Sullivan (see No. 18). After holding two minor positions he was appointed organist of St. Andrew's, Wells Street, W., where he made the music of the church service famous. From here he went to St. Anne's, Soho, where he produced, for the first time in England, Bach's *St. John* Passion music. His revival of the *St. Matthew* Passion music and of Handel's *Jephthah* were noteworthy events, the former being given in Westminster Abbey. For fifteen years he was musical adviser to the firm of Novello, and backed up by this firm he organized a body of amateur singers, known as Barnby's Choir, which gave a series of concerts in St. James's Hall. For upwards of twenty years he was precentor and director of music at Eton College. In 1892 he was appointed principal of the Guildhall School of Music, a post he held till his death in 1896. Amid all these numerous public engagements he found time for composition, which included an oratorio *Rebekah,* a large number of services, anthems and part-songs, and nearly 250 hymn-tunes. In 1872 he edited *The Hymnary,* and in 1883 his setting of Psalm xcvii., 'The Lord is King,' was heard at the Leeds Festival. Barnby's hymn-tunes have been criticized for various reasons, but his own words may be recalled in justification of his style : ' It has always appeared strange to me that musicians should be found who, whilst admitting that seventeenth-century tunes were very properly written in what we may call the natural idiom of that period, will not allow nineteenth-century ones to be written in the idiom of the day.'

106, 535—Pavia.

PAVIA (or SOLDAU) is an old thirteenth-century German melody of unknown origin. See note on this tune at No. 535.

107—Bishopthorpe.

BISHOPTHORPE is usually credited to Jeremiah Clark (see No. 72), but there is no definite proof that he is the composer. It has not been traced earlier than Dr. Miller's *Psalms of David for the use of Parish Churches* (1790), where it is called BISHOPTHORPE, and assigned to Clark.

108—Kilmarnock. See No. 50.

109, 546—Wareham.

William Knapp is remembered to-day by his fine psalm-tune, WAREHAM. It first appeared in 1738 in the composer's *Sett of New Psalm-Tunes and Anthems,* where it is in triple time as it is known to-day. But in his *New Church Melody* he began to experiment with his tune, changing the name to ' Blandford Tune,' and putting it in common time, producing a very ' jiggy ' effect. Posterity has not approved of the change, and the way the tune is sung now is but little altered from the original form.

Knapp, who was a native of Wareham, in Dorsetshire, spent a large part of his life at Poole, where he was parish clerk at St. James's Church for thirty-nine years. Possibly he compiled his psalmody books for use at that church. In some of his tunes he shows that he had an eye (or an ear) for effect. For instance, in two tunes in the book referred to, which are written in four parts, he adds, ' A low Bass to the Chorus, which might be sung by two or three deep Voices together with the Four upper Parts.' He has localized his book by christening the tunes with names of towns and villages that will be familiar to all who know their South Dorsetshire. Another example will be found in SPETISBURY (No. 511), a welcome revival of a long neglected tune. He died in 1768, and was buried ' somewhere near the old town wall.' There is a curious reference to him in a pamphlet published in 1734 by a 'land waiter in the Port of Poole,' wherein the writer prays to be delivered from certain terrible people and things, including 'Will Knapp,' which seems to indicate that he was not a popular holder of the office of parish clerk.

One of the editions of his book contains Knapp's portrait with the inscription 'Guil Knapp ætat 54 A.D. 1753,' which suggests that he was born in 1698, and not in 1688, as sometimes stated.

110—Hollingside.

HOLLINGSIDE was written by Rev. J. B. Dykes (see No. 36) for *Hymns Ancient and Modern* (1861). It is named from the cottage where he lived at Durham, which was about half-an-hour's walk from the cathedral, and it used to be a joke in the neighbourhood that Dr. Dykes was always late in starting for service, and had regularly to run the whole way. However, he always arrived in time, though occasionally so out of breath that on more than one occasion one of his clerical brethren had to volunteer to commence the service for him.

111—Southwell.

SOUTHWELL is from *Hymns Ancient and Modern* (1861). The composer, Herbert Stephen Irons, was a nephew of the brothers Stephen and Sir George Elvey. Born at Canterbury in 1834, he became a chorister at the cathedral under T. E. Jones. After studying music under Stephen Elvey at Oxford he was appointed organist at St. Columba's College, a large public school at Rathfarnham, near Dublin. He remained here only a few months, as the offer of the organ at Southwell Minister proved a more powerful attraction. From Southwell he went to Chester as assistant organist to Frederic Gunton. After three years' service there he accepted an appointment at St. Andrew's Church, Nottingham, where he remained till his death in 1905.

8

112—Narenza.

NARENZA is probably a German traditional melody without any very definite origin or source. It has been traced back to a collection formed in 1584 by Johann Leisentrit(t), where it is found in a seven-line form. Its present form is due to W. H. Havergal, who gave it the present name in his *Old Church Psalmody* (1847).

Little is known of Johann Leisentrit(t) save that he was born at Olmütz in the early half of the sixteenth century, held various church positions, and published three collections of hymns and chorales.

113—Laudes Domini.

LAUDES DOMINI, by Sir J. Barnby (see No. 105), was composed for the 1868 edition of *Hymns Ancient and Modern,* and set to the hymn 'When morning gilds the skies.'

114—Millennium.

MILLENNIUM belongs probably to the middle part of last century. It was in the 1876 *Methodist Hymn-Book,* was sent into the Appendix in 1904, and has now been restored to its former position. Nothing is at present known of its origin or history.

115—Ascalon.

ASCALON. Many a web of romance has been woven around this somewhat unromantic air. That it is a 'Crusaders' melody,' as has frequently been stated, or that it belongs to the period of the Crusades, or even hundreds of years after, may at once be dismissed as a too lively flight of the imagination. The demand for a tune of this metre (6.6.8,6.6.8) was created when the Rev. Benjamin Rhodes wrote his hymn 'My heart and voice I'll raise,' in 1787. The earliest tune to the hymn appeared in Rippon's *Selection of Psalm and Hymn-Tunes* (1806), where it was called DALSTON, the composer probably being Aaron Williams (see No. 554).

The resemblance between the opening bars of DALSTON and ASCALON will be noticed.

Rhodes' hymn came into use in Methodism in 1831, and DALSTON (with two or three other tunes, long since forgotten) held the field till 1876. Meanwhile another tune had made its appearance, heralded by a paragraph on p. 178 of *Evangelical Christendom* (1850). It ran thus :

An unexpected treasure was discovered in 1850 in the guise of a Crusader's Hymn. It was found in Westphalia amid a number of other curious relics, and according to the traditional text by which it was accompanied this hymn used to be sung by the German Pilgrims on their way to Jerusalem. It may, therefore, be regarded as a national air of that time.

A musical note calls this one of the most remarkable discoveries of modern research. It achieved a great popularity at the time of its discovery. It has already become a chief favourite with the people, and is sung by all classes and ages from the shepherd on the hillside to the lisping urchin in the nursery. At a

missionary meeting lately held in the Principality of
Lippedetmold it was commenced by three voices only,
yet, ere the third verse was reached hundreds joined
in the heart-stirring song of praise. From that period
it has been progressing from meeting to meeting
through the Rhinish provinces and thus bids far to
rival the popularity of P. Gerhardt's celebrated hymn
'Befiehl du deine Wege' (Commit thou all thy ways).

We are told how the Halls of Kothen echoed to its
melody and there, where a few years since the Friends
of Light held their sittings and triumphed in the
thought of having deposed King Jesus from His
Throne, this hymn was eagerly copied and travelled
thence to many distant and far-scattered dwellings.

The tune was published in leaflet form, set to an
English translation of a German hymn 'Schönster Herr
Jesu,' of unknown authorship, but dating from 1677.

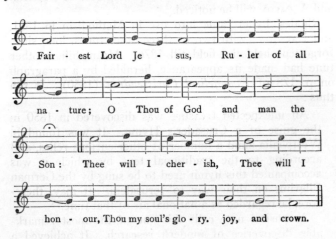

Fair - est Lord Je - sus,   Ru - ler of   all
na - ture;   O   Thou of God   and   man the
Son :   Thee   will I   cher - ish,   Thee   will I
hon - our, Thou my soul's glo - ry.   joy,   and   crown.

The tune was approved by Dr. Allon, and inserted in
his *Congregational Psalmist* (1861), also in the *Bristol
Tune-Book* two years later. The source of the tune in
the former work was given as 'Crusader's Melody,'

Meanwhile the tune had appeared in a very unexpected quarter, being used by Liszt as the subject of the trio in the ' Crusaders ' March in his oratorio *St. Elizabeth,* and it is also introduced in the ' Praeludium ' to the sixth scene. The late C. A. Barry, who wrote the Introduction to the English version of *St. Elizabeth,* said that the air ' was derived from an old Pilgrim's song supposed to date from the time of the Crusaders.' This statement was made later than 1862, for Liszt did not finish his oratorio till August of that year. On writing to Mr. Barry (in December, 1903) for further information about the tune he replied that the only information he could give was that in the full preface to the work, Liszt thanked Herr Cantor Gottschlag for introducing him to the old ' Pilgrim's Song.' A letter to this gentleman asking for further information produced no result for the simple reason that he had died a few years previously.

It then became necessary to examine any available sources of information, and on consulting Wilhelm Baümker's *Index* ASCALON (but not so named) was discovered in Vol. II. After giving two melodies to ' Schönster Herr Jesu ' Baümker says, ' another melody in use in the district of Glaz is found in Hoffmann and Richter's *Schleswige Volkelieder,* Leipzig, 1842.' On referring to this collection of folk-songs ASCALON was found amongst the religious songs set to the words just quoted. Hoffman, in his preface, says :

> In the summer of 1836 I visited a friend in the country. Towards evening I heard the hay-wardens sing. I made inquiries. They sang folk-songs which to me seemed worthy of collection. For this purpose I associated myself with my friend Richter. We divided the work between us; to him fell the musical portion, to me the rest.

Thus is the origin of ASCALON settled, at any rate for the present. It is not a ' Crusaders' Melody,' but a modern Silesian song which cannot be traced earlier than 1842.

A paragraph about the origin of ASCALON appeared in the *Musical Times* for October, 1916, where it is stated that 'the original source has now been traced to a melody in a Choralbuch (1819) by J. G. Schicht.' Here is the tune referred to:

It requires a vivid imagination to look upon this as the original source of ASCALON.

116 (i)—Sing we the King.

SING WE THE KING was composed by Christopher Luke Wiseman when he was about twelve years old, and he now confesses that he is not very proud of it! He was born in 1893 at Birmingham, and his musical tendencies were developed by his father (Rev. F. L. Wiseman) who brought him up on Handel, and by his mother, who guided him in the paths of Schumann and Brahms. He soon formed very definite ideas about psalmody, and still maintains that 'the German chorales are the finest possible expression of religious feeling in hymns.' After leaving Cambridge (where he gained distinction in Mathematics and Science) he became an assistant master at Kingswood School, Bath, and proved an invaluable supporter of the music master, Alfred Beer, in his schemes for the advancement of music in the school. On his appointment as Headmaster of Queen's College, Taunton, he paid special attention to developing a love of good music amongst the boys. He managed to form an orchestra, but not without difficulty, and deficiency in the

wood-wind department caused him to study both the oboe
and the clarinet in order to teach the young idea. (He
was less successful with the flute.) The result has been
the formation of a capable orchestra in the school, and
the development of a love of good music in the boys.
He has used the gramophone with good effect, and has
established a library of records ranging from Byrd to
Bax. Recitals are given on Sunday evening after church,
and the boys listen attentively, appreciating the *Valkyrie*
and *The Meistersingers* equally with Brahms' symphonies. Mr. Wiseman believes strongly in music as an
educational force, and his experiments in teaching the
violin to a whole class at a time have proved satisfactory.

116 (ii)—The Glory Song.

THE GLORY SONG is by Charles H. Gabriel, who was
born in 1856 at Kilton, Iowa. At the age of seventeen,
he started out to hold singing schools and travelled
widely. He had a fine natural tenor voice and considerable dramatic power, and was associated at various
times with Sam Jones, Billy Sunday, and E. O. Excell in
evangelistic services. In 1900 he wrote THE GLORY SONG,
which has been translated into twenty languages, and has
sold to the number of 20,000,000 copies. He was editor
for the Rodeheaver Company for a dozen years, and
compiler of a dozen music collections. He also wrote
cantatas and three operettas. His poems, recently
printed, show a wide range, some being in the negro
dialect, and others reveal a real sympathy with child
life. He was a member of the Methodist Church.
Gabriel died at the home of his son in Hollywood,
California, in 1932.

117—Berlin.

BERLIN is adapted from the ' Lied,' the second number
in Mendelssohn's *Festgesang* for men's voices and brass
instruments. The work was composed in celebration of

the invention of printing, with which the name of Guthenburg is associated, and the festival was named after him. Mendelssohn subsequently arranged the chorus for mixed voices, and W. H. Cummings, at the time organist of Waltham Abbey, adapted it to Wesley's 'Hark! the herald-angels sing.' It became popular, and Cummings got Messrs. Ewer and Co. to publish it in leaflet form in 1856. It next appeared almost simultaneously in Chope's *Congregational Tune-Book* and *The Wesleyan Sunday School Tune-Book*, both published in 1858. The latter was a small oblong blue covered book which had a long run of popularity. It contained BERLIN (called NATIVITY) in a four-line form, with the first two lines of the hymn used as a refrain. Since those days BERLIN, under a variety of other names has remained the standard setting for Wesley's hymn.

When the translation by W. Bartholomew of the libretto of *Festgesang* was published in England, Mendelssohn wrote to the publishers expressing disapproval. He said, 'I think there ought to be other words [than those written by Bartholomew] to No. 2, the "Lied." If the right ones are hit at, I am sure that piece will be liked very much by the singers and the hearers, but it will *never* do to sacred words. There must be a national and merry subject found out, something to which the soldierlike and buxom motion of the piece has some relation, and the words must express something gay and popular, as the music tries to do it.'

Felix Mendelssohn Bartholdy was born at Hamburg in 1809. On his family moving to Berlin he studied music under Berger and Zelter, the latter introducing him to Goethe, at whose house he spent several weeks. He made rapid progress in music, winning the approval of many notable musicians including Moscheles, with whom he struck up a lasting friendship. The boy's father, anxious for his future, took him to Paris to obtain Cherubini's advice, who after hearing him said 'He will do well.' Back he went home and the young

composer kept hard at work, producing symphonies,
operas and other compositions in rapid succession till in
1826 he wrote his overture to the *Midsummer Night's
Dream,* at which he had been working, pruning and
trimming for about twelve months. In 1829 his
enthusiasm for Bach found an outlet in a performance of
the St. Matthew Passion music, the first time it had been
heard since Bach's death. A visit to England followed,
the first of nine he paid to this country, and after a
successful season in London, he visited Scotland and
Wales. Returning home he paid his last visit to Goethe,
and then had a tour in Italy, about which he has left a
series of vivid word-pictures in his letters. His first
settled appointment was as director of music at Düsseldorf, but owing to internal quarrels he was glad to leave
for Leipzig to conduct the famous Gewandhaus concerts.
He was now at work on *St. Paul,* which was first
heard at Düsseldorf and in England (at Liverpool)
in 1836. He projected another oratorio founded on the
life of St. Peter, but this was given up in favour of
Elijah, the scheming of it taking many years. Meanwhile he produced his *Lobgesang, Walpurgisnact,* and
other famous overtures and choral works culminating in
the production of *Elijah,* which he conducted at the
Birmingham Festival of 1846. After a return visit to
England the following year to conduct *Elijah* in London,
he heard of the death of his sister. The blow proved too
much for a system already weakened by excitement and
overwork, and he died in November, 1847, to the great
sorrow of the whole musical world.

118—Adeste Fideles.

ADESTE FIDELES. There are two stories concerning
the origin of this tune, one which assigns it to John
Reading, a second, far less widely spread, which
announces ' Marcas Portugal ' as the composer. This

claim is given in detail in Duffield's *English Hymns*
(1886), where we find the following statement :—

The 'Portuguese Hymn,' to which the ADESTE
FIDELES has usually been sung, was the composition
of Marcas Portugal. He was the chapel-master of the
King of Portugal, and died at Rio de Janeiro over fifty
years ago. The tune was originally employed as an
offertory piece, and Dom Joao VI, in whose service the
composer had a position, came to Brazil in 1808.
Marcas Portugal accompanied him thither, and
remained when his royal master returned to Europe.
When Dom Pedro II, who is the grandson of Dom
Joao, was a little boy, the old composer still led the
chapel services, and Dr. Fletcher, in his *Brazil and the
Brazilians,* fixes the date of his death in 1834. In the
preface to the ninth edition of Dr. Fletcher's work
this fact is authoritatively stated, and it is added that
Marcas (or Marcos) Portugal wrote several operas as
well as much sacred music. These were popular in
the early part of the present century, both in Portugal
and Italy. The claim, therefore, that Reading (otherwise Redding) was the composer of this celebrated tune
falls to the ground. It is worthy of passing note that
the earliest composer on the Western continent was
Antonio Carlos Gomez, who came from the very land
where the body of Marcas Portugal rests.

The proper name of the individual here referred to is
Marcus Antonio da Fonseca, who received the nickname
of ' Il Portogallo,' which subsequently came to be looked
upon as his real name. As he was born in 1763, the
claim set up for him collapses, as the tune was certainly
in use more than a dozen years previous to that date.

The claim of Reading as the composer of the melody
is not so easily disposed of. In the life of her father,
Vincent Novello, Mrs. Clarke makes the following
definite statement :

The ADESTE FIDELES, although a composition by an

Englishman named John Reading (who also wrote DULCE DOMUM), obtained the name of ' The Portuguese Hymn ' from its having been heard by the Duke of Leeds at the Portuguese Chapel, who imagined it to be peculiar to the service in Portugal. Being a Director of the Ancient Concerts, his Grace introduced the melody there, and it speedily became popular under the title he had given it.

There are two musicians bearing the name of John Reading, the first being organist of Winchester Cathedral, and subsequently of Winchester College, his period of service at the two places extending from 1675-92. John Reading No. 2 was born in 1677, and held positions as organist at Dulwich College, and also at St. John's Church, Hackney. The late Dr. Cummings, who went very carefully into the possible claims of either of the Readings to the music of ADESTE FIDELES, came to the conclusion that the Dulwich and Hackney Reading had nothing whatever to do with it. There is no trace of any such music, or anything like it in his compositions, nor is he known to have set any Latin words to music. ' On the other hand,' wrote Dr. Cummings, ' the older Reading of Winchester did compose GRACES and the DULCES DOMUM with Latin words, and, judging by the music, it seems to me that the man who composed the latter might well have been the author of ADESTE FIDELES '—(*Notes and Queries*, May 21, 1881).

After all, this is mere surmise, and until proof positive is forthcoming there is no reason why the name of John Reading should be given as the composer, although the editor of the most recent tune-book—*The Congregational Hymnary*—appears to have more definite information on the subject, as he unhesitatingly ascribes it to John Reading without a query, though he is careful not to commit himself as to which of the Readings he prefers.

Having thus disposed of the claims set up on behalf of Messrs. Reading and ' Portugal,' let us see what further light can be thrown on the story of this famous melody. In 1901 Messrs. Cowan & Love issued their book dealing with the music in *The Church Hymnary,* and in their account of ADESTE FIDELES they state that it is found in a manuscript volume preserved at Stonyhurst College, near Blackburn. It is the work of John Francis Wade, a priest who seems to have occupied part of his time in writing out music for the use of wealthy Lancashire families. The book is dated 1751, at which time Stonyhurst was in the possession of the Sherburns, an old Lancashire Roman Catholic family that had held the manor for upwards of two hundred years.

The Henry Watson Musical Library at Manchester contains a similar book to the one at Stonyhurst College, but appears to be a year earlier. This is also the work of the copyist-priest. It is probable that Wade commenced his Lancashire tour in Manchester, but the original provenance of the volume is not known. The photograph of the page containing ADESTE FIDELES is reproduced from the manuscript in possession of Henry Watson Music Library, by the courtesy of the Manchester Libraries Committee. (See plate.)

119 (i)—Woodford Green.

WOODFORD GREEN is one of the new tunes included in the *Methodist Hymn-Book* (1933). The composer, William Parkyn, was born in 1881, and began his experiences as an organist at the early age of seven, when he played a tune at evensong at Kirkley parish church. He played his first full service at Crouch End Presbyterian Church at the age of fourteen, and promptly applied shortly afterwards for the full position on the resignation of the organist, Goddard Plowman, but was thought to be too young. He continued his studies under Plowman, and also under Josiah Booth (see No. 850). His first important appointment was at East Finchley Congregational Church. In 1928 he became organist and

A Profe for Chriftmas

ADéste fidéles, læti triumphántes, venite, venite in Béthlehem. Natum vidéte Regem Angelórum, venite adorémus, venite adoré=amus, venite adorémus Dóminum. Deum de Deo, lumen de lúmine, geftant puéllæ vif=

See No. 118, p. 100.

director of the music at the Methodist Central Hall, East Ham, where he also directs the popular concerts which have been so successful. He has done a considerable amount of work as accompanist to famous professional singers, and has taken an active part in the work of the Free Church Choir Union.

119 (ii)—Iris.

IRIS is from *The Oxford Book of Carols,* where it is set to ' Angels from the Realms of Glory.' It is said to be an old French carol, but of doubtful origin.

120—Yorkshire.

YORKSHIRE is by John Wainwright, who was born at Stockport in (or about) 1723, and became organist of the parish church. After his marriage in 1746 he settled in Manchester, but still kept up his organ work at Stockport. When Byrom wrote ' Christians, awake ' is not known, but at Christmas, 1750, he entered in his diary :

> The singing men and boys, with Mr. Wainwright, came here and sang ' Christians, awake.'

This carol performance probably took place at the corner of Hanging Ditch and Hunter's Lane, in Manchester, though Byrom also had a ' country residence ' at Kersal.

Wainwright did not at once proceed to publish his tune; he may have thought little of it, but others thought differently. The tune began to get about, and attracted the attention of Caleb Ashworth, a Lancastrian of musical ability who had settled as a Nonconformist parson at Daventry. He occupied his spare time in preparing collections of psalmody, and in the first, which was published about 1760, he included Wainwright's tune, not to ' Christians, awake,' but to the metrical rendering of Psalm l. from the old version :

The mighty God, th' Eternal hath thus spoke,
And all the world he will call and provoke,
E'en from the East, and so forth to the West :
Out of Sion, which place he liketh best,
God will appear in beauty most excellent,
Our God will come before that long time be spent.

How Ashworth got hold of Wainwright's tune we do
not know, but although a minister, he certainly had a
curious idea about questions of copyright. He was, however, quite ready to confess his sins, and suggests in one
of his prefaces that in including other people's property
in his collection he is giving them good advertisement!
So he inserted Wainwright's tune in this form :

Peculiar Measure. MORTRAM.
Old 50th Psalm Tune.

MORTRAM is probably a misprint for MOTTRAM, a
Cheshire village. Wainwright did not like this appro-
priation of his tune, so he set to work to publish a
collection of his tunes and announced its coming in an

advertisement in Harrap's *Manchester Mercury* for October, 1766, describing himself as organist of the Collegiate Church (history records that he was actually assistant organist). He did not name his tune to Byrom's hymn, and the first to call it ' Stockport ' was Ralph Harrison (see No. 389).

Wainwright died in 1768 and was buried in Stockport churchyard. In 1810 the church was destroyed, and the tower blown up, many of the tombstones being destroyed or scattered abroad. Early in this century the stone that had marked Wainwright's grave was dug up in a garden in Turncroft Lane. Opportunity was taken of the discovery to reveal Wainwright's name, and a tablet was placed in the church to his memory. The name YORK-SHIRE is a complete misfit, as the tune has no association with the county.

121—Bonn.

BONN is the melody originally set to Gerhardt's hymn ' Warum sollt ich mich denn grämen,' no translation of which is in general use. It is by J. G. Ebeling, Cantor of St. Nicholas Church, Berlin. He formed a collection of Gerhardt's hymns and issued them in sets of a dozen each, with instrumental accompaniments. The original melody by Crüger, to Gerhardt's hymns has not survived. Ebeling was born at Lüneberg in 1637. He succeeded Crüger as precentor of St. Nicholas Church, Berlin, and afterwards he became professor of music and poetry at the Gymnasium at Stettin, where he died in 1676.

122 (i)—Spean.

SPEAN was written by Sir F. Bridge at the request of the editor of *The Quiver* for insertion in that magazine in 1878. The name is taken from the river in Inverness-shire, Scotland, which was the scene of Sir F. Bridge's fishing exploits.

Sir John Frederick Bridge was born at Oldbury,

Worcestershire, and he commemorated the event by naming one of his tunes after that town (No. 179). He was brought up as a chorister at Rochester Cathedral, and thus received the training which is essential to the career of a successful church musician. Here also he imbibed his love of fishing, and his devotion to the art rivalled that of S. S. Wesley. After holding two organist appointments in the Home Counties he was appointed organist at Manchester Cathedral, and after seven years' service there he removed to Westminster Abbey, where he became 'Permanent Deputy Organist during the lifetime of James Turle.'

In 1882 Sir Frederick was appointed full organist, and when in 1918 he retired with the rank of Emeritus Organist his service to the Abbey had extended over a period of forty-three years. During that time he had successfully officiated at two Coronations, as well as at the Queen Victoria Jubilee and Diamond Jubilee Services, and on many other historic occasions connected with the Abbey. He was knighted after the Diamond Jubilee, was created M.V.O. in 1902, and became C.V.O. in 1911.

Sir Frederick took a prominent part in the initiation of various schemes planned for the advancement of musical knowledge and education. Specially, however, will he be remembered as the founder of the Organists' Benevolent League, which came into being in 1909. He led a busy life, and certainly had no time for being idle. He composed, he lectured, he edited old musical works, and he wrote his autobiography under the name of *A Westminster Pilgrim.* When a friend congratulated him on the cheerful character of his book of memoirs, he replied, 'Oh, well, of course, I've had some unpleasant times; I could have put in a lot of them. But what's the use of remembering those things?' Such was the secret of his long life and of his professional success. He always made the best of everything and caused his genial presence to be felt wherever he happened to be.

In 1897 he edited *The Westminster Abbey Tune-Book,*

an excellent collection which has suffered strangely from neglect. In 1904 he readily accepted the position of musical editor for the *Methodist Hymn-Book,* then in course of preparation. His compositions ranged from large choral works to anthems, part-songs (chiefly humorous), carols and hymn-tunes. He passed away at his residence in the Cloisters, Westminster, in March, 1927.

122 (ii)—Epiphany Hymn.

EPIPHANY HYMN is by Joseph Francis Thrupp, who was born in London in 1827. He was educated at Winchester and at Trinity College, Cambridge, being made a Fellow of the College in 1854. He entered the Church in 1852, and was for some years actively associated with the work of the S.P.C.K. He was a biblical scholar of some eminence, and published a translation of ' The Song of Solomon.' He also edited a collection of psalm- and hymn-tunes. EPIPHANY HYMN was contributed by him to Turle's *Psalms and Hymns for Public Worship* (1863), and popularized by its insertion in the *Bristol Tune-Book* published in the same year, where the tune is called EPIPHANY, and dated 1848.

123—Stille Nacht.

STILLE NACHT (or HOLY NIGHT) was composed by Franz Gruber in 1818. He was born in 1787 at Hochburg, near Linz (Austria). He was a schoolmaster at Arnsdorf, afterwards an organist at Hallein, near Salzburg, where he died in 1863.

124—Oxford.

OXFORD is a name that disguises John Goss's (see No. 12) hymn-carol ' See, amid the winter's snow,' which was composed for the series of carols edited by Bramley and Stainer, 1870.

125—Bethlehem.

BETHLEHEM is said to have been written by Sir Joseph
Barnby for a 'University Hymn-Book' for use in the
Chapel of Harvard University, 1891, but the present
authorities of the College do not appear to have any
knowledge of the transaction.

126—Vom Himmel Hoch.   See No. 42.

127 (i)—Oran na Prasaich.

ORAN NA PRASAICH—the Gaelic for 'The Song of the
Manger'—was written for the *Methodist Hymn-Book*
(1933). The composer, George Frederick Brockless, was
born at Fritwell (Oxon.), in 1887. He received his
education at New College School, Oxford, and gained a
choral scholarship at Queen's College. Before he
attained his twenty-first birthday he had secured his
diplomas of L.R.A.M. (in piano teaching), A.R.C.M.
(solo performer), and F.R.C.O. Thus equipped he sailed
for S. Africa to take up the position of organist at the
Commemoration Church, Grahamstown, and music
master at Kingswood College. The musical services at
the church were chiefly liturgical, and under Mr. Brockless were marked by great taste and efficiency. During
his term of office he opened a new organ in the church
which had been erected by a firm at Capetown. On
returning to England he added to his distinctions by
taking his Mus.B. degree at Durham, advancing to the
doctorate in 1928. After holding the position of organist
at Hornsey parish church he is now organist and choirmaster at St. Barnabas Church, Kensington. He is also
director of the music department of Battersea Poly-
technic, where the students rank as internal students of
London University. In 1933 he succeeded Dr. Wostenholm as musical adviser to the Methodist Tune-Book
Committee. Dr. Brockless has had wide experience in
directing large organisations. He has acted as conductor

of the Toc H Festivals at the Albert Hall, London, and also at the Crystal Palace. He was the musical director of the Pageant of Essex (1932), and was in 1934 conductor of the pageant play 'The Rock,' which was performed at Sadler's Wells Theatre in aid of the Bishop of London's Fund.

127 (ii)—St. Winifred.

ST. WINIFRED was composed for *The Methodist Sunday School Hymn and Tune-Book* (1889), by the Rev. Sidney Joseph Palmer Dunman. Born at Bridgwater in 1843, he soon displayed musical ability, and one of his chief services to Methodism was in connexion with its psalmody. He was a member of the committee that compiled the *Wesleyan Tune-Book* (1876). He was at that time well known as a composer, and several of his compositions were included in Kaffir, Japanese, Italian, and other tune-books. He entered the Wesleyan ministry in 1864, and was held in great esteem in the various circuits in which he worked till his death in 1913.

128—A Virgin Most Pure.

A VIRGIN MOST PURE is from a collection of carols made by William Sandys, and published in 1833. From this source also came THE FIRST NOWELL (No. 131), and SANDYS (No. 597).

William Sandys was born in London in 1792, and became a solicitor. He was devoted to music, and gave much time and attention to the antiquarian side of the art. His *Selection of Christmas Carols* was a valuable contribution to carol literature. He was also part-author with S. A. Forster of a *History of the Violin* (1864).

129, 276, 960—Winchester Old.

WINCHESTER OLD appears to be an adaptation by George Kirbye of Tye's melody for Chapter viii. of his settings of *The Actes of the Apostles* (1553).

George Kirbye was an East Anglian of whom nothing is known till Thomas East published his whole *Book of Psalms* in 1592, when Kirbye was employed to arrange some of the tunes, including WINCHESTER OLD. East, in his preface, says that he entrusted the work of arranging to those whom he knew to be ' expert in the Arte,' which suggests that Kirbye was a musician of some standing. In 1597 he published a ' first set ' of madrigals. He died at Bury St. Edmunds (which was probably his birthplace) in 1634.

130—Noel.

The first four lines of NOEL were adapted by Sullivan from a melody given to him by a friend. He added four more lines and set the total result to Dr. Sears' hymn in *Church Hymns* (1874), of which he was the music editor. The first four lines bear a strong resemblance to the tune of the old carol ' Dives and Lazarus ' in the Appendix to the *Oxford Book of Carols* (No. 5), which is a variant on the tune of the Mummers' Carol ' A glorious Angel from Heaven came,' noted by the Rev. John Broadwood before 1843, as sung by Sussex Tipteerers (Mummers) after their play of St. George. It is probable that the first half of Sullivan's tune belonged to this carol, as well as being sung to ' Dives and Lazarus.' A version very like the above named *Oxford Carol Book* variant is set to ' Dives and Lazarus,' as a traditional tune, in Bramley and Stainer's *Christmas Carols*.

131—The First Nowell.

THE FIRST NOWELL is from the same source as No. 128.

132—Orient.

ORIENT was written by Stanford for Novello's collection of *Christmas Carols*, 1894.

Sir Charles Villiers Stanford was born at Dublin in 1852. He commenced his career at Cambridge as organ scholar of Queen's College, and whilst still an under-graduate he succeeded his master, Dr. J. L. Hopkins, as organist at Trinity. He brought fresh life to the University Musical Society, and also gained distinction as a classical scholar. In after years he retained his love for the organ, and his recent compositions for the instrument have been highly appreciated by organists. Stanford's contributions to church music were not numerous, nor have many of them become widely known. Everyone is familiar with his service in B flat, which has become a classic. The section for evening use was written whilst he was organist at Trinity. Although he used to say that there were far too many hymn-tunes already in existence he did not fail to add to the number. Some of them will be found in that excellent collection *The Westminster Abbey Tune-Book,* and this setting of ' As with gladness ' is familiar to everybody. As a composer he has touched all branches of the art and succeeded in every one, but to what extent only the trying test of years can tell. It has been suggested that had he been content to free himself from the trammels of an academic career, and give free play to his unfettered genius, then he might have accomplished still greater things. No one has ever questioned his scholarship, or his ready command over all the forms of music, and yet the fact remains that his greatest works have been practically ignored by his own generation, and to-day they lie idle on the shelf.

But when Stanford was content to forget his masters and let himself go, drawing unreservedly on his natural resources—when he got ' out of the class-room into the open air '—then he gave his best to the world; witness his *Songs of the Sea* and other classic songs, his *Revenge,* and *Shamus O'Brien,* his Irish Symphony, and his *Stabat Mater.* His *Three Holy Children* and *Eden* were produced at Birmingham in 1885 and 1891, but though they were both received with enthusiasm at the time, their very names are well-nigh forgotten. Stanford used to say that the only memorial a composer wants is that his works should be published and performed and so live after him.

133 (i)—Kirkbraddan.

KIRKBRADDAN, by the Rev. Edward Charles Walker, appeared originally in the *Hymnal Companion* (second edition, 1877). Nothing is known of this composer, except that he contributed some tunes to various hymnals, including the *Bristol Tune-Book*.

133 (ii)—Foundation.

FOUNDATION is adapted from Haydn's (see No. 16) Symphony in D (No. 15).

It is the tune originally selected by S. Baring-Gould to be sung to his ' Onward, Christian Soldiers ' in 1865. It had earlier adventures, as for instance, in *The Wesleyan Sunday School Tune-Book* (1857) where it was made to fit an Iambic 7.6.7.6. to the hymn :

When His salvation bringing.

The original adaptation appears to be due to Gauntlett, who arranged the melody in the *Comprehensive Tune-Book* (1851), which he edited.

134—Hatfield.

HATFIELD is said to be from one of the editions of the *French Psalter* (1539-1565) but this is probably an error, as it undoubtedly belongs to the succeeding century. It is associated with E. C. Hamberg's hymn ' Jesu, meines Lebens Leben,' and in the music edition of the *Moravian Liturgy* (1914) the tune is credited to Wolfgang Wessnitzer, ducal organist at Celle, in the province of Hanover. His dates range from about 1615 to 1680.

135—Dura.

DURA, by H. J. Gauntlett (see No. 7), was introduced by him into the *Wesleyan Tune-Book* (1876), but it is uncertain whether that was its first appearance.

136, 855—Newbury.

NEWBURY is from *The English Hymnal* (1906). The tune belongs to a Christmas Mummers' Carol, noted at Kingsclere, Hants., 1897, by Miss M. G. Arkwright, which begins

> There are six good days all in a week,
> All for a labouring man;
> But the seventh is the Sabbath of our Lord Jesus
> Christ,
> The Father and the Son.

It is also found in Miss Broadwood's *English Traditional Songs,* as 'The Hampshire Mummers' Christmas Carol.'

137—Cranham.

CRANHAM was written by G. Holst (see No. 30) for Miss Rossetti's hymn ' In the bleak mid-winter ' in the *English Hymnal* (1906).

138—Hermitage.

HERMITAGE was written for, and first appeared in, *Songs of Praise* (1925). R. O. Morris was educated at Eton and Oxford. He entered the Royal College of Music, and is now one of its professors. His compositions have been chiefly instrumental. A symphony of his (in D) was heard at the B.B.C. Festival in January, 1934. It is dedicated to the composer's brother-in-law, Dr. Vaughan Williams. He has also written part-songs and a chorus—' Corinna's Maying '—with orchestral accompaniment. He is the author of *Contrapuntal Technique in the Sixteenth Century* (1922).

139—Dunfermline. See No. 37.

140, 811—St. Cecilia.

ST. CECILIA, also BUCKLAND (No. 277), are both taken from *The Merton Tune-Book* which the composer (with the help of H. W. Sargeant) compiled in 1863.

The Rev. L. G. Hayne was born at Exeter in 1836. After leaving Queen's College, Oxford, he took holy orders, and also his musical doctorate, and was appointed organist at Eton College, where he remained three years, when he became rector of Mistley and vicar of Bradfield, in Essex, where he died in 1883.

141—Berkshire. See No. 48.

142—Adoration. See No. 58.

143—In Dulci Jubilo.

IN DULCI JUBILO has been traced back in some form or other to the fourteenth century, and further research may reveal still earlier origins. The original words are said to have been sung by angels to a certain Henry Suss (14th century), who was then induced to join in a dance with his celestial choir. The jubilant strains of this old carol easily accommodate themselves to the story. The music is found in various sixteenth-century ' song-books,' including Klug's (1535). An arrangement of it by J. S. Bach will be found in C. P. E. Bach's *Collection* (No. 143) in 3-4 time, and also in the *Oxford Carol Book* (1928) in 6-4 time.

144—Love Unknown.

LOVE UNKNOWN was written for Samuel Crossman's hymn ' My song is love unknown,' and appeared in *Songs of Praise* (1925).

John Ireland, son of Alexander Ireland, formerly editor of *The Manchester Examiner,* was born at Bowden, Cheshire, in 1879. After leaving Leeds Grammar School he studied music at the R.C.M. under Stanford. For some years he exercised considerable restraint in composition, and then came his orchestral prelude *The Forgotten Rite.* He has specialized in chamber and piano music, notably the piano *Rhapsody, Prelude* and *London Pieces.* His setting of Masefield's ' Sea-Fever ' has proved very popular. Ireland's output is small, the reason being probably that he only writes when the spirit moves him.

145—Clinton.

CLINTON was contributed by C. H. H. Parry to *The Songs of Praise* (1876).

Born at Bournemouth in 1848, Parry devoted the greater part of his life to the art for which he had shown great predilection both during his schooldays at Eton, his college life at Oxford, and afterwards when engaged in business in the City of London. Amongst his teachers at this period were H. Hugo Pierson and W. Sterndale Bennett, whilst during his residence in London he came under the influence of Edward Dannreuther.

Parry's father, who was a painter of repute, and also somewhat of a musician (he composed the tune ST. BENEDICT, *Wesleyan Tune-Book,* 1876), was opposed to his son's taking up music as a profession, but circumstances combined to overcome this opposition, and he soon occupied a prominent position both as a composer and teacher. Many honours fell to his lot, notably the Professorship of Music at Oxford University, which he held from 1899 to 1908, and the honourable position of Director of the Royal College of Music. His influence in this position was wide-spread, and he gained both the respect and love of a large number of pupils, amongst whom may be mentioned Arthur Somervell, Benjamin

Dale, Walford Davies, and Coleridge Taylor. He died in 1918.

As a composer Parry's chief work was accomplished in the realm of choral music, and he wrote a remarkable number of works of this kind, many of which were composed for the Three Choirs' Festivals, and also for those held at Leeds, Birmingham, and Norwich. At the last-named place his still popular *Pied Piper of Hamelin* was produced in 1905, while of other works that have come from his pen we have the oratorios *Judith* (1888), *Job* (1892), and *King Saul* (1894). His *Blest Pair of Sirens* was written for and produced by the Bach Society in 1887.

In some of his choral works the composer was responsible for the libretto. In *Judith,* for instance, he adapted the words of the Apocrypha to suit his own devices, connecting the extracts with verses of his own composition. His extensive knowledge of every form of contrapuntal device, and his ready skill in utilizing the same, are ever manifest in his principal choral works. He strove to achieve great things, but no amount of mere scholarly writing will atone for lack of true inspiration, and it is not, therefore, surprising that with but very few exceptions, his great choral works have recently been rarely heard. As a song-writer he excelled, and in his English Lyrics of some fifty songs the most notable feature is the sense of structure, well illustrated in the sustained sweep of 'Through the ivory gate,' and the cumulative interest and easy evenness of 'Bright Star,' a song which he thought his best.

But if his music shows little signs of immortality, it may be safely asserted that his valuable contributions to the literature of music will long perpetuate his name and fame. His study of the life of Bach is already a classic, while his contributions to the *Oxford History of Music* and to Grove's *Dictionary* reveal great abilities both as a profound historian and a keenly discerning critic of the various epochs of the history of music. Other works by which he will be remembered are *The Evolution of the Art of Music, Style in Musical Art,* and *Studies of the Great Composers.*

146—Philippine.

PHILIPPINE was composed for Mrs. R. E. Roberts' hymn ' O Lord, Thy people gathered here,' by her husband, R. E. Roberts, and included in *Songs of Praise* (1925).

Robert Edwin Roberts was born at Llangerniew, Denbighshire, in 1878. After leaving Ellesmere School, Shropshire, he went to Durham University. After ordination he became a minor canon, and subsequently precentor at Peterborough Cathedral. More recently he has been precentor at St. Martin's, Leicester, and dean and proctor in Convocation. He compiled *The Transition Tune-Book* (1924), and has taken an active part in the movement to raise the tone standard of church music.

147—Salvator.

SALVATOR was composed by M. B. Foster, for Stopford Brooke's hymn, ' When the Lord of Love was here,' and first appeared in *Worship Song* (1905).

Myles Foster was the son of the famous artist Birket Foster. He was educated at Brighton and at Guildford Grammar School. From boyhood he took an interest in music, and used to recall how he was promised a shilling ' if he did not kick the dentist.' He refrained, and spent the coin in buying Boosey's edition of *The Hymn of Praise,* little thinking that in after years he was to become that firm's musical adviser. After a year or two in a stockbroker's office, during which period his desk held more MS. anthems than share lists, he drifted off into music, and worked with Battison Haynes, who edited the music edition of the *Methodist Free Church Hymns* (1889). He also studied under Arthur Sullivan, who instilled in him the doctrine that the student who wished to write full scores should at least understand the fingering of every orchestral instrument. This so impressed Foster that he studied the 'cello, oboe, and clarinet.

Foster held appointments at H. R. Haweis's church in Westmorland Place, at that time famous for its singing, and at St. Alban's, Holborn. He is, however, best remembered as master of the music at the Foundling Hospital (1880-1892), where he fully maintained the traditions of the beautiful Sunday afternoon services. He composed cantatas, duets and other vocal music, and compiled a *History of the Philharmonic Society* (1913). His *Anthems and Anthem Composers* is a useful work of reference. He died in 1922.

148—Credo.

CREDO was written by Stainer (see No. 20) for J. H. Gurney's hymn 'We saw Thee not when Thou didst come' in the 1875 edition of *Hymns Ancient and Modern*.

149—Artavia.

ARTAVIA was specially written by Dr. E. J. Hopkins (see No. 103) for Jean Ingelow's verses in the *Congregational Church Hymnal* (1887).

150—Margaret.

MARGARET is from *Children's Hymns and Tunes* (1876), by the Rev. Timothy R. Matthews, a native of Bedfordshire, having been born at Colmworth in 1826. He was the son of the Rev. T. R. Matthews referred to in one of Edward Fitzgerald's letters as 'my noble preacher.' Having passed through Bedford Grammar School he became a private tutor at Windsor, where he began a life-long friendship with George Elvey (see No. 11).

In 1853 Matthews was ordained to the curacy of St. Mary's, Nottingham, where he laboured with great zeal and success for six years. There he founded the Working Men's Institute, which earned him the gratitude of many. In 1859 he accepted the sole charge of North Coates, a small parish in the Lincolnshire marshes, where pluralism had long been rife. Church life in the district was at a low ebb, and all the conditions were dreary in the extreme. The church was in a dilapidated state; the people were alienated by neglect, and the place was isolated and depressing. Undaunted, however, by indifference and opposition, he pursued his way, gradually bringing about an improvement in the life of the parish. He gained considerable renown as a composer of simple, melodious hymn-tunes. He edited *The Village Chant Book* and *The Village Organist*. As an instance of the rapidity with which his tunes were composed, it may be mentioned that when the Rev. (afterwards Bishop) Walsham How wrote asking him for six tunes for *The Children's Hymn-Book*, all six were composed and dispatched within twenty-four hours. He was a great lover of trees, many of which he planted about the church and school and in the garden in which he delighted to labour. Many years ago he said to a friend, ' When my time comes, I hope I shall find a garden awaiting me.' He resigned the living of North Coates in 1907, and spent the last two years of his life with his son, the Rev. R. N. Matthews, at Tetney, where he was Vicar.

151—Who is He?

WHO IS HE (or LOWLINESS), by B. R. HANBY, appeared in *Chapel Gems* (1866), an American publication for which Hanby and G. F. Root were responsible. He was for some years associated with the music-publishing firm of Root and Cadby in Chicago, and wrote a good deal of vocal music for them, including the once-popular ' Darling Nellie Gray.' He died in his thirty-fifth year in 1867.

152—Nazareth.

NAZARETH is by T. E. Perkins, who was the son of a
Baptist minister. He was born in 1831 at Poughkeepsie,
New York. His life was devoted to the upbuilding of
church music, but because he did not travel much, he
was little known personally. He compiled many books,
especially for the use of Sunday schools. In 1863 his
Shining Light appeared; the next year *The New Shining
Light.* Then followed *The Sacred Lute, Sabbath Carols,
The Psalm King,* and the *Mount Zion Collection of
Secular and Sacred Music.* He wrote or arranged the
tune LUNDIE used in the *American Methodist Hymnal*
with Mrs. Bonar's ' Fade, fade, each earthly joy,' also
the present tune for Etta Campbell's ' Jesus of
Nazareth passeth by.' He died in 1912.

153, 590—Antwerp.

ANTWERP, by W. Smallwood, probably first appeared
in the second series (1881) of the *Bristol Tune-Book.*
It has been stated that it is adapted from the composer's
anthem ' The path of the just,' but this is not correct.

William Smallwood was born at Kendal on the last
day of December, 1831. His father, who was a bandmaster and teacher of singing, placed him under Dr.
Camidge for the organ, and he received singing lessons
from Henry Phillips, a famous bass singer of the period.
At the age of fifteen Smallwood was appointed organist
of the parish church of his native town, a post he
retained for half a century. He composed a large
quantity of pianoforte music, and many of the elders of
the present day were brought up on his *Pianoforte Tutor.*
Some of his compositions were very popular with young
musicians.

154 (i)—Kingsfold.

During 1917-18 Sir Hugh Allen held a series of hymn-
singing practices at the Sheldonian Theatre, Oxford. On

those occasions hymns were not merely sung through in the indifferent and careless manner that characterizes the efforts of the average church-goer, but each one was exhorted to join in and do his best. Faults were pointed out and corrected as the work proceeded. On one occasion the hymn had scarcely got started when Dr. Allen reminded the audience that one of the early petitions of the church service was ' O Lord, open Thou our lips,' and yet he could scarcely see a mouth open anywhere. It was, he said, somewhat inconsistent for them to express such a desire, and then make no effort to follow it up. Another important point he insisted on was a careful attention to phrasing, and on no account would he allow his singers to take breath at the end of a line when the music ran straight on into the next one.

In order to give the singers every opportunity to do their best, hymn-sheets were provided, with the airs of most of the tunes printed thereon. Choir and people sang in unison, and each tune was rehearsed a line at a time, the result being that a new tune was soon picked up. One of these was an arrangement of KINGSFOLD for unison singing, and this is the setting that has been adopted for this book.

KINGSFOLD is an old air of unknown origin and date. It is found in the *English Hymnal* (1906), and it got there from Miss Broadwood's *English Country Songs* (1893), where a note at the foot says that it was ' noted by A. J. Hopkins, F.S.A., in Westminster. He knew it as LAZARUS, probably because it was set to some verses relating at length the story of Dives (or Diverus) and Lazarus.' The air has been put to various uses, including a song formerly very popular beginning :

> O my boy Dan is an Irishman,
> And a broth of a boy was he,
> And I wept and I wailed
> When the good ship sailed
> Away to Amerikee.

154 (ii)—Vox Dilecti.

Vox Dilecti was composed by Dr. Dykes (see No. 36) for Dr. Bonar's hymn in the Appendix to *Hymns Ancient and Modern* (1868).

155—Bedford.

Bedford has had a somewhat chequered career. No one knows exactly when it came into existence, and its end is certainly not yet. It is not disputed that William Weale was the composer (or possibly the adapter). He was organist of St. Paul's, Bedford, from about 1715 till 1727, when this entry appears in the church registers :

> September 4, 1727. Bury'd—Mr. William Weale, organist.

It has not hitherto been possible to trace the appearance of the tune before the publication of Francis Timbrell's *Divine Music Scholar's Guide,* which is, unfortunately, undated, but seems to range between 1715 and 1723. The former date is given for the copy in the British Museum, but without any circumstantial evidence to support it. The tune soon started on its long career of usefulness. After two or three earlier appearances John Wesley requisitioned it for his 'Foundery' Tune-Book, but strangely distorted the rhythm, inserting it in this form, using the tenor (or C) clef for the air :

It will be noticed that Wesley went wrong at the bar marked x, and never got right again with his barring system, the result being suggestive of a club-foot movement. But the tune received much more grievous treatment at the hands of William Gardiner, who published a volume of *Sacred Melodies* in 1812. He decided in his own mind that BEDFORD would strut along in a more dignified fashion in common time, so he dressed it up in 2-4 rhythm with the explanation, 'I have changed the key to D, and written it in common time, a measure that is more stately, and better accords with the solemn grandeur in which it is disposed to move.'

And so it stood in its new but ill-fitting garb till recent years, when attempts have been made to restore the tune to the original form in which Weale created it. It appeared with a special note to that effect in the 1904 *Methodist Hymn-Book,* but in the present book the 4-4 rhythm has been preferred. One wonders what its fate may be in future years!

Little is known of the composer, but he was probably a native of Bedford. His appointment as organist is thus recorded in the minutes of the Corporation (it was a town appointment) :

> It is ordered that Wm. Weale, jun., Esq., is made choyce of to be Organist to the Organs of St. Paul's parish to play thereon he qualifying himselfe soe as to be fitt & capable of performing & playing upon the same instrument duly then he is to have the sallary agreed upon by the sd. Corporation to the sd. Organist.

There is a quaintness in the expression that Weale was 'made choyce of to be Organist to the Organs.'

It may be assumed that he was a young man who would soon make himself 'fitt' for the post, as he took the degree of Bachelor of Music at the University of Cambridge in 1719.

156—St. Luke.

St. Luke is No. 28 in a *Collection of Easy Litanies* (1852), where it is set to the old Latin hymn :

> Deus tuorum militum
> Sors et corona premium,
> Laude canentes martyris
> Absolve nexu criminis.

The composer of the tune is unknown.

157—St. Catherine.

St. Catherine. The Rev. S. Flood Jones, the composer of this tune, was connected with Westminster Abbey for several years as deputy Minor Canon, Minor Canon, and finally Precentor, holding this post from 1868 till his death in 1895.

158—Submission.

Submission is by Edmund Gilding, an eighteenth-century London organist who was one of the contributors to Riley's *Parochial Harmony* (1762), in which the tune appears, and where it is called St. Edmund's Tune from the fact that he was organist at the church of St. Edmund the King, in Lombard Street. He was also organist at St. Martin's, Ludgate Hill, holding the two positions concurrently.

159—Fingal.

Fingal was selected for insertion in the 1885 *Scottish Hymnal,* where it was set to H. W. Baker's hymn, ' I am not worthy, holy Lord.'

J. S. Anderson was born at Crail, Fifeshire, in 1853. He learnt music from Dr. G. C. Martin, who was at that time private organist to the Duke of Buccleugh. He also studied the organ under Dr. A. L. Peace. He was at one time organist at Nicolson Square Methodist Church, Edinburgh, and subsequently held other appointments at various churches in the city, including St. Andrew's parish church, George Street. He was a member of the committee which prepared the *Revised Church Hymnary,* and also of the music sub-committee.

160, 563—Redhead No. 66. See No. 13.

161—Tell Me.

TELL ME (full title is TELL ME THE OLD, OLD STORY) was contributed by W. H. Doane to an American collection called *The Silver Spray* (1868). A freshly harmonized version was contributed by Sir Joseph Barnby for the *Bible Christian Sunday-school Hymnal* (1892).

William Howard Doane, who was born in Preston, Conn., in 1832, was a manufacturer who was also an enthusiastic musical amateur, and who took great interest in choral work. He published several collections of melodies, and also assisted in the production of others. He was a contributor to *Sacred Songs and Solos.*

162—Löwenstern.

LÖWENSTERN takes its name from the composer, Mätthäus von Löwenstern, who was both poet and musician, though his abilities in the latter direction seem to have been limited to setting his own hymns to music. He was somewhat of an experimenter in verse, writing in imitation of antique forms which did not always readily lend themselves to the restraint of the chorale form. Born in 1594 at Neustadt, in Silesia, his musical abilities gained him a position as music director at Bernstadt, and he also held political office under various German princes and magnates. He died in 1648. He wrote about thirty hymns with music, which were published some four years before his death.

163—Gillingham.

GILLINGHAM (also known as BROCKHAM and CONFIDENCE), by Jeremiah Clark (see No. 72), is from *The Divine Companion, or David's Harp New Tun'd* (1709), where it is assigned to Psalm 121, 'Up to the hills I lift mine eyes.'

164—Shebbear College.

SHEBBEAR COLLEGE was contributed by the composer to the *Methodist School Hymnal* (1910).

John Dawson Hands was born at Newark in 1878. He was educated at Bedford Grammar School, and acted as organist of St. Paul's Wesleyan Church, Bedford, from 1900 to 1906, when he was appointed resident music-master at Shebbear College, N. Devon. On leaving there he became organist at St. Paul's, Kingsbridge, S. Devon, and assistant master at the Thames Nautical Training College. His next appointment was assistant master at Liverpool Collegiate School, where he also had charge of the music. In 1922 he went to live at Clacton-on-Sea, where he is now (1934) organist of Christ Church. He received his early musical education under Dr. Harding at Bedford, and also under Drs. Cuthbert Harris and C. H. Kitson. His tune takes its name from the College in N. Devon with which he was associated.

165—Heinlein.

HEINLEIN came from the *Nurnbergisches Gesangbuch* (1676), the composer being given as 'M.H.,' which is supposed to signify Martin Herbst (c. 1654-1681). He held various posts at Eisleben, but there are no records of him as a musician, nor of his musical abilities.

166—Childhood.

CHILDHOOD is from *Hymns of the Kingdom*. According to a somewhat indefinite note in the preface this tune is the result of the combined efforts of 'a small community of minds.'

167—St. Aëlred.

ST. AËLRED, composed by J. B. Dykes (see No. 36),
dates from 1861, when it first appeared in R. R. Chope's
Congregational Hymn and Tune-Book (1861), a useful
collection intended for congregational singing, and not
specially for the Congregational Church. In its original
form the tune ended in the minor key, and in quadruple
time :

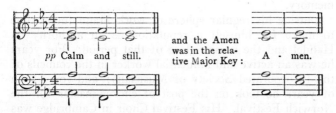

pp Calm and still. and the Amen was in the relative Major Key : A - men.

This was altered to the current ending in the Appendix
to *Hymns Ancient and Modern* (1868).

168—Stanley.

STANLEY was composed by Dr. Mann for Stanley's
hymn ' Lord, it is good for use to be,' at the request
of the committee of the *Wesleyan Tune-Book* (1876),
and first appeared in that book.

Born at Norwich in 1850, Arthur H. Mann, became a
' Trial boy ' at the Cathedral, under Dr. Buck, and in
1860 he passed on to the position of chorister at a salary
of £2 per annum. The training he received was of a
most laborious character, singing, ever singing, from
early morning until night, even to a late hour. Such a
dose of it did the boy have that when his voice broke
he vowed he would never sing again, and he never did !

Mann's first appointment after leaving Norwich in
1870 was at the Collegiate Church of St. Peter's, Wolverhampton, whence he moved to Tettenhall parish church
in the following year. There he stayed till 1875, when

he went to Beverley Minster for six months and then, on July 17, 1876, he took his first service at King's College Chapel, Cambridge, where he was destined to remain till his death in 1930. For some years he held the important position of director of the music at the Leys School, where his influence on the boys was great. He usually presided at the organ in the school chapel at the evening service, and the impression he made on some of the boys by the beauty of his accompaniment is still a treasured memory.

Outside his regular sphere of work Mann found time to make for himself a reputation as an authority on Handel and the musical lore of that period. For years he was an active and influential worker in the councils of the Incorporated Society of Musicians; and for a term of years he took on the post of chorus-master for the Norwich Festival. His Festival Choir in Cambridge was long one of the acknowledged meeting-grounds—none too many—of town and university, and if its performances fell behind those of the University Musical Society in the distinguished visitors whom Sir C. V. Stanford was able to bring in from outside, they certainly did not suffer by comparison in respect of accurate and effective presentation of great oratorios, including Parry's *Judith,* Elgar's *Dream of Gerontius,* and Beethoven's *Choral Symphony.*

But with all his effective and important work outside, it was in King's College Chapel that Dr. A. H. Mann did his best work; and the service there remains one of the outstanding features of the Cambridge of former days. The introduction of a system of choral scholarships greatly enriched the choir in the matter of tenor and bass soloists, while the King's Choir School gave him the opportunity of training an adequate succession of choristers, the result being a remarkably uniform excellence in the work done in the Chapel.

As an organist he distinctly belonged to the cathedral type rather than the concert type; and, it may be added, to the cathedral type of a period before the specifications and literature for organs had been so radically affected by the requirements of concert performances. Handel, Mendelssohn, Rheinberger, and Widor constituted his favourite sources for voluntaries, and he would always laughingly declare that he had no time to practice, and therefore could not give recitals. There was just a measure of truth in his self-depreciation; that he had voluntarily chosen other fields than that of recitalist was undoubtedly the case, but those who heard him play works like Rheinberger's Sonata in E flat minor, Merkel's Sonata in G minor, the Mendelssohn Sonatas, and Widor's Symphony in G minor, knew what he could do as an organist pure and simple. His service-playing was of a style distinctly his own, and wonderfully well suited to the building in which he officiated. The contrapuntal devices which abounded in his accompaniments to the Psalms might have proved disconcerting to some choirs, but at King's the result was both interesting and congruous. Mann's compositions were few, and his range did not extend beyond church music.

169—Sidmouth.

SIDMOUTH is by Benjamin J. Dale, and was composed by request for the *Methodist Hymn-Book* (1904). He is the son of the late Mr. C. J. Dale, a musician who was well known as the musical director at Holly Park Methodist Church, London, N., some years ago. He was a prominent member of the committee that compiled the 1904 *Methodist Tune-Book,* and he also took an active part in the musical life of North London. Mr. B. J. Dale was born in 1885 in Highbury, and soon showed a natural aptitude for music. An overture, *Horatius,* by him was performed at a London concert when he was only fourteen years old, and was very highly spoken of by the critics. During his student years at the Royal Academy of Music Dale wrote his Pianoforte Sonata in D minor, which was performed for the first time in 1905. This fine work at once brought him into prominent notice, and a recognized authority declares it to be 'one of the most important compositions in the British repertoire.' Dale next turned his attention to the viola, and he has produced some notable works for that instrument which have been interpreted by Lionel Tertis, its greatest living exponent.

Mr. Dale was in Germany when the war broke out and his opportunities for composition were limited. Since his return home he has been actively engaged in teaching. He has in past years acted as organist at City Road Chapel, and also at St. Luke's Church, W. His church compositions include a cantata ' Before the paling of the stars ' for chorus and orchestra, and a few carols.

170—All of Thee.

ALL OF THEE, by the Rev. James Mountain, first appeared in his *Hymns of Consecration and Faith* (1876). The composer was trained for the ministry of the Countess of Huntingdon's Connexion, but he subsequently became by conviction a Baptist, and was an accredited minister in the Baptist Church. He died in 1933 in his ninetieth year.

171—Jesus, I Will Trust Thee.

JESUS, I WILL TRUST THEE (RELIANCE), by Ira D. Sankey, is No. 14 in *Gospel Songs* No. 4 (1881).

172—Manchester.

MANCHESTER is by Robert Wainwright, the son of John Wainwright (see No. 120), and elder brother of Richard (see No. 326). Born in Manchester in 1748, he showed great musical ability, and in his eighteenth year competed for the position of organist of Halifax parish church, where a new organ had recently been erected by Snetzler. How he came off second best is thus related by Dr. E. Miller (see No. 182) :

The candidates first of all drew lots. My friend Herschel drew the third lot, the second performer was Mr. Wainwright, afterwards Dr. Wainwright, of Manchester, whose finger was so rapid, that old Snetzler, the organ builder, ran about the church exclaiming, ' Te tevil, te tevil, he run over to key like one cat, he vil not give my pipes room for to shpeak.' During Mr. Wainwright's performance I was standing in the middle aisle with Herschel. ' What chance have you,' said I, ' to follow this man?' He replied, ' I don't know, I'm sure fingers will not do.' On which he ascended the organ loft, and produced from the organ so uncommon a fullness, such a volume of slow, solemn harmony, that I could by no means account for the effect.

In 1767 Wainwright was appointed organist of the Old Collegiate Church, Manchester (now the Cathedral), retaining the position for eight years, when he went to Liverpool as organist of St. Peter's Church. He died in 1782.

173, 771—Euphony.

EUPHONY, by H. Dennis, was first published in 1850 in a magazine called *The Soul's Welfare*, where it appeared as a L.M. tune to ' Sweet is the work, my God, my King,' the first two and the last lines being repeated. The original name was EUPHONIA, which was shortened to EUPHONY by the composer.

Henry Dennis was born at Tickenhill, Derbyshire, in 1818. He entered the choir of the Baptist Church at such an early age that he had to stand on a stool to allow of his voice sounding forth. He spent the last forty years of his life at Hugglescote, in Leicestershire, living on an ancestral farm which had been in his mother's family over two hundred years. He did valuable work for the Baptist community there, and also wrote a number of tunes and other pieces, which had a large sale. Nor was his good

work confined to the church, for he served as a guardian
of the poor for many years, and his position and
influence made him respected by all parties and creeds.
In spite of his Nonconformity he was somewhat of a
Conservative in politics, and used to look back upon the
old times of Protection as some of England's best and
happiest days. Dying in 1887 he was buried at Hugglescote, and on his memorial stone are engraved on an open
music scroll the first two lines of EUPHONY.

174—St. Wilfrid.

ST. WILFRID was contributed by A. E. Floyd to the
Methodist School Hymnal (1910).

Dr. Alfred Ernest Floyd was born in Birmingham
(where his father, the Rev. C. H. Floyd, was a Wesleyan
minister) in 1877. He was educated at Bradford
Grammar School and the Leys School, Cambridge.
After acting for a time as deputy organist at Winchester
Cathedral he became organist of Llangollen and Oswestry
parish churches. He is now organist of St. Paul's
Cathedral, Melbourne, Australia, and has acted as
musical critic of the *Melbourne Argus*. He has done a
good deal of work as a lecturer and musical
adjudicator.

175—St. Mary.

ST. MARY is from the Welsh metrical version of the
Psalms by Edmund Prys. Its publication in 1621 was
certainly an event of great importance in the literary
history of Wales. The title of the book was *Llyfr y
Psalmau*. No publishers' name is given, and the title-
page simply indicates that it was printed in London in
1621. It contains twelve tunes, some of them—such as
the ' Old 100th ' and ' Old 113th '—being taken from the
English Psalter. Of the others, one makes its first
appearance in Prys' Psalter in this form, with B natural :

Prys wrote his version in simple metres so that the Psalms could be easily sung by the common people, and the Rev. H. Elvet Lewis tells us that this Psalter is still one of the chief treasures of Welsh hymnology. The tune was included by Playford in his *Whole Book of Psalms* (1677), and since that date no tune-book has been complete unless it included ST. MARY.

The following tradition is recorded about Prys:

> A certain person named Dr. Coch, of Yspytty Igan, had some grudge against the Archdeacon, and once, when the latter was conducting Divine service in Maentwrog Church, this Coch, accompanied by a number of followers, came to the church to seize him. Prys was informed of this fact, but he pretended to take no notice of it, and went through the service as usual. When it was over he ventured out in spite of the danger, and seized hold of a short ladder which was used by the sexton when digging graves. This impromptu instrument of warfare he began to wave around in such a threatening manner that none of his enemies ventured to close with him, and so he managed to pass through in safety to the place where his pony was tied up. Having mounted him, he rode off, and was soon at a safe distance from his pursuers.

176—Gethsemane.

GETHSEMANE (MAN OF SORROWS), by P. Bliss, is from No. 6 of the American *Gospel Hymns* (1891). It is also found in *Sacred Songs and Solos* (1883).

Philip Bliss was born at Clearfield County, Pennsylvania, in 1838. In early life he was associated with the Methodists, and worked under G. F. Root in conducting music classes in Institutes and Sunday schools. In 1871 he became connected with the First Congregational Church at Chicago, both as a chorister and as superintendent of the Sunday school. Three years later he joined D. W. Whittles in evangelical work. He was killed in a railway accident in 1876. The original form of his name was Philipp Bliss, but in an unfortunate moment he took a fancy to disconnecting the last ' p ' of his Christian name, and called himself P. P. Bliss, to the lasting confusion of his biographers.

177—Herzliebster Jesu.

HERZLIEBSTER JESU is the tune composed for Heermann's hymn by Johann Crüger (see No. 10) in his *Neues Volkömliches Gesangbuch* printed at Berlin in 1640. The tune is used three times by Bach in his *St. Matthew Passion,* and twice in the *St. John Passion.*

178, 549—Simplicity.

SIMPLICITY or, more correctly, SONG 13, is by Orlando Gibbons (see No. 24).

179—Oldbury.

OLDBURY was composed by Sir J. F. Bridge (see No. 122) for the 1904 edition of the *Methodist Hymn-Book.* He named the tune after his native town in Worcestershire.

180—Horsley.

HORSLEY is from *Twenty-Four Psalm Tunes* (1844). It is named after the composer, William Horsley, who was born in London in 1774. From his early instructors in music he got more kicks than ha'pence, but his prospects brightened on his becoming acquainted with J. W. Callcott, who encouraged him to persevere in glee-writing, in which he was afterwards so successful. After some three years as organist at Ely Chapel, Holborn, he was appointed assistant organist at the Asylum for Female Orphans, succeeding Dr. Callcott as full organist in 1802, retaining the position for fifty-two years, when a difference of opinion between him and the Asylum Committee led to his being dismissed. In 1838 he succeeded R. J. S. Stevens as organist at the Charter-house ' at a salary of £70 and a room set apart and a fire provided when necessary for his use on those days upon which his duty requires his attendance at the Hospital.' Horsley was one of the judges appointed by Miss Hackett to award the Gresham prizes she had offered for the best anthem. S. S. Wesley sent in his ' Wilderness ' for the competition, but the judges gave preference to Goss's ' Have mercy upon me, O God ' (one of the judges said that the ' Wilderness ' was not cathedral music !).

181—Atonement.

ATONEMENT belongs to the sixteenth century period of the Old Brethren's Church of Bohemia and Moravia. In the music edition of the *Moravian Liturgy and Hymns* (1914), it is said to be from the 1566 *Kirchengesänge* of the Bohemian Brethren. MIT FREUDEN ZART (No. 415) is from the same source. The origins of these melodies and their composers are alike unknown, but we may infer a good deal from this extract from a letter written by Andrew Stefan and John Kalef, two Bishops of the Bohemian Brethren, to the Emperor Frederick III. It is dated October 12, 1574 :

> Our ancestors, living among the Papists, as we also do at this day, adopted, as an attraction for persons of that description, the practice still continued by us, of singing many of our hymns to the old Gregorian tunes. And as others have borrowed our tunes, so have we borrowed many from others, especially the Germans, some of which we hear are in other languages sung to worldly songs, which not unnaturally gives offence to those who happen to recognize them.
>
> Some such profane melodies, as we may call them, have also been knowingly introduced by well-meant musicians, in hopes that the common people would be then more easily drawn on to learn the truth by means of tunes to which they were but too much accustomed; and since this was done with a good intention, we were unwilling to oppose it, more especially as we learned that the Germans had done the same.
>
> Still, it would be better if the authors of the hymns likewise composed the tunes without borrowing from others, as was the case amongst the ancients, the same persons being both musicians and poets. But these faculties are not possessed by all. We will therefore pay attention to this matter hereafter, God permitting. Yet the measures and tunes are in themselves innocent, and free from blame, and become ennobled or degraded only by the language and the sentiments of which they are the channels. Devout persons care less for the manner than the matter.

In the *Bohemian Tune-Book* (1566), the melody of ATONEMENT is set to the hymn ' Nun seht und merket, lieben leut,' by Johannes Jelecky, a priest of the Brethren's Unity, ordained in 1555, and subsequently their President. The hymn has not passed into current use. The present form of ATONEMENT is due to James Turle (No. 73), who inserted it in his *Psalms and Hymns with Tunes* (1865). The tune has also been used as a D.C.M.

182—Rockingham.

ROCKINGHAM in its present form first appeared in Dr. E. Miller's *Psalms of David* (1790), to which reference is made below.

Edward Miller was the son of a stone-mason, or, as he was then called, pavior, at Norwich, and was born in that city in 1735. He was apprenticed to his father's business, but not finding it to his liking, he ran away from home in order to follow up the study of music, for which he had already shown great predilection. He made his way to London, and became a pupil of the great Dr. Burney, with whom he formed a lasting friendship. Being a skilled flute player, he obtained a place in Handel's orchestra, and was also present at the rehearsals which the great composer used to hold at his house in Brook Street. Thus he saw and heard a good deal of what went on there, and he has recorded the following incident :

About the year 1753 a minor canon of Gloucester Cathedral offered his services as a singer, which Handel accepted, and he was employed in the choruses. Not satisfied with this department, Handel acceded to the Canon's request that he should sing a solo, so that his voice should appear to better advantage. But he sang so badly that the audience instantly hissed him. When the performance was over, by way of consolation, Handel made him the following speech, ' I am very, very sorry for you, indeed, my dear sir; but as you go back to your church in de country, God will forgive you for your bad singing; dese wicked people in London, dey will not forgive you.'

In 1756, Miller was appointed organist of the parish church at Doncaster on the recommendation of Dr. Nares, organist of the Chapel Royal, and held this position for over half a century. His salary at the commencement was £30, and with this he had to be content for the first two years of his appointment. In 1767, when he had attained the age of thirty-two, he applied for an increase in salary, and the Corporation, ' taking into consideration the dearness of provisions, and his business as a teacher of music not being so extensive as usual,' agreed to allow him the sum of forty guineas a year. In 1798 a further annual grant of ten guineas was voted to him ' to provide an organ blower, and also a proper person to instruct eight children in singing.'

In 1786 Miller took his degree of Mus.D. at Cambridge, and four years later he issued his *Psalms of David,* which had an immediate success, as nearly five thousand subscribers, from George the Third downwards, gave in their names, whilst the King also forwarded Miller a present of £25 in token of appreciation of his work. It was in this work that ROCKINGHAM made its first appearance, and its origin may be traced to a tune-book in Miller's possession, called :

A SECOND SUPPLEMENT TO PSALMODY IN MINIATURE, Containing an addition of new Hymn-Tunes, chiefly used at the Lock Tabernacle, Tottenham Court, Lady Huntingdon's and Mr. Wesley's Chaples, Dissenting Meetings, etc., etc., many of which are not in any other Collection.

Although the book is not dated, internal evidence leads one to conclude that it was issued about 1780.

This particular copy of Dr. Miller's contains several notes which are undoubtedly in Miller's handwriting, and the most interesting of these appears under the tune TUNBRIDGE, where he has written :

Would make good long M.

TUNBRIDGE. P.M.

All ye that pafs by, &c.

Here, then, we have the undoubted genesis of ROCKINGHAM. When Miller's book appeared in 1790 the editor had carried out his idea about TUNBRIDGE and it appears in the *Psalms of David* as ROCKINGHAM.

It will be noticed that Miller acknowledges that 'part of the melody' is derived from another source, and thus, although we are indebted to him for the tune in its present form, he cannot be looked upon as the actual composer.

It is uncertain when the tune was first associated with Watts's hymn 'When I survey the wondrous Cross,' but the association is found in Goddings' *The Parochial Psalmodist* (1833), and the combination is also found in the first issue (1861) of *Hymns Ancient and Modern*.

Miller was held in high esteem by his fellow towns-
men, and in 1774 the Freedom of the Borough was conferred on him. Of his eight children, William inherited
his father's musical gifts (see No. 628). Miller died
in 1807 and was buried within the walls of the parish
church.

183—Love Divine.

LOVE DIVINE was contributed by Sir John Stainer
(see No. 20) to the 1889 edition of *Hymns Ancient and
Modern*.

184 (i)—Vexilla Regis.

VEXILLA REGIS, ADORO TE (691), and VENI CREATOR
(779), are the only three examples of plain-song melodies
in the book. Their history is rather beyond the scope of
this work. It will be sufficient to say that each melody
has from the earliest times been associated with its hymn.

'Vexilla Regis prodeunt' = The Royal banners
forward go. 569 A.D.

'Adoro te devote, latens deitas' = Thee we adore, O
hidden Saviour, Thee. c. 1260 A.D.

'Veni Creator Spiritus, Mentes tuorum visita' =
Come, Holy Ghost, our souls inspire. Ninth century.

184 (ii)—Breslau.

BRESLAU is a much altered form of a melody that
originally appeared in *As hymnodus Sacer*, a collection
of twelve 'agreeable spiritual songs, mostly new' published at Leipzig in 1652. The composer is unknown.
The melody was used by Mendelssohn in *St. Paul*. The
reference to Clauder's Psalmody in M.H.B. is incorrect.

185, 287—Stabat Mater.

The tune STABAT MATER has been traced to the
Maintzisch Gesangbuch published at Mainz in 1661 in
this form:

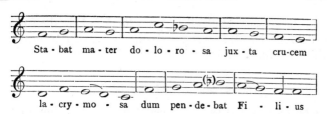

Sta - bat ma - ter do - lo - ro - sa jux - ta cru - cem

la - cry - mo - sa dum pen - de - bat Fi - li - us

Its first known appearance in England was in a book called ' *The Evening-Office of the Church,* according to the Roman Breviary, containing the Vespers for all Sundays and Festivals throughout the year. In Latin and English. To which is added A PIOUS ASSOCIATION at Public Meetings once a month, &c. . . . London. Printed for J. Marmaduke, in May's Buildings, St. Martin's Lane, 1748.'

This book contains thirty-nine Latin hymns, with translations, and on page 392 is STABAT MATER DOLOROSA, set to the following plain song melody, which is here given in modern notation :

Our modern acquaintance with the tune is due largely to its inclusion in the *Bristol Tune-Book* (1863), as an 8.8.7. to the hymn ' At the Cross, her station keeping.' From this collection it was transferred to the *Wesleyan Tune-Book* (1876) where it is described as an ' Ancient Latin Melody,' and transformed into a 7.7.7. to the words ' Holy Ghost, my Comforter,' with a pretty trickle of quavers at the end of the second line. In the 1904 *Methodist Hymn-Book* the trickle disappeared, and the melody was reharmonized, still doing duty as a 7.7.7.

In the present *Methodist Hymn-Book,* it is in the form of 8.8.7. at No. 185, set to a six-line hymn of that metre, whilst at No. 287 it is made to fit a 7.7.7. metre.

186, 974—God of the Living.

God of the Living is named from the first line of a hymn by J. Ellerton. It was written by Everard W. Hulton for the 1889 edition of *Hymns Ancient and Modern.* It was dropped from the 1904 edition of the same work, but kept alive by being included in the *Methodist Hymn-Book* of the same year.

Everard Hulton was born at King's Lynn in 1845. He was educated at Oxford and also at Cologne Conservatoire. He acted as organist at St. Luke's, Chelsea, from 1870 to 1904.

187—St. Cross.

St. Cross was written by Dr. Dykes (see No. 36) for this hymn in *Hymns Ancient and Modern* (1861).

188—Darlington.

Darlington. The source of this tune is at present unknown. It is not found in the *Hallelujah,* as stated in the *Methodist Hymn-Book.*

189—Nicht So Traurig.

Nicht So Traurig is usually ascribed (but without definite proof) to J. S. Bach. It is found in his *Vierstimmige Choral-gesänge* (1769), where it is in the key of C minor.

John Sebastian Bach was born at Eisenach in 1685. He came of a musical ancestry, entering life amid the strongest influence of German Protestantism, and this had a remarkable and permanent effect on his career. Left an orphan at ten years, he passed under his brother's care, but soon learnt all that the latter could impart. He then joined the choir of St. Michael's, Luneberg, and when his voice broke he acted as accompanist. But he had only a poor instrument at his disposal, so he moved to Weimar, and thence to a municipal church at Arnstadt, where a new organ attracted him. He remained here two years, frequently going to hear other organists, and occasionally getting into trouble for neglect of duty. His next appointment was at the Duke's Court at Weimar, and here he commenced the output of church cantatas which, upon his death, amounted to nearly three hundred. Finding Weimar not to his liking he accepted the position of capellmeister at Cothen, where he wrote a large number of instrumental works, including Book I of the *Forty-eight Preludes and Fugues*. His next and final move was to St. Thomas's Church, Leipzig, where he accepted the office of cantor. He now turned his attention once again to choral work, and soon after his arrival he produced the music of the *St. Matthew Passion*, which was followed by the *St. John Passion*, the *Mass in B minor*, and the *Christmas Oratorio*. He also continued his series of church cantatas, and added the second twenty-four to the Preludes and Fugues. Towards the end of his life his eyes began to give him trouble, largely owing to overstraining them when young. An operation proved unsuccessful, and he became totally blind. The end soon came, and on July 28, 1750, there passed away the man ' to whom ' (as Schumann said) ' music owes about as great a debt as religion owes to its founder.'

190—Fons Amoris.

FONS AMORIS, by F. Luke Wiseman (see No. 5), was written for the *Methodist School Hymnal* (1910).

191—Pelham.

PELHAM, by F. Giardini, is from the same source as MOSCOW (see No. 880).

192—St. Drostane.

St. Drostane was composed by Dr. Dykes to this hymn for Chope's *Congregational Hymn and Tune-Book* (1862).

193—Burford.

Burford has had a long career. First appearing in John Chetham's *Book of Psalmody* (1718), it passed into Gawthorne's *Harmonica Perfecta* (1730) as Burford, thence into Wesley's *Foundery Tune-Book* (1742), under the name St. John's, and the *Divine Musical Miscellany* (1754), as Burford. At last it found its way into Dr. Miller's *Psalms of David* (1790), where it was ' said to be Purcell's '—a myth which has prevailed ever since, even to the appearance of the *Congregational Hymnary* (1916). Dr. W. H. Cumming and Barclay Squire, both of them recognized authorities on Purcell's music, were quite unable to place it in any of the composer's works, and thus Dr. Miller's suggestion is finally disposed of. But Miller was not the first to be responsible for the assignment. The story of the destruction of Epworth vicarage and Wesley's marvellous escape is well authenticated, so also is this story :

> Among other relics rescued from the flames was a bit of scorched paper that was found by the rector the next day, and which had on it a hymn that he had composed a few days earlier, beginning ' Behold the Saviour of mankind,' set to a tune (by Purcell) now known as Burford.

Although the tune may have been known in 1709 when the fire took place, it has not hitherto been found in print till nine years later. Whether the story is true or not, it is a fact that John Wesley inserted it in his ' Foundery ' Tune-Book in 1742.

The strains of this tune were heard frequently in Birmingham Town Hall during 1842. The death of the organist, George Hollins, led to the appointment of a successor, and the four judges, J. A. Novello, John Goss, Knyrett and T. A. Walmisley, drew up a scheme of tests for the candidates, the first being ' to play BURFORD psalm-tune, with prelude on the diapason, and an interlude between the first and second verses.' The successful candidate was James Stimpson.

John Chetham is said to have been a musical clergyman at Skipton and Rotherham, but there are no records of him at either place. The Skipton registers disclose a John Chetham, schoolmaster, in 1725, and in 1739-40, he is described as ' Mr. John Chetham, curate.' His burial is recorded as taking place on June 26, 1746. In the *Transactions of the Lancashire and Cheshire Antiquarian Society*, 1916-17, there is a record of a letter from the musician's son in which he says that John Chetham was born ' at a place called Ashton under line a little village between Cheshire and Lancashire. He was educated at Deckerfield School. . . . After he left the school he entered into orders and then settled in Yorkshire, where he did reside at Skipton.' Then follow particulars about the family. Whether John Chetham was related to the famous Humphrey Chetham is not certain. It is very doubtful if he could have had any acquaintance with Purcell's music, and BURFORD is quite probably a local effort whose composer is unknown.

194—Llyfnant.

LLYFNANT was composed by John Cluley for the *Methodist Hymn-Book* (1904).

Mr. J. Cluley was born at Willenhall in 1856, and for over fifty years he was organist and choirmaster in some of the Nonconformist churches in the neighbourhood. In 1861 he commenced his musical career by accepting an appointment as organist at the Baptist Chapel in Lichfield Street, Willenhall. From here he moved to another Baptist Chapel in Little London (in the same district). Here he remained till 1893 when he was appointed to the Wesleyan Chapel in Union Street. Here he remained for nearly thirty years, when ill-health compelled him to give up the organ, though retaining the office of choirmaster. He has composed a good deal of anniversary and similar music.

195—Merthyr Tydfil.

MERTHYR TYDFIL (or DIES IRAE), by Joseph Parry is from the enlarged (1870) edition of *Llyfr Tonau Cynulleidfaol,* originally published in 1859.

Dr. Joseph Parry was born at Merthyr Tydfil in 1841 at a cottage in Cyfartha that now attracts its hundreds of visitors—especially from America—annually. At nine he worked in a mine and at twelve he became a puddler in the celebrated Cyfartha Steelworks. During these years Parry sang in the Bethesda Chapel choir as an alto, but he could get no one to be interested in him. He was musical but knew no music. Indeed, in 1858 Parry wrote, ' I am seventeen years of age, and know not a note of music.'

In 1855 the family emigrated to America, where he started on his Eisteddfodic career, a fact which made him competitive in all his work.

From 1860 to 1866 he won at will in as many competitions as he entered for, both in America and Wales. He boasted that he was never beaten in competition. His first big prize at nineteen was for ' A Temperance Vocal March.' Six years later he won £30 at the Chester National Eisteddfod for a cantata entitled *The Prodigal Son.* Most of the compositions that brought him prizes during these years also brought him publishers who gave him very good publishing terms. More than this, the prizes brought him prominence in America, and made his appointment as organist and choirmaster at New York churches easy.

Not only Welsh people of Wales and America, but Parry himself realized that he needed training if he was to climb higher. And the funds came. At twenty-seven he returned from America with his family, and entered the Royal Academy of Music, where for three years he studied composition under Sterndale Bennett, singing under Manuel Garcia, and the organ under Dr. Steggall. He was the winner of many prizes each year, and at the end of the third year won the highest prize the Academy offered in those days—the Silver Medal. While at the Academy he obtained his Mus.B. (Cantab.), the first Welshman to do so.

During another visit to America Parry was offered the newly endowed music chair at Aberystwyth in 1874. He was glad of the opportunity to return to Wales. The professorship lasted only six years, but these years at Aberystwyth gave Parry the time to read for his Mus.D., which he took at Cambridge. The work prepared by him for this degree was his oratorio *Jerusalem*, which was performed at King's College, Cambridge, under the composer's direction. Numerous compositions followed, *Blodwen* and other operas, oratorios (including *Emmanuel* and *Saul of Tarsus*), and part-songs and hymn-tunes in rapid succession. His ' Codwer Hwyl' for male voices, is widely known. He died in 1903.

196—Church Triumphant.

CHURCH TRIUMPHANT, by J. W. Elliott, was contributed by him to *Church Hymns* (1874).

James William Elliott was born at Warwick in 1833. After being trained as a chorister at Leamington he held various country organ appointments, including the parish church at Banbury, where he stayed two years. In 1862 he moved to London, and finally settled at St. Mark's, Hamilton Terrace, St. John's Wood, where he remained thirty-six years. In 1871 Sullivan invited his aid in preparing the music edition of *Church Hymns,* which was published three years later. In this work Elliott contributed several tunes which Sullivan duly acknowledged, and also thanked him ' for the very valuable assistance he has rendered by his good counsels, his sound judgement, and his untiring energy in the more laborious department of manual work.'

Outside his church work Elliott did good service for young people, and his settings of nursery rhymes and songs for children had a long run of popularity, whilst his fine song ' Hybreas the Cretan ' is still remembered as one of the most popular songs of a previous generation. He was for some years musical adviser to a prominent London firm, a position for which his personal qualities fitted him admirably. He resigned his position at St. Mark's a year or two before his death, which took place in 1915.

197—Beneath the Cross of Jesus.

BENEATH THE CROSS OF JESUS. The first appearance of this tune is uncertain, but it was probably in an early edition of *Sacred Songs and Solos.* Sankey relates how he composed the tune at the home of Dr. T. J. Barnardo, and it was sung next day at a meeting held in the Hall in Bow Road, London. It is in No. 1 of the American *Gospel Hymns.*

198—Cross.

CROSS is taken from the Supplement (1912) to the *Primitive Methodist Hymnal,* where it is said to be an ' Old Melody.' There is no reason to doubt the statement.

199—Near the Cross.

NEAR THE CROSS is by W. H. Doane (see No. 161), and is from an American collection called *Bright Jewels* (1869).

200—Old German.

OLD GERMAN is a somewhat staid and sober form of a rather lively tune that John Wesley placed at the beginning of his *Sacred Melody* (1761), where it was in this form :

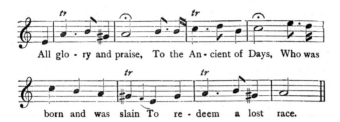

All glo - ry and praise, To the An - cient of Days, Who was

born and was slain To re - deem a lost race.

There are traces of BREMEN (No. 504) running through it, but its origin has yet to be discovered.

201—Martyrdom.

Like many another famous melody, MARTYRDOM is not the composition of a skilled musician, but has its origin in the fertile brain of a countryside amateur. Hugh Wilson was born in 1764, at the Ayrshire village of Fenwick, which lies about four miles north of Kilmarnock. He received his education in the village school, but his knowledge and skill in music was gained entirely by his own exertions. On leaving school he learnt the shoemaking trade with his father, spending his spare time in the study of music and mathematics. A favourite pastime of his was the designing of sundials, and it is said that one constructed by him may still be seen in his native village. About the beginning of last century he left Fenwick for Pollokshaws, where he made the acquaintance of a Mr. Dunn, in whose mills he occupied a responsible position till his death in 1824.

Wilson composed many tunes, but only two of these appear to have been published, viz.: MARTYRDOM and CAROLINE, and the latter is not now in use. While on his death-bed the composer caused his manuscript tunes and a few poems to be destroyed—a circumstance that is to be regretted, as there may well have been other work as excellent as MARTYRDOM. This tune was composed before Wilson left Fenwick, from which village it took its first name; and, indeed, in the churches there until lately it was still announced under that title. It was originally written in duple-time, and first published on single slips with the melody and bass only for the use of teachers in psalmody classes.

The story of MARTYRDOM has been the cause of much antiquarian dispute, since for many years the very name of the composer was unknown. It is said that on one occasion legal action was taken to protect the copyright, when two of Wilson's relations named Fulton proved that Wilson not only composed the tune, but taught it in his classes at Fenwick at least twenty-five years before. The evidence thus brought forward satisfied the sheriff, who gave it as his decision that Wilson was the composer. The tune first appeared in triple time in R. A. Smith's *Sacred Music* (1825). Miss Gilchrist suggests that R. A. Smith may have misunderstood the name ' Fenwick,' and thought the tune was named after the martyred Covenanter, James Fenwick, and so re-christened it MARTYRDOM.

202, 768—Passion Chorale.

PASSION CHORALE was originally a love song by Hans Leo Hassler in his *Lustgarten neuer deutscher Gesänge*, in which were also included ' balletti, galliards and intrades ' for 4, 5 and 8 voices. The melody was a five-part setting of a song beginning ' Mein Gmüt ist mir ver wirret von einer jungfrau zart ' (' My heart is distracted by a gentle maid '). The tune soon got adapted for church use, being set in 1656 to Gerhardt's ' O Haupt voll Blut und Wunden,' and with the English translation ' O sacred Head once wounded,' the tune is still associated. Hassler, who was born at Nürnberg in 1564, became an organist at Augsburg. Some years later he went to Vienna, where he became the Court director of the music. This chorale is used extensively by Bach, who did not hesitate to vary the melody (see No. 72, in the *St. Matthew Passion*). In fact by altering the melody and varying the treatment he made it serve the most opposite sentiments.

203—Shaftesbury.

SHAFTESBURY was composed by Sir J. F. Bridge at the request of John Dobson, who wanted it for his *Tunes New and Old* (1864). Thirteen editions of this book were published, the last being in 1877, after which date it fell into disuse owing to the publication of the *Wesleyan Tune-Book* in the previous year. John Dobson was a Manchester man, and secured Bridge's co-operation whilst the latter was organist of Manchester cathedral.

204—Easter Morn.

EASTER MORN. In 1708 there was published in London a small tune-book with the title :

Lyra Davidica, or a Collection of Divine Songs and Hymns, partly New Composed, partly Translated from the High-German, and Latin Hymns : and set to easy and pleasant tunes, for more General Use.

The music Engrav'd on Copper Plates.

Isa. xxiv., xvi., xiv., xv.

From the (Wing) of the Earth we have heard Songs; Even Glory to the Righteous; They shall Sing for the Majesty of the Lord; They shall Cry aloud from the Sea; Wherefore Glorify ye the Lord in the Isles of the Sea.

EASTER MORN makes its first appearance in this collection under the title of THE RESURRECTION. (See Frontispiece.)

This is a very scarce book, the copy in the British Museum being the only one known.

In all probability the book was a private venture—Dr. Julian credits it to ' some Anglo-German of the Pietist school of thought '—and its rarity at the present day is probably due to the fact that very few copies were printed. The compiler tells us in his preface that his object has been to introduce 'a little freer air than the grave movement of the Psalm-tunes, as being both seasonable and acceptable,' and he goes on to say, 'In Germany, where they have abundance of divine songs and hymns, set to short and pleasant tunes, the peasant at his plow, the servants at their labour, the children in the street . . . make use of these for the expression of their mirth; and have no such custom as we unhappily labour under, of ballads and profane songs.' And he concludes by expressing the hope that his book 'may yield a grateful savour both to God and man.'

Elsewhere in the preface we are told that the basis of the work was 'a collection of compositions for private use, in which are two or three of the German hymns; to which others were recommended to be Added by some of that Nation, and Encouragement given of good Acceptance, if they were made Publick,' and the editor intimates that he has 'many more of this kind by him,' expressing a hope that they may be published at some future time 'for the Use of the greater Proficiency both in Musick and Religion.'

No name of any compiler, editor, or composer appears on the title-page, or in any other part of the book, the only individual mentioned being 'William Patersen,' to whom the book is 'Humbly Inscribed' in very stilted and somewhat incomprehensible language. The *Lyra* contains twenty-five tunes and thirty-one hymns. A general analysis of the sources of the tunes shows that nine are German chorales, two are Latin melodies, and nine are English, and were probably written for the work. The remainder are probably English, but do not make a first appearance in the *Lyra*.

205—Llanfair.

LLANFAIR. There is considerable doubt as to the composer of this tune. *The Handbook to the Church*

Hymnary states definitely that it is by Robert Williams, a blind basket-maker who was a native of Anglesea, and that the tune is in a MS. music-book belonging to him ' dated July 14, 1817,' also that it appeared in print in J. Parry's *Peroriaeth Hyfryd* (1837). But more than one composer has claimed this tune as his own, and there was a Robert H. Williams, a contemporary of the above, who also wrote hymn-tunes. The chief authorities content themselves with simply calling this tune ' Alaw Gymreig ' (Welsh Air), a safe remark common in Welsh hymnals for a tune whose origin is uncertain. The Rev. E. Ebrard Rees, who has examined a large number of tune-books in an attempt to trace this tune, says : ' Many of the early Welsh hymn-tunes appeared under various titles and various authors. To avoid trouble some of the tunes were designated " Welsh air "; but many of them were traditional Welsh airs that were put down on paper by people who claimed them as their own. LLANFAIR seems to belong to this class.'

206, 967—Morgenlied.

MORGENLIED was contributed by F. C. Maker to the 1881 Supplement to the *Bristol Tune-Book*. He was born in Bristol in 1844, and spent the whole of his life in the city. Like many other composers he began his musical career as a choir boy in the cathedral during the time Corfe was organist. One of his fellow-choristers was George Riseley, who afterwards became organist of the cathedral and the Colston Hall.

Maker held several organ appointments in the city, including Clifton Downs Congregational Church, and finally became organist and choirmaster at Redland Park Congregational Church, of which the late Rev. Urijah Thomas was the minister. This position was held for thirty years, until his retirement about 1910.

During this period he lived a busy life and held many

important musical appointments, including the following : Accompanist to the Bristol Festival Choir from its inauguration, when Alfred Stone was the chorus master; visiting professor of music at Clifton College for twenty years, under W. F. Trimnell, who was the resident music master at that time; conductor of the Bristol Choirs Association, which consisted of several of the Free Church choirs, who united for the purpose of giving special musical services, and rendering church cantatas. This society did much for Free Church music in its time, and introduced a large quantity of good church music to the various choirs.

It was by the merest accident that he became known as a composer. Alfred Stone, who was a prominent Bristol musician a generation ago, was appointed editor of the *Bristol Tune-Book,* and wanting some tunes of a special character, asked Maker if he had any such. He responded by handing over a number of tunes which so pleased Stone that several were at once accepted, and so the name of F. C. Maker as a hymn-tune composer was brought before the public. Later on, many of these tunes found a place in new hymnals and have become established favourites with many. In addition to hymntunes Maker was successful in other fields of composition and his anthems and a cantata, *Moses in the Bulrushes,* have enjoyed a large circulation. Maker spent his closing years in retirement, dying at the advanced age of eighty-three.

207—Würtemberg.

WÜRTEMBERG is supposed to be by Johann Rosenmüller, but the ascription is doubtful. There is ' rather an apocryphal story ' to the effect that Rosenmüller, whilst acting Music Director at Leipzig, had been guilty of certain indiscretions with some of his pupils. He was convicted and put in prison, but managed to escape and went to Hamburg. Whilst there he sent a letter to the

Elector, Johann Georg at Dresden, praying for release and enclosing a hymn which a friend had written for him together with a tune of his own to which he had set the words. The chorale is found in *Hundert geistliche Arien,* published at Dresden in 1694.

208, 836—Ellacombe.

ELLACOMBE has had a somewhat eventful career since it appeared amongst a collection of melodies published at Mainz by X. L. Hartig in 1833. In England it started life as a D.C.M., then got adapted to a 7.6. (8 lines Iambic) metre; the result being doubtful, it was sent back to the D.C.M. compartment, only to find itself returned once more to the company of the 7.6. metre. A still earlier appearance of the melody is found in *Gesang-Buch der Herzogl Wirtemburgischen Katholischen Hofkapelle* (1784), where it is found as 'Melody No. 1b.' This collection was made for use in the private chapel of the duchy of Wirtemburg.

209, 886—Gratitude.

GRATITUDE, by G. W. Martin, is from one of the numbers of his *Part Music Series* (1862).

George William Martin was born in London in 1828. He was a chorister at St. Paul's Cathedral, and sang in the choir at the coronation of Queen Victoria. He became music master at St. John's Training College, Battersea, and was also organist of Christ Church, Battersea. In 1860 he formed a large choir under the name of the National Choral Society, giving a series of oratorio concerts at Exeter Hall. For the use of his choir he composed and arranged a quantity of part music, including 'The Pilgrim Song' (see No. 542), and the present tune. In 1864 he formed a choir of about a thousand voices for performance of the 'Macbeth' music

12

at the tercentenary celebrations of Shakespeare's birth.
In 1871 he organized a series of concerts at the Albert
Hall ' to place within the reach of all classes a high-class
performance of madrigals, glees, and part-songs, inter-
spersed with solos, vocal and instrumental, by the best
artistes.'   Martin's later years were clouded, and he died
a pauper in Bolingbroke House Hospital, Wandsworth,
in 1881.

210—Christ lag in Todesbanden.

CHRIST LAG IN TODESBANDEN is an old German melody
of unknown origin.   Its earliest known appearance in
print was in Johann Walther's *Gesangbuchlein,* which
was one of three hymn-books associated with Luther
published in 1524.   Dr. A. W. Wilson points out that the
tune is partly based on phrases from a twelfth-century
air ' Christ(us) ist erstanden.'

211—Christ Arose.

CHRIST AROSE, by the Rev. Dr. Lowry, is from
Brightest and Best, an American collection published in
1875.   Dr. Lowry was a baptist clergyman in Plainfield,
New Jersey.   He composed many tunes, characterized by
lively rhythm and simple harmonies.   Born at Philadelphia in 1826, he was educated at Lewisburg University,
and then held various pastorates, becoming professor
of rhetoric in his old university.   He died in
1899.

212—Salve, Festa Dies.

SALVE, FESTA DIES (Hail, festal day) was contributed
by Sir Joseph Barnby to the 1889 edition of *Hymns
Ancient and Modern.*

213—Maccabæus.

MACCABAEUS. This famous tune is from *Judas Maccabaeus* (1746), but Handel originally designed it for *Joshua,* which appeared in the following year. *Judas* was composed at the suggestion of Frederic, Prince of Wales, who thought such a work would fittingly celebrate the victory of his brother, the Duke of Cumberland, at Culloden (1745), which greatly aroused the enthusiasm of Londoners. Handel readily accepted the commission, and himself selected the subject of his new oratorio, which he decided should illustrate the story of the great Jewish hero Judas Maccabaeus.

An interesting story is told about Handel's own opinion of the chorus ' See, the conquering hero comes.' Soon after it was completed he played it to a friend who, in answer to the question ' How do you like it? ' answered, ' Not so well as some things I have heard of yours.' ' Nor I, either,' said Handel, ' but you will live to see it a greater favourite with the people than my other finer things.' Certain it is that in this particular instance Handel has proved a true prophet. As Rockstro says, in his life of the composer, ' It is as true to nature as the most priceless picture that was ever painted. If it needed no great amount of learning to produce it, it exhibits an infinity of knowledge—knowledge of men, and things, and circumstances and feelings, which it paints so clearly that a child may read its story.'

Streatfeild, in his *Handel,* says of this music that it is ' one of those brave immortal things upon which the touch of Time is powerless.' This chorus has had some strange adventures. It soon became popular, and was made use of in a manner that the composer never anticipated. On August 12, 1762, a son was born to George III, and some loyal poet, to celebrate the occasion, burst forth thus :

> To George and Charlotte, happy pair,
> A son is born, a Royal Heir.

> Bring ev'ry Gem from chrystals bred
> To crown the lovely Infant's head.
> Britons, all hail th' auspicous morn
> When George and Charlotte's son was born.

The 'lovely infant' afterwards became George IV.
This impromptu verse was fitted (with some difficulty,
it is true) to 'See the conquering hero,' and was 'Sung
by Mr. Lowe at the Theatre in the Haymarket on his
Night at the Performance of Alexander's Feast.'

In 1779 Admiral Keppel was charged with various
derelictions of duty during an engagement with the
French. The charges were proved to be 'malicious and
ill-founded,' and the Admiral became the hero of the
day; bonfires blazed in his honour, the rioters drank his
health, the publicans painted his head on their signs, and
a poet burst out with this song, which he fitted, with no
little difficulty, to the music of 'See the conquering hero
comes,' with original additions :

> See brave Keppel, see He comes,
> Sound the Trumpet, beat the drums.
> Sons of Neptune, Laurels bring,
> Deck his Brow, and to him sing.
> Ride triumphant o'er the Main,
> Check the Pride of France and Spain.

214—Belgrave.

BELGRAVE is by William Horsley (see No. 180) and
was first published in *National Psalmody,* an extensive
collection of tunes collected and edited by Benjamin
Jacob in 1817.

215—Victory.

VICTORY is a very much altered form of this *Gloria
Patri et Filio* by Palestrina, belonging to a ' Magnificat '
in the third mode :

Notice how from the fifth bar the tenor takes up the chant. This itself is built up from a chant in the same mode, which is the canto fermo of the above :

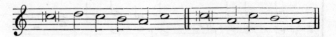

W. H. Monk adapted his tune from this, flattening his B everywhere, and adding an ' Alleluia ' out of his own head. He also put the whole in E, yet Sir Richard Terry, in tracing this development, points out that Palestrina never wrote in this key. Monk probably did this out of consideration for his congregation.

Some twenty miles east of Rome, up amongst the hills, lies the town of Palestrina, the modern descendant of the ancient Praeneste, whose praises Horace used to sing, though he complained of its cold winds. Here, in 1525 (or 1526) was born Giovanni Pierluigi, who, when in after years he became famous, was called Pierluigi da Palestrina, and so the name of his birthplace became the cognomen of one of the most famous musicians in history. Very few details are known about his life, but in the course of the centuries many stories, more or less authentic, have been associated with his name. One of the most popular is the oft-repeated statement that whilst in Rome Palestrina was a pupil of Goudimel, a statement which has brought about much strife between rival biographers, some of whom rashly state that Goudimel was never in Rome, whilst others are equally ready to affirm that he was.

Another legend is to the effect that young Gianetto, as he was called, was singing in the streets of Rome when his voice attracted the attention of a choirmaster, who promptly secured him as a promising recruit to his choir. But there is no foundation for this incident, especially as the boy's parents were apparently well off, and there was no reason why their offspring should have been sent to Rome to sing in the streets.

When these and similar statements are disentangled from historic fact there remains little to be told about Palestrina's career. He made such progress in his musical studies in Rome that before he was twenty he was appointed organist of the cathedral in his native town, which goes to prove that thus early in life he had won the esteem of his fellow-citizens. This was in 1544, and three years later it is said that the fortunate youth married a wealthy citizen's daughter.

In 1551 Palestrina was appointed master of the choir at St. Peter's, Rome, and three years later he published his first volume of masses, which he dedicated to Pope Julius III, who appointed him one of his singers in his private chapel, although the musician was technically incapable of holding the position, being both a Benedict and a layman. This led to disaster under another Pope, Paul IV, who initiated a series of reforms, which led to Palestrina's dismissal. But he had already made a name for himself as a composer, and within two months he was invited to the post of chapel-master at the Lateran, where he remained for six years, when he was transferred to a similar post at the Church of Santa Maria Maggiore. Here he remained for ten years, when he was once more elected to his old office of *maestro* at the Vatican. By this time he stood out as a composer of the first rank amongst the polyphonic writers of the day, and he was commissioned to write a Mass that should be the type of true Church music. He wrote three, of which *Missa Papae Marcelli* was accepted as the standard.

Palestrina wrote his music in four, five, or more parts, and for a full choir. It is most effective when sung without accompaniment. In studying or in listening to his compositions it is important to remember that the division of phrases and sentences by means of bars was entirely unknown in his day, and so the bar lines which are now inserted are not necessarily indications of accent. Thus there is rhythm in his music, but not time in the sense that we understand the term now. Nor is there any clear indication of key, although signatures are now added, just as bars are, for the sake of convenience.

Palestrina led a strangely quiet and uneventful life, devoted entirely to the best interests of his art. He epitomized his career thus : ' From my youth I have devoted myself to the study of music, and many are of opinion that I have accomplished something in this direction, though I am fully conscious how little it really is. Yet all my progress in this study I am determined to use solely for the glory of God in songs of praise.'

216—St. Albinus.

St. Albinus. In 1852 the Rev. W. J. Blew, a hymn-writer of considerable ability, issued his *Church Hymn and Tune-Book,* having Gauntlett associated with him as musical editor. This publication inaugurated a new era in tune-books, and formed the model on which *Hymns Ancient and Modern* (1861) and other collections were founded. Gauntlett wrote a large number of original tunes for the book, of which St. Albinus is one, originally composed to ' Angels to our jubilee,' a translation from the Latin by Blew, which has now passed out of use. St. Albinus originally had the fifth note dotted, instead of the third, as now printed.

217—Wetherby.

Wetherby was written by S. S. Wesley for *The European Psalmist* (1872).

Samuel Sebastian Wesley was the eldest son of Samuel Wesley by his second alliance, and grandson of the Rev. Charles Wesley. His father was careful to develop and train the boy's natural instinct for music, and in his tenth year he became a chorister at the Chapel Royal. He frequently appeared in public, and on one occasion

George IV was in the audience when Wesley sang at Brighton, and his display so delighted the King that he presented the lad with a gold watch.

At the age of seventeen Wesley received his first appointment as organist. This was at St. James's, Hampstead Road. In 1829 he accepted the double appointment at St. Giles', Camberwell, and St. John's, Waterloo Road. A year later he included Hampton-on-Thames as a third appointment, though his duties here were in the evening only. This parochial work ceased in 1832, when he became organist of Hereford Cathedral, and whilst here he wrote his two famous anthems, 'The Wilderness' and 'Blessed be the God and Father.' These, with his other anthems and services, have placed Wesley in the front rank of composers of church music. In 1835 he married Marianne Merewether, daughter of the Dean of Hereford. Wesley was a faithful son, frequently writing home to his parents and giving them wise advice about money matters. He himself was beginning to find it difficult to make both ends meet. ' I wish I was a Dean,' he wrote, on hearing that his father-in-law had been made a Canon of Windsor, an office which added £1,400 to his salary.

Shortly after his marriage Wesley accepted the post of organist at Exeter Cathedral, where he remained seven years. During this period he took his doctor's degree in music at Oxford (being excused the Mus.B. examination). In 1842 he became organist at Leeds parish church. During his residence in the north he wrote his famous Service in E. In 1849 Wesley made another move, this time to Winchester Cathedral. In 1865 he was asked to preside at a trial of candidates for the post of organist at Gloucester Cathedral, but before the examination began he intimated that he would like the post himself, and was at once accepted. Here he remained till his death in 1876. Memorials at Exeter, Leeds and Gloucester remind the visitor of the life work of this great musician.

218—The Foe Behind.

THE FOE BEHIND was composed by the Rev. Olinthus R. Barnicott at the request of the committee for the *Wesleyan Tune-Book* (1876).

Dr. Barnicott was originally a Wesleyan minister, but about 1880 he decided to take orders in the Church of England. For many years he was vicar of the parish church of Stratton-on-the-Foss, near Bath, and those who heard him preach there used to say that his sermons had ' a true Methodist ring' about them. He was much esteemed by his parishioners, who felt they had lost a true friend when he passed away in his sixty-fourth year in 1908. In a letter written some years ago Dr. Barnicott said that he had a distinct recollection of composing portions of ' The foe behind' whilst walking on the sea-shore.

219—Dudley.

DUDLEY, by E. F. Rimbault, appeared in *Psalms and Hymns for Divine Worship* (1867).

Edward Francis Rimbault was born in Soho, London, in 1816. His father was Stephen Francis Rimbault, who was organist of St. Giles-in-the-Fields, London, had studied music in Germany, and was well known in England as an arranger of overtures, &c., for the piano, as well as a composer of some merit. He wrote three grand sonatas for flute and piano. Young Rimbault became a pupil of his father, as well as of Samuel Wesley and Dr. Crotch. At sixteen years of age he was appointed organist of the Swiss Church, Soho, and after his resignation of this appointment, he was successively organist of several churches and chapels. Early in life he directed his attention to the study of musical history and literature, and at the age of twenty-two delivered a series of lectures on the history of music in England. Two years later—in 1840—he became attached to the Musical Antiquarian Society (eventually becoming its secretary) and he forthwith began editing the musical

publications of the Motet Society. In the course of
the next few years he edited a collection of Anglican
chants; the order of daily service according to the ' use '
of Westminster Abbey; a reprint of Lowe's *Brief Direction for the performance of Cathedral Service*; Tallis's
Responses; Merbecke's 1550 Book of Common Prayer
noted; a volume of unpublished Cathedral services, and
a reprint of Dr. Arnold's *Cathedral Music*, besides books
of carols.

Rimbault was responsible for the historic part of that
famous work *The Organ* (1870), E. J. Hopkins preparing
the technical chapters.

220—God is Ascended.

GOD IS ASCENDED was conveyed from the *Oxford Book
of Carols* (1928), where it is said to be taken from David
Corner's *Collection* (1631).

221—Ascension.

ASCENSION was written by Dr. Monk for the first
(1861) edition of *Hymns Ancient and Modern.*

W. H. Monk was born in the west of London in 1823.
His early love of music took him to the concerts of the
Sacred Harmonic Society, and at these he got impressions
and formed ideas which strengthened and developed as
he grew older. He learned the organ from Thomas
Adams, a famous player of the time, and thus became
qualified to take a series of organ appointments which
culminated at St. Matthias, Stoke Newington, where he
was in charge of the music from 1852 till his death in
1889.

The Oxford Movement, with its demands for the
improvement of church music, attracted his attention,
and he became interested, with others, in the establishment of the *Parish Choir*, which became the musical
journal of the movement. This he edited from the
fortieth number till it ceased to exist in 1853. In 1858

Sir Henry Baker, vicar of Monkland, Herefordshire, brought together about twenty clergymen with a view to producing a hymn-book which should supersede those then in use. The fact is that up till then metrical psalmody had been viewed with suspicion by many who looked upon it as too suggestive of the Reformation. There was even some doubt expressed as to the legality of the use of hymns in the church, and 'an acute legal friend' was requested to investigate the matter. The result was satisfactory, and then this band of workers was free to proceed with their self-appointed task. A committee was formed in 1859, with Sir Henry Baker as chairman, and in the following year a 'words only' edition of *Hymns Ancient and Modern* was published. A music edition at once became essential and W. H. Monk was invited to act as editor. This music edition was published in 1861, an Appendix in 1868, an enlarged edition in 1875, and a complete edition in 1889. Monk died on the eve of its production. On the day before his death he sent the final proofs to the publisher, saying that he had finished the work, but did not expect to live to see it published. Two years later a memorial cross was erected over his tomb in Highgate cemetery, the expenses being defrayed by public subscription.

222—Hermann.

HERMANN (properly HERMAN) is probably by (or adapted by) Nicolaus Herman, and is found in his *Die Sontags Evangelia,* which he published at Wittenberg in 1560. Bach, in this present adaptation, altered Herman's tune considerably. Little is known of the composer except that he was at one time organist and choirmaster at Joachimsthal, in Bohemia, until a bad attack of gout compelled him to resign. He died in 1561. He is said to have been 'an ardent lover of music and a very good organist.' This arrangement of the chorale is from Bach's cantata No. 67 ('Hold in affection Jesus Christ').

223—Rex Gloriae.

REX GLORIAE, by Henry Smart (see No. 12) appeared in the Supplement to *Hymns Ancient and Modern* (1868).

224—London New.

LONDON NEW is from the *Scottish Psalter* of 1635 (see No. 37). It was originally called NEWTOWN.

225—Dulcina.

DULCINA is taken from a MS. book of songs in the British Museum. It is not the old tune DULCINA ('as at noon Dulcina rested').

226—Triumph.

TRIUMPH was composed by Dr. Gauntlett for the *Church Hymn and Tune-Book.* See No. 216.

227—Salzburg.

SALZBURG is ascribed to Jakob Hintze in the 1658 edition of Crüger's *Praxis Pietatis Melica.* It has been much altered from the original form. Hintze acted as editor of the work after Crüger's death.

228—Austria. See No. 16.

229—Festus.

FESTUS is a much-altered and reduced form of an eight-line chorale from Freylinghausen's *Gesangbuch* (1714), where it is set to a D.L.M. hymn by Wolfgang C. Dessler 'Mein Jesu dem die Seraphinen.' This was translated by John Wesley and appeared in his *Hymns and Sacred Poems* (1739) as 'Jesu, whose glory's streaming rays.' This was in the 1904 *Methodist Hymn-Book.* Dessler's hymn also appeared in the 1704 Freylinghausen's *Gesangbuch* set to LUSATIA (or DESSLER) (see No. 280).

230—Rejoice and be Glad.

REJOICE AND BE GLAD is a tune of unknown origin. It is taken from the *Revival Tune-Book* (1864).

231—Blairgowrie.

BLAIRGOWRIE was composed at the request of the Committee for Edward Shillito's hymn 'Away with gloom, away with doubt!' in the *Methodist Hymn-Book* (1933).

Robert George Thompson was born at Middlesbrough in 1862, and he spent the whole of his life there, or in the neighbouring town of Stockton-on-Tees. He was educated at the Wesleyan Day School, receiving his musical education from Mr. Felix Corbett, though he was to a large extent self-taught. He spent some years at the Westminster Training College in Horseferry Road, S.W., and to the end he retained pleasant memories of his sojourn there. He figured in the College band as a clarinettest, though the troublesome 'quacking' of the instrument led him to give it up subsequently. He always spoke highly of Dr. Ralph Dunstan, the director of the music at the College, and ever found him kindly and helpful. After leaving Westminster he became an assistant master at the Wesleyan Day School in Middlesbrough. His first organ appointment was at Newport Road Baptist Church, whence he went to Grange Road United Methodist Church. Eager to gain a more extensive knowledge of church music, he accepted the appointment of organist and choirmaster at Holy Trinity Church, Stockton, in 1895, where he remained for eight years.

He was instrumental in forming a Wesleyan Choir Union, which included upwards of thirty choirs from the various part of the district. An Annual Festival was held in Middlesbrough Town Hall, in which some thousand choristers participated. He had a special gift for training choirs of children, and their young voices were a notable feature in the soprano of the choruses by Handel and other composers.

His compositions were confined chiefly to vocal music. His cantata *Arise, Shine,* and many of his anthems achieved wide popularity. For some years he was organist at the Park Methodist Church, Middlesbrough, and he died in harness early in 1934.

232—Adam.

ADAM is a tune that has long been popular in the Primitive Methodist Church. Its source and composer are both unknown.

233—Irene.

IRENE is from Freylinghausen's *Gesangbuch* (1704) (see No. 89). It is in John Wesley's *Foundery Tune-Book* (1742), where it is called SAVANNAH TUNE.

234, 578—Cambridge.

CAMBRIDGE, by Ralph Harrison, is from Volume I of his *Sacred Harmony* (1784) (see No. 389).

235—Torquay.

TORQUAY, by W. Youens, was contributed by him to the Supplement (1912) to the *Primitive Methodist Hymnal* under the name ' Confidence.'

William Youens was born at High Wycombe in 1834. He was by trade a basket-maker. As an amateur musician he did excellent work, and was for some years choirmaster at Oxford Road Free Methodist Chapel. He was also a bandmaster, and gave music lessons in his spare time. He wrote a large number of anniversary leaflets. He died in 1911.

236—Oldham Street.

OLDHAM STREET is by John Howgate, of Manchester, who, about 1820, published *Sacred Music* containing ' Twenty Hymn and Psalm-Tunes.' The collection, which is undated, was published by subscription, and contains both OLDHAM STREET and WORSLEY (see No. 270). Howgate named his tunes after Manchester localities. Nothing appears to be known about him.

237—Windsor.

WINDSOR is an early example of the adaptation of a melody as a hymn-tune. In the first year of Queen Mary's reign (1553) a book was published bearing this title :

The
ACTES OF THE APOSTLES
translated into Englyshe Metre and
dedicated to the Kynges most excellent
Majestye by Christofer Tye
Doctor in Musyke and one of the
Gentylmen of hys graces most honourable
Chappell, wyth notes to
eche Chapter, to synge and also to
play upon the Lute
Very necessarye
for studentes after theyr studye,
to fyle theyr wyttes and also
for all Christians that
cannot synge to
reade the good and
Godlye Storyes
of the lyves of Christ ad Hys
Apostles.

This book was dedicated to Edward VI, and bears the inscription :

HYNDER NOT MUSYKE.

Dr. Christopher Tye, who was probably an East

Anglian by birth, was brought up as a chorister at King's College, Cambridge. In later years he devoted himself chiefly to church music, but his compositions, though interesting to the student, are not of the kind to make a popular appeal. In his 'Actes' the music is decidedly superior to the versification. WINDSOR is adapted from this melody, which Tye composed for his verses for Chapter III :

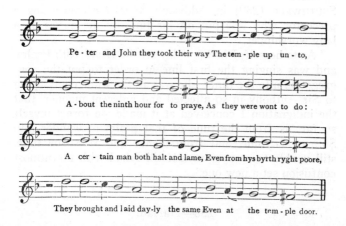

Pe - ter and John they took their way The tem - ple up un - to,

A - bout the ninth hour for to praye, As they were wont to do :

A cer - tain man both halt and lame, Even from hys byrth ryght poore,

They brought and laid day-ly the same Even at the tem - ple door.

It appears to have been abbreviated and turned into a C.M. tune by William Damon 'late one of Her Majesties Musitions' (see No. 239), who issued a 'Booke of Musicke' in 1591. The tune received its first christening by Thomas Est (1592), who called it SUFFOLK TUNE. This name did not please Ravenscroft (1621), who called it WINDSOR or EATON, and under the former name it is still known. In Hart's *Scottish Psalter* (1615), it is called DUNDIE TUNE, and it is still known as DUNDEE in Scotland.

Although Dr. Tye was a prolific composer it would appear that Queen Elizabeth did not show much partiality for his music. It is related that on one occasion,

13

when playing something at the Chapel Royal ' which contained much music, but little to delight the ear,' the
Queen sent him a message saying that he was playing
out of tune. Tye promptly sent the verger back with
the message that Her Majesty's ears were out of tune.
Probably the verger thought it was more than his place
or even his life was worth to deliver himself of the
message.

There is an amusing reference to WINDSOR and also to
SOUTHWELL (239) in Addison's *Spectator* concerning a
precentor who was put off his tune by the antics of a
lady worshipper.

' As to herself, I had one day set the Hundredth Psalm,
and was singing the first line in order to put the congregation into the tune; she was all the while courtseying
to Sir Anthony in so affected and indecent manner, that
the indignation I conceived at it made me forget myself
so far, as from the tune of that psalm to wander into
SOUTHWELL tune, and from thence into WINDSOR tune,
still unable to recover myself till I had with the utmost
confusion set a new one.'

238—Harlan.

Lowell Mason, the composer of HARLAN, takes rank
as a musical reformer with such apostles as Mainzer,
John Curwen, Hullah and Waite. He was one of the
first in America to agitate for universal musical
education, and while the Handel and Haydn Society and
the Boston Academy were educating the public to
appreciate the highest music, he was labouring with a
success worthy of his zeal and perseverance to make
singing and the reading of ordinary vocal music as
common an acquirement as the simple rules of arithmetic
or the outlines of geography.

Lowell Mason was born at Medfield, Mass., in 1792.
His early youth was divided between weaving straw hats
and conducting choirs. Finding the former employment

somewhat monotonous he went off to Savannah and became a bank clerk, but still keeping up his favourite pursuit of conducting and writing music for choirs. He also amassed a quantity of MS. tunes and anthems, and having put them into form he returned to the North to find a publisher. He failed in his search, but the Handel and Haydn Society of Boston heard about his collection through their organist, G. K. Jackson, and after lengthened bargaining they agreed to issue the collection as their own work! This was in 1822, and during the following thirty years or so upwards of 50,000 copies of the various editions were sold.

After a further period of five years in the Savannah bank Mason accepted an offer to settle in Boston as a professor of music and choir leader. He now entered on his great scheme for spreading a universal knowledge of music. His first step was to gather together classes to whom he imparted his methods of teaching, which were based upon a thorough study of the system of Pestalozzi —awakened their enthusiasm, and thus soon had an able body of disciples to aid him in a project which he had for some time cherished—nothing less than making singing and reading music compulsory branches of instruction in the public schools! Anything more hopeless could hardly have been planned. He was obliged to prove that children could be made to comprehend the meaning of staves and notes—a page of music being then to most people as strange as a column of hieroglyphics. He did prove it, by concerts of children, whom he and George James Webb (see No. 821) had taught.

Another project of his was the calling together conventions of music-teachers and amateurs. These, continuing ten or twelve days, were occasions of very great interest and value. Lectures on musical topics, especially upon the art of teaching singing-classes, with constant practice, and, finally, a concert or two, in which the members took part, filled the time, and those who

attended carried away with them their first and never-
fading impression of the glorious power of choral
song.

Simultaneously with all these labours, the press was
teeming with collections of vocal music by Mason alone,
or in conjunction with Webb, for every possible demand
—from the infant school to the societies for singing the
highest music. Their sale was enormous. Single collections were distributed by hundreds of thousands. Not
alone sacred music, but glees, madrigals, and four-part
songs, for men's voices, women's voices, a mixed chorus,
English, German, French, Italian, anything that was good
of its kind that could be found in the large library which
their editor had collected.

Mason accumulated a wonderful collection of books,
nor did he confine himself to such as he could read. He
collected not for himself only, but for posterity. Hearing
that Professor Dehn, of Berlin, was disposed to sell the
finest and completest collection of the works of Matheson
and Marpurg—that in the Royal Library at Berlin
excepted—he immediately commissioned a friend to
secure them, though there was not one among them that
he himself could read. He also purchased C. H. Rinck's
great collection, and after his death Mason's family
presented his library to Yale College.

Mason edited a very large number of hymn-tune
collections, all of which have had their day and ceased
to be. A few of his compositions survive, characterized
by extreme simplicity. He would frequently select his
themes from the great composers, and clothe them in a
metrical dress. Others were founded on Gregorian
themes, but he had a natural fount of melody and could
write independently of external sources. The tune under
notice, HARLAN, also known as OLIVET, which is the
original title, made its first appearance in Hastings and
Mason's *Spiritual Songs*. Here is the original form of
the tune, taken from a copy of a tune-book in Mr. F. J.
Metcalf's library :

My faith looks up to Thee, Thou Lamb of Cal - va - ry;

Sa - viour di-vine : Now hear me while I pray, Take all my

guilt a - way; O   let me from this day Be whol - ly Thine.

In Inverness cemetery is a tombstone to the memory of an old precentor of the Free High Church choir. On it is engraved ' My faith looks up to Thee ' with the tune in Tonic Sol-fa.

239—Southwell.

SOUTHWELL first appeared in Damon's *Psalmes of David in English Meter, with Notes of foure parts set unto them* (1579). There are two separate editions of this psalter, the result of a misunderstanding. John Bull, whose name was not uncommon in the days of Queen Elizabeth, was a citizen and goldsmith of London. He used to devote his evenings to the pursuit of music, and amongst those who shared his pleasures was William Damon (or Daman) ' one of her Majestie's Musitions.' One of their occupations was the singing of psalm-tunes, and Damon used to compose them for his friend's private use only, and does not seem to have devoted that care and attention to the work he otherwise might have done. Consequently, he must have been much dismayed when in 1579 a book appeared entitled, ' *The Psalms of David* . . . with notes of foure partes set unto them by Guilielm Damon for John Bull. . . . Printed by John Daye.' Bull's reason for publication is seen in the preface (written by another friend, E. Hake), in which the writer specially refers to the profaning of God's divine service by music ' by over curious, yea and I may say by over tragicall, dismembrying, not only of words, but of letters and syllables, in the holy psalms and anthems.'

Now Damon was much concerned at this unauthorized publication of his work, which, he says, reflected no credit on his skill as a musician; so twelve years after-wards (rather a long interval!) he published a corrected edition of the book containing the tunes ' most excellently by him composed into four parts, in which sett the Tenor singeth the church tune.' In the same year he issued yet another edition, ' in which sett the Highest part singeth the Church tune ' (1591).

240—L'Omnipotent.

L'OMNIPOTENT is a tune composed or adapted by Louis Bourgeois for the *Genevan Psalter* (1551), where it is set to a metrical version of Psalm cx.

241—Welwyn.

WELWYN is from the ' Arundel Hymns.'
Sir Alfred Scott Gatty, K.C.V.O., was better known

as a composer of songs than of hymn-tunes. He composed a large number of songs of all kinds, of which his Plantation Songs gained him fame. This was supported by his 'True till Death,' which formerly had a great vogue. He was born at Ecclesfield Vicarage, Yorks., in 1847, and died in 1918.

242—Stuttgart.

STUTTGART is probably by C. F. Witt who, in conjunction with A. C. Ludwig, edited a collection named *Psalmodia Sacra*, published at Gotha in 1715.

Christian Friedrich Witt was born about 1660. He was a native of Attenburg, where he was court Kapellmeister. He wrote a number of compositions which have not stood the test of time, and he is now remembered only as the reputed composer of this tune.

243, 700—Ishmael.

ISHMAEL was written for *The Hymnal Companion* by C. Vincent, who was the musical editor. He also contributed ST. DOROTHEA (No. 459) and ST. CYRIL (No. 633) to the same work.

Dr. Charles Vincent, son of an organ-builder and music dealer at Sunderland, was born at Houghton-le-Spring, Durham, in 1852. He was a chorister at Durham Cathedral, and studied music under the organist, Dr. Philip Armes (see No. 781). After a few years as organist at the parish church, Monkwearmouth, he went to Leipzig for three years, and returned to be organist at Tavistock. He then went to London to act as organist of Christ Church, Hampstead (1883-1891). In 1893 he went to South Africa as an examiner for Trinity College, and to Australia in the same capacity in 1897. In 1893 he commenced the *Organist and Choirmaster* in association with C. W. Pearce and E. J. Hopkins. In connexion with this journal he commenced a music-publishing business, securing in time a valuable lot of copyrights. He also founded the firm of Rogers & Co., piano factors. He retired from his various undertakings a few years ago and retired to Hendon, where he died in 1934.

244—St. Magnus. See No. 72.

245 (i)—Lancashire.

LANCASHIRE was composed by Henry Smart (No. 12) whilst he was organist at Blackburn parish church (1836) for a missionary meeting. It was set to ' From Greenland's icy mountains.' It did not appear in any printed collection till 1867, when it was inserted in *Psalms and Hymns for Divine Worship* (see No. 27).

245 (ii), 793—Herrnhut.

HERRNHUT (or CRÜGER) is a very much altered form of a melody in Crüger's *Praxis Pietatis Melica* (see No. 10). It has undergone much editing, and the present form is that adapted by W. H. Monk for *Hymns Ancient and Modern* (1861).

246—Ephraim.

EPHRAIM, by Henry Temple Leslie, appeared in *Clifton Conference Hymns,* which he assisted in preparing, probably whilst he was organist at the church of St. Mary-le-Port, Bristol. He took an active part in temperance work and edited a good deal of leaflet and other music. He died at Sandown, Isle of Wight, in 1876, in his fifty-second year.

247—Gopsal.

GOPSAL. In 1826 Samuel Wesley received permission from the authorities at the Fitzwilliam Museum, Cambridge, to overhaul the MS. music in their collection, and make copies of any that he desired. On September 20 he wrote thus from the Castle Inn, Cambridge, to his wife :

' All goes on well here : I have already copied six famous fine Hymn-tunes *from Handel's own Manuscript*, and what is uncommonly fortunate, they are all set to my father's own words, so that my dear father's poetry must have highly delighted Handel. This circumstance will much forward the work.'

What Wesley meant by saying that he had copied *six* tunes will probably never be known. Doubtless it was a slip, as only three are known to exist.

He at once proposed to publish them, but having no funds to enable him to issue them at his own risk and expense, he resolved to approach the chiefs of the Methodist society. He therefore wrote to the Rev. Thomas Jackson, in his capacity as editor of the *Wesleyan Methodist Magazine* to this effect : ' I take the liberty of addressing you upon a subject which appears likely to prove both of interest and utility, especially to the Wesleyan Connexion. Having been honoured by the University of Cambridge with a Grace, authorizing me to transcribe and publish any portions of the very valuable musical manuscripts in the Library of the Fitzwilliam Museum—of which privilege I have lately assiduously availed myself—I was very agreeably surprised at meeting with three hymn-tunes (most noble melodies), composed by our great Handel (in his own handwriting) and set to words of my good father. The first hymn is :

> Sinners, obey the Gospel-word ;

the second :

> O Love Divine, how sweet Thou art ;

and the third :

> Rejoice, the Lord is King.'

Jackson undertook the responsibility of publication, and the tunes were thus announced in the *Wesleyan Methodist Magazine* of January, 1827 :

178 THE MUSIC OF THE

The FITZWILLIAM MUSIC, never before published : *Three Hymns*: the words by the late Rev. Charles Wesley, A.M., of Christ Church College, Oxford; and set to music by George Frederick Handel, faithfully transcribed from his Autography in the Library of the Fitzwilliam Museum, Cambridge, by Samuel Wesley, and now very respectfully promoted to the Wesleyan Society at large. Price 1s. 6d.

A proposal to issue an edition in a harmonized form was not carried out. The sale of the folio edition was brisk for a time, and then the demand came to an abrupt end. A photographic reproduction of Handel's original MS. of the tunes appeared in *The Choir* for March, 1930.

The three hymns with their tunes were :

' Sinners, obey the gospel word.' Original title—THE INVITATION. Now known as CANNONS.

' O love divine, how sweet thou art.' Original title— DESIRING TO LOVE. Now known as FITZWILLIAM.

' Rejoice, the Lord is King.' Original title—THE RESURRECTION. Now known as GOPSAL.

They subsequently appeared in several collections, but GOPSAL is the only one in the present *Methodist Hymn-Book*. It is so called from Gopsal, near Atherstone, formerly the residence of Charles Jennens, who compiled the libretto for Handel's *Messiah*.

248, 676—St. George.

ST. GEORGE (or ST. OLAVE) was composed by Dr. Gauntlett for *The Church Hymn and Tune-Book* which he edited together with the Rev. W. J. Blew (1852).

249—Evelyns.

EVELYNS was composed by W. H. Monk for the 1875 edition of *Hymns Ancient and Modern*. See No. 221.

250—Ashley.

ASHLEY has frequently been credited to Martin Madan, but it is not found in any tune-book that he was associated with. The tune appeared in the first volume of the *Gospel Magazine* (1774), where it is simply called 'A hymn.' It is also found under the name RAMSGATE in Isaac Smith's *Collection of Tunes,* which, though undated, is usually put down to 1770. In both of these works the tune is anonymous, nor does it seem to have become generally popular till after its appearance in the *Companion to the Wesleyan Hymn-Book* (1849), where it is still without a composer's name.

251—Worship.

WORSHIP, by Johann Michael Haydn, is from Latrobe's *Sacred Music* (1806), which contains various adaptations from the composer's works.

Michael Haydn was born at Rohrau in 1736, and became a chorister at St. Stephen's, Vienna, where he soon supplanted his brother as soloist owing to Joseph's voice breaking. He acquired considerable skill on the organ and was soon able to act as deputy organist at the cathedral. In 1762 he entered Archbishop Sigismund's employment at Salzburg, where he frequently met Mozart, who on one occasion wrote two compositions for his friend to save Haydn's salary, which his employer had threatened to stop owing to the musician's illness.

Haydn spent the remainder of his days at Salzburg. When the French entered the city in 1801 the composer lost much of his property, but his brother came to his rescue and supplied him with funds. Joseph Haydn thought highly of his younger brother, maintaining that his church compositions were superior to his own in earnestness, severity of style and sustained power. Michael, who certainly had confidence in his own powers, once said, 'Give me good librettos and the same patronage as my brother, and I should not be behind him.' He died in 1806.

252—Pilgrim Brothers.

Pilgrim Brothers was adapted by Sir J. F. Bridge from a movement in C. H. H. Parry's symphonic ode *War and Peace,* sung at the Albert Hall by the Royal Choral Society on April 30, 1903. It was written expressly for the Society, and had indirect reference to the close of the Boer War. One of the numbers 'The Marching Song of Peace,' struck Sir F. Bridge as a suitable subject for a hymn-tune. He submitted his idea to the Committee of the 1904 *Methodist Hymn-Book,* and it was promptly accepted.

253 (i)—Burton.

Burton was written by J. T. Lightwood at the request of the Rev. Henry Burton, who was not satisfied with the setting of his hymn ' Break, day of God, O break,' in the *Methodist Hymn-Book* (1904). It was originally printed as a leaflet (1905) and inserted in the *New People's Hymnary* (1922).

253 (ii)—Arncliffe.

Arncliffe was written for Dr. Burton's hymn at the request of Sir J. F. Bridge, for insertion in the 1904 *Methodist Hymn-Book.* Its composer, Wilfrid E. Sanderson, who was born in 1878, is the son of the Rev. Thomas Sanderson, Wesleyan minister. After two years' business experience Sanderson decided to adopt the musical profession and spent some time with Bridge, whom he assisted in providing some harmonies for certain tunes in the *Methodist Hymn-Book,* and also in revising the proofs. In 1907 he was appointed organist of Doncaster parish church, resigning the office in 1924. He has specialized in song-writing, one of his earliest being ' My dear soul,' which had the advantage of being sung by Dame Clara Butt. His other works include ' The Valley of Laughter,' ' Drake goes West,' and ' Shipmates o' Mine.'

254—Highwood.

HIGHWOOD was originally written by Sir R. R. Terry at Lord Runciman's suggestion for Mrs. Gurney's hymn, ' O perfect love.' This is its first appearance in a hymnal.

Richard Runciman Terry, who is a nephew of Lord Runciman, was born at Newcastle-on-Tyne in 1865. His boyhood was spent partly near Amble, not far from Blyth, and here he used to listen to the crews of the sailing ships singing shanties. These inspired him with a love of these quaint ditties, on which in after life he was to become a noted authority. His parents were keen amateur musicians, his mother having a rich soprano voice which so delighted an impresario that he suggested that she should be trained for operatic work, a tempting proposal which was declined from religious scruples. When Terry was eleven he had advanced sufficiently in technique to be allowed to play the organ at church at the week-day services during Lent. This duty caused him much anxiety, and indirectly inspired him with a dread of church bells to this day, the reason being that their cessation whilst he was at the organ reminded him that it was time for the voluntary, and he was invariably seized with stage fright.

He was educated at Oxford, and also at Cambridge, where he won a choral scholarship at King's College, and founded the Cambridge University Musical Club for the study of chamber music. He also acted as music critic of the *Cambridge Review,* and his pontifical opinions brought him into touch with Villiers Stanford, at whose house he made the acquaintance of Joachim, Piatti, and other famous instrumentalists who were occasionally invited to play any new chamber work he had composed. There, too, he had the pleasure of hearing Madame Schumann, unquestionably the greatest interpreter of her husband's music.

After leaving Cambridge Sir Richard decided to enter

the music profession, and became organist and music master at Elstow School near Bedford, where he gave choral works suited to the capacity of the choir. His next appointment was as organist at St. John's Cathedral, Antigua, W.I., where he had a choir composed of coloured men and boys. He gradually introduced women's voices. A dangerous attack of malaria drove him back to England, and on taking up the appointment of music master at Downside School, and organist of the Benedictine Abbey to which it is attached, he began working hard with the boys on Palestrina's music. Some of the monks were members of the choir, and the fact that both monks and boys knew their Latin, and were therefore thoroughly acquainted with the meaning of what they sang, made artistic results more evident than those obtainable with professional singers. In 1901 he was appointed director of the music at Westminster Cathedral, a position he retained till 1924. He has made a special study of the music of the English polyphonic period, and has brought to light many long-forgotten compositions by Tudor composers. His published compositions include masses, motets, and services. In this he had as a co-worker the late Dr. Ralph Dunstan, whose knowledge of polyphonic music was both extensive and profound. Sir Richard is a skilled choir trainer, and his golden rule for young choirmasters is well worth recording :

Never repeat a piece of music at full practice until you have made the choir fully aware of your reason for doing so. Nothing disheartens them so much as the cry ' Now we will do that over again.' It is an indication of helplessness on the part of the choristers.

255—Sleepers, Wake.

SLEEPERS, WAKE (WACHET AUF, or NICOLAI) is by Philipp Nicolai, and is from the Appendix to his *Freuden Spiegel* (1598), a religious treatise with a supplement of four hymns and two tunes. Both melody and hymn appeared together, though the melody does not appear to be entirely original, the first line being apparently based on the fifth Gregorian tone. But that does not interfere with its claim to rank amongst the finest of the German chorales.

In 1597, during a fearful pestilence in Westphalia, where Nicolai was pastor of the town of Unna, more than fourteen hundred persons died in a very short time, and from his window he saw the funerals pass to the graveyard close at hand. It was these scenes of sorrow and death that inspired him to write his great 'Watchman' hymn and its accompanying melody, 'Wake, awake, for night is flying.' The seventh and eighth lines of the melody have been used with wonderful effect by Handel in the 'Hallelujah Chorus':

The kingdom of this world   is be - come

Bach has built one of his cantatas (No. 140, WACHET AUF) on the chorale, and Mendelssohn uses it in his overture to *St. Paul*.

Philipp Nicolai was born in 1556. After passing through the University of Erfurt he went to Wittenberg, and then became a Lutheran pastor. He was frequently involved in controversy at various places, notably with the Catholics and Calvinists. After the pestilence referred to he became pastor of St. Katherine's Church, Hamburg, and here he died in 1608.

256—There's a Light upon the Mountains.

THERE'S A LIGHT UPON THE MOUNTAINS was written in 1908 by M. L. Wostenholm at the request of the Rev. Dr. Burton, author of the hymn.

Dr. Maurice L. Wostenholm is a son of the manse,

his father, the Rev. Henry Wostenholm, being formerly a well-known Wesleyan minister. Born at Hastings in 1887, the boy soon developed a natural taste for music. He received his first lessons from Mr. Henry Hill, organist of Queen Street Wesleyan Chapel, Scarborough. When his father removed to Nottingham, the young musician passed under the care of Dr. C. H. Kitson, then of Leicester, with whom he remained five years. During a part of this period he acted as organist for two years at Musters Road Wesleyan Church, Nottingham.

In 1910 he was, after competition, appointed organist at the Central Hall, Birmingham. Here the musical portion of the services and the training of the choir were both in the hands of the Rev. F. L. Wiseman, whose enthusiasm and ability in this direction are widely known and appreciated. Needless to say, with this excellent combination of strong choir-master and skilful organist, the music at the Central Hall attained a high degree of excellence. Three anthems were regularly given on Sundays, one at the morning and two at the evening service, while Mr. Wostenholm's skill enabled the fine organ to be heard to great advantage.

But although the young musician had secured one of the best Nonconformist positions in Birmingham, he was by no means inclined to rest on his oars. Eager to become master of his instrument, he put himself under the care of Mr. C. W. Perkins. In 1913 he had the honour of being chosen to give a series of three organ recitals before the British Association, assembled in Birmingham for conference.

Meanwhile, he pursued his theoretical studies under the direction of Dr. A. G. Iggulden, of Reigate, a gentleman of whom he speaks in the highest terms; and such progress did he make that he was able to take the degree of Bachelor of Music at Durham in 1912. He also holds the Licentiate Diploma of Trinity College, London. The next step was the writing of an 'exercise' for the

Doctor's degree, and in June, 1915, he received the welcome news that it had met with the approval of the
examiners.

When Mr. Wiseman left Birmingham in 1913, Dr.
Wostenholm took sole charge of the musical arrangements at the Central Hall.   He was also at this period
appointed director of the Saturday night concerts, which
were run during the winter months.   In 1918 he was
appointed music master at King Edward School,
Birmingham, when the school came under the Board of
Education.   Dr. Wostenholm has the distinction of being
the first to hold this important position.   Ill-health
necessitated his retirement from all professional work in
1931, and from the same cause he was obliged to resign
in the following year the position of musical adviser to
the Committee appointed to prepare the music for the
new *Methodist Hymn-Book*.

257—Veni Immanuel.

VENI IMMANUEL has not been definitely traced to an
earlier source than *The Hymnal Noted* 1854).   It is
said to have been copied from a French missal in the
National Library at Lisbon, but who copied it is not
known, nor has the missal ever again been seen.   The
suggestion that it is 'composed' of a selection of fragments of plain-song is scarcely plausible.   Savants are
not entirely agreed about its tonality, some say it is in
the Aeolian mode, and others that it is Dorian, with an
excursion into Hypo-Lydian in the last two lines.   It
found a place in the *Wesleyan Hymn-Book* (1876) under
the name EPHRATAH.   The editor, Dr. Gauntlett, did not
like the flattened seventh at the end of the second and
sixth lines, and inserted a sharp to the D, and so it
appeared in the *Wesleyan Tune-Book*.   He also engaged
in an acrid correspondence with W. H. Monk on the subject, as he published curious harmonies in the first edition
of *Hymns Ancient and Modern* which he (Monk) sub-

14

sequently revised. Gauntlett published his own arrangement as a leaflet in 1865. Mr. Francis Burgess, an accepted authority on plain-song, maintains that VENI IMMANUEL is in the ' first Plainsong Mode,' and there we may leave it.

The *Hymnal Noted* was compiled by Thomas Helmore at the request of the Ecclesiological Society, a body of church people who devoted themselves to attempting the reformation of church music. Born in 1811, Helmore was educated at Mill Hill School. After leaving Oxford he entered the Church and in 1846 he succeeded William Hawes as master of the choristers at the Chapel Royal, St. James's. Amongst those who came under his care was Arthur Sullivan, who harmonized four of the melodies in *The Hymnal Noted* for his master.

258—Beverley.

BEVERLEY, by W. H. Monk, is taken from the 1875 edition of *Hymns Ancient and Modern* (see No. 221).

259—St. Sepulchre.

ST. SEPULCHRE is from Chope's *Congregational Hymn and Tune-Book* (1862). It was composed in 1856. The Cooper family included a wonderful succession of organists who ruled over the music of St. Sepulchre's Church, Newgate Street, throughout the nineteenth century. They were, with the dates of their tenures of office :

George Cooper I —   -1799.
George Cooper II —1799-1843.
George Cooper III—1843-1876.
George Cooper IV—1876-1899.

George Cooper No. III is the composer of ST. SEPULCHRE. He was, perhaps, the most gifted member of the family. His father was assistant organist to John Goss at St. Paul's Cathedral. When No. III. was a youngster a pupil of his father's, on going to the house for his lesson, saw Master George in a dirty brown pinafore, busy with his knife shaping a boat out of a piece of wood. His sister suddenly appeared on the scene, with the message, ' George, father says you are to go,' and the boy reluctantly gave up his boat and went off grumbling. The pupil subsequently asked the father where the boy was going to. ' Oh,' was the reply, ' he's got to go to St. Paul's to take the service.' The boy was only twelve years of age at that time, but his ' professional ' life had already begun, and from that day to his death his organ work and his pupils occupied all his time. One of his earliest appointments was to St. Benet's Church in Upper Thames Street, where in after years (1854-1856) Stainer also officiated. Cooper was also one of the organists of the Chapel Royal, where the duties, though by no means exacting, were always faithfully performed by him.

At St. Sepulchre's Cooper's wonderful playing used to attract large audiences, and many of his admirers used also to gather at St. Paul's to hear him ' play the people out ' when doing duty for John Goss. He was also organist and music master at Christ's Hospital, and one of the attractions of the public suppers in the great hall was to hear Mr. Cooper ' touch the instrument with his well-known power and skill.' George Cooper the Third did little in the way of original composition, but his ' Arrangements for the Organ ' had a great vogue some years ago, and they still deserve attention. He attained great fame as a teacher, one of his most celebrated pupils being the late Sir Walter Parratt. Cooper once told a pupil to call at a friend's house in a certain street. ' I don't remember the number,' said he, ' I think it is number five, but anyhow, his door-scraper sounds G.'

Cooper was the first editor appointed to superintend the production of the new *Wesleyan Tune-Book,* which was published in 1876. Both he and his successor, Dr. Gauntlett, passed away whilst the work was being carried on, and it was completed by Dr. E. J. Hopkins. Cooper's contributions to organ literature were numerous. The adaptations of various works by the great composers were skilfully done, and his 'Organ Arrangements,' 'Organist's Assistant,' and 'Organist's Manual,' were for many years an essential part of the organist's equipment.

260 (i)—Vision.

VISION, by Sir Walford Davies (see No. 44), was written for a sixpenny 'Supplementary Tune-Book for use with existing Collections' issued in 1915 under the title *In Hoc Signo : Hymns of War and Peace.*

260 (ii)—Battle Hymn.

BATTLE HYMN. Mystery surrounds the origin of this famous air. Louis Elson, in his *History of American Music* says that previous to the Civil War of 1861 the melody was first brought into use as a hymn-tune in Charleston, S.C., where it was used in Methodist camp meetings to a hymn beginning

> Say, brother, will you meet us
> (*repeated three times*)
> On Canaan's happy shore.

Soon after the outbreak of the war a certain Captain Hallgreen, who was stationed with a battalion of Massachusett's Infantry at Fort Warren, heard two recruits singing this camp-meeting hymn, 'Say, brothers, will you meet us.' He took a fancy to the melody, and taught it to his soldiers, and soon the original words disappeared in favour of some impromptu words to which the melody and rhythm of the air readily lent itself. There was a popular Scotch soldier named John Brown, who lost his life in trying to cross a river during the retreat of the Union forces. This incident, allied with the popularity of the man, combined to make a sort of hero of him, and he thus became the subject of a new set of verses to the old tune, which were as follows :

(1) John Brown's body lies a-mouldering in the grave,
    John Brown's body lies a-mouldering in the grave,
    John Brown's body lies a-mouldering in the grave,
        But his soul is marching on.

    (*In each verse the line is repeated as above.*)

(2) He's gone to be a soldier in the army of the Lord,
        His soul is marching on.

(3) John Brown's knapsack is strapped upon his back,
        His soul is marching on.

(4) His pet lambs will meet him on the way,
        They go marching on.

There are two other verses, and at the end of each verse comes the refrain :—

> Glory, Hally, Hallelujah !
> Glory, Hally, Hallelujah !
> Glory, Hally, Hallelujah !
> Hip hip hip hurrah !

The melody has sometimes been attributed to a certain W. Steffe, of whose career nothing is known.

The tune soon became national property, and Mrs. Edna Dean Proctor attempted to make the words more worthy of the occasion by writing some verses in honour of the more celebrated John Brown of Harper's Ferry. It was this version that found its way to England, and was made popular by a troop of Christy Minstrels who were performing in this country during the sixties of last century. It was called the ' Celebrated American Army Hymn.'

Old John Brown's body lies a-mouldering in the grave,
And all because he tried to free the negro and the slave.
Old John Brown's body lies a-mouldering in the grave,
    But his soul is marching on.
        Glory, glory, hallelujah !
        O glory, glory, hallelujah !
        Glory, glory, hallelujah !
        His soul is marching on.

There is another and more romantic story given about the source of the music. Charles G. Leland, in discussing the ' Voodoo ' songs of the negroes of the United States, has an interesting reference to the tune. He acknowledges it to have been adapted to a ' hymn ' used by American Methodists at their camp-meetings, and suggests that it was probably some kind of Voodoo song of purely negro origin, giving the following instance to prove his contention. A certain Lieutenant Chandler, in describing one of Sherman's marches during the Civil War, says that during a halt in an out-of-the-way corner of Georgia, the Federal band struck up ' John Brown's Body.' Great was the amazement of the soldiers to see a number of negro girls come out one by one from the deserted houses, and, forming a circle round the band, dance in a grave and dignified manner without smiling, as if in some kind of a magical or religious ceremony. The dance over, they disappeared. The band played other airs, but the girls did not reappear; and their modest and earnest deportment on this occasion made an impression on the spectators. Inquiry of an old negro woman elicited the fact that the air was known as the ' wedding tune,' that it had no connexion with hymns or songs, and that the coloured girls all believed that they must dance whenever they heard it played or they never would be married.

Another and perhaps earlier form of the tune occurs in the American revival melody, ' Say, brother, will you meet me.' Both hymn and music were brought over to this country by Mr. John Macgregor, of the Temple, who asked Dr. E. J. Hopkins to make a four-part arrangement of it. It was published in 1859 for Mr. Edmund Macrory (author of *Notes on the Temple Organ*), and presented by the two Benchers to the Ragged School Shoe-black Society, for whose benefit it was sold.

In a letter to his friend William Amoy, written April 22, 1865, O. W. Holmes wrote :

The song of the war is, after all, the John Brown song. To be sure some of the verses are nonsense or worse, but the first stanza and one at least of the others, with the tune, closing with Hallelujah, come nearest to the Marseillaise in effect and as an expression of the feeling of the time, of all that the war has produced.

261—Saltash.

SALTASH (PLYMOUTH or PLEADING SAVIOUR) is from the collection of tunes formed for use in Plymouth Church, Brooklyn, U.S.A. (1855), famous for the ministry of Henry Ward Beecher. John Zundel (see No. 431) was the director of the music, and the tune may possibly be his.

262, 956—Derbe.

DERBE. In the 'Large Minutes' of the Methodist Conference published in 1780, there are references to singing, and a series of injunctions to the preachers appear, amongst these being :

No. 12. Recommend our Tune-book everywhere, and if you cannot sing yourself, choose a person or two in each place to pitch the tune for you.

Needless to say, the spirit of Wesley pervades all these recommendations, and the reference here to 'our Tune-Book' deals with *Sacred Harmony,* which had just been issued. This was the last tune-book published by Wesley, though a smaller edition was issued in 1789. The name was originally DERBY, and why it was changed to DERBE is a mystery. It is set (in *Sacred Harmony*) to the hymn :

Away with our fears,
Our sorrows and tears,

whilst 'Come, let us anew' is set to a curiously jumpy,

spasmodic tune, long since forgotten, called NEW YEAR'S
DAY.

In a copy of *Sacred Harmony* preserved at the Methodist Conference Office in City Road, London, there is an
interesting note by John Wesley. He has crossed out
the music of the tune NEW YEAR'S DAY, evidently dis-
approving of it, and written in the margin a note to the
effect that DERBY would be more suitable for 'Come, let
us anew.' It is uncertain when his suggestion was
adopted, but DERBY has been for over a century the
recognized tune for 'Come, let us anew.' This is the
original form of the tune, the composer being unknown :

A - way with our fears, Our sor-rows and
tears, The spi - rit is come, The spi - rit is
come, The wit - ness of Je - sus, The wit-ness of
Je - sus, re - turn'd to his home.

263, 962—St. George's, Windsor.

ST. GEORGE'S, WINDSOR (or ST. GEORGE), by Sir G. J.
Elvey (see No. 11), was written for Montgomery's 'Hark
the sound of jubilee,' and was included in *A Selection of
Psalm and Hymn-Tunes* (1858), edited by E. H. Thorne.

264—Helmsley.

HELMSLEY first appeared in John Wesley's *Select
Hymns with Tunes Annext* (1765) in this form :

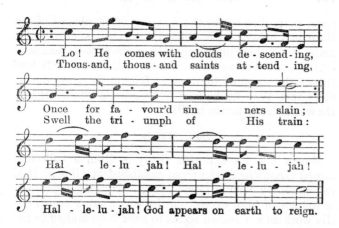

Lo! He comes with clouds de-scend-ing,
Thous-and, thous-and saints at-tend-ing,
Once for fa-vour'd sin - ners slain;
Swell the tri-umph of His train:
Hal - le-lu - jah! Hal - le-lu - jah!
Hal - le-lu - jah! God appears on earth to reign.

Four years later it was included in Madan's *Lock Hospital Collection,* the name being changed to HELMSLEY and the melody to the form it now takes. Wesley, in his *Sacred Harmony* (1780) adopted Madan's version, but retained the original name OLIVER'S. Various attempts have been made in the past to show that the tune was adapted from some contemporary songs and operatic airs, but these myths have now been finally dispelled and there is no doubt that we owe the tune to Thomas Olivers, one of the best known of Wesley's helpers. He was born at Tregynon, Mont., and was brought up to the shoemaking trade. He led a wild and dissolute life until, when he was about twenty-five years of age, he came under the influence of Whitefield, and associated himself with the Methodists. Wesley employed him for a time as corrector for the press, but he was a much greater success as an evangelist. He died in 1799.

265—Bromsgrove.

BROMSGROVE was written by H. A. Dyer for the *Public School Hymn-Book* (1919). It was published after his death. The composer was the son of A. E. Dyer, for some years director of the music at Cheltenham College. Born in Cheltenham in 1878, H. A. Dyer studied music under his father, ultimately taking his Mus.B. degree at Oxford. He became music master at Bromsgrove School (hence the name of the tune). Joining the army during the Great War he became a Lieutenant in the R.F.C. He was killed in action in 1918.

266—Meyer.

MEYER (or ES IST KEIN TAG) is from a collection named *Geistliche Seelenfreud* published at Ulm in 1692 and edited by Johann David Meyer. Nothing appears to be known of him, except that he was a town councillor. His work as a musician seems to have been limited to the production of the book referred to.

267—Alleluia.

ALLELUIA was composed by S. S. Wesley (see No. 217) for the 1868 Supplement to *Hymns Ancient and Modern,* set to Dix's ' Alleluia ! Sing to Jesus.'

268, 533—Nox Præcessit.

NOX PRÆCESSIT was written in 1873 for *The Christian Hymnal* (1875), where it is set to Sir E. Denny's advent hymn ' Bride of the Lamb, awake, awake.'

John Baptiste Calkin belonged to a family of musicians, his father being a prominent music teacher, whilst one of his brothers, George, is remembered for his organ music and arrangements. J. B. Calkin was born in London in 1827. In his twentieth year he succeeded E. G. Monk (see No. 668) as organist at St. Columba's College, a Protestant public school at Rathfarnham, near Dublin. Six years later he returned to London and held various church appointments, including ten years at Woburn Chapel. He held the diploma of F.R.C.O. and was also a member of the Philharmonic Society. He was a professor at the Guildhall School of Music, and his abilities in this direction are manifest from the fact that ten recitals were given by his pupils. One who knew him says that 'his moral influence over the students that came under him was strong.' He composed in various styles, but he is remembered chiefly by his services and his hymn-tunes. One of his pupils, James Langran (see No. 772), used to speak in high terms of Calkin's musical gifts. 'Besides being an accomplished performer he was a composer quite at home in all styles— the part-song, the church service, anthems, organ music, and music for his own particular instrument, all are excellent, and bear the mark of a highly cultured musician.' He died in 1905.

269, 716—St. Godric.

ST. GODRIC was composed by Dr. Dykes for Isaac Watts's 'Lord of the worlds above' in Chope's *Congregational Hymn and Tune-Book* (1862).

270—Worsley.

WORSLEY is by John Howgate. See No. 236.

271—Diademata.

DIADEMATA was composed by Sir G. J. Elvey (see No. 11) for the Appendix (1868) to *Hymns Ancient and Modern*.

272—Truro.

TRURO appeared originally in *Psalmodia Evangelica* (1789), but bears no composer's name. It has been attributed to Dr. Charles Burney, but without any known reason. Other tunes by him have his name attached, and the doctor was not the kind of man to let any off-spring of his go unacknowledged. That he was quite capable of writing a hymn-tune is evident from the florid long metre he wrote for William Dixon's *Psalmodia Christiana* in the same year (1789). Lacking proof to the contrary, TRURO should be assigned to the anonymous tunes. Burney contributed eight tunes to Madan's *Lock Hospital Collection* (see 479).

Charles Burney was born at Shrewsbury in 1726. He was educated at the King's School, Chester, and it was at the cathedral that, as he said, ' I saw and heard the first organ I ever touched.' It was a great day for him when he caught sight of Handel smoking his pipe and drinking a bowl of coffee at the Exchange Coffee House. On returning to Shrewsbury he had lessons from his brother James, and then went to London to study under Dr. Arne. His first organ appointment was at St. Dionis Backchurch, Fenchurch Street (now destroyed), and from here he went to St. Margaret's, King's Lynn. Here his organ and harpsichord pupils, and the care of a young family (his daughter Fanny was born here), kept him fully employed till 1760, when he returned to London. In 1769 he took his Mus.D. degree at Oxford, and then paid two visits to the Continent, recording his experiences in *The Present State of Music in France and Italy*, which was followed by two more volumes detailing his travels in Germany. After his return he commenced his *History of Music*, the last of the four volumes being published in 1789. After residing in St. Martin's Lane for some years he accepted the post of organist at Chelsea Hospital, which he retained till his death in 1814.

273—Down Ampney.

DOWN AMPNEY is from *The English Hymnal* (1906). It is by R. Vaughan Williams, and is named from the village near Cirencester, Gloucestershire, where he was born in 1872. After leaving Charterhouse he went to Cambridge, and studied at the R.C.M. under Parry and Stanford. His only practical experience in church music was gained whilst he was organist for three years at South Lambeth parish church. He has written three *Preludes* for the organ on Welsh hymn-tunes. In 1906 he edited the *English Hymnal,* and in 1925 *Songs of Praise,* a revised edition being published six years later. He has always taken an interest in folk-songs, and has done practical work in collecting them in various countries. Examples of his diligence are seen in some of the melodies derived from folk-songs in the present *Methodist Hymn-Book.* 'In all his activities he has refused to be bound by material restrictions' (says an article in *Grove*). 'The fact that a work of his own is published will not prevent his altering a passage,' and proof of this statement was forthcoming when he required a modification in his tune SINE NOMINE just as the proof was being returned to the printers when the production of the present *Methodist Hymn-Book* was in progress. His principal works (many of them founded on folk-song melodies) include *On Wenlock Edge* (song cycle), *Songs of Travel* and other songs, *Hugh, the Drover* (opera), Symphonies, *Sancta Civitas* (oratorio) and Mass in G minor.

274—Winchester New.

WINCHESTER NEW is adapted from a melody in the *Musikalisches Handbuch* published at Hamburg in 1690. It next appeared in Freylinghausen's *Gesangbuch* (1704), and is one of the tunes brought to England by John Wesley, who inserted it in his *Foundery Tune-Book* (1742) calling it 'Swift German Tune.' The tune was recently known as CRASSELIUS, a German hymnist who was entirely innocent of composing chorales.

275—Newhaven.

NEWHAVEN (or LUTON) is by the Rev. George Burder. Born in London in 1752, he was brought up to the business of an engraver. After being associated with the followers of George Whitefield for a time, he entered the ministry, and became pastor of a Congregational church in Lancaster. During his ministry here he used to visit other places, and became well known in the north-west of England. He had his full share of adventure and persecution, and his services were often interrupted by noisy scoffers. On one occasion, when he was at Preston, the preaching-room happened to be over a cock-pit used for theatrical purposes, and both minister and players had engagements in their respective quarters on the same evening. The singing upstairs interfered with the proper performance of the play, which was *Romeo and Juliet,* and the congregation were considerably startled to see the Romeo of the evening enter hurriedly in full costume, with drawn sword in hand, and demand that the service should be stopped at once, for no one could hear what his Juliet was talking about! Finally, he became so violent that the service had to be given up. From Lancaster Burder moved to Coventry, where he established the first Sunday school in the town (1785), and whilst there he issued a collection of hymns which was widely adopted by the Nonconformists. He spent the last thirty years of his life in London, and during this period he took an active part in the formation of the Religious Tract Society and the British and Foreign Bible Society, and also acted as secretary of the London Missionary Society. He died in 1832.

276—Winchester Old (see No. 129).

277—Buckland.

BUCKLAND is by the Rev. L. G. Hayne (see No. 140).

278—Ardwick.

ARDWICK was composed by Dr. Gauntlett for the first edition of *Tunes New and Old* (1864). (See No. 7.)

279—Drumcondra.

DRUMCONDRA is by Canon D. F. R. Wilson (see No. 770).

280—Lusatia.

LUSATIA (or DESSLER) is from Freylinghausen's *Gesangbuch* (1704) (see No. 229).

281—Walsall.

WALSALL has been in continual use ever since it appeared in *A Choice Collection of Psalm-Tunes, Hymns and Anthems, For the Delight and Improvement of all who are Truly Lovers of Divine Musick,* and to this is added 'Taught by William Anchors,' but he omitted to give the composer of WALSALL, or of any of the tunes in his collection (*c.* 1721).

282—Pembroke.

PEMBROKE has long been a useful tune for this 8.8.6, 8.8.6 metre though its popularity was imperilled by the awkward harmonies provided for it by Dr. J. C. Bridge in the *Methodist Hymn-Book* (1904).

James Foster (1807-85) was organist of the Bristol Tabernacle, and greatly interested himself in psalmody. He was also an amateur organ builder, and during his apprenticeship to the joinering trade he built himself a small four-stop organ which he enclosed in a Spanish mahogany case. Subsequently he added a second manual, the notes of which he connected to the reeds of a seraphine (a predecessor of the harmonium) but the experiment was not a success, as the reeds did not keep in tune with the pipes.

PEMBROKE was written for Waite's *Hallelujah* (1842), and from this it was transferred to the *Bristol Tune-Book* (1863).

283—St. Cuthbert.

ST. CUTHBERT was written by Dr. Dykes for Miss Auber's hymn in *Hymns Ancient and Modern* (1861).

284—Illsley.

ILLSLEY. John Bishop's fame rests almost entirely on
two tunes from his *Sett of New Psalm-Tunes in four
parts*, which he published at the beginning of the
eighteenth century.   In the title to his book he names
himself as 'Organist of the College at Winton,' otherwise Winchester.   In 1729 he was appointed organist at
the Cathedral, his rival for the post being James Kent,
' who was esteemed a better player, but the age and
amiable disposition of the former (Bishop) coupled with
the sympathy felt for some family misfortune he had
suffered, induced the Dean and Chapter to give him the
appointment.'   Bishop was buried in the cloisters of the
College Chapel, and a lengthy Latin inscription bears
ample testimony to his worth, besides recording that he
was ' very skilled in the science of music.'   His tunes
ILLSLEY and LEICESTER (No. 500) are both from the
' Sett ' already mentioned.

285—Calm.

CALM.   The first known appearance of CALM is in the
Leeds Tune-Book, which was published in 1868, where it
is headed ' There is a Calm, 8.8.8.4, presented to the
Editor,' but there is no further indication amongst the
acknowledgements in the index as to where the tune
came from.   The title given above is taken from a hymn
by Montgomery :

> There is a calm for those who weep,
> A rest for weary pilgrims found :
> They softly lie and sweetly sleep
> Low in the ground.

The tune was also published in leaflet form about the
same time by B. W. Barwick, Market Place, Keighley,
set to Keble's ' Sun of my soul,' and is stated to be
' published by the kind permission of the composer.'   It
bears the name VESPERE or ILKLEY.   Subsequently it

appeared in various hymnals, but always anonymously. However, on its appearance in the *Methodist Hymn-Book* (1904), several correspondents wrote to explain that it was the work of Dr. Dykes, and in the second and subsequent editions of that book it has always been ascribed to him.

This tune was the origin of a curious myth in the *Strand Magazine* (1895). The writer, in his article ' Some notable Hymns,' after referring to three tunes for ' Sun of my soul ' said :

> I have had lent to me a fourth tune, also by Dr. Dykes, which has never before been published, and is, in fact, quite unknown. It was given in MS. by Dr. Dykes, shortly before his death, to a friend, among whose papers it has lain for many years. A short while since, however, the owner of these papers died, and his widow sent me the tune, to use as I thought fit. The tune is very beautiful, and I give it for the benefit of my musical readers.

The writer was quite wrong in his statement, as the tune had been in print for some years, and appeared also in *Church Praise* (1883), nor was the handwriting anything like that of Dr. Dykes.

286—North Coates.

NORTH COATES is from a collection of tunes named *Congregational Melodies* (1862), and takes its name from the village where the composer, the Rev. T. R. Matthews, was rector (see No. 150).

287.—Stabat Mater. See No. 185.

288—Christus.

CHRISTUS, by the Rev. W. Blow, appeared in the enlarged (1881) edition of the *Bristol Tune-Book*.

William Blow was born in 1819 at Goodmanham. At

15

Peterhouse, Cambridge, he was a friend of Sir William
Thompson, electrician. He was ordained in 1847, and
held the vicarage of Layer Breton, Herts., from 1855 till
his death in 1887. He was a skilful violinist, and at one
time possessed the finest collection of violins in the
country, including specimens of the art of Stradivarius,
Amati, and Joseph Guarnerius, which formed a conspicuous feature at the Inventions Exhibition of 1885. He
was a lineal descendant of Dr. John Blow, who was one
of the glories of the school of English Church musicians
in the eighteenth century.

289—St. Agnes.

ST. AGNES (also called ST. AGNES, DURHAM) was composed by Dr. Dykes for the hymn ' Jesus, the very
thought of Thee,' and first appeared in Grey's *Hymnal
for use in the English Church* (1866). This was edited
by the Hon. Rev. J. Grey, who in his preface acknowledged Dyke's ' long continued zeal and patience.'

290—Charity.

CHARITY was written by Dr. Stainer for the 1868
Appendix to *Hymns Ancient and Modern*.

Sir John Stainer was born in London, June 6, 1840.
At the age of seven he was a chorister in St. Paul's
Cathedral, and seven years later he was appointed
organist and choirmaster at St. Benedict's (or St. Benet),
Thames Street. His first organ tutor was George Cooper,
deputy organist under John Goss at St. Paul's. One day,
when both the great men were away for the day, Stainer
was taking the service, and at the close a stranger, who
proved to be Sir F. A. Gore Ouseley, came to the cathedral
to ask Goss to find him an organist for his newly founded
College at Tenbury. Instead of Goss he found the boy
Stainer at the organ ' getting on very comfortably,' and
later in the day he wrote asking him to go to Tenbury.
Here he remained three years drinking in all he could

from the famous library there, until in 1859 he went on trial to Magdalen College, Oxford, and after two months was elected organist. At the same time he entered St. Edmund's Hall as an undergraduate, and in due time took both his M.A. and Mus.D. degrees. He led an active life at Oxford conducting various choral and other societies, and on leaving to accept the proffered position of organist at St. Paul's Cathedral in succession to John Goss, he was the recipient of a notable testimonial, subscribed for by dons and undergraduates at Magdalen.

Goss was a worthy musician and a fine composer, but not a disciplinarian, so when Stainer came he found he had a different task to perform. How he succeeded is now a matter of history. He combined ready tact with a kindly disposition, and soon made the service as famous for beauty as it had formerly been for slovenliness. He instituted oratorio services, making them a special feature at certain seasons of the year.

After sixteen years' service failing eyesight compelled him to retire, when he received the honour of knighthood from Queen Victoria. In 1889 he succeeded his old friend Ouseley as Professor of Music at Oxford. Stainer was a skilful organist, though his exploits as a recitalist were limited. He was, however, frequently to be heard at the Crystal Palace, and also as accompanist at the oratorio concerts at the Albert Hall. He had in early years a wonderful facility for extemporization in the style of Bach, but ' later on the trammels of a knowledge of counterpoint and of the correct treatment of fugue ' somewhat interfered with his natural skill.

With the exception of an oratorio, *Gideon,* written for his Doctor's degree, Stainer attempted no large choral work, but his cantatas, notably the *Crucifixion,* have long been popular. *The Daughter of Jairus* and *St. Mary Magdalen* were written for the Three Choirs Festival at Worcester and Gloucester respectively. He wrote a large number of anthems, of which ' The Morning Stars

Sang Together ' is a notable example, and his numerous hymn-tunes are characterized by strength and easy flow of melody. Stainer died at Oxford in 1901 and was buried in Holywell cemetery. It has been well said of him that ' he was one of the very few touched with the radiance of the inner life of sacred music.'

291—Cassel.

CASSEL appears to have been a melody that was current in Germany for many years until Johann Thommen appropriated it for a collection published at Basil in 1745 called *Erbaulicher Musicalischer Christen Schatz,* where it is an eight-line tune. The Rev. H. Parr abbreviated and slightly altered it for his *Church of England Psalmody* (1889).

292—Manchester. See No. 172.

293—Attwood.

ATTWOOD is adapted from Thomas Attwood's anthem ' Come, Holy Ghost,' which has become a classic and finds a place in the repertoire of every church choir. The late Mr. John S. Bumpus related the following interesting story which he had from J. G. Boardman, an old organist, who in his young days was a chorister under Attwood at St. Paul's :

At that time the St. Paul's boys, like the ten children of the Chapel Royal, resided under the roof of their master, Mr. William Hawes; but they were allowed to sleep at their own homes on Saturday nights. An ordination was to be held at St. Paul's on Trinity Sunday, 1833. On the preceding day the Bishop of London (Blomfield) requested Attwood to set the ' Veni Creator ' to music specially for the solemn occasion; which he did. It was Attwood's custom on

Sunday mornings to drive from Norwood to St. Paul's in a gig drawn by Peggy, a steady-going pony. His route included the Brixton Road, where, at Union Cottage, Cranmer Road, North Brixton, resided Master J. G. Boardman. Attwood was kindheartedness itself, and it was the custom for young Boardman to be on the lookout for a ' lift ' in the old organist's gig. On this particular occasion the gig appeared in sight with its occupant busily engaged in writing, the reins being thrown over the back of Peggy, who knew her way to St. Paul's quite as well as her master. It turned out that Attwood was putting the finishing touches to the vocal parts of his anthem ' Come, Holy Ghost,' for it was his invariable custom to write these parts out with his own hand whenever his compositions were sung at St. Paul's or at the Chapel Royal. Placing the completed treble solo in Johnny Boardman's hands, Attwood said that he wished him to sing it at that very morning's service. The young chorister duly obeyed, and, without previous rehearsal, sang the solo, to the complete satisfaction of both the composer and the Bishop.

Thomas Attwood's father was a coal merchant by trade, but, like the famous Thomas Britton, he found consolation in music, and performed both on the viola and the trumpet. The son was born in 1765, and after a careful musical training, he showed such an ability that the Prince of Wales (afterwards George IV) sent him to Italy to study. From Naples he went to Vienna, and here it was that he made the acquaintance of Mozart, becoming the only English pupil that the great composer ever accepted. Some mementoes of the connexion have been preserved. On one occasion Attwood wrote in a boyish hand opposite his exercise ' Thomas Attwood presents his compliments to Mr. Mozart, and hopes he will find the exercise satisfactory, as he has left no possible room for correction ! ' On another example

Mozart wrote, probably as a rejoinder to the above, 'You are an ass.'

In 1796 Attwood was appointed organist of St. Paul's Cathedral, one of the unsuccessful candidates being Charles Wesley, who was passed over on account of his name, which proved to be an offence to the cathedral dignitaries. Attwood seems to have shone more as a composer than a performer, but he will always be remembered as an able exponent of the school of English church music, and he was amongst the first to raise it from the depths to which it had fallen since the death of Dr. Boyce in 1779.

For some years Attwood resided on Beulah Hill, Norwood—the house is still standing—and here he often entertained Mendelssohn during his early visits to England. He used frequently to accompany Attwood to St. Paul's Cathedral, sitting by him as he played the service, and then taking his place at the close and playing the voluntary. On one occasion the congregation were so charmed with the playing that many of them lingered too long to suit the pleasure of the vergers, who wanted to get home to their dinners, so they conceived an evil plot, and induced the organ blower to desert his post. The wind went out with a groan and a sigh, and the voluntary came to an untimely end. Mendelssohn showed his esteem for his old friend by dedicating his three organ preludes and fugues to him. Attwood died in 1838, and was buried beneath the organ in the cathedral. In addition to his church music he wrote a number of operas, and some of his songs enjoyed considerable popularity. His 'Christmas Eve' glee is a characteristic example of English vocal music.

294—Sion.

Although SION is stated to be by Benjamin Milgrove (No. 66), it is not found in any of his works, and proof that he wrote it is wanting.

295—Joseph.

JOSEPH is a slightly more harmonious epithet than
' Helfer meiner armen seele,' by which this melody is
known in some collections. It is from the same source
as No. 689, but it has been so altered from the original
that it is doubtful if the composer, George Joseph, would
recognize it. The present form of the melody is from
the *English Hymnal*, where it is said to be ' slightly
adapted.' Here is the original form :

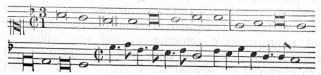

from which it will be seen that the adapter has effectively
disguised it.

296—Heinlein. See No. 165.

297—Angelus.

ANGELUS was originally composed in 1888 by R.
Jackson for a Sunday-school festival at Oldham, and
issued in leaflet form.

Robert Jackson, who was born at Oldham in 1842,
received his musical education at the Royal Academy of
Music and subsequently became organist at St. Mark's,
Grosvenor Square, W. He returned to Oldham in 1868
to succeed his father, who had been organist at St. Peter's
Church for nearly forty-eight years. Robert Jackson
was a good executant and an excellent choirmaster, and
the Oldham Musical Society and the Werneth Vocal
Society gained great fame under his direction. He
remained at St. Peter's for forty-eight years, retiring in
1914. A few years previously he was presented with a
portrait of himself in oils, which now hangs in the Oldham
Art Gallery. His compositions were limited to hymn-
tunes, of which he produced a large number. He died
in 1914.

298—Bowden.

BOWDEN is from S. S. Wesley's *European Psalmist* which was published in 1872, after it had been in preparation for many years. On May 2, 1854, Wesley, in response to a query about the book, said that between four and five hundred pages ' have already been engraved these three years.' Five years later, in answer to further complaint, he wrote to the *Musical World* confessing that the publication had been delayed ' longer than was absolutely necessary,' and was inclined to blame the engraver for not being able to commence the work. He had returned some subscriptions and was willing to return more. ' More than three-fourths of the work had been engraved for several years past.' But it was not till 1872 that the *European Psalmist* finally appeared.

299, 372—Arne's.

ARNE'S and ARLINGTON (see No. 272) are both derived from the same source, though this fact is not at once apparent. They are founded on this slow movement in the overture to Arne's opera *Artaxerxes* :

ARLINGTON (sometimes called ARTAXERXES) appeared as a hymn-tune in Harrison's *Sacred Harmony* (Vol. I, 1784). The responsible adapter of the longer form of ARNE'S has not been traced. It is found in *Booth's Psalmody, The Companion,* and also in the *Wesleyan Tune-Book* (1876). Dropped in 1904, it has once more found favour.

300—St. Beuno.

ST. BEUNO, by J. C. Bridge, was composed for *The Westminster Abbey Hymn-Book* (1883, music edition 1897), edited by J. F. Bridge.

Dr. Joseph Cox Bridge, younger brother of Sir Frederick Bridge, was born at Rochester in 1853. He became a chorister in the cathedral under John Hopkins, whose assistant he became. He then studied under his brother, J. F. Bridge, whilst the latter was organist at Manchester Cathedral, and then became organist at Exeter College, Oxford, taking his degrees at the University. In 1877 he was appointed organist at Chester Cathedral, a post which he held with distinction till 1925. He revived the Chester Musical Festivals, writing a pamphlet on their previous history. He lectured on various subjects, notably the remarkable set of recorders which are preserved in Chester Museum. In 1908 he was appointed professor of music at Durham University, holding the position till his death in 1929. He wrote an oratorio, *Daniel,* and also church music, and was the author of several antiquarian papers on musical subjects.

301—Simeon.

SIMEON, by S. Stanley, is from his *Twenty-four Tunes in four parts, composed chiefly to Dr. Watts's Psalms and Hymns* (c. 1796).

Samuel Stanley was for a long time one of the leading figures in the musical life of Birmingham. Born in 1767, he became an accomplished player on the violoncello, and performed at various towns in the Midlands about 1790 and onwards, while in 1792 he fulfilled an engagement at the Vauxhall Gardens, London. He also played at the Birmingham Festivals of 1799, 1802, and 1817, and his opinions on the correct performance of Handel's music were quoted authoritatively for many years after his death. At one period of his life he kept the Crown Tavern in Great Charles Street, but this does not seem to have interfered with his holding the appointment of leader of the singing in the Carr's Lane meeting-house. He afterwards took up a similar position at Ebenezer Chapel, in Steelhouse Lane, and under his leadership the musical services at this place became renowned far and wide. He published two sets of tunes, the first being *Twenty-four Tunes in Four Parts* (c. 1796). Among these are SHIRLAND, STONE-FIELD, WARWICK, SIMEON, WILTON, CALVARY, and KENT. The second set contains nineteen tunes, none of them known at the present day, though SUTTON COLD-FIELD and STAR OF BETHLEHEM were formerly popular. Both these books were ' Printed for the author, Banbury Street, Birmingham,' but contain no publisher's name, and are now very scarce. After Stanley's death in 1822 his widow published a third book, containing twenty original tunes and eleven arrangements. From the title-page she seems to have been living at 31, Cannon Street, at the time. About 1828 a reprint was issued of all Stanley's tunes, which had a wide circulation and is still to be met with. A tablet erected to his memory used to be on the wall of the school behind Ebenezer Chapel, bearing the following inscription :

Sacred to the memory of Samuel Stanley, who for the space of thirty-four years conducted the singing of the congregation which now worships in Ebenezer Chapel. He departed this life on the 29th day of October, 1822, in the 55th year of his age, greatly respected by a large circle of friends, but by no one more than his surviving widow, who erects this monument as a feeble testimony of her regard to his memory.

302—Tiltey Abbey.

TILTEY ABBEY, by A. H. Brown, was originally printed in a leaflet collection, but the date in uncertain. Arthur Henry Brown was born in 1830, and his love of music, and diligence in practising, led to his appointment as organist of Brentwood parish church when he was only about ten years of age, retaining the post till he reached his fiftieth year. Subsequently he became the official organist at Brentwood School Chapel, a post he retained till his death.

In recalling his early experiences Brown said :

In those days church music was at a very low ebb, as indeed were all things ecclesiastical. When at the age of ten and a half years I became organist of Brentwood Church, my instrument possessed only one manual, five stops and no pedals. This was placed in a west gallery, and was supported on either side by a choir of National School children, the boys on one side and the girls on the other. The music was that of the *Mitre* hymn-book, and between each verse of the hymns interludes were played, which not infrequently disconnected the sentiment of the words. Only the canticles were chanted, to MS. tunes obtained from several sources. The service ended with a sermon delivered by a preacher in a black gown and black gloves, from a three-decker planted in the centre of the church, perhaps as an exemplification of the *beauty* of holiness. This took place thrice every Sunday, at eleven, three, and six-thirty, and as the congregation escaped I played a voluntary.

He remembered also how, on one occasion, when the rector of a neighbouring parish, of Swedish nationality, rose in the body of the church after the anthem had been sung, and turning to the west gallery, addressed the singers thus : ' Shentlemen, I shall be vary moch obliged if you will sing that all over again,' which was accordingly done.

The name of A. H. Brown has been known to church musicians for many years. He was a most prolific composer of all kinds of church music, and he must have written upward of eight hundred hymn-tunes and carols, many of which were published by himself. Undoubtedly his best-known tune is ST. ANATOLIUS (see No. 951) composed in 1862. This was printed with eight others in pamphlet form. It attracted the notice of W. H. Monk, and was included in the second (1868) edition of *Hymns Ancient and Modern.* Thus it started on a journey which reached the far corners of the world, and which is certainly not yet completed. Mr. Brown considered that the best of all his tunes was ALL ANGELS, a long metre tune, which was set to 'Lo round the throne a glorious band' in several hymnals.

He was an ardent and active cyclist. On his eighty-fifth birthday he rode to Thaxted and back, a total distance of twenty-five miles, to attend a patronal festival. He died in 1926.

303 (i)—Bentley.

BENTLEY was contributed by Hullah to *Psalms and Hymns for Divine Worship* (1867).

John Hullah was born at Worcester in 1812. When quite young he was brought to London, where the rest of his life was spent. When seventeen he was placed under the famous glee-composer, William Horsley, and afterwards studied singing under Crevelli at the Royal Academy of Music. He became known as a composer by his music to Charles Dickens' opera, *The Village Coquettes,* produced in 1836. When the fame of Mainzer's popular singing classes reached England, Hullah conceived the idea of founding a similar institution in his own country. He went to Paris, only to find that Mainzer's classes had been discontinued. The work of Wilhem (whose true patronymic was Bocquillon), who in 1835 had been appointed Director-General of Musical Instruction in all the French schools, was now, however, beginning to bear fruit, and early in 1840 Hullah revisited Paris to observe these results at first-hand. A year after his return he began, at Exeter Hall, those classes for popularizing vocal music, and especially for instructing teachers, which eventually became one of the most phenomenal successes in the whole history of musical education. So great was the number attending them and the gratitude of his pupils, that a hall—St. Martin's Hall, in Long Acre—was specially built for his classes and concerts, and presented to him. Unfortunately, after some thirteen years' use, it was destroyed by fire, to meet which loss its owner was presented with a handsome testimonial. It is reckoned that in twenty years some 25,000 pupils passed through his hands. In 1872 he became Inspector of Music in training colleges, and was also organist of the Charterhouse. His song, 'The Three Fishers,' is still remembered. His *History of Modern Music* and a collection of his *Lectures* are useful works of reference. He died in 1884.

303 (ii)—Nyland.

NYLAND is from the revised edition of *The Church Hymnary* (1930), where it is said to be a ' Finnish Folk Melody,' and that appears to be all that is known about it.

304, 607—Tallis' Ordinal.

TALLIS' ORDINAL is from Parker's *Psalter* (see No. 943). Tallis wrote eight tunes for it, each in a different mode, and a supplementary tune, now known as TALLIS' ORDINAL, for the hymn, ' Veni Creator.' The tune takes its name from the fact that the hymn was used at the Ordinal, or the Ordering of priests and deacons.

Thomas Tallis (he spelt his name Tallys) was born early in the sixteenth century. The exact year of his birth is uncertain, and there are few reliable facts about his early life. It is certain that he was organist at Waltham Abbey, but when the monasteries were dissolved by Henry VIII he lost his appointment. He was, however, solaced by the king with the office of Gentleman of the Chapel Royal. To the superior virtue of political consistency this sixteenth-century musician can no more lay claim than the traditional Vicar of Bray. A Roman Catholic organist at Waltham Abbey, he easily turned to Protestantism, and set his famous ' Preces,' ' Responses,' and ' Litany ' to the second Prayer Book issued by King Edward VI in 1552. When Queen Mary ascended the throne Tallis was once more converted to Roman Catholicism, but under Elizabeth his Protestantism was so strongly marked that the queen made him organist at the Chapel Royal, Greenwich. Tallis died November 23, 1585, and was buried in the chancel of old Greenwich Church. Of his many compositions the best-known now, or at any rate the most familiar, is the music to the Responses and the Litany. Some of his anthems have been reprinted in recent years. His most important work was the *Cantiones Sacrae,* which contained sixteen motets by him. His celebrated motet, ' Spem in alium non habui,' was written for eight five-part choirs, i.e. forty voices in all. It was revived by Dr. A. H. Mann in 1889.

305—Richmond.   See No. 1.

306, 769—Spanish Chant.

SPANISH CHANT is first found in this country in *A Collection of Psalms and Hymns* made by Montagu Burgoyne, the music edited by J. MacDonald Harris, 1827. It appeared with the name MADRID a year earlier in America as *The Spanish Hymn,* arranged by Benjamin Carr. This is the earliest known form of the tune :

It does not appear that the air has anything to do with Spain, nor is there any records of the Spaniards ever having used it as a chant, or in any other form. The composer of CASTLE STREET (A.T. 13) also known as LUTHER'S CHANT, had a fancy for using the word 'chant' in naming his tunes (also MISSIONARY CHANT, 1039 *Primitive Methodist Hymnal*). Perhaps he is responsible for SPANISH CHANT. It belongs to his period.

307, 575—St. James.

ST. JAMES probably made its first appearance in *Select Psalms and Hymns for the use of the Parish Church and Tabernacle of St. James's, Westminster* (1697). In a later edition, the sixth, published in 1704, the word 'Tabernacle' in the title is replaced by 'Chappel.' This church stands on the south side of Piccadilly and is a well-known feature with its bare churchyard and outside pulpit. The tune was inserted without any composer's name, but it is assigned with good reason to Raphael (or Ralph) Courteville, sometimes spelled Courtaville, or Courtivill. He was one of the children of the Chapel Royal, and on September 7, 1691, seven years after its consecration, he was appointed the first organist of St. James's Church, Piccadilly, at a salary of £20 per annum and £4 for an organ-blower. If, as has been assumed, he lived until June, 1772, he must have held the organistship for eighty-one years. It is possible, however, that he was succeeded in 1735

by his son, bearing the same name, although the change
is not recorded in the vestry minutes. That there was a
Raphael Courteville, junior, in existence at that time
(1735) is proved by a monument to his wife in the
church, who died on May 27 of that year; moreover
there is a volume of Italian music in the Bodleian Library
which was owned in the eighteenth century by 'R.
Courtivill, junior, in Bury Street, St. James's, London.'
One of these Courtevilles, either father or son, entered
into the political arena, and wrote an article in defence
of the Government of the day. Its opponents objected,
and playfully punned on the writer's name, dubbing him
'Court-evil.'

ST. JAMES is one of the many unfortunate tunes that
have passed through many editions, and got straitened in
the process. The original melody has four crochets at
the end which add greatly to its charm :

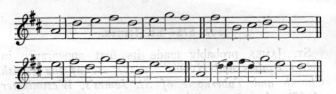

308—Ravenshaw.

RAVENSHAW. Dr. W. Bäumker affirms this to be the
melody of 'Ave hierarchia' (fifteenth century). It
occurs in Weisse's *Collection* (see No. 638) of 1531, and
in various later collections. It is found (in conjunction
with another melody) in Bach's *Choralgesänge*. The
present adaptation was made by W. H. Monk for *Hymns
Ancient and Modern* (1861).

309—Bethsaida.

BETHSAIDA was written for the *Methodist Hymn-
Book* (1904) by Miss Rosalind F. Bridge, daughter of
Sir Frederick Bridge. She was born in 1884 at the

Cloisters, Westminster Abbey, and studied music at home, learning harmony from her father, and the piano and violin from visiting masters. In 1907 she married Dr. Edward Stainer, F.R.C.P., second son of Sir John Stainer, the famous organist of St. Paul's Cathedral. The musical tradition of the family is being upheld. Their eldest daughter is a 'cello scholar of Trinity College, and their second son obtained an organ scholarship at Christ's College, Cambridge.

310, 941—Companion.

COMPANION is by R. S. Newman. It was published with others in a small selection of twenty-two original tunes with the title, *Hymns for School Festivals, Harvest Thanksgiving and other Services.*

COMPANION was originally called A HYMN FOR EVENING, and set to J. Ashcroft Noble's ' Lord Jesus, in the days of old.'

Richard Stinson Newman was born in Wednesbury in 1850. On going to live in Wolverhampton he took up the study of music and became organist of Trinity Wesleyan Church, where he remained for thirty-five years, resigning through ill-health. He retired to North Wales and settled at Abergele, where he died in 1927. During his retirement he found consolation in composing, and proposed to issue a new collection of his hymn-tunes, but the work was never completed.

311—Montgomery.

MONTGOMERY. Not many tunes have been so repeatedly re-christened, or done duty for so many metres, as the one now usually known as MONTGOMERY. Amongst its various names are BURTON, NEWTON, BLOOMSBURY, ST. ANDREW and ST. GEORGE. Another name, MAGDALEN, is of more consequence, as it appears to furnish a clue to the source of the tune. Its first known appearance is in :

16

The Tunes and Hymns as they are used at the Magdalen Chapel. Properly set for the Organ, Harpsichord and Guittar.

To hear Montgomery twanged off a ' Guittar' would be a new experience to-day. The editor of this collection was Thomas Call, organist of the Magdalen Chapel, and its date, thanks to the researches of Mr. J. R. Griffiths, has been assigned to 1762.

The tune appears to have received its name Montgomery for the first time in the second volume of R. Harrison's *Sacred Harmony,* which was issued about 1780. Harrison, who was for some time minister of Cross Street Chapel, Manchester, puts the tune in the key of E, but does not give any composer's name. However, his tune-book had a large circulation, and as he composed several of the tunes therein, to which, however, he was always careful to affix his own name, some editors assumed that Montgomery might also be his, and he was credited with its composition in many subsequent tune-books. But there was no foundation for this assumption; and it should also be remembered that in 1762, when the tune first appeared, Harrison was only fourteen years of age, and was going to school at Warrington Academy.

In *Sacred Harmony* the tune starts on the fifth note of the scale. Why the name Montgomery was given to it is not known. Harrison was for a time at Shrewsbury, and may have visited the Welsh town, or he may have had associations with the place, but this is only surmise. James Montgomery, the hymnist, was not ten years of age when this tune-book first appeared, so we cannot associate him with it.

In 1806 appeared a cumbrous oblong volume called *Devotional Harmony,* wherein the editor, L. B. Seeley, christened the tune Bloomsbury, and assigned it to Stanley, the blind organist of St. Andrew's, Holborn, and this error has been frequently repeated.

Seeley was a bookseller living in Ave Maria Lane, and what his qualifications were for editing a tune-book we cannot say, but this is immaterial—tune-books have been edited by all sorts of unsuitable people. Suffice it to say that Stanley's compositions have been carefully searched by Mr. J. R. Griffiths, but without success, and the assumption that he was the composer may be promptly dismissed. Seeley appears to have had a printing works at Buckingham, and it must be allowed that the music printing in this volume is greatly to his credit.

312, 445—New 113th.

New 113th is from Dr. W. Hayes' *Sixteen Psalms* (see No. 55) where it is set to Merrick's version of Psalm cxxxiv., so why it has been christened New 113th is not apparent.

313—To God be the Glory.

To God be the Glory is by W. H. Doane (see No. 161), from his *Songs of Devotion* (1870).

314—Wonderful Love.

Wonderful Love, by the Rev. F. Luke Wiseman (see No. 5), first appeared in the *New People's Hymnary* (1922).

315—St. Raphael.

St. Raphael, by E. J. Hopkins (see No. 103), is from R. R. Chope's *Congregational Hymn and Tune-Book* (1862), where it is called St. Giles. The composer renamed it in his *Temple Church Choral Service* (1867).

316—Jesus Saves.

Jesus Saves is by W. J. Kirkpatrick, who was born in 1838 at Duncannan, Pennsylvania. He served during the Civil War as fife major and principal musician in the

91st Regiment Pennsylvania Volunteers from November, 1861, to October, 1862. In 1916 one of the churches in Philadelphia devoted an evening to his music, including his hymns, anthems, and solos, with an address on his musical work. His first editorial work was in 1859 on a book, *Devotional Melodies,* which contained eighty-six of his tunes. He studied the organ under David B. Wood, a blind musician, who also taught Adam Geibel, a musician blind from infancy. Kirkpatrick has contributed to more than eighty different collections of tunes, in one or other of which the zealous student will doubtless discover JESUS SAVES, WILL YOUR ANCHOR HOLD? (634), and AWAY IN A MANGER (860). The books are not available in this country, except a very few in private libraries. He died in 1921.

317—Whosoever Will.

WHOSOEVER WILL, by P. Bliss (see No. 176) is from No. 6 of the American *Gospel Hymns* (1891).

318 (i)—Cross of Jesus.

CROSS OF JESUS appeared originally in Stainer's cantata, *The Crucifixion,* which was specially composed for the choir of Marylebone Parish Church. The first rendering took place on February 24, 1887 (Ash Wednesday). The composer conducted, the late W. Hodge was at the organ, and he played the accompaniments with such skill, succeeding in producing the very effects that Stainer desired so admirably, that the composer would never consent to write orchestral accompaniments for the cantata.

The following explanatory note on the subject and scope of the cantata appeared in the first edition :

This work is an attempt to supply the want, long felt, of an easy and short form of Passion music, suitable for use in ordinary parish churches. It is composed for two solo voices, a tenor and a bass—and for the church choir. At intervals hymns occur, in which the whole congregation can join. The performance will probably not exceed forty minutes in duration, thus giving an opportunity for a short address, if desirable. No orchestra is required, the accompaniment being specially adapted for the organ only; much of the expense usually attending Passion services will be, therefore, avoided.

318 (ii)—Omni Die.

OMNI DIE is stated to be from a *Gesangbuch* edited by David Corner in 1631. The present version is from the *English Hymnal* (1906), where it is said to be 'arranged by W. S. Rockstro.' It would be interesting to know the authority for this statement, as Rockstro died in 1895.

319, 574—Wellspring.

It has been frequently asserted that WELLSPRING is adapted from a 'Mass' by D. S. Bortnianski, but it appears to be impossible to verify this statement. Two of the chief authorities on Russian music in this country know nothing of Bortnianski's 'masses' (he appears to have written one), and the writer of the notice of the composer in 'Grove' is dead. The Bortnianski theory may therefore be set aside until more definite information is obtainable.

WELLSPRING (also known as WELLS, and ST. PETERSBURG and SHANGANA) is found in Tscherlitzky's *Choralbuch* (1825), set to a hymn beginning 'Ich bete an die Macht der Liebe,' and here it is stated to be from a mass written in 1822. A correspondent, writing in 1904, said, 'This melody is not used in Russian churches, but is played in public on semi-religious occasions, as, for instance, at the "blessing of the waters," which takes place at St. Petersburg on January 6. It is also played

on the bells of the churches of St. Peter and St. Paul.'
In the first edition of Grove's *Dictionary*, under the
article Zapfenstreich, a description is given of the
serenade which formerly terminated the annual
manoeuvres of the German army. There was a torch-
light procession, in which from 1,000 to 1,400 instrumentalists took part, with the addition of buglers,
trumpeters, and drummers. After an introduction of
eight bars, this ' Zapfenstreich ' (or quickstep) is played,
and when this is finished the ' Retraite ' of the combined
cavalry bands follow, and then comes this prayer, played
by the combined bands :

The famous conductor, V. Safonov (who died in
1918) said that the tune was a Russian folk-song, ' Kol
sla-ven,' but this statement has not hitherto been verified.
It seems that the tune first appeared in this country as
a long metre in a *Collection of Psalms and Hymns*
formed by Montagu Burgoyne in 1827, the music being
edited by J. MacDonald Harris. (See No. 306.)

320—Stephanos.

STEPHANOS is by H. W. Baker, first chairman of the
committee that compiled *Hymns Ancient and Modern* in
1861. To the later editions he contributed both hymns
and tunes, including STEPHANOS in the 1868 Appendix,
and ST. TIMOTHY (No. 926) in the 1875 edition. Sir
H. W. Baker, Bart., was born in London in 1821, and
after leaving Trinity College, Cambridge, he was
presented to the vicarage of Monkland (see No. 19).

321 (i)—Even Me.

EVEN ME, by W. B. Bradbury, first appeared in an American publication called *The Golden Shower* (1862).

Bradbury was born at York, Maine, in 1816. Both his parents were good musicians and vocalists, and from them the boy inherited his musical tastes. Before he was fourteen he could play a variety of instruments, but not the organ, as it was not known in his home. In early manhood he went to Boston to study music with a local professor. Here he became acquainted with Lowell Mason, and G. Webb, and entered their Academy of Music. For the next few years he was occupied in teaching at Boston and in Maine, and then went to take an organ in New York. In 1847 he visited England and Germany, where he remained studying at Leipzig. He was present at Mendelssohn's funeral on November 4, 1847, and two years later he was back in the States. For some time he worked with L. Mason, T. Hastings, and G. Root in conducting conventions, and then entered the piano business with his brother. Ill-health compelled him to give up his many engagements, and he died at his home at Montclair, N.J., in 1868. Bradbury published a large number of tune-books, the most popular being *The Shawm and the Jubilee,* rivalled only by *The Golden Chain.*

321 (ii)—Even Me.

The second tune EVEN ME is by the late Mrs. Hornabrook, wife of the Rev. John Hornabrook, and sister of the Rev. F. L. Wiseman. It first appeared in the *New People's Hymnary* (1922). Mrs. Hornabrook was a gifted amateur, and had the advantage in early life of receiving lessons from Walter Macfarren. She died in her eightieth year in 1930.

322—Christ Receiveth.

CHRIST RECEIVETH, by James McGranahan, is from *Songs of the Gospel,* published in America in 1880.

323—Fulda.

The source of FULDA (or WALTON) will be found in a collection published by William Gardiner of Leicester, with the title :

Sacred Melodies from Haydn, Mozart, and Beethoven, adapted to the best English poets and appropriated to the use of the British Church (1812).

This collection proved a happy hunting-ground for tune-book editors for more than half-a-century. Many adaptations that are still in use made their first appearance here, and whatever opinion may be held about the musical legality or the appropriateness of this particular form of hymn-tune, it is certain that Gardiner not only dealt skilfully with the melodies he selected, but also treated them, as a rule, with more reverence than is usually shown. In the 'advertisement' to the second volume Gardiner intimates his intention of stating the sources of the melodies 'in an essay to be annexed to the second volume of the words.' It does not appear that this essay ever got into print, which is a pity, for although most of the 'melodies' have long since been traced to their various sources, the mystery surrounding the long-metre tune FULDA has never been solved. Gardiner ascribes it to Beethoven, but the best authorities fail to identify it as the work, in any shape or form, of that composer. In a subsequent publication called *Music and Friends* (1838) Gardiner says of FULDA that 'it is somewhere in the works of Beethoven, but where I cannot now point out ' —nor, up to the present, can any one else.

Gardiner, who was a stocking manufacturer by trade, was an enthusiastic musical amateur, and was associated with many of the musical festivals in this country. He appreciated the highest forms of music, and he enjoyed the friendship of some of the most celebrated musicians of his time. His admiration for Beethoven's genius led him to offer the great composer one hundred guineas for an overture to the oratorio *Judah,* which

Gardiner had compiled from the works of Handel and
other composers; but it appears that this letter never
reached Beethoven.

He claimed to be the first to introduce Beethoven's
music into England, and there are good grounds for his
claim. Mrs. T. Fielding Johnson, in her *Glimpses of
Ancient Leicester,* relates how, in 1794, the Abbé Dobler,
an accomplished German musician, being obliged for
political reasons to leave his native country, was offered
a home in England by the Hon. Mrs. Bowater, who lived
at the North Leicestershire village of Little Dalby, and
whose acquaintance he had made on the Continent.

Whilst staying here the Abbé was introduced to
Gardiner, and subsequently showed him a violin trio in
E flat written by Beethoven, who was then seventeen
years of age. On looking over the composition,
Gardiner's interest was aroused, and having invited some
local violinists to try it, the trio was played over in
Leicester in 1794, this being several years before any of
the composer's works were heard in London. His early
enthusiasm for Beethoven had an interesting sequel half
a century later. In the year 1848 he went over to Bonn,
the birth-place of Beethoven, in order that he might be
present at the unveiling of a statue to the great composer. Well-known musicians and other people of high
and low degree were present, including Queen Victoria
and the Prince Consort. Gardiner died in 1853 in his
eighty-fourth year.

324—Bryn Calfaria.

BRYN CALFARIA is by William Owen, of Prysgol,
Caernarvon, and appeared in his *Y Perl Cerddorol,* Vol.
II, 1854.

William Owen was born at Bangor in 1813. His
father was employed at the celebrated Penrhyn quarries.
Like so many musicians who became famous, he
developed his musical qualities very soon. In his early

life it was foretold that he would be a star in the musical firmament of the Principality, for he used to sing at work until the galleries of the quarry rang with the echoes of his song. While he was yet a young lad of eighteen he composed his first tune set to a popular hymn, the result being that he was criticized very severely for his daring, and was told to write new tunes to new hymns.

There is much truth and suggestiveness in this criticism. It is less easy to sing the tunes of William Owen to new words than it is in any other case. He composed his tunes to certain hymns, and it seems like divorcement to separate them. BRYN CALFARIA is wedded to the revival and evangelistic words of the Welsh hymn ' Gwaed y groes sy'n codi fynny.' However well other words go to the tune, the Welshman cannot in his own mind separate these Welsh words from the melody. And there is no adequate translation of them in English.

When he was thirty-nine years of age he published *Y Perl Cerddorol* (The Pearl of Music), which contained a number of selected musical compositions from his pen, most of which were hymn-tunes. So popular was this work that a second edition was called for immediately. He died in 1893.

325—Elim.

ELIM (also HESPERUS or WHITBURN) had a curious start in life. In 1861 there was some correspondence in the *Penny Post* on the subject of a suitable tune for Keble's ' Sun of my soul.' The correspondence continued into the following year, when contributors sent in tunes of their own as being (in their opinion) the most suitable for the words. Amongst these was the tune under notice, unnamed and unassigned, but an editorial note in the April (1862) number of the *Penny Post* said :

To S.C.C. we are indebted for the tune No. 6. Our correspondent omitted to give it a name (if it has one) or to mention that of the composer; still we are inclined to agree with S.C.C. that it is very suitable for Keble's Evening Hymn.

Nothing more was heard of the tune till the appearance in 1866 of Grey's *Hymnal for use in the English Church* with accompanying Tunes, in which it was inserted with the name of WHITBURN, the composer being given as Henry Baker, who kindly supplied this account of the history of the tune :

> The hymn-tune WHITBURN or HESPERUS, was written by me in 1854 (when at Exeter College, Oxford), but never, to my knowledge, in print until 1866, when it was inserted, with my permission, by Dr. J. B. Dykes, of Durham, in Mr. Grey's Hymnal to ' Sun of my soul.' I remember seeing the tune in the number of the *Penny Post* you allude to, some years after 1862, but have no idea who S. C. C. was. Many of my friends were very familiar with the tune when written, and probably it was much handed about in MS. for some years, and the name was lost. When Bishop Bickersteth's book came in about 1871, the tune was in it without a name, and I wrote to him claiming it, and asking to make a few corrections. This was done, and it was named HESPERUS, hence the two names.

Baker was an amateur musician, but sufficiently enthusiastic to take his bachelor's degree in music in 1867. He was a civil engineer by profession. He died at Wimbledon in 1910.

326—Liverpool.

LIVERPOOL (also known as NEWMARKET and WAIN-WRIGHT) is by Richard Wainwright, son of John Wainwright (see No. 120), and brother of Robert (see No. 172). He was born in Manchester in 1758 and in 1775 succeeded his brother Robert as organist at the

Collegiate Church, holding a similar position at St. Anne's Church. In 1782 he went to Liverpool as organist at St. Peter's. He died in 1825. His tune LIVERPOOL was composed whilst he was there, and printed in *A Collection of Hymns,* originally compiled for the children at the Bluecoat School.

327—Anima Christi.

ANIMA CHRISTI. The source of this will be found in Chappell's *Popular Music* (1855), as THE STAINES MORRIS TUNE. It is found without words in the first edition of Playford's *Dancing Master*. It probably belongs to the time of Queen Elizabeth, if not still earlier :

328—Come unto Me.

COME UNTO ME was written by Dr. Dykes for *Hymns Ancient and Modern* (1875).

329—Old 104th. See No. 45.

330—Llangloffan.

LLANGLOFFAN is found in Rev. D. Evans's *Hymnau a Thonau* (1865). It is an old Welsh melody, but its origin is at present unknown.

331—Behold Me Standing.

BEHOLD ME STANDING is by Mrs. Joseph Fairchild Knapp, who was the daughter of Dr. Walter Palmer. Born in New York City, N.Y., in 1839, she married Joseph Fairchild Knapp, the founder of the Metropolitan Life Insurance Company of New York, one of the largest companies carrying industrial insurance. Both she and her husband were members of the Methodist Church, and much of their wealth was dispensed in charitable and philanthropic work. Her annual income after the death of her husband was $50,000. She was one of the most famous hymn-writers in the country, and during her travels in Europe, she was invited to Sheffield and was given such a reception as was never before accorded a musician in that city. A letter from the secretary of her son states that 'his mother, Mrs. Phebe Palmer Knapp, died July 10, 1908,' at Poland Springs, Maine. BLESSED ASSURANCE (see No. 422) was published in 1873. Another composition, OPEN THE GATES OF THE TEMPLE, is much used at church dedications.

332—Entreaty.

ENTREATY was written by Sir H. Coward at the request of the committee of the Wesleyan Sunday-school Festival at Sheffield in 1889. It is here set to the hymn for which it was originally composed.

Dr. Coward, who was born in Liverpool in 1849, has always been an ardent advocate of tonic sol-fa, and his introduction to the system dates from his three months' attendance at the Parish Church Schools in Sheffield, in which town he has lived since he was about eight years of age. A few years later he took up the study of the system seriously, and he pursued the subject till he had mastered it, taking practically all the certificates that the Tonic Sol-fa College had to offer him. A still greater success attended his attack on the Oxford University musical degree. In the Mus.B. examination Sir Hubert Parry asked him a question on a subject which he had fortunately specialized in, whilst the paper work gave him no trouble. How he managed to find time to proceed to and obtain his doctorate five years later reads almost like a romance, but the sequel thereto deserves to be told here in full:

Shortly after this I met a friend who had obtained the degree at a previous examination, who said to me: 'I suppose that having reached the summit, you will now take it easy, as I am doing?' I asked him to explain, and he continued: 'Well, to me the degree was merely a means to an end—namely, to secure a standing as a professor of the pianoforte in ladies' schools. This I have attained; therefore I shall never again put pen to paper.' I told him that my view was just the reverse of his. Instead of the degree marking the end, it was just a starting-point. It gave the holder a right to be considered, and to demonstrate his ability, but for any one to shield himself behind his doctorate is to bring it into disrepute, and to create the notion that a doctor of music may be as dull as many D.D.'s.

Sir Henry has a wonderful record as a choir trainer and chorus master. Some of the finest choirs in the north of England have honoured themselves by appointing him as their conductor, whilst many of our leading composers have readily acknowledged the magic of his wand. And, then, how boundless has been his enthusiasm! Not content with taking choirs to Paris, to Germany, and to Canada, he set the seal on his fame by the world tour of his celebrated choir, a feat which is now recognized as one of the most remarkable musical undertakings of the century.

Sir Henry has composed several cantatas which have had a remarkable popularity. He is the author of an important work on *Choral Technique and Interpretation* (1914), and his *Reminiscences* give an intimate insight into the life work of a notable musician.

333, 603—Attercliffe.

William Mather, composer of ATTERCLIFFE and CANADA (No. 807), was born in Sheffield in 1756 and acted as organist at St. Paul's Church from 1788 to his death in 1808. He kept a music shop at what was in those days No. 11, Norfolk Street, and from here he published in 1806 his ' *Sacred Music,* consisting of twenty-six Psalm and Hymn-Tunes in Score with six Anthems.' Mather secured a fine list of subscribers for his venture, including the Right Hon. Lord Harewood. The choirs of the parish church, St. Paul's, and St. James's all subscribed for five copies each of Mather's tunes, and many country choirs, including the ' Ancient Society of Singers at Matlock,' also indulged in a copy. Mather did not name his tunes, but two of them have been christened ATTERCLIFFE and CANADA. The former has also been known as BETHPHAGE. It got badly mauled in the *Methodist Hymn-Book* (1904), but has now been restored to its pristine condition.

334 (i)—Good Shepherd.

GOOD SHEPHERD was written by Sir Frederick Bridge (see No. 122), for the *Methodist Free Church Hymns with Tunes* (1889). The original name of the tune was NINETY AND NINE. The name was changed to GOOD SHEPHERD for the *Methodist Hymn-Book* (1904) by the composer.

334 (ii)—The Ninety and Nine.

THE NINETY AND NINE is from *Sacred Songs and Solos* (1874).

Ira D. Sankey was born on a farm in Edinburgh,

Pennsylvania, in 1840. His family subsequently moved to Newcastle in the same State, and he soon began to take an active part in church affairs, being leader of the church choir. None of his ancestors were musical, and he had no special musical training, but, as he once said of himself, ' I sang from childhood, I was literally full and running over with music.' He first met Moody at the International Convention of the Y.M.C.A., held at Indianapolis in 1871. Here he was introduced to W. H. Doane, composer of the once famous PRODIGAL CHILD, and the impression the singing of the air made on the audience roused in Sankey a great desire to be able to use his voice with similar effect. The opportunity soon came. Moody engaged Sankey to join him in an evangelistic career, and thus did the famous Moody and Sankey combination originate.

They were invited to England in 1873 and began a remarkable series of meetings at York. They visited many other centres, including Scotland, where exception was taken to Sankey's harmonium as being a ' sinfu' instrument,' whilst many ministers were troubled about the use of hymns that were not in authorized collections. From Scotland the missioners went to Ireland, where even the Roman Catholics crowded to hear them, and on returning to England they visited the chief towns in the country.

The origin of the tune THE NINETY AND NINE may best be told in Sankey's own words :

When Mr. Moody and I were holding revival meetings in England and Scotland, I was travelling one day from Glasgow to Edinburgh. I was reading a newspaper as the train sped along, when my eye fell on a poem about a shepherd and his sheep. I read it through, and at once felt it would make a great song if it were set to music. I tore it out and put it in my scrap-book, thinking that some time I might compose music for it.

Next day the subject of the meeting in Edinburgh was 'The Good Shepherd.' At the close of the meeting, after Dr. Andrew Bonar had spoken, Mr. Moody rose and said, 'Mr. Sankey, have you any hymn appropriate to the occasion for a solo?' I had nothing save the poem I had found on the train the previous day. I felt that would be exceptionally appropriate, but I was unable to use it, as no music had as yet been written for it. Suddenly the impression came upon me: 'Sing the hymn and make the tune as you go along.' It was almost as if I had heard a voice, so vivid was the sensation. I yielded to it, and taking the little newspaper slip and laying it on the organ before me, with a silent prayer to God for help, I commenced to sing.

Note by note, the music was given me clear through to the end of the tune. After the first verse, I was very glad I had got through, but overwhelmed with fear that the tune for the next verse would be greatly different from the first. But again looking up to the Lord for help in this most trying moment, He gave me again the same tune for all the remaining verses, note by note. The impression made upon the audience was very deep. Hundreds were in tears.

Mr. Moody left the pulpit, and, coming to my side at the organ, said: 'Where did you get that? I never heard anything like it in my life.' He at once closed the meeting with prayer—asking God to bring home to the Shepherd's fold many a poor wanderer— and pronounced the benediction. In such a God-given way was THE NINETY AND NINE born.

335—Pass Me Not.

PASS ME NOT, by W. H. Doane (see No. 161), was contributed by him to *Songs of Devotion*, an American collection published in 1870.

336—He Lifted Me.

HE LIFTED ME, by Charles H. Gabriel (see No. 116), is from Alexander's *Gospel Songs* (1908). The tune was probably written in 1905.

337—Wondrous Love.

William G. Fischer, the composer of WONDROUS LOVE, was born at Baltimore in 1835. From 1858-1868 he was professor of music in Gerard College in Philadelphia. He was a skilful leader of large bodies of singers, and directed a choir of a thousand voices at some of Moody and Sankey's meetings. At the bicentenary festivals to commemorate the landing of William Penn, he conducted a choir of Welsh singers. He was a member of the Christ Methodist Episcopal Church in Philadelphia. He died in his seventieth year in 1912. His compositions were confined to hymn-tunes, of which he composed about two hundred.

338—Rescue.

RESCUE (or RESCUE THE PERISHING) was contributed by W. H. Doane (see No. 161) to an American collection called *Songs of Devotion* in 1870. A newly harmonized version was made by Sir Joseph Barnby for the *Bible Christian Sunday-school Hymnal* (1898).

339—Wrestling Jacob.

WRESTLING JACOB, by S. S. Wesley (see No. 365), is from *The European Psalmist* (1872), which he edited (see No. 298).

340—David's Harp.

DAVID'S HARP is by Robert King, who was one of the king's musicians in the reign of Charles II, also under William and Mary. He composed songs, also music for the ode on St. Cecilia's day written by Thomas Shadwell, the poet laureate. The ode is still in existence, but the

music has disappeared. King also wrote music for an
ode celebrating the birthday of John Cecil, Earl of
Exeter. He was one of the contributors to *The Divine
Companion* (1709), from which this tune is taken. The
dates of his birth and death are unknown.

341—Shirland.

SHIRLAND, by Samuel Stanley, is from the same source
as SIMEON (see No. 301).

342, 382—Byzantium.

BYZANTIUM (or JACKSON'S) is from *Twelve Psalm-
Tunes,* and eighteen single and double chants which the
composer, Thomas Jackson, published in 1780. The tune,
which was unnamed, was set to some verses from the
metrical version of Psalm xlvii. Little is known of the
composer except that he was organist of Newark Parish
Church, but he seems to have been a pushful individual,
to judge from the number of subscribers—upwards of
300—that he secured for his *Twelve Psalm-Tunes.*
Flushed with success he sent out a leaflet containing
proposals for publishing by subscription a book of
'Sixteen Marches,' but the proposal did not arouse
enthusiasm and nothing more was heard of it. He died
in his sixty-sixth year in 1781.

343—Jena.

JENA is the name assigned in the present tune-book to
a melody set to a Christmas hymn, 'Das neugeborne
Kindelein' (the new-born child), by Cyriacus Schneegass
(1546-1597). He belonged to the University of Jena,
and this probably accounts for the name of the tune.
It is found in a *Gesangbuch* (see No. 466) edited by
Melchior Vulpius in 1609.

344—Dorchester.

DORCHESTER is a modern name for the well-known
HYMNUS EUCHARISTICUS, which is found in a folio

volume of MS. music in the library of Christ Church, Oxford. It dates from the seventeenth century, and the tune carries an explanatory note:

> This hymn is sung every day, in Magdalen College Hall, Oxon, Dinner and Supper; through the yeare for the after grace by the Chaplains, Clarks and Choristers there. Composed by Benjamin Rogers, Doctor of Musique of the University of Oxon, 1685.

Whether the Latin hymn ('Te Deum Patrem colimus') is the work of Rogers is doubtful. The tune is also known under other names, such as TE DEUM PATREM, CHAPEL ROYAL, and BAMPTON.

The custom of singing on the top of Magdalen College tower on the first of May dates from early in the sixteenth century, and took the form of a concert lasting about two hours. A drenching shower of rain one May morning about 1790 put an end to a lengthened performance, and since then the singing of the HYMNUS EUCHARISTICUS has sufficed to maintain the old custom unbroken.

Benjamin Rogers, who was born at Windsor in 1614, commenced his musical career as a chorister at St. George's Chapel, Windsor, where he also served as a 'singing man' during the Civil War of Charles I's reign. He achieved a great reputation as a composer, and, says Anthony Wood, he 'composed several sets of ayres of four parts to be performed by violins and an organ which . . . were sent as great rarities into Germany to the Court of Archduke Leopold, and often played by his own musicians.'

At the Restoration, Rogers was employed to write special music for a banquet given by the City of London to Charles II, and this 'being admirably well done, gave great content, and the author being present, obtained a great name for his composition and a plentiful reward.'

The doctor's reputation extended as far as Sweden, where some of his compositions were given in the presence of Queen Christiana.

After acting as organist at Eton College for four years he was appointed to Magdalen College, Oxford, and here his eccentric and wayward behaviour finally got him into serious trouble on account of a series of irregularities, and he was at last dismissed. One reason assigned for this was his neglect of duty and 'troublesome behaviour in the Chapel, where he would talk so loud in the organ loft that he offended the company and would not leave off, though he hath been sent to by the President not to make such a scandalous noise there.' Also there were frequent complaints of him from the clerks, to whom especially the Chanter he used to be very cross, in not playing services as they were willing and able to sing, but, out of a thwarting humour, would play nothing but Canterbury tune, wherein he minded not the honour of the College, but his own ease and laziness.

Dr. Rogers had a different story to tell to the effect that ' he was ejected in consequence of the misconduct of his daughter, who had carried on an intrigue with the College porter.'

As the College granted Dr. Rogers a pension, assisted his widow, and bore the expenses of her funeral, it would appear that he was very highly respected. When his beautiful HYMNUS EUCHARISTICUS is sung from the top of the magnificent tower of Magdalen College at five o'clock in the morning annually on May Day it is usually listened to by a large audience gathered in the thoroughfare below.

Dr. Rogers was a great church musician, of whom it is on record that ' he was esteemed the prime composer of the nation.' Whether this be true or not the fact remains that after a lapse of more than 200 years his music may still be heard in our great cathedrals.

345—Isleworth.

ISLEWORTH was composed by Dr. Samuel Howard (see No. 81) for *Melodies for the Psalms of David,* a work compiled as a music companion for Christopher Smart's metrical version of the Psalms (1765).

346—Valete.

VALETE, by Arthur Sullivan, was composed for *Church Hymns* (1874).

347—York.

YORK is one of the twelve Common Tunes (see No. 37) in the Scottish Psalter of 1615, where it is called THE STILT. Thomas Ravenscroft included it in his Psalter (1621), and placed it under his ' Northerne ' tunes, calling it YORKE. Its popularity is thus referred to by Sir John Hawkins in his *History* (Vol. II), ' the tenor part (i.e. the air) of this tune is so well known, that within memory half the nurses in England were used to sing it by way of lullaby; and the chimes of many country churches have played it six or eight times in four and twenty hours from time immemorial.'

348—Christopher.

CHRISTOPHER is a melody that has undergone several modifications since it appeared in one of Christopher Peter's collections of tunes (1655), some of which were his own compositions. He was for some years a music director (or Cantor) in Guben (not far from Frankfurt-on-the-Oder). Little is known of his career.

349—Carey's.

CAREY'S (or SURREY) appeared in John Church's *Introduction to Psalmody* (1723), set to Addison's hymn, ' The Lord my pasture shall prepare.'

Henry Carey was born in (or about) 1692. There is some uncertainty about both his parentage and the place of his birth, and little is known of his early life. In 1715 he commenced writing operas for the stage, composing the music for most of them. In 1732 Rich, the manager of Covent Garden Theatre, brought Carey and J. F. Lampe (see No. 411) together, and the collaboration of the two resulted in a successful series of operas, the association being an imperfect resemblance to the Gilbert and Sullivan combination of recent years. Their most successful production was *The Dragon of Wantley*, a clever skit on the productions of the Italian opera school. The partnership ended with Carey's death in 1743 and two years later Lampe came under the influence of the Methodist movement. The claim made by Carey's son that his father composed the National Anthem has not been admitted. Carey's claim to fame now rests on his hymn-tune and on his famous song, 'Sally in our Alley.'

350—Plaistow.

PLAISTOW is found in T. Call's *The Tunes and Hymns as they are used at the Magdalen Chapel, properly set for the Organ, Harpsichord and Guittar,* by Thomas Call, Organist (c. 1762).

PLAISTOW is a fanciful name for this tune, as originally the only heading is ' Tune. To THE UNKNOWN WORLD,' and set to:

> Hark, my gay friend that solemn toll
> Speaks the departure of a soul.

No composer's name is attached, and the tune may be Mr. Call's own. Nothing is known about him except that his lodgings (as he informs the public in his title page) were ' at Mr. Bennetts' Stay Ware House, near Great Turnstile, Holbourn.'

351—Calvary.

CALVARY is by Lewis Hartsough, who was born in 1828 in Ithaca, New York. At the age of twenty-three he entered the ministry of the Methodist Episcopal Church. Ill-health compelled his ultimate resignation, and he retired to the Rocky Mountains, where he started the Mati Mission, and became its first superintendent. Advancing years compelled him at last to abandon active work, and he retired to Mount Vernon, Iowa, where he died in 1919. He was a poet-musician, and wrote many hymn-tunes. He also edited the music edition of *The Revivalist* (c. 1868). The words and music of Hartsough's most popular hymn, 'I hear Thy welcome voice,' were written in 1872. They were first published in a monthly magazine called *Guide to Holiness*. A copy of this was sent to Ira D. Sankey, who inserted it in his *Sacred Songs and Solos,* and there its popularity commenced. The tune was not originally named, but bore as the heading the first line of the hymn.

352—St. Bride. See No. 81.

353 (i)—Misericordia.

MISERICORDIA, by Henry Smart (see No. 12), was written by him for the 1875 edition of *Hymns Ancient and Modern.*

353 (ii)—Gainsworth.

GAINSWORTH is from *A Church Hymn and Tune-Book* (1858), edited by C. H. Purday, who composed the tune. See No. 612.

354—St. Werburgh.

ST. WERBURGH was composed in 1873 by Sir R. P. Stewart for the *Irish Church Hymnal* (1874) of which he was editor. Stewart was born in Dublin in 1825, and learnt music as a chorister at Christ Church Cathedral, where he became organist at the age of nineteen as well as at St. Patrick's Cathedral. On being appointed Professor of Music at Dublin University, he at once endeavoured to raise the credit and status of the degrees in music. He demanded that candidates should in future give evidence that they had received a good education in general subjects.

Stewart was undoubtedly a musician of great gifts, and as a skilful, and indeed a great organ player, he was widely known and respected. The late Sir Charles Stanford, who learnt composition and orchestration from Stewart, used to speak highly of his skill, and he has put on record his memories of the first organ lessons he received from him. 'Remember,' Stewart would say, 'remember that your left hand is a tenor, and not a bass,' and the first exercise Stewart proposed for his youthful pupil was the 100th Psalm, which he wrote out, placing the melody in the pedals coupled to the four-foot flute on the choir without any pedal stops, and the lower parts only given to the hands. 'To a beginner,' added Stanford, 'this sensation somewhat resembled the topsy-turvydom experienced by those who have looped the loop.'

When Mendelssohn's organ sonatas were first published Stewart was so full of enthusiasm over them that he used to retreat to Christ Church Cathedral, where he was organist, and work at them day after day till he knew them by heart, then on the Sunday following he played the first Sonata as a voluntary. Naturally the freshness of the music greatly aroused the curiosity of his friends, and they came up to the organ to know all about it. Great was their astonishment to find no music on the desk, and Stewart mischievously refused to give any information, and reproved them for their ignorance of the classical works for the organ!

Stewart was a strong advocate of Bach's music, notably his organ works, at a time when the composer's compositions did not figure very often on recital programmes in this country. The great composer was his chief deity. Some who heard him used to condemn the speed at which he played many of the Preludes and Fugues, 'but,' says Stanford, 'recent authorities have held that Bach himself played his music so quickly that his pupils despaired of imitating him.' Stewart's interpretations were also criticized, but Stanford points out that they were only anticipating methods of phrasing on which Schweitzer lays such stress.

Stewart was very proud of the share that Ireland had in the first production of *Messiah*. In one of his letters he says:

> The English critique writers have lately taken up the trick of ignoring Handel's visit to *Ireland* (which lasted nine months) in 1741-2. The British lords nagged the poor man and drove him over to Ireland, and nearly killed him by paralysis and worry. *We* rescued and petted him, till the others grew ashamed of themselves.

On one occasion Stewart was playing the accompaniments to Handel's *Samson* in the Ulster Hall, Belfast, when his eyesight, never very strong, quite failed him, just as the tenor was commencing his solo, 'Total eclipse.' He turned to a friend who was near the organ and said, 'I can't see,' and then proceeded to accompany the rest of the oratorio entirely from memory. Fortunately the attack was only temporary, and it soon passed away.

He found little time for composing. He had an easy flow of melody, and understood all the intricacies of the art, but for various reasons he never developed on these lines. Moreover, he was a stern self-critic, and did not hesitate to destroy much that he wrote, but which did not come up to his standard. He relates how he made a 'holocaust' of his setting of Psalm cvii., on the ground that 'one weak work was extant the less in this world,' and he adds, 'I think I also burned two orchestral overtures and a symphony.' His high standard in worship music is evident from the way in which he edited the *Irish Church Hymnal*. He died in 1894.

355—Dalkeith.

DALKEITH is by Thomas Hewlett, who was born at Oxford in 1845. From 1865 to 1871 he was organist at the Duke of Buccleugh's private chapel, and soon after his appointment he contributed DALKEITH to the *St. Albans' Tune-Book* (1866). He was also organist in Edinburgh successively at St. Peter's Episcopal Church, St. Mary's Roman Catholic Church, and Newington Parish Church. He died in 1874, and was buried in Newington Cemetery, where his resting-place is marked by a monument erected by the members of the Edinburgh Choral Union in 'acknowledgement of his musical talent and his great ability as organist of that Society.' Hewlett wrote several other hymn-tunes, but only DALKEITH has survived.

356—Sovereignty.

SOVEREIGNTY is by John Newton, and first appeared in *The Pilgrim*, a collection of twenty-eight original tunes by him. No copy of the first edition is known to exist, but the dates of the second and third editions are 1839 and 1845. SOVEREIGNTY was originally composed for the hymn, 'Great God of wonders, all Thy ways,' by Samuel Davies, to which it is set in the present *Methodist Tune-Book*. In some recent Welsh hymnals such as E. Stephens' *Ail Lyfr Tonau ac Emynau* (1879) the name is changed to HUDDERSFIELD without any apparent reason, as the composer had nothing to do with that town.

John Newton was born in 1802 at Rice's (now called Riste's) Place, Barker Gate, Nottingham. He attended with his parents at Castle Gate Congregational Chapel till his marriage in 1824. After that he attended Zion

Chapel, and it was here that his musical talent was recognized. He was allowed to reorganize the choir, and in many ways greatly improved the musical part of the service. He was by trade a 'twist-hand' (lace maker), and frequently whilst at his work, when a favourite hymn occupied his thoughts, he mentally wove round the words the music they suggested to him; thus he began to compose hymn-tunes. The melody which stands first in his manuscript book of hymn-tunes is Agnus Dei, composed for the hymn 'Thou dear Redeemer, dying Lamb.'

About 1830 a depression in the lace trade was the cause of his removal to Beeston, near Nottingham. A new Wesleyan chapel had just been completed there, and John Newton was requested to gather together a choir, and make all the arrangements for the musical part of the service. This he did with great success for four years, and composed many tunes for the hymns he found in use. Wishing to publish his work, he canvassed the town and county for subscriptions, and in 1834 was able to defray the expenses of printing his first book, which he named *The Pilgrim*, in memory of the long tramps he had had.

In 1834 a revival of the lace trade recalled him to its centre in Nottingham, and in the same year he was appointed choirmaster of Parliament Street Chapel (Methodist New Connexion). This post he held for eight years, and during this time most of his music was composed. He introduced special musical services for important seasons, which were much appreciated.

Becoming associated with the Nottingham Choral (later Sacred Harmonic) Society, Newton's compositions took a wider range, and oratorio music, with orchestral accompaniment, and anthems for the church services, proceeded from his pen. Some of his compositions were performed in the Mechanics Hall, Nottingham, with full orchestral accompaniment. He published various collections of psalmody, most of them being now very scarce. SOVEREIGNTY gained a fresh lease of life by being included in the Appendix to the *Methodist Hymn-Book* (1904).

357, 504—Marienbourn.

MARIENBOURN is from John Wesley's 'Foundery' Tune-Book (1742). It appears to be founded on BREMEN (No. 504) a tune also known as NEUMARK from the name of its composer. MARIENBOURN possesses the turns and graces that are lacking in BREMEN, which, however, was not quite elaborate enough for the Herrnhut and the Methodist eighteenth-century singers. BREMEN became very popular after its introduction, and it is possible that in a series of congregational vocalizations it got twisted into MARIENBOURN.

Georg Neumark was a native of Thuringia. He suffered many hardships in early life, but at last his prospects improved and he obtained a position as tutor in a family living in Kiel. In gratitude he wrote both hymn and tune No. 504. He returned later to his native district and held various offices under Duke Wilhelm II, of Saxe-Weimar, including that of Court Librarian. He died in 1681, having been afflicted with blindness during the last few months of his life.

358, 978—Redhead No. 47.

REDHEAD No. 47. See under No. 13.

359—St. Martin.

ST. MARTIN is by James Hallett Sheppard, who sent it for inclusion in the *Wesleyan Tune-Book* (1876). Its somewhat unusual metre has not been conducive to popularity. As the hymn to which it is set ('Out of the depths I cry to Thee') is a translation of Luther's 'Aus tiefer Noth,' it would seem that Luther's own chorale would have been the most suitable setting, as in *Hymns Ancient and Modern.*

J. H. Sheppard was born in 1835. He was an 'organist and vocal composer of merit,' but no details of his career are available. He died at Clapham early in 1879.

360—Blockley.

BLOCKLEY is adapted from a song 'Leaning on Thee,' by T. Blockley, who was a music-publisher in London about 1870-1880.

361—Old 23rd.

OLD 23RD. Charles Wesley's hymn (No. 371):

> And can it be that I should gain
> An interest in the Saviour's blood?

disputes with No. 361:

> Where shall my wondering soul begin?

the claim to be the hymn written by Charles Wesley on Tuesday, May 23, 1738, and sung 'with great joy' on the following night, when John Wesley 'was brought in triumph by a troop of friends' to his brother's lodging in Little Britain after his conversion. In the preface to the *Methodist Tune-Book* (1904) we are told that the hymn (there said to be No. 358), is set to the OLD TWENTY-THIRD PSALM-TUNE, partly because it is believed to be the tune sung on that occasion.

Interesting as the suggestion is, there is absolutely no proof of it, and the theory is wholly untenable. The phrase 'Old Psalm-tune' is always used to refer to the tunes set to the metrical versions of the Psalms in the 'Sternhold and Hopkins' edition, such as the OLD 81ST or OLD 100TH. Occasionally it may include a tune found in the musical edition of Tate and Brady's 'New Version,' but the OLD 23RD does not occur in either of these. The source from which it is derived is *Melopeia Sacra*, a collection of sacred songs set to music by Andrew Roner (1721). Here we find the melody of the so-called OLD 23RD, set to Addison's version of Psalm xxiii. :

> The Lord my pasture shall prepare.

There is an 'introducing base' of sixteen bars, and at the end of the song is a 'ritornel,' or interlude of twenty-four bars.

Roner's book was published in 1721, and during the next thirty years or so there is no trace (so far as is at present known) of the air referred to. But someone was evidently at work on it, adapting it and moulding its form into that of the hymn-tune, and at last it appeared in its new form in 1754 in a book entitled *The Divine Musical Miscellany*, where it is called KINGSWOOD TUNE. For upwards of a century the OLD 23RD passed out of use, and was then revived and inserted in a much-altered form in the 1904 *Methodist Hymn-Book*, with the melody considerably adapted and shorn of its former glory. Here is the original form :

KINGSWOOD TUNE.   Psalm 23rd.   ADDISON. P.M.

The Lord my pas - ture shall pre-pare, And feed me with a shep - herd's care; His pre - sence shall my wants sup - ply, And guard me with a watch - ful eye; My noon - day walks He shall at - tend, And all my mid - - night hours de - fend.

362, 695—Mainzer.

MAINZER. Joseph Mainzer, the composer of the tune
which bears his name, well deserves to take his place
amongst the apostles of choral singing in the mid-
Victorian era. Born at Trêves, the son of a butcher, he
received his musical training at the Cathedral School of
his native town. He began to learn music at the age of
seven, and three years later he would gather his mates
together to sing choruses. He also learnt to play several
instruments, but as he grew older he decided in favour
of the profession of a mining engineer. But the hard
work undermined his health, and he reverted to his first
love, which was henceforth to be his sole occupation.
He went on a tour through Germany and Italy making
the acquaintance of prominent musicians, and he also
took lessons from Rinck. In each town he visited he
(to use his own words), 'created choruses, because
teaching was to me a passion, and so was music. In
Rome I united all the German, Swedish, Danish, and
Hungarian artists in classes. Among them were men
of the very first talent in the art. In the ruined
Coliseum of the eternal city did we raise our voices,
singing together, in the silent hours of night, the
grandest compositions of the greatest masters of the
art.'

Then his wanderings ceased, and he settled in Trêves
as a teacher of music. Brought up as a Roman Catholic,
he had been made a priest in 1826, and then an Abbé.
But serious doubts now began to influence him, bringing
about 'a period of reflection and ferment of the soul.'
The result was that he renounced Catholicism, and
finding himself at variance with his old friends, he left
his native town. His biographers, however, assert that
there were other reasons, sympathy with the Polish
Revolution bringing him into trouble with the Prussian
Government. Visits to Brussels and Paris followed,
everywhere seeking an opportunity for putting into

execution his fondly cherished scheme for free singing classes for working men. At Paris he succeeded in attracting some 3,000 workmen to his classes, but this was at a time when revolution was in the air, and the Government, suspecting sedition in the gathering together of such large numbers, broke up the classes, and Mainzer decided to try his fortunes in Great Britain. He brought no introductions, he knew scarcely a word of English, and he discovered that the English Government had decided to support Hullah's singing system. In no way daunted, he set to work to learn the language, and within two months of his arrival in England he issued the first number of *The National Singing Circular,* to be followed in a few months by the first number of his *Musical Times* in July, 1842, the forerunner of the present journal of that name which J. A. Novello started two years later.

Mainzer's one idea was that everybody should sing, and no ' community singing' advocate of the present day is more insistent than he was. To further his object he issued his famous pamphlet, *Singing for the Million.* He fought a famous battle in spite of the opposition of the professors, indeed he even started a normal school for professors of music who wished to learn his system, granting them free admission. In 1842 he accepted an invitation to visit Edinburgh, and remained there five years, accomplishing wonders, though he failed in his application for the vacant Reid Professorship of Music at the Edinburgh University. In 1845 he issued his *Standard Psalmody of Scotland,* wherein appeared the tune named after him. According to James Love it had been published a short time previously, set to Psalm cvii. After five years' residence in Scotland, Mainzer left for Manchester, where he continued his work till ill-health laid him aside and death terminated his labours in 1851. It is interesting to remember that one of Mainzer's chief supporters was W. E. Hickson, a shoe manufacturer of London, who worked on Mainzer's

18

lines, and who, in 1836 published *The Singing Master,* which contained his national hymn, ' God bless our native land ' (No. 880).

363, 393—Ich Halte Treulich Still.

ICH HALTE TREULICH STILL is found in *Musicalisches Gesangbuch*, a collection of 954 melodies (' Geistriche Lieder und Arien ') published at Leipzig. This was formed in 1736 by Georg Christian Schemelli, who had been a pupil at the Thomas-schule at Leipzig. Only one of the songs bears the name of J. S. Bach, and it is a matter of much curious and indeed fruitless speculation as to the other probable composers. ICH HALTE may be by J. S. Bach, and then again it may not, and that is all that can be said.

364—Wirksworth.

WIRKSWORTH occurs in *A Book of Psalm-Tunes* edited by James Green. The fifth edition is dated 1724. An earlier form of the tune is found in Chetham's *Psalmody* (see No. 193). The composer is unknown.

365—Faith.

FAITH, by S. S. Wesley (see No. 217), is from Kemble's *Psalms and Hymns* (1864).

366, 934—Epworth.

EPWORTH (or LOUGHTON) is found in Part III of *The Psalmist* (1838). The production of this work was due to some enthusiasts connected with the Baptist Church formerly in Devonshire Square, Bishopsgate, E.C. Being thoroughly tired of Rippon's tune-book, they set to work to form a collection of their own. Having made their selection, they entrusted the technical work to Vincent Novello, who obtained further contributions from S. Wesley, W. Horsley, J. Turle and others. The work was issued in four parts, the complete edition forming a standard work for many years.

Charles Wesley, eldest son of the hymn-writer, was born at Bristol in 1757. From his earliest years the boy showed great talent for music, and his wonderful precocity aroused the enthusiasm of some of the leading musicians of the time. When the family removed to London Charles and his brother Samuel gave a series of subscription concerts at their father's house in Marylebone which extended over seven seasons (1778-1785). Young Wesley's gifts as a player attracted the attention of George III, and Wesley paid frequent visits to Windsor Castle, where his playing of Handel's music greatly delighted the king. Wesley would have made a name for himself in the profession, but his father was opposed to his taking any public appointment, otherwise he would have accepted the position of organist at St. George's, Windsor, which the king offered him. After the Rev. Charles Wesley's death the prejudice against the very name of Wesley prevented young Charles from obtaining some of the most lucrative posts of the day, including St. Paul's Cathedral (1796), and Westminster Abbey (1802). 'We want no Wesleys here!' was the remark that greeted him when he applied for the Cathedral post. After his father's death Wesley resided with his mother and sister, fulfilling social engagements, ever occupied with the works of his beloved Handel, and giving occasional music lessons, also tendering advice about the erection of new organs. At last, in 1817, came the offer of the organ at the new parish church of Marylebone at a yearly salary of £100. He had for a short time previously acted as organist at Chelsea Hospital, but he did the work largely by deputy, and the governors did not approve of this. In 1822 he edited a revised edition of *Sacred Harmony*. Five years later he was invited to open the new organ in Brunswick Chapel, Leeds, but he sent his brother Sam in his place. Rumours that a pension was to be granted him led Wesley to submit a memorial to the king, but nothing came of it. His last days were spent at his harpsichord, and in his last hours he played in imagination with his feeble fingers as if the instrument lay beneath them. His end came on May 23, 1834. His compositions were confined to concertos, songs, and a few anthems.

367, 881—Lincoln.

LINCOLN is from T. Ravenscroft's *Psalter*. See No. 45.

368—St. Swithin.

ST. SWITHIN (or SWITHIN, or CHELSEA) is found in Isaac Smith's *Collection of Psalm-Tunes* (c. 1770) (see No. 519), no composer's name being given. In later tune-books it is ascribed to Jesser, but nothing is at present known about him, not even his Christian name. He may have been a West Country man, for a certain 'Mr. Jesser' of Frome, is mentioned in the eighteenth century *Diary of a West Country Physician* (1934) as taking his part in some musical activities in the town.

369—Purleigh.

PURLEIGH was contributed by A. H. Brown (see No. 302) to the first edition of *Hymns Ancient and Modern* (1861). 'It was written some years earlier on a piece of waste paper one Sunday morning before service in Romford Church.'

370—Confidence.

CONFIDENCE is by William Moore, who was born in Manchester in 1811. From his youth he showed a love of music, and at the age of nineteen he became a teacher of instrumental music. From about 1832 to 1837 he was organist of St. Mary's Church, Rochdale, and CONFIDENCE was composed during that period. In 1838 he went as organist to Albion Chapel, Ashton-under-Lyne, and seven years later another move found him installed at a new instrument in Cavendish Chapel,

Manchester, which had just been opened by Sir George
Smart. Moore remained here for thirty-one years, when
he resigned his office, and lived in retirement till his
death in 1880. The original name of CONFIDENCE was
ELY. It has also been known as ACCRINGTON.

371 (i)—Sagina.

SAGINA is by Thomas Campbell, and is so named in his
Bouquet containing twenty-three original tunes, published
in 1825. Except that he was a native of Sheffield nothing
further is known of the composer. The tune has also
been known as SAGIORA, and a claim made that some
J. Goldie from the Isle of Man was the composer, but
there is no foundation for the statement.

371 (ii)—Lansdown.

LANSDOWN. Alfred Beer, the composer of this tune,
was born at Great Barr, Birmingham, in 1874. He
received his early education from his father. As a boy
he showed musical ability, and was for some time a
chorister. In this capacity he had the honour of taking
part in the diocesan festivals at Canterbury Cathedral.
He subsequently became a pupil teacher at Dereham,
Norfolk, and at the same time took music lessons from
Dr. Horace Hill, whose name is ever associated with
the Norwich Musical Festivals. His desire to advance
led him to aim for the L.R.A.M. diploma, and for this
purpose he put himself under Oscar Beringer. Meanwhile he kept up his scholastic work, acting as assistant
master at Mr. Conquest's school in Biggleswade, and also
at a private school in Margate.

In 1904 he was attracted by an advertisement for a
music master at Kingswood School. This he applied
for and was successful in obtaining the post. There he
remained till 1928, when ill-health compelled him to
resign. He retired to Minehead, where for a short period
he acted as organist-choirmaster at the Baptist Church,
returning to old associations in Bath in 1933.

Four of Mr. Beer's tunes in the book are written to 6-8's metre. This choice is due to the late Mr. Workman, formerly headmaster at Kingswood, who complained to Mr. Beer that good tunes of that metre were sadly wanted, especially to certain hymns. Thus did LANSDOWN (No. 371) come into being in 1904, and MOUNT BEACON (No. 610) in 1905, to be followed at intervals by ANCHOR (No. 375) and EIDE (No. 668). The writing of TENAX (No. 523), originally called NEW KING STREET, was also due to Mr. Workman's influence. LANSDOWN and MOUNT BEACON are local Bath names and EIDE takes its name from a beauty spot in Norway.

Eyesight trouble has prevented Mr. Beer from accomplishing many schemes he had in view. This was the case when he sat for his Mus.B. degree at Oxford, when the time allotted for the various papers did not prove enough owing to his eye infirmity. Sir Hubert Parry fully realized the difficulty that Mr. Beer laboured under, and the kindly and spontaneous letter of sympathy that the Professor of Music wrote him is one of Mr. Beer's treasured possessions.

372—Arlington. See No. 299.

373 (i)—A Babe is Born.

A BABE IS BORN is from Bramley and Stainer's *Christmas Carols,* but the tune seems to have been taken from Husk's *Songs of the Nativity,* where it is attached to a different carol beginning :

> All you that in this house be here,
> Remember Christ that for us died,
> And spend away with modest cheer
> In loving sort this Christmas tide.

Husk's carol is from *New Carolls for this Mery Time of Christmas* (1661), where it is directed to be sung to the tune of 'Essex's Last Good Night' (Robert

Devereux, second earl of Essex, beheaded Ash Wednesday, 1600-1). It is quite possible that the above carol tune is a traditional version of this old ballad tune. It is undoubtedly a folk-tune, and belongs to a large family group of linked traditional airs, sung to melancholy ballads such as 'Lord Bateman,' and 'My true love once he courted me.' Chappell, in his *Popular Music,* prints an 'Essex's Good-night,' but this belongs to another Essex lament in a different form.

373 (ii)—Ely.

ELY is named ST. CATHERINE in Turle and Taylor's collection of psalms and hymn-tunes (1844) called *The People's Music-Book.* The composer, Thomas Turton, was a Yorkshireman by birth. At Cambridge he gained great distinction in mathematics, being senior wrangler in 1805. After ordination he was made regius professor of Divinity at Cambridge, and in 1820 became Dean of Peterborough. Twelve years later he was appointed Dean of Westminster, and in 1845 Sir Robert Peel appointed him to the see of Ely. He was actively engaged in religious controversies, but found opportunity to indulge in his love of art, and also to devote time to music.

374—Jesus Saves Me Now.

JESUS SAVES ME NOW. The composer of this tune is unknown, nor does it appear to have any history.

375 (i)—Madrid.

MADRID is by William Matthews. Born in 1759 he spent his early life at his native town of Ilkeston. Later he went to live at Nottingham, where he became a stocking maker. He devoted much of his spare time to music and became a successful choirmaster and teacher.

He published a good deal of music, chiefly hymn-tunes and anthems, of which MADRID still remains popular. In his later years Matthews changed the stocking trade for that of music-seller, opening a shop in Houndsditch. He died in 1830.

375 (ii)—Anchor.

ANCHOR, by Alfred Beer. See No. 371 (ii).

376—Traveller.

TRAVELLER is a very much altered form of a tune of the same name in John Wesley's *Sacred Harmony* (1780), this being the original form:

It is set to the hymn, ' Come on, my partners in distress,' and this may account for the name of the tune. The melody is adapted from a song by Henry Holcombe, a popular eighteenth-century song composer. He was born, according to some accounts, in Salisbury about

1690. He appeared as a boy prodigy singer on the London stage, and when his voice broke he took to teaching singing and the harpsichord.

377, 594—St. Michael.

St. Michael is a shortened form of the tune set to Psalm cxxxiv. in Day's *Psalter* (1562). It originally appeared in *Pseaumes octante trois,* published at Geneva in 1551. The tune has been subject to many variations from the original melody. The present form seems to be due to Dr. Crotch in his selection of psalm-tunes published in 1836.

378—Dublin.

Dublin has come down through the *Methodist Hymn-Book* (1904) from the *Wesleyan Tune-Book* (1876) where it is said to be inserted ' By permission of H. H. Bemrose.' James Love, in his *Scottish Church Music,* gives currency to a story that a copy of this tune was presented in MS. to John Dobson in 1845 with the intimation that it was by Sir John Stevenson. Dobson evidently did not think much of it, for he did not insert it in either edition of his *Tunes New and Old* (1864 and 1876). Its earliest recorded appearance was under the name Howard in John Wilson's *Selection of Psalm-Tunes,* published at Edinburgh in 1825. In this collection the tune is anonymous. Its ascription to Sir John Stevenson certainly lacks corroboration.

Sir John Andrew Stevenson was born in Dublin in 1762. He was connected as a chorister and then as Vicar Choral with the Cathedrals of Christ Church and St. Patrick. He composed a large quantity of church music, most of which is now forgotten. He did excellent work as the arranger and musical editor of the ' Irish Melodies,' for which Thomas Moore wrote the words. Some people still remember him with gratitude as the adapter of the once popular tune VESPER HYMN to the hymn, ' Hark! the vesper hymn is stealing.' He died in 1833.

379—Nunhead.

NUNHEAD is found in a book of melodies published at Leipzig in 1713, collected and edited by Daniel Vettes, a Leipzig organist. There is no direct proof that he composed NUNHEAD or any other of the chorales in the collection. It is set to a hymn by Behm (' Das walt 'Gott Vater und Gott Sohn'), which has never gained recognition in English hymnals. The melody is amongst those adapted and harmonized by J. S. Bach in his *Choral-gesänge*. NUNHEAD is also known by the first four words of Behm's hymn.

380—Hyfrydol.

HYFRYDOL is by R. H. Pritchard.

When a new tune-book is issued there will always be a certain number of fresh melodies that will arouse special interest, and when the *Methodist Hymn-Book* (1904) was issued HYFRYDOL was one of the tunes that earned this distinction. It was sung everywhere, and a generous elasticity in its rhythm enabled enthusiasts to fit it to other metres than the one for which it was written. Perhaps the greatest iconoclasm was the attempt to fit it on to Dr. Burton's great missionary hymn ' There's a light upon the mountains.' The tune even obtained the distinction of an appearance in the *Daily Mail*. This was on the occasion when Mr. Lloyd George addressed a meeting at the Queen's Hall in 1914 in support of the movement to organize a regiment of London Welshmen for service abroad with the new Army. A music programme was arranged, and the choral selections included HYFRYDOL, which was sung to the hymn, ' Marchog, Iesu,' the first verse of which, as translated by the Rev. Elvet Lewis, runs thus :

Ride to battle, ride victorious,
 Gird, O Christ, Thy glittering sword;
Earth can never stand before Thee,
 Nor can hell itself, O Lord:
In Thy name such glory dwelleth,
 Hostile armies faint with fear,
And the wide creation trembleth
 When it feels Thee coming near.

Rowland Hugh Pritchard was born at Graienyn, near Bala, on January 14, 1811. He was a grandson of the bard Rowland Hugh, after whom he was named. He was fond of music from boyhood, and composed the hymn-tune HYFRYDOL when he was about twenty years of age. Throughout his life he devoted much time and thought to the study of music, and even during his last illness he tried to write down the melodies that kept coming to him. He was the owner of a good voice, and did much useful work as a choir conductor. He possessed an attractive personality, and his musical enthusiasm touched all who came in contact with him.

Pritchard's love of music and his devotion to the art led him to neglect the essentials necessary to a successful business life, and he was nearing the Psalmist's allotted span when circumstances compelled him to leave his home and take up a position with a business firm at Holywell. He did not long survive the change, and passed away on January 25, 1887. During his last illness the head of his firm paid him every attention, and finally undertook most of the funeral expenses. He was buried in Holywell cemetery, where a monument was a few years ago erected to his memory.

Pritchard composed a large number of hymn-tunes, and also assisted in the editing and compilation of collections. In 1844 he published *Cyfaill y Cantorion* (*The Singers' Companion*), which consisted chiefly of his own compositions. Another of his works, *Y Fasged Gerddorol* (*The Singers' Basket*), contained a series of ten lessons for children, some of them being written in verse. He also contributed a number of tunes to Welsh tune-books, and some anthems by him appeared in the *Haleluwia* (1849). According to the Rev. J. Mearns HYFRYDOL made its first appearance in print in the *In Memoriam Casgliad o Donau* (1876), but Dr. Patrick has found it in *Halelwiah Drachefn*, edited by Griffiith Roberts in 1855.

381—Keston.

KESTON, by Dr. A. E. Floyd (see No. 174), appeared first in the *Methodist School Hymnal* (1910).

382—Byzantium. See No. 342.

383—Tottenham.

TOTTENHAM is from *Parochial Psalmody* (1823), edited by Thomas Greatorex, who may have composed the tune, though no name is attached to it. Greatorex, who was born at North Wingfield, Derbyshire, in 1758, studied music under Dr. Benjamin Cooke, organist of Westminster Abbey. He had the good fortune to enjoy the patronage of the Earl of Sandwich, whom he assisted in oratorio performances at the Earl's seat near Huntingdon. In 1781 Greatorex was appointed organist of Carlisle Cathedral, but after three years he resigned and spent some time in travelling on the continent. He ultimately settled in London, and took an active part in its musical life. In 1819 he was appointed organist at Westminster Abbey and conducted festivals at Birmingham, York, Derby and elsewhere. He seems to have enjoyed royal patronage for on one occasion George, Prince of Wales, said to him, ' My father (George III) is Rex, but you are Greater Rex.'

384, 388, 478—Angels' Song.

ANGELS' SONG, or, more correctly, SONG 34, is by Orlando Gibbons, set to Wither's versification of Luke ii. 13 :

> Thus Angels sung, and thus sing we;
> To God on high all glory be;
> Let Him on earth His peace bestow,
> And unto men His favour show.

Hence the name of the tune. SONG 9 (PALATINE) is practically the same tune with two additional lines. (See No. 24.)

385—Tytherton.

TYTHERTON is by Lewis Renatus West, a contemporary and friend of C. I. Latrobe (composer of FULNECK, No. 440). West was educated at the Moravian school at Fulneck, near Leeds, and after many changes took charge of the Moravian Church at Tytherton, Wilts. He died in 1826 and was interred in the burial ground attached to the church.

386—Wilton.

WILTON, by Samuel Stanley, is from the same source as SIMEON, No. 301.

387—Warwick.

WARWICK, by Samuel Stanley, is from the same source as SIMEON, No. 301.

388—Angels' Song. See No. 384.

389—Warrington.

WARRINGTON is by Ralph Harrison, who was the eldest son of the Rev. William Harrison, minister of a Society of Protestant Dissenters in the Derbyshire village of Chinley. Ralph was born in 1748, and at the age of sixteen he was sent to Warrington Academy, where he remained several years, becoming a tutor during his last two years. This Academy was the cradle of Unitarianism in the eighteenth century, and though it only existed for twenty-nine years, many famous men passed through it. The head tutor was Dr. Aikin, whose daughter, Mrs. Barbauld, is still remembered as the authoress of the famous *Hymns in Prose for Children*, and the equally famous *Evenings at Home*.

After leaving Warrington, Ralph Harrison had charge of an Independent chapel at Shrewsbury for two years, and he then accepted an invitation to the pastorate at Cross Street Chapel, Manchester, in 1771, remaining there for forty-three years. He also opened a school for boys, and subsequently took an active part in establishing the Manchester Academy in 1786, serving as classical tutor for the first three years of its existence.

It is certain that Harrison took a great interest in music, though we have no evidence that he ever received any training in the art. However, he gave practical evidence of his appreciation of the value of psalm-singing by publishing in 1784 a collection of psalm-tunes under the name *Sacred Harmony*, and this was followed by a second series issued seven years later.

In a somewhat lengthy introduction, Harrison declares that he ' boasts no extraordinary talent in music, and is sensible how much better qualified many others are for the undertaking; but as they have in general thought proper to decline it, his attempt will be the more excusable,' and he hopes his collection will contribute to assist and improve this pleasing part of worship.

The first part contains ' the more easy tunes, and such as are suitable to congregations in general,' whilst in the second part he includes ' tunes in a greater diversity of style, more fit for practitioners or choirs of singers.' ' I have,' he says, ' purposely avoided those more light and flimsy airs which debase the subject to which they belong, are principally recommended by novelty, and whilst they are the most difficult to be learned, soonest cloy and satiate.'

Sacred Harmony was well received by the Press. Here is a contemporary notice :

This work is much more correct than publications of this sort usually are. The introduction is written with great clearness and good sense . . . and several of the tunes by the author do him credit.

In his collection Harrison inserted some of his own compositions, but only two of them—WARRINGTON (L.M.) and CAMBRIDGE (No. 234, S.M.) have survived. The former is a fine bold melody which will deservedly have a long lease of life. Many of the old psalm-tunes are included, nor was Harrison averse to adaptations, for he calls Arne, Handel, Corelli, Purcell and others to his aid. Here we find the opening theme of ' O Father whose almighty power ' (*Judas Maccabaeus*) arranged as a six-lines-eights. Several tunes already in print he helped to popularize, such as MELCOMBE, MONTGOMERY, DARWALL'S and DURHAM (or HUDDERSFIELD, S.M.). Harrison remained in office at Cross Street till his death in 1810.

390—Mount Sion.

MOUNT SION is adapted from the Andante movement of an instrumental quartet by I. J. Pleyel.

Ignaz Josef Pleyel was born at a village in Lower Austria in 1757. After studying under Haydn for some years he went to Italy, staying there six years. On returning he was made Kapellmeister at Strasburg Cathedral. In 1791 he was invited to conduct some concerts in London, when he suddenly found himself brought into rivalry with his old master Haydn. The strife between the supporters of the two musicians was keen whilst it lasted; but in the end Pleyel's supporters retired defeated. Haydn felt no jealousy towards his rival, nor was the quarrel of Pleyel's doing. ' I go to all his concerts,' said Haydn, ' for I love him.' Pleyel returned to Paris and settled there as a music publisher. He started a piano factory in 1807, and the inscription,

'Pleyel, Wolff and Co.' is still to be seen on pianos. Pleyel produced a vast amount of instrumental music but nearly all of it is now forgotten.

391—Baca.

BACA, by the Rev. W. H. Havergal, is in his *Hundred Psalm and Hymn-Tunes* (1859). It was composed in 1841. There is a reference to the tune in the *Memorials of Frances Ridley Havergal*. She heard it sung in church to her own hymn, and wrote to a friend :

> I was so overwhelmed on Sunday at hearing three of my hymns touchingly sung at Perry Church. I never before realized the high privilege of writing for 'the great congregation,' especially 'I gave My life for thee' to the tune BACA.

392—St. Patrick.

ST. PATRICK is adapted and arranged by Sir Charles Stanford from an air (No. 1048) in the *Complete Petrie Collection,* arranged to be sung to 'The Hymn of St. Bernard, *Jesu dulcis memoria.*'

392—Deirdre.

DEIRDRE is from *The English Hymnal,* where it is said to be 'adapted from an ancient Irish melody,' possibly No. 139 in the 'Petrie' collection.

393—Ich Halte Treulich Still. See No. 363.

394 (i)—Just as I am.

JUST AS I AM was written by Sir Joseph Barnby for the *Home and School Hymnal* (1892).

394 (ii)—Howcroft.

HOWCROFT was written for the Supplement (1912) to the *Primitive Methodist Hymnal,* by George Trotter.

Born in Stockton-on-Tees in 1866, he was for some time organist at the Primitive Methodist church in Paradise Row, Stockton (where his father-in-law, Mr. J. Howcroft Riley, was conductor for half a century). Besides HOWCROFT he wrote two other tunes for the *Primitive Methodist Hymnal Supplement,* and has composed songs that have proved popular in the north of England. The Rev. J. G. Bowran (' Ramsey Guthrie ') said of him, ' We have heard very few who were able to enter into the thought and spirit of hymns as he could do.' He died in 1917.

395—Shipston.

SHIPSTON is adapted from an old melody described as from Warwickshire in *English County Songs* (Broadwood and Maitland, 1893). These ascriptions to counties, or to localities in the case of traditional songs are somewhat indefinite; for example, Shipston-on-Stour, which apparently gives its name to the tune, is not in Warwickshire. The song is known as ' Bedlam City,' also as ' Don't you see my Billy coming?' and tells of the lament of a maiden for her Billy, who was slain in the war. She has a vision of him ' surrounded by clouds of glory and guardian angels.'

396—Skelmorlie.

SKELMORLIE was contributed to the *Methodist Hymn-Book* (1904) by the Rev. W. F. Moulton, an amateur musician of wide knowledge and considerable attainments. He learnt music from Dr. A. H. Mann, organist of King's College, Cambridge, and gained considerable facility as a player. He served on the committee for selecting the music for the *Methodist School Hymnal* (1910). He was associated with Cliff College for eleven years previous to his death in 1929.

19

397—Calvary.

CALVARY, by Samuel Stanley, is from the same source as SIMEON, No. 301.

398—Nutbourne.

NUTBOURNE is from the *Sarum Hymnal*, edited by Aylward in 1870.

Theodore E. Aylward belonged to a musical family in Salisbury. His father was organist of St. Martin's Church in that city, and also had a wide knowledge of instruments from an organ to a concertina. He had nine sons and daughters, seven of whom entered the musical profession, in which they all distinguished themselves. Thus 'T.E.' born in 1844, was brought up in a musical atmosphere, and distinguished himself as a trombonist in a volunteer band that his father conducted. At the age of eighteen he was articled to S. S. Wesley, who was then at Winchester Cathedral. Wesley, according to Mr. Aylward, did not do much directly to teach his pupils, but he let them watch and observe, and his uncertain ways gave them constant opportunities. They never knew, for example, if he would turn up at a service, and thus they had to be always ready to take the organ stool. Wesley at this time was organist of Winchester College as well as of the Cathedral, and it was Mr. Aylward's duty to play at the College service on Saturday evening and at two services on Sunday which took place before and after the Cathedral services.

When Wesley moved to Gloucester Aylward went with him, and assisted him in arranging for the Three Choirs Festival. Aylward's first appointment was at St. Matthew's, Cheltenham, whence he moved to St. Columba's, Rathfarnham. After a brief stay he returned to Salisbury to succeed his father at St. Martin's. Earl Nelson, whose seat was a short distance from the city, was just then compiling the *Sarum Hymnal*, and he appointed Aylward as his musical editor. For this work he wrote his tune NUTBOURNE, and other contributors were Barnby, Stainer and Goss. Having finished this work Aylward went to Cardiff, and for six years was organist at Llandaff Cathedral. He also formed the Cardiff Choral Society, which he conducted till 1876, when he was appointed organist of Chichester Cathedral. After eleven years he once more returned to Cardiff, where he spent the remainder of his long life, being for some time organist at St. George's Church. He was actively engaged in the Cardiff Festivals of 1892 and 1895 and also in 1902. He died in his ninetieth year in 1933.

399—Morna.

MORNA is from *Original Church Music*, by C. H. Perrot, of Sheffield, published in 1873. Six years later he issued another collection called *Cantica Ecclesiae Nova*, which contained forty-eight tunes set chiefly to peculiar metres. Perrot completed this work whilst he was living at Rotherham. The latest information gives his dates as 1842-1910.

400—Consecration.

CONSECRATION (or PATMOS) is by the Rev. W. H. Havergal, and is from his *Psalmody* (1871). It is the 'proper' tune for his daughter's 'Take my life and let it be.'

The music to which Miss Havergal invariably sang this hymn, and with which it was always associated in the publications over which she had any influence, was her father's tune, PATMOS, and the family's desire is that this course may be followed by others. (*Julian*, p. 1114.)

It is not quite clear why the name CONSECRATION has been substituted for PATMOS in the present book.

401—Nativity. See No. 85.

402—Faith of our Fathers.

FAITH OF OUR FATHERS is from *Catholic Hymn-Tunes*, a set of original compositions by Augustus Edmonds Tozer, who was born at Sutton, Cheshire, in 1857. He studied music at the R.A.M., and also the National Training School for Music (which in 1882 became the R.C.M.). Brought up as a Congregationalist, the music of the Anglican Church attracted him, influenced largely by attending the services at Westminster Abbey. He was organist at St. Mary Magdalene, St. Leonard's-on-Sea, and also at St. Gregory's Priory Church, Cheltenham. He gradually drifted into the Roman Catholic Church, and was appointed music director at the Church of the Sacred Heart, Brighton. The work that he did for his newly-adopted church was recognized by Pope Leo XIII, who conferred on him the order of Chevalier of the Pontifical Order of St. Sylvester. He died in 1910. He published a good deal of church music, edited the *Catholic Church Hymnal*, and was associated with his friend (but no relation), Dr. Ferris Tozer, of Exeter, in ' A Book of Solutions of Examination Exercises.' Dr. A. E. Tozer was a man of great ability and remarkable diligence. In May, 1895, he passed his examination as a Bachelor of Music at Oxford. He at once set to work on the exercise for his doctorate. It was accepted, and he passed the final Mus.D. examination in November of the same year, a very unusual performance. According to the conditions at Oxford he could not proceed to the doctor's degree for five years after taking the bachelor's degree, so he had to wait about four and a half years before having the doctor's degree conferred.

403—Christ for Me.

CHRIST FOR ME is probably adapted from a German volkslied. There are several tunes of similar character in Erk's *Lieder-Schatz*, Vol. I, especially the Swabian MADELE, RUCK, RUCK, RUCK, dated 1828, which has a refrain in waltz-time which was probably danced as well as sung. Another revival tune sung to CHRIST FOR ME was the Tyroler-lied WANN I IN DER FRUH AUFSTEH' (1814), with yodel refrain, known in England (but without the yodelling) as PRETTY POLLY HOPKINS. There seems to have been an invasion of these volkslieder tunes about the middle of last century. The last-named is in Richard Weaver's *Tune-Book* (1862).

404—David's Harp.

DAVID'S HARP, by J. Daniel, first appeared in *The Psalmist* (1842) with the name BROADMEAD. Its inclusion in the *Bristol Tune-Book* (1863) called attention to the tune, and it was selected for the *Methodist Tune-Book* in 1876. Nothing is known at present of the composer, but the original name of the tune suggests that he had some connexion with Broadmead, a district in Bristol.

405—God be in my Head.

GOD BE IN MY HEAD, by Sir H. Walford Davies, was first published in leaflet form in 1910. It was included in the 1912 Festival Service Book of the London Church Choir Association for use at St. Paul's Cathedral, and has since been used in several similar collections. It was included in the *Fellowship Song-Book* (1915) and subsequently in *Hymns of the Kingdom* and *A Student's Hymnal*. The present *Methodist Hymn-Book* is the first church hymnal to contain the melody.

406—Harwich. See No. 66.

407—Hungerford.

HUNGERFORD is from *The Hallelujah*, a collection of tunes originally formed by J. J. Waite in 1842, an enlarged edition being published in four parts in 1849, edited by Dr. Gauntlett, who wrote a number of tunes for it, but with unusual modesty, omitted to put his name to them.

The good work done by the Rev. John J. Waite in promoting congregational singing throughout the country deserves permanent record. Born at Hereford in 1808, he devoted himself so energetically to work in his youth that the strain proved too much for him, and he became totally blind before he was eighteen. He entered the ministry of the Congregational Church, and held pastorates at Ilminster and Hereford. Being very fond of music, he observed with regret the indifference of many congregations to the musical part of the service, and he determined to devote his life and substance to the advancement of congregational psalmody. As he was unable to find amongst existing tune-books any particular one that would suit his purpose, he issued from his house in Bristol the first edition of his *Hallelujah*, or *Devotional Psalmody*. In a long essay prefixed to this book he enunciated the principles on which he proposed to work, the most novel being his suggestion that the congregation should be taught to sing in parts. It contained tunes of a more severe type than was common in the middle of last century. He held meetings throughout the country at various Nonconformist churches for the advancement of harmonized hymn-singing, making use of a system of numbers, by which he maintained that any one could soon learn to sing at sight. He had a great objection to tunes in triple time, and altered BEDFORD and others in accordance with his views. Waite, who was singularly patriarchal in appearance, died in his sixtieth year in 1868.

408, 949—St. Bernard.

ST. BERNARD is generally ascribed to John Richardson, but Messrs. Cowan and Love point out that he may have adapted it from the following melody in a Cologne tune-book of 1741 :

John Richardson was born in Preston in 1816. He was educated at the Catholic day-schools in Fox Street, and was for a time a chorister at St. Wilfrid's Catholic Church. At the age of thirteen he went to Liverpool, where his fame as an alto singer had preceded him, and he was engaged at St. Nicholas' Catholic Church. He was apprenticed to Mr. Gillow, a house decorator, but his love for music was too great to allow him to enter thoroughly into trade, and on the expiration of his apprenticeship he commenced teaching music in 1836. In the previous year he had been appointed organist of St. Mary's, and after holding that appointment for two years he returned to St. Nicholas, this time as organist, a position he held for twenty years. During this period he was prominent in the musical life of Liverpool, and many well-known local musicians received their training at his hands, amongst whom may specially be mentioned two who have since attained world-wide renown, W. T. Best and Sir Charles Santley.

Richardson won the prize of the Liverpool Catch and Glee Club for his glee, ' O fill the wine-cup high,' and for which he also received a silver snuff-box from an admiring circle of friends. At the opening of the Sailors' Home in Liverpool by H.R.H. the Prince Consort, he was commissioned to write a song, ' Speed me on,' for the occasion, which was sung by Mrs. Shand, and produced a great effect. In 1844 he was appointed music-master at St. Edward's College, and continued in that position for thirteen years. During his residence in Liverpool he composed a large quantity of music for

church use, and also edited a collection of motets, hymns,
vespers and other compositions, which were issued in
three books and dedicated to the Right Hon. Lord
Arundel of Wardour. He also composed several pieces
at the special request of Cardinal Newman, who presented him with a magnificent ring in acknowledgement
of his talents. Similar presentations were made to him
by His Holiness the late Pope Pius IX and by Cardinal
Wiseman, in recognition not only of his musical genius,
but also of his great services to the Catholic Church.
After upwards of thirty years' residence and active life
in Liverpool, his health broke down. A great domestic
calamity overtook him, his wife and two children falling
victims to scarlet fever. After a severe illness he gave
up his engagements in Liverpool, and returned to his
native town in 1860.

At this time the head of the Catholic College at Ushaw,
County Durham, was the Rev. Dr. Newsham, a man of
considerable musical ability and great enthusiasm. At
his invitation Richardson went to reside at Ushaw
College. Two years previously he had set to music an
ode by Cardinal Wiseman for the College jubilee. This
work is laid out in ten movements, all of great beauty.
The first, with its exquisite melody and free running
accompaniment, is very suggestive of Mozart. The whole
work is of a very high order, and were it set to words
more adapted to general use, would well repay revival.

After leaving Ushaw he resided at Warrington for a
time, and whilst here, he wrote music to the first Psalm
(Beatus Vir) for the choir of St. Alban's Church. He
subsequently returned to his native town, where he died
in 1879.

409—Sharon.

Sharon, by T. Wallhead, of Belper, first appeared in
the *Wesleyan Tune-Book* (1876).

410 (i)—Ridge.

Ridge is from Samuel Wesley's *Original Hymn-Tunes*

adapted to every metre in the Collection of the Rev. John Wesley, A.M. (1828). The book contains some fine tunes, and Wesley was so particular about the correct accent of the words, that in many cases he has added alternative bars to fit the changing accent of the verses—an excellent plan in theory, but not perhaps conducive to united congregational singing. Wesley received much praise for his collection, but the financial results were unsatisfactory, which wrung from him his famous declaration :

> If Puncheons, or Pipes, of Flattery, could either have fattened, or enriched a Man, Sir John Falstaff had been a very shrimp, and King Croesus a mere beggar, in comparison of   S. WESLEY.
> *August* 19, 1828.

Samuel Wesley, younger son of the Rev. Charles Wesley, was born at Bristol in 1766. When only three years old he could play and extemporize on the organ, and by the time he was eight years old he knew all Handel's overtures by heart, and composed an oratorio, *Ruth*, which is now preserved in the British Museum. When the father removed to London Sam and his brother commenced a series of subscription concerts in the Marylebone home. When he was in his eighteenth year it was reported that he had joined the Roman Catholic Church, but this he afterwards firmly denied, observing that though their music attracted him to their church, their doctrines had never influenced him. An unfortunate accident in 1787 greatly affected his subsequent career, as he was frequently the victim of long spells of illness and occasionally insanity. From about 1800 onwards, he became deeply interested in the works of J. S. Bach, which were at that time scarcely known in England, and Wesley is now regarded as the first apostle of the great composer's music in this country. In this work he received support from Benjamin Jacob, C. Horn, and V. Novello. Wesley was recognized as the leading organist of his day, but he never held any position of importance. His choral works *In exitu Israel, Confitebor, Exultate Deo,* to mention only a few, place him in the front rank of English church composers. The limitations of the English organ of his time prevented his leaving any important work for the instrument, and his numerous piano pieces were chiefly of a fugitive nature. Shortly before his death he spent an evening with Mendelssohn at Christ Church, Newgate Street. This was on September 12, 1837, and four weeks later he passed away.

410 (ii)—Ascension.

ASCENSION was composed by Gauntlett for the *Wesleyan Tune-Book* (1876). (See No. 7.)

411—Dying Stephen.

DYING STEPHEN is from Lampe's *Hymns on the Great Festivals* (1746), referred to below. It takes its name from the seventh line of the fourth verse of the hymn.

Both John and Charles Wesley were acquainted with several of the leading musicians of their day, but though John found little time to devote to their company, his brother evidently keenly enjoyed their society, and in few homes did he find more of the flow of soul than in that of John Rich, the proprietor of the Theatre Royal, Covent Garden, and inventor of that once popular form of entertainment known as pantomime, with all its delights of harlequin and columbine.

For his second wife Rich married a widow named Stevens, who, from being a barmaid at a coffee-house, had become Rich's housekeeper. At one time she had been an actress, but after hearing a sermon preached by Charles Wesley at West Street Chapel she had renounced the stage, much to her husband's disgust. Subsequently, however, Rich approved of the change, and even accepted some of the tenets of Methodism, which caused Smollett to assert that 'the poor man's head, which was not naturally very clear, had been disordered with superstition, and he laboured under the tyranny of a wife and the terror of hell-fire at the same time.'

It was in Rich's house that Charles Wesley was introduced to John Frederick Lampe (pronounced 'Lampeh'), who was connected with the Theatre Royal, and this acquaintanceship had important results on Methodist psalmody. Born in Saxony in 1703, Lampe seems to have had a careful and complete musical training, and although we know practically nothing of his early life, it is evident that when he came to this country at the age of twenty-three his musical talents were promptly recognized, and he at once received an appointment as bassoon player at Covent Garden Theatre, and also in Handel's band, while tradition says that he had the reputation of being one of the finest players of the time on his instrument.

Rich, who had an aptitude for discovering talent, soon found that his bassoon player was capable of higher flights. A successful playwright of the time was Henry Carey, whose reputation still flourishes on the strength of the 6-8's hymn-tune CAREY'S (see No. 349), and the ballad, 'Sally in our Alley.' He was not only a prolific writer of music, but he was a skilled librettist, and consequently Rich introduced him to Lampe in order that the two might collaborate. The association proved remarkably successful, the partnership bearing an imperfect resemblance to the Gilbert and Sullivan combination of recent years. Their most successful attempt was *The Dragon of Wantley,* a clever and amusing skit on the Italian operas of the time.

Towards the close of 1745 Lampe was brought into touch with the Methodist movement. Writing in his diary under the date November 29, 1745, John Wesley says : 'I spent an hour with Mr. Lampe, who had been a deist for many years, till it pleased God by the "Earnest Appeal" to bring him to a better mind.'

It is not necessary here to follow out the development

of Lampe's religious opinions, but it is pretty certain that he found the companionship of Charles Wesley more congenial than that of his brother, as both poet and musician had naturally much in common, and the acquaintance thus begun soon ripened into close friendship. Lampe now turned to a form of composition to which, so far, he had been a stranger. Acting on a suggestion of Charles Wesley's, he set two dozen of the poet's hymns to music, and the joint effort was published towards the end of 1746, with the title—

Hymns on the Great Festivals, and other occasions.
   London: Printed for M. Cooper, at the Globe in Paternoster Row, and sold by T. Trye, near Gray's Inn Gate, Holborn; Henry Butler, in Bow Churchyard; the booksellers of Bristol, Bath, Newcastle-upon-Tyne and Exeter; and at the Musick-shops.   1746.

Most of these tunes are in that florid style which might be expected from one who had been associated with the stage; but although they do not seem easy to sing— they are certainly not what we should now call ' congregational '—they took the fancy of the Wesleys and their followers, and every endeavour was made to promote the use of them amongst the ' Societies.'
   There is ample proof that, in spite of their difficulties, it is evident that they soon became popular. Charles Wesley, writing to a friend in December, 1746, makes a reference to the composer, and ends up by saying: ' His tunes are universally admired here among the musical men, and have brought me into high favour with them.' In another letter, this time to his wife, who possessed considerable musical ability, he asks her how many of Lampe's tunes she could play, but her answer is not recorded.
   Another proof that Lampe's tunes were popular amongst the Methodists of his time is found in the fact that the *Harmonia Sacra,* a large oblong volume specially issued for use amongst Methodists, contains no less than

twenty tunes by him as well as some of his songs selected from *The Ladies' Amusement,* and which strike one as being somewhat out of place in a Methodist tune-book.

In 1749 Lampe visited Dublin (see under IRISH, No. 503), and two years later he was in Edinburgh, where he died after a brief illness, and was interred in Canongate Churchyard. The memorial stone has now so far crumbled away as to leave the inscription almost illegible. His sudden death was a great grief to Charles Wesley, and he wrote a fine lyric ode in memory of his friend. Here is one of the nine verses :

> Enroll'd with that harmonious throng,
> He hears the unutterable song,
>   The unutterable name;
> He *sees* the Master of the Choir,
> He bows, and strikes the golden lyre,
> And hymns the glorious Lamb.

412—Deliverance.

DELIVERANCE was composed by Dr. Gauntlett for the first edition of *Tunes New and Old* (1864).

413—Harington.

HARINGTON is adapted from a glee by Henry Harrington (originally ' Harington '). He was born at Kelston, about three miles from Bath, in 1727. After graduating at Queen's College, Oxford, he qualified as a doctor of medicine, and settled for a time in Wells. During his student years he devoted much time to music, whilst his poetic talent took shape in several effusions, notably ' The Witch of Wokey,' a legend of the Cheddar Cliffs, which subsequently found a place in Bishop Percy's *Reliques.*

In 1757 he came to Bath, where he spent the remainder of his life, intermingling his professional duties with much music-making, and he also took a prominent part in municipal affairs, serving as mayor of the city in 1793. The Rev. R. Warner, one of Bath's historians, speaks highly of Harrington's charm of manner, which had such an effect on his patients that his visits were in themselves almost as efficacious as his medical prescriptions.

For many years the good doctor was a conspicuous figure in the streets of Bath, recognized everywhere by his well-defined features and his eccentric, old-fashioned garb. Tall, thin, and with an inclination to stoop as he walked, he looked older than his age warranted. He wore the triangular hat and the powdered, full-bottomed wig of an earlier period, the whole of his suit—his court dress, deep-pocketed waistcoat, and knee breeches—were all cut from the same sombre-hued cloth, and when he went out walking he invariably held his handkerchief to his mouth as a perpetual preventive against chills.

This description of him does not seem to suggest that there was a vein of humour lurking beneath such a solemn exterior, but such is the case. Many of his glees, catches, and other vocal music are set to humorous verses as, for example, his 'Laughing catch,' and another describing the excitement caused amongst the bath-chairmen and the pump-room waiters on seeing a new visitor arrive. His 'What shall we sing,' was written after hearing 'Non nobis Domine' sung incorrectly. The music has a comic effect, representing three blundering singers who get wrong at the start, and then proceed to blame each other, each insisting that he is right, and the others wrong. His serious glees include 'Retirement,' from which the present tune is adapted. He died in 1816.

414—Holly.

HOLLY (or HOLLEY) is by George Hews. He was for a time concerned in a piano factory in Boston, U.S.A., and took a prominent part in the musical life of the city. He died in 1873 in his sixty-eighth year.

415—Mit Freuden Zart.

MIT FREUDEN ZART is from the same source as ATONEMENT (No. 181), but it has been much altered from its original form.

416—Charterhouse.

CHARTERHOUSE is by Alexander Samuel Cooper. Born in London in 1835, he became a pupil of Dr. E. J. Hopkins and also studied the piano under Charles Hallé. In 1855 he was appointed organist at Trinity College, Glenalmond, and two years later succeeded H. S. Irons at St. Columba's College, Rathfarnham. Subsequently he held several organist's appointments at various London churches, and in 1880 became organist at St. Paul's, Covent Garden. For two years (1866-68) he was organist at Tonbridge Grammar School. He died in 1900.

417—Normandy.

NORMANDY is by Chrétien Bost, a Swiss historian and divine. He was a minister at the Evangelical Church at Geneva. He published a *History of Christianity,* and also a *History of Brethren of Bohemia and Moravia.* The tune first appeared in *Chants Chrétiens* (1833).

418—Samson.

SAMSON is adapted from the chorus, 'Then round about the starry throne' in Handel's oratorio *Samson* (1742).

419—Binchester.

BINCHESTER, by Dr. W. Croft, is from *The Divine Companion,* 2nd edition (1709).

420, 788—St. Merryn.

ST. MERRYN was written by H. A. Harding at the request of the committee for the 1904 *Methodist Hymn-Book.*

Harry Alfred Harding was born at Salisbury in 1856. From boyhood he practised the piano diligently, sometimes devoting eight or nine hours daily to his work. When about fourteen he obtained his first engagement, undertaking to act as accompanist to a travelling pantomime company, but this he soon relinquished. He then had organ lessons from Dr. C. W. Pearce, and in his seventeenth year he was appointed organist at Sidmouth parish church. He stayed here sixteen years, availing himself of holiday periods to further his knowledge of music under good masters. After declining an offer to go to Philadelphia, he was appointed organist of St. Paul's Church, Bedford. He soon took a prominent part in the musical life of the town, and for many years held a distinguished position in the borough. In 1907 he was appointed Hon. Secretary of the Royal College of Organists. His compositions include church music and a cantata, *Mucius Scaevola*, and he wrote some theoretical works. He died in 1930.

421—I am so Glad.

I AM SO GLAD is also known as JESUS LOVES EVEN ME. It is by P. Bliss, and was composed by him for an American collection called *The Crown* (1871). A version harmonized by Sir Joseph Barnby was published in the *Bible Christian Sunday-school Hymnal* (1892), though he found the task rather difficult.

422—Blessed Assurance.

BLESSED ASSURANCE is by Mrs. Joseph Fairchild Knapp. See No. 331.

423—Constance.

CONSTANCE, by Arthur Sullivan, appeared in the *New Church Hymn-Book* (1874).

424—Mount Ephraim.

MOUNT EPHRAIM, by Benjamin Milgrove, is from the same source as No. 66.

425—Springtide Hour.

SPRINGTIDE HOUR was written by Sir Joseph Barnby for the *Methodist Sunday-School Tune-Book* (1881). It is named from the first words of J. S. B. Monsell's hymn :

> The springtide hour
> Bears leaf and flower.

426—Laudate Dominum.

LAUDATE DOMINUM, by Sir H. H. Parry, is a successful adaptation of the final chorus of his anthem, ' Hear my words, ye people.' It was published as a hymn-tune in the second supplement of *Hymns Ancient and Modern* (1916).

427—Wiltshire. See No. 57.

428—Monmouth.

MONMOUTH is by Gabriel Davis who, whilst living at Portsea, published about 1800 his *Sacred Music*, which contained ' Forty Psalm-tunes of various measures,' besides other music. MONMOUTH is from this work and appears as a long metre tune in the key of F. Nothing is known of Davis except that he was leader of the music in the Baptist Chapel at Portsea. His enthusiasm for psalmody is evident from the fact that he was a subscriber to Dixon's *Psalmodia Christiana,* published in 1789.

429 (i)—God of my Life.

GOD OF MY LIFE. This melody, a study in five-four time, first appeared in a collection of the Rev. F. Luke Wiseman's tunes made at the suggestion of the late Rev. W. F. Moulton, and issued in 1915 under the title *Songs of the Twelve Hours.*

Melodies in quintuple measure were formerly of rare occurrence. Examples are found in Handel's *Orlando,* Chopin's *Sonata in C minor,* and elsewhere. Tartini, in

20

his *Trattato di musica* (1754) says that 'quintuple pro-
portion is useless in melody and cannot be performed,'
but he obviously knew nothing about folk-songs, in
which the rhythm frequently occurs.   It is used by
William Reeve, organist of St. Martin, Ludgate, at the
words, 'Come, stain your cheeks with nut and berry' in
his *Gypsies Glee* (1796). H. C. Banister, in his *Text-
book of Music,* refers to an irregular measure of five
crotchets in Mendelssohn's 'Rivulet' Rondo.   Mr.
Wiseman's experiment is probably one of the earliest to
appear in a collection of hymn-tunes.

429 (ii)—Heaton Norris.

HEATON NORRIS is by John Grimshaw, a Manchester
musician and probably a local organist who published a
book of tunes early last century. The collection was
dedicated to the Rev. J. Clewes, rector of St. John's
Church, so it is quite possible that Grimshaw was
organist at that church.

430—Giessen.

GIESSEN is from the *Comprehensive Tune-Book*
(1851), which was edited by Dr. Gauntlett, and the tune
may possibly be by him, though no composer's name is
attached. It was originally called HOXTON.

431 (i)—Love Divine.

LOVE DIVINE (or BEECHER) is by John Zundel, who
was born in 1815 at Hochdorf. He received a thorough
training in music, gained experience as organist in a
Lutheran Church at St. Petersburg, and also acted
as bandmaster of the Imperial Horse Guards.   In
October, 1847, he crossed to America and became
organist at the First Unitarian Church in Brooklyn.
After another appointment he became organist of
Plymouth Church in Brooklyn. During the twenty-eight
years at this church he resigned and then returned on
three separate occasions. After another appointment at

Michigan he returned to his native country, where he died at Cannstadt in 1882. Zundel was closely associated with Henry Ward Beecher, and they prepared two hymnals for use at the Plymouth Church. The first was *Temple Melodies* (1851), but it did not meet with Beecher's approval, partly because many of the hymns were selected without his approval. The next venture was the *Plymouth Collection,* a massive work which had a wide circulation, though at first it was greeted with storms of protest owing to the admission of hymns by Roman Catholic poets. The selection of tunes was made by Charles Beecher, brother of the church minister, but Zundel was the responsible musical editor, and, as editors are prone to do, he included twenty-eight of his own tunes. That Beecher had a high opinion of his organist is evident from his testimony that 'Mr. Zundel has co-operated with me for nearly twenty years in building up congregational singing in Plymouth Church.'

431 (ii)—Bithynia.

BITHYNIA (or CORINTH) is by Samuel Webbe (see No. 75). This unfortunate tune has not yet recovered from the surgical operation it underwent before admittance into the *Methodist Hymn-Book* (1904). The original form of the sixth line was :

and organists and singers of an older generation will always so sing it.

432—St. Bees.

ST. BEES was composed by Dr. Dykes for Chope's *Congregational Hymn and Tune-Book* (1862), in which it was set to Bishop How's hymn, 'Jesus, name of wondrous love.' It was adapted to Cowper's hymn, 'Hark my soul,' in *Hymns Ancient and Modern* (1875).

433, 447—Aldersgate Street.

ALDERSGATE STREET and HAMPSTEAD (No. 767), were composed by Dr. E. F. Horner for the 1904 edition of the *Methodist Hymn-Book*.

Egbert Foster Horner studied music under Sir F. Bridge. He was organist at St. John's Church, Westminster, and became closely associated with Trinity College, London, and other educational undertakings. He acted as one of the examiners in music at Durham and London, and in 1928 was appointed Dean of the Faculty of Music at London University. His compositions were confined to organ and church music. He died in 1928.

434—Allgütiger, Mein Preisgesang.

ALLGÜTIGER, MEIN PREISGESANG, by G. P. Weimar, is from his *Choral-melodien Buch,* published at Erfurt in 1803, which contains a few other compositions of his own, besides this tune. The composer, Georg Peter Weimar, was born at Stotternheim, Saxe Weimar, in 1734. After receiving instruction from local professors he became a court musician, and also a cantor at Erfurt, and music director of the Gymnasium. He composed church music and cantatas, and vocal exercises. He died in 1800, and his collection of chorals was edited by J. C. Kittel, one of the last pupils of J. S. Bach. It is said that Kittel inherited a full-length portrait of Bach, and that when his pupils satisfied him he would draw aside the curtain and reveal the portrait as the best reward he could offer them.

435—Lovest Thou Me?

LOVEST THOU ME? was composed by the Rev. F. L. Wiseman for the *Methodist School Hymnal* (1910).

436—It Passeth Knowledge.

IT PASSETH KNOWLEDGE, by I. D. Sankey (see No. 171), is from an American publication called *Gospel Hymns* (c. 1883).

437—My Jesus I Love Thee.

MY JESUS I LOVE THEE. This tune does not appear to have any history, and the composer and origin are alike unknown.

438, 755—St. Chrysostom.

ST. CHRYSOSTOM, by Sir Joseph Barnby, originally appeared in the *Musical Times* for December, 1871. In the following year it was inserted in Messrs. Novello's *Hymnary,* of which Barnby was editor.

439, 774—Saffron Walden.

SAFFRON WALDEN, by A. H. Brown (see No. 302) appeared in the *Hymnal Companion* (1890).

440—Fulneck.

FULNECK, by C. Ignatius Latrobe, first appeared in Seeley's *Devotional Harmony* (1806), where it is called MARYLEBONE. It was originally in triple time. Editors of subsequent hymnals tried to improve on this, and after appearing in a hybrid condition—the first two lines in common time and the last four in triple—it finally emerged in common time, and is thus found in most modern hymnals. The *Moravian Liturgy* (1914) retains the triple time. The tune takes its name from Fulneck, in Yorkshire, where some of the Moravian Brethren from Fulneck in Moravia established a settlement in 1748. Here Latrobe was born in 1758. He possessed great musical ability, and amongst other works he published six volumes of *Selections of Sacred Music from the Works of the most eminent composers of France and Germany.* A large number of fine compositions were thus introduced into this country for the first time. He died at the Moravian Settlement in Fairfield, near Manchester, in 1836.

Latrobe was intimate with the leading musicians of his time, and he has left an interesting account of a visit Haydn paid to him.

'When he entered the room he found my wife alone, and as she could not speak German, and he had scarcely picked up a few English words, both were at a loss what to say. He bowed with foreign formality, and the following short explanation took place:

'H.—"Dis, Mr. Latrobe house."

'The answer was in the affirmative.

'H.—"Be you his Woman?"

'"I am Mrs. Latrobe," was the reply.

'After some pause he looked round the room and saw his picture, to which he immediately pointed and explained: "Dat is me. I am Haydn!" My wife instantly, knowing what a most welcome guest I was honoured with, sent for me to a house not far off and treated him with all possible civility. He was meanwhile amused with some fine specimens of Labrador spar on the chimney-piece, which he greatly admired, and accepted of a polished slab. Of course, I hastened home, and passed half an hour with him in agreeable conversation.'

441—Dominica.

Dominica, by H. S. Oakeley, was written for the revised edition of *Hymns Ancient and Modern* (1875). Sir Herbert Stanley Oakeley was born at Ealing Vicarage in 1830. He soon gave evidence of musical gifts, and especially of his fine sense of pitch. He was educated at Rugby, and after a short period at Bath he went to Christ Church, Oxford, and for four years took a prominent part in the musical life of the University. After leaving he spent some years as musical critic of the *Guardian*, and in touring in foreign countries. On one of his expeditions he met with an accident in the Alps which made him practically a one-legged organist for the rest of his life. In 1865 he was appointed Reid Professor of Music at Edinburgh, defeating such notable candidates as Stainer, George Macfarren, Gauntlett and Hullah, the last-named running Oakeley very close. It was said that he owed his election to the casting vote of W. E. Gladstone, chairman of the Governors. The appointment was an unpopular one, as he was regarded as an 'amateur,' and he never entirely lived down the opposition caused by his election. But he did his duty worthily, and his lectures and organ recitals did much to popularize the instrument when it was regarded with suspicion in Scotland. He resigned his professorship in 1891, and died twelve years later. He wrote a good deal of music for church use, including anthems, services, and hymn-tunes. Many of his anthems have been heard at important functions, and his EVENING AND MORNING is still highly esteemed. His well-known Quadruple Chant was composed in 1853 for use in Canterbury Cathedral, where a memorial brass was erected to his memory in 1907.

442—Lynton.

LYNTON was written by Arthur James Jamouneau for the *Methodist Hymn-Book* (1904). The composer was born in Guernsey in 1865, a descendant of an old Huguenot family. He received his musical education at home, and on coming to England he was for some time a music master in a school in the South. About 1896 he settled in Hull, and devoted all his time to the composition and publication of Sunday-school music and other sacred compositions. For many years he was associated in membership with the Queen's Road Wesleyan Church, Hull, but he never held any appointments as organist. He died in 1927.

443—Loughborough College.

LOUGHBOROUGH COLLEGE was originally written by the composer for his hymn for use on All Saints' Day (' For the brave of every race '). It is taken from *Songs of Praise*. The Rev. George Wallace Briggs was ordained in 1889 after taking a First Class in the Classical Tripos at Cambridge. He was curate at Alverthorpe for two

years before going to sea as a naval chaplain. He was
subsequently tutor at the London College of Divinity
and vicar of St. Andrew's, Norwich. He has been
rector of Loughborough since 1918 and canon of
Leicester since 1922. He is a proctor in Canterbury
Convocation, and has been Select Preacher at Cambridge.
In March, 1934, he was appointed to a vacant canonry
at Worcester.

444, 827—Frogmore.

FROGMORE, called by the composer 'a tunelet for a
hymnlet,' was written for the hymn to which it is set
by Sir Walter Parratt for the *Methodist Hymn-Book*
(1904). He was born in 1841 at Huddersfield, where
his father, Mr. Thomas Parratt, and his brother, Mr.
Henry Parratt, held in succession the organistship of
the parish church for the long period of ninety-two
years. As a child Sir Walter first acquired his love for
church music at this church. Then the organ stood in
the west gallery, and with it the mixed choir of something less than a score of grand Yorkshire voices. Mrs.
Sunderland, the famous soprano of the county, was the
leading vocalist. She used to sing 'Comfort ye,' from
the *Messiah*, and it was not an uncommon thing for solos
written for other than soprano voices to be transposed
in order to suit her voice.

At the age of twelve he entered a choir school and
played the organ at St. Peter's Chapel in Pimlico, S.W.,
and on one occasion he even accompanied the anthem at
St. Paul's Cathedral; and also took lessons from George
Cooper (see No. 259). After these adventures the boy
returned to Huddersfield to succeed his brother at St.
Paul's Church. At this period of his life he was
essentially 'Handelian,' and his voluntaries were usually
selected from the oratorios. Mr. Ben Stocks, a former
president of the Huddersfield Choral Society, tells an
interesting story of young Parratt's remarkable memory.
Stocks was a candidate for the position of bass soloist

at St. Paul's Church. He had only one copy of the music, and on arriving at the church he told young Parratt that no other copy was available. He asked to be allowed to look the song over, and then said he thought he could manage without the music. This he did, and afterwards pointed out two notes which Stocks had sung wrong! Parratt failed in his applications for the post of municipal organist both at Newcastle and Leeds, but he found a safe harbour as private organist to Lord Dudley at Witley Court. After seven years' peaceful country life he once more returned to the busy north, this time as organist at Wigan parish church, a position that has been held by many distinguished musicians.

Four years later he succeeded Stainer as organist at Magdalen College, Oxford. His departure from Wigan caused general regret, for his Sunday evening post-service recitals had proved a great attraction. Ten years elapsed and Parratt made his final move, this time to St. George's Chapel, Windsor, as successor to Sir George Elvey, a position he retained till his death in 1924. During his professional career he had many other appointments—Professor of Music at Oxford, and also professor of the organ at the R.C.M., and Master of the King's Music. He was knighted in 1892. Mention should be made both of his marvellous memory and his skill as a chess player. An illustration from Dr. Shinn's *Musical Memory* will illustrate this:

In one of the lodgings attached to St. Michael's College, Tenbury, some eight or ten men were assembled. Von Holst and Sir Walter played on the piano in turn such music as was asked for and always from memory. This went on for some time, when the chess-board was brought out and Sir Walter proposed to play two men in consultation, while he remained at the piano, still playing anything asked for either from Bach, Mozart, Beethoven, Mendelssohn or Chopin. He never looked at the chess-board, but continued to converse with those around, who did all they could to distract him, although without success. His memory never failed for at least an hour, when the game was won by him, and he told us how he had been watching the chances of a poor fly which had become entangled in a spider's web.

445—New 113th. See No. 312.

446—Culross.

CULROSS is one of sixteen ' Common Tunes ' contained in a 1634 edition of the *Scottish Book of Common Order.*

447—Aldersgate Street. See No. 433.

448—St. Margaret.

ST. MARGARET. Dr. A. L. Peace thus related the origin of this tune in a letter to a friend : ' It was composed in 1884 during the time the music of the *Scottish Hymnal,* of which I was the musical editor, was in preparation. I wrote it at Brodick Manse, where I was on a visit to my old friend, Mr. M'Lean. There was no tune of that particular metre available at that time, so I was requested by the Hymnal Committee to write one specially for Dr. Matheson's hymn. After reading it over carefully, I wrote the music straight off, and may say that the ink of the first note was hardly dry when I had finished the tune.' An interesting circumstance may be mentioned. When King Edward was at Cairo he attended service in one of the churches when Matheson's hymn was sung, and so impressed was he with it that he made a special inquiry as to the composer of the tune.

Albert Lister Peace was born at Huddersfield in 1844. He was only nine years old when he was appointed organist at Holmfirth parish church. After holding various other appointments in the neighbourhood he went to Glasgow in 1866 as organist of Trinity Congregational Church. In 1877 he was appointed organist of St. Andrew's Hall, and two years later, of Glasgow Cathedral. After the death of W. T. Best he was appointed (after competition) organist of St. George's Hall, Liverpool. He was fond of retelling an anecdote he heard in his boyhood of the young lady who went into a music shop and asked the assistant for Mozart's *Jemima* symphony. After careful deliberation the young man brought out Mozart's 'G minor' symphony, which proved to be the piece required. Before Peace left Huddersfield he had the honour of playing to S. S. Wesley, who was on a visit to the town. Great was his delight the next day to receive a flattering testimonial from the famous organist.

449—Eden.

EDEN is by T. B. Mason (and not by Lowell Mason), and appeared in *The Sacred Harp* (1836), edited by him. The tune was originally called MONTGOMERY.

Timothy Battle Mason was born at Midfield, Mass., in 1801. He became a professor of music in Cincinnati, and founded an important choral society there. Here he died in 1861.

450—Edgware.

EDGWARE. The 'composer' of this tune is unknown. It appears to be made up of a series of phrases that are familiar to all churchgoers. The tune is taken from the *Primitive Methodist Hymnal* (1889).

451—Sursum Corda.

SURSUM CORDA is by George Lomas, who was born at Birch Hall, Bolton, in 1834. He learnt the elements of music as a chorister, and later he continued his studies under Dr. Steggall for the organ, and Sterndale Bennett for composition. During his residence in London he occasionally acted as deputy organist at various churches. Returning to Lancashire he was organist at Didsbury

parish church, and subsequently at Emmanuel Church,
Barlow Moor (Manchester), where he officiated for
twenty-six years. During this period he took his
bachelor's degree in music at New College, Oxford. He
remained in active work till his death in 1884. His
three tunes in the present book were all composed for
the 1876 edition of *The Bristol Tune-Book*.

452—Stella.

STELLA appeared as a hymn-tune in *Easy Hymn-
Tunes, with the words in full, adapted for Catholic
Schools*. This was edited by Henri Hemy in 1851-52.
The tune is an old one, and was sung to secular words
before reaching the sanctuary. Hemy used to say that
he heard some children singing it when he was in the
village of Stella, near Newcastle, hence its name. Others
maintain that it is called STELLA from the first line of
the hymn to which he set it, ' Hail, Queen of Heaven,
the ocean star,' the name really being ' Stella Maris '
(Star of the sea). In 1858 this tune appeared as
COVENTRY in *The Wesleyan Sunday School Tune-Book*,
set to a hymn of unusual metre:

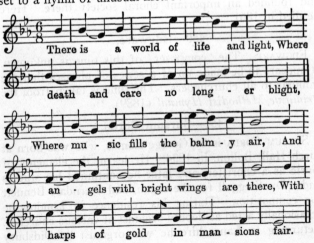

There is a world of life and light, Where
death and care no long - er blight,
Where mu - sic fills the balm - y air, And
an - gels with bright wings are there, With
harps of gold in man - sions fair.

STELLA is well known to the inhabitants of Bath, as it is played on the bells of the Abbey two or three times every Monday morning all the year round. By a slight stretch of the imagination it is not difficult to detect a resemblance between STELLA and 'Bonnie Dundee.'

453—O my Saviour, hear me.

O MY SAVIOUR, HEAR ME, was contributed by Hubert P. Main to *Brightest and Best,* an American Collection published in 1875. The composer was born in 1839 at Ridgefield, Connecticut. For many years he was a member of the music firm of Biglow and Main, founded by his father in New York, and publisher of the Moody and Sankey collections and similar works. He composed music for more than a thousand songs, hymn-tunes and anthems, besides compiling and editing song-books for church and Sunday schools. He was also a great authority on the history of hymns and tunes, and ever ready to supply information about them. After his death in 1925 part of his extensive collection of books was sold to the Newberry Library in Chicago. He was a member of the Methodist Church in Newark.

454—St. Frances.

ST. FRANCES is by G. A. Löhr. Born at Norwich in 1821, he became a chorister at Magdalen College, Oxford, and then returned to Norwich to act as assistant organist to Dr. Buck. In 1845 he was appointed organist at St. Margaret's, Leicester, where he remained till his death in 1897. ST. FRANCES was composed for Bemrose and Adlington's *Chorale Book* (1861).

455, 456—Martyrdom. See No. 201.

457—Arabia.

ARABIA is by W. J. White, an unobtrusive composer of whom little is known. He lived at St. Albans at the beginning of last century, and in or about 1824 published *New Sacred Melodies,* of which a writer in the *Imperial Magazine* said that ' tunes better calculated to inspire a congregation with feelings of true devotion have seldom been seen or heard.' ARABIA is one of the melodies commended thus highly. Another of them, ' Sprowston Lodge,' was frequently heard some years ago, but it has now lost ground.

458, 892—Song 1. See No. 24.

459—St. Dorothea.

ST. DOROTHEA was written for the *Hymnal Companion* by Dr. Charles Vincent. (See No. 243.)

460—Tiverton.

TIVERTON is ascribed to a certain ' Grigg,' but no one appears to have traced him. The tune first appeared in Rippon's *Psalm and Hymn-Tunes* (c. 1795). There are no grounds for assuming that he is the same person as Rev. Joseph Grigg, hymn-writer.

461, 647—Cheshire.

CHESHIRE (originally CHESSHIRE) is from Thomas Este's *Whole Book of Psalmes with their wonted Tunes, as they are sung in Churches,* which was published 1592. The Psalter is important, as it supplies the earliest examples of names being given to tunes. Only three are christened, CHESSHIRE being one of them.

Thomas Este (or Est), music publisher, flourished during the reign of Elizabeth, and produced some remarkable epoch-making works from his press in Aldersgate Street.

462—Ibstone.

IBSTONE was composed by Miss Maria Tiddeman and included in the revised edition of *Hymns Ancient and Modern* (1875). The tune takes its name from the village where the composer's father was rector.

463—Westminster New.

WESTMINSTER NEW was contributed by Dr. Nares to Riley's *Parochial Harmony* (1762), where it is called WESTMINSTER, and included as a ' New Tune.'

James Nares was born at Stanwell, Middlesex, in 1715. He entered the choir of the Chapel Royal, and studied music under Dr. Pepusch. His first appointment was as assistant organist at St. George's Chapel, Windsor, and then, at the early age of nineteen, he was made organist of York Minster in succession to Edward Salisbury. ' What,' said the retiring organist, when the youthful Nares presented himself, ' is that child to succeed me ? ' The ' child ' took an early opportunity of showing what he was capable of, for when a difficult service had been chosen he played it a semitone below the given key, and emerged successfully. On being asked why he did so, he replied that it was only to show what a *child* could do. After twelve years at York, where he made an excellent reputation as a trainer of boys' voices, he was appointed to the Chapel Royal, St. James's, and also Master of the Children. These offices Nares resigned in 1780, and died three years later. He composed a large number of anthems and services, also harpsichord lessons and two treatises in singing.

464—Coleshill.

COLESHILL cannot exactly be called an original conception, as it bears a strong resemblance to other tunes of the period, from which its various parts have apparently been assembled. In its present form it is found in *The Psalmes of David in Metre* (1644), which the editor, the Rev. William Barton, ' set to the best Psalm-Tunes in two parts, viz. Treble and Bass '—to use his own words. Hamish McCunn introduced COLESHILL into his cantata, *The Cameronian's Dream*, produced at Edinburgh in 1890.

465—Leamington.

LEAMINGTON is from Arnold and Callcott's *Psalms* (1791), where it is called LLANDAFF TUNE. It is a tune that has easily adapted itself to the demands made upon it. Starting life as a D.C.M. it has also served as a 6-8's, and is now doing duty as a 7's and 6's. Here is the original melody:

The composer, Dr. Samuel Arnold, was born in London in 1740, and became one of the Children of the Chapel Royal. On entering the musical profession he had ambitions to shine as an operatic composer, but having lost £10,000 by various speculations, he turned his attention to church music, and in 1783 was appointed organist and composer to the Chapel Royal. Ten years later he succeeded Dr. Cooke as organist at Westminster Abbey, doing his work chiefly by the aid of deputies.

Arnold gained such distinction as a composer and conductor that in 1773 he was offered the degree of Mus.B. and Mus.D. by Oxford University, but he declined these honours, preferring to gain his degrees in the ordinary way. Arnold fell in with the custom of his age by writing oratorios, one of which, *The Prodigal Son,* had a short career. When Arnold submitted an exercise for his degree at Oxford, the Professor of Music, Dr. W. Hayes, returned it unopened, saying, ' Sir, it is unnecessary for me to scrutinize an exercise composed by the author of *The Prodigal Son.*'

In 1769 Arnold obtained the lease of the once famous Marylebone Gardens, but though he maintained the music at a high level, he failed to make a success of his bargain, and retired after four years' struggle. His most important works were the editing of Handel's works in forty volumes, which he undertook at the request of George III, and his three volumes of *Cathedral Music,* with a fourth containing the organ parts. Only a few of the numbers in the work have stood the test of time.

466—Pastor.

PASTOR is also known as BREMEN and (from the German hymn for which it was probably originally written) CHRISTUS DER IST MEIN LEBEN. This hymn, with the present tune, is found in *Ein schön geistleich Gesangbuch,* compiled by Melchior Vulpius in 1609.

467—Psalm 32.

PSALM 32. In 1636 George Sandys published his *Paraphrase upon the Psalms of David,* and two years later a second edition was issued containing musical settings by Henry Lawes of some of the versions. The present tune is the setting for Psalm xxxii.

Two more tunes from the same source are used in the present Tune-Book, 472 (BATTLE) and 505 (PSALM 8).

Lawes, who was born at Dinton, in Wiltshire, in 1595, probably inherited his taste for music from his father, Thomas Lawes, who was vicar-choral at Salisbury Cathedral and also organist of St. Martin's Church. Whether the boy was ever a chorister of the Cathedral is not recorded, but in due time his father entrusted his musical education to Giovanni Coprario, a famous musician of those days, who thus disguised his plain

21

English name of John Cooper. The fact that the Earl of Hertford paid for the lad's musical education seems to suggest that the father was already moving in high society, and this introduction served Lawes in good stead, for he was soon able to reckon the daughters, and possibly the sons, of the aristocracy amongst his pupils.

At the age of thirty Lawes was appointed a 'pistler,' i.e. one who reads the Epistle at the Communion Service, an office concerning which little seems to be known, except that the salary attached to it was six shillings and eightpence, though how often it was paid is not recorded. Probably it was an annual salary. Further distinctions awaited him, for he was made a gentleman of the Chapel Royal, and also 'of the private musick to King Charles the First.' He was a staunch Royalist, but his enthusiasm did not lead him to take up arms on behalf of the King. Thus he appears to have escaped the fate which befell so many of Charles's followers during the Commonwealth, and at the Restoration his music found expression in an anthem, 'Zadock the Priest,' which he wrote for the Coronation of Charles II.

Henry Lawes is remembered to-day by his psalm-tunes, but more especially by his association with Milton in the creation of the Masque of Comus, which was performed at Ludlow Castle in 1634. In 1653 he published his first book of *Ayres and Dialogues for One, Two and Three Voices.* Two more books subsequently came out, and Burney declared that the three sets contained 'the choicest songs that have been composed these forty years past.' Praise such as this was rarely awarded by the good doctor, and he evidently thought highly of Lawes.

There is a pleasing vein of sarcastic humour running through Lawes' Preface, which he addresses 'To all Understanders or Lovers of Musick.' He mildly reproves certain publishers who had been pirating his compositions. One of them had printed 'about twenty of my Songs, whereof I had no knowledge till his Book

was in the Presse,' and the pirate had found his invest-
ment so profitable that he was eagerly searching for
more of Lawes' songs. But the composer did not
approve, especially when he found his music being
credited to other composers, or, as he quaintly puts it, ' I
have found many of mine that have walkt abroad in
other men's names; how they came to lose their
Relations and be Anabaptiz'd, I think not worth
examining.' He then goes on to condemn those who are
continually extolling the music of foreigners in
preference to English productions.

But the full resources of his wrath are reserved for
those of his fellow-countrymen who think every language superior to their own native tongue, and so, ' to
make them a little sensible of this ridiculous humour,'
Lawes selected from an index some titles of old Italian
songs, set them to music, and gave out that it came
from Italy ' where it hath passed for a rare Italian song.'
The result seems to have pleased him so much that he
caused it to be printed at the end of his first book of
Ayres with the title ' Tavola,' which merely signifies
' Table of Contents.'

Lawes died in 1662, and was buried in the Cloisters
of Westminster Abbey, but the actual spot is unknown.

468 (i)—Horbury.

HORBURY was composed by Rev. J. B. Dykes whilst on
a visit to a friend at Horbury, near Wakefield, the special
object of his visit being to make his first confession.
The tune first appeared in *Hymns Ancient and Modern*
(1861).

468 (ii)—Nearer to Thee.

NEARER TO THEE was brought over from America
about 1870 by a friend of the Rev. Nehemiah Curnock,
and subsequently introduced into the 1876 *Wesleyan
Tune-Book*. Nothing is known at present about the
composer or the original source of the tune.

468 (iii)—Nearer, my God, to Thee.

NEARER, MY GOD, TO THEE was written by T. C. Gregory (see No. 98) during the summer of 1932. The composer points out that 'it should be sung in the rhythm of speech.'

469—Song 24. See No. 24.

470—Selma. See No. 54.

471—Berkshire. See No. 48.

472—Battle.

BATTLE is by Henry Lawes, from the same source as No. 467. It was originally set to Psalm xxxi. in George Sandy's metrical version, and ought to be so named, like the other tunes (467 and 505) by Lawes. The name BATTLE, which is given to the tune in *Songs of Praise,* is about the most inappropriate that could possibly have been devised.

473—Nettleham.

NETTLEHAM was composed by request for the *Methodist Hymn-Book* (1904) by G. J. Bennett.

Dr. George John Bennett was born at Andover in 1863. He was a chorister in the choir at Winchester College, and in 1878 proceeded to the R.A.M., having won the Balfe scholarship. On leaving he spent three years in Germany, studying for a time under Rheinberger. On returning to England he was appointed a professor at the Royal Academy, and acted as organist at St. John's, Wilton Road (near Victoria Station). In 1895 he succeeded J. M. W. Young as organist at Lincoln Cathedral and from that time took an active part in the musical life of the city. He formed a musical society and organized five Musical Festivals. In 1925 he was elected Sheriff of Lincoln. He was ever ready to place his services at the disposal of others, and readily assisted, either by organ recitals or by wise advice, in advancing the interests of music in the county. He died in 1930.

474—Alverstoke.

ALVERSTOKE was first published in a collection of original tunes by J. Barnby in 1883. The first hymn-book in which it was included seems to have been the *Methodist Free Church Tune-Book* (1892), under the title, ' Still, still with Thee.'

475—I Need Thee.

I NEED THEE, by R. Lowry (see No. 211), is from the *Royal Diadem*, an American publication issued in 1872.

476—Greenland.

GREENLAND is adapted from a *Mass* by Johann Michael Haydn (see No. 251). The history of this tune has been somewhat involved. In the *Wesleyan Tune-Book* (1876) it is set to Cowper's ' Ere God had built the mountains,' but owing, apparently, to a lack of suitable double short metres at the time, it was slightly contracted and then set to a hymn of that metre. In the former case its origin was ascribed to some unknown ' Lausanne Psalter,' but as a D.S.M. Haydn got the credit of it.

477—Gersau.

GERSAU was contributed by L. M. White to the *Methodist Hymn-Book* (1904).

Lewis Meadows White was born in 1860 in the City of London, his father, the Rev. L. B. White, being vicar of St. Mary Aldermary. He learnt music from E. Deane, the organist of St. Mary's. After being trained for the Church he was ordained in 1884 in Norwich Cathedral to the curacy of Cromer. He has been vicar of Potter Heigham and Repps with Bestwick since 1911, and has just (1934) been made an Honorary Canon of

Norwich Cathedral. He has done much musical work in Norfolk, and has frequently given organ recitals at East Coast watering places. His Christmas Carol 'Ye earthly choirs' (words by the composer's brother) won the first prize in a carol competition instituted by the *Organist and Choirmaster* in 1896, and proved very popular.

478—Angels' Song. See No. 384.

479—Hotham.

HOTHAM is by the Rev. Martin Madan, and first appeared in John Wesley's *Sacred Melody* (1765).

Martin Madan was born in 1726, and educated for the legal profession, but gave it up in 1751 and entered the Church. He gained great renown as a preacher, and his aristocratic connexion gave him considerable influence, in spite of his Methodist tendencies. He was also a skilled musician, and appears to have assisted John Wesley when the latter was preparing his *Sacred Melody* in 1765, to which Madan contributed HOTHAM, which was the recognized tune for 'Jesu, lover of my soul' till HOLLINGSIDE appeared in 1861. When Madan wrote it he was minister at the chapel of the Lock Hospital, and under his auspices oratorios were frequently performed there. He made it a rule to commence with a hymn-tune, while another was frequently introduced in the course of the performance. In 1769 Madan published his *Collection of Psalms and Hymn-Tunes, never published before*. This last remark was scarcely correct, as both HOTHAM and HELMSLEY had previously appeared; but another well-known tune here makes its first appearance as 'A Hymn to the Trinity,' now usually known as Moscow (No. 880). Many of the plates from which this work was printed are still in existence. In later life Madan's peculiar views on the subject of marriage got him into trouble, and he retired into private life till his death in 1790. Samuel Wesley (see No. 48) was an intimate friend of his and used frequently to visit him in his retreat at Epsom.

480—Babylon's Streams.

BABYLON'S STREAMS is adapted from a melody in Thomas Campion's *First Book of Ayres,* set to a metrical version of Psalm cxxxii.

> As by the streams of Babilon
> Farre from our native soyle we sat.

It has been much altered from its original form, which certainly did not consist of a string of minims like the present version.

Thomas Campion (or Campian) was a Londoner by birth (c. 1575). He passed through Cambridge without taking a degree, and then, after a long sojourn abroad, he entered the medical profession. What training in music he had there is no record to show, but that he was an accomplished musician is evident from the 'Books of Airs' that he composed. He wrote no music specially for church use. One of his most beautiful songs is 'Never weather-beaten sail.' Its tune was formerly adapted as a 'sevens and sixes' under the name KINGSWOOD (*Wesleyan Tune-Book,* 1876). He died in 1619.

481—Victory.

VICTORY, by Haydn Keeton, was composed by him specially for the 1904 edition of the *Methodist Hymn-Book.*

Dr. H. Keeton was born at Mosborough, near Chesterfield in 1847. His father had been a parish church organist for forty-nine years, and so the boy had an excellent training. He became a chorister at St. George's Chapel, Windsor, where he studied under Sir George Elvey, and also made the acquaintance of Hubert Parry, then a young Etonian. The young chorister was always ready to accept any addition to his somewhat slender income, and he therefore readily closed with Hubert Parry's suggestion that he should, for a fee, make a fair copy of Parry's exercise for his Mus.B. degree.

After two years' teaching in Windsor and the neighbourhood and acting as organist at Datchet Church, he obtained the position of organist at Peterborough Cathedral, and master of the choristers. This position he held till his death in 1921. His output as a composer was limited to a few anthems, but he did important work in assisting Bishop Westcott in producing *The Paragraph Psalter*. He was fond of his garden and greatly enjoyed country life. His friend, Sir Frederick Bridge, once told this story about Keeton:

For many years he came to me in Scotland and enjoyed it greatly, learning to land salmon, and taking a hand in shooting. He had never done much of this, and was a little troublesome sometimes. He was so afraid of catching cold that he would walk about and eat his lunch instead of sitting down with us. This mattered little, but he rather annoyed my keeper more than once. He delighted in shooting a wood, but when placed at the spot to which the game was being driven, he was inclined to march up and down like a sentry, instead of standing motionless. He kept his own blood in circulation, but he also kept the rabbits in circulation, and they ran back towards the beaters, instead of towards Keeton. He liked going to the Scots kirk at Glass, and he was with me when the minister scored off us so well—a story I have told elsewhere. The lady organist was ill. We went and offered to play, and as we took the hymn paper from the parson I said, ' It will be all right; we shall both take part in the playing.' ' Oh! yes,' said my friend the parson, ' It will be all right. We are *no' very particular at Glass* ! '

482—Clarion.

CLARION was written by Myles B. Foster (see No. 147) for the *Congregational Mission Hymnal* (1890).

483—Defiance.

DEFIANCE was composed by Dr. M. L. Wostenholm (see No. 256) for the 'Choir' series of anthems in 1912.

484—From Strength to Strength.

FROM STRENGTH TO STRENGTH, by E. W. Naylor, was composed for the hymn 'Soldiers of Christ, arise' for the *Public School Hymn-Book* (1919).

Dr. Edward Woodall Naylor was the son of John Naylor, organist of York Minster. He was born at Scarborough in 1867 whilst his father was organist at St. Michael's Church in that town. His son was brought up as a chorister under his father at York. On leaving the Minster choir he obtained a choral scholarship at Emmanuel College, Cambridge, and from there he entered the R.C.M. After holding the position of organist at St. Michael's, Chester Square, and St. Mary's, Kilburn, he returned in 1898 to Emmanuel College as organist, and was also a music master at the Leys School. He greatly improved the Emmanuel choir, and wrote services and anthems for their use. His lectures on music gained him considerable reputation, and in 1926 he was appointed University lecturer on musical history. He died in 1934. Dr. Naylor's literary works include *Shakespeare and Music* and *The Poets and Music*. In 1909 he obtained a prize offered by Messrs. Ricordi for an opera, the successful work being called *The Angelus*. A feeble libretto militated against its success. It was revived in 1921.

485—Azmon.

AZMON was written in 1828 by Carl G. Glaser, a native of Wessenfels, Germany, where he was born in 1784. The first instructor of this composer was his father, and later he studied at the Saint Thomas School in Leipzig under Johan Adam Hiller and August Eberhard Muller, who taught him the pianoforte, and Campagnoli, who

taught him the violin. In 1801 he went to Leipzig to
study law, but he was more interested in music than
in briefs, so he gave up jurisprudence and settled in
Barmen, where he spent the remainder of his years as
a teacher of pianoforte, violin and voice. He also
directed choruses and opened a music shop in Barmen,
which he carried on until his death on April 16, 1829.
His compositions were many, including motets, school
songs and instrumental music.

486—Justification. See No. 79.

487—Praise.

PRAISE is from No. 2 of *Four Setts of New Psalm and
Hymn Tunes in three and four parts,* which the com-
poser, Anton Radiger, ' adapted for Divine Worship in
General.' There are twelve tunes in each ' Sett ' (1790).
PRAISE is written for three voices, set to the hymn :

> To Father, Son and Holy Ghost,
> Be praise amid the heavenly host
> And in the Church below.

The composer named his tunes ' from the sentiment of
the hymn,' hence the name ' Praise ' from the second
line.

Radiger was born in 1749 at Chatham, of German
parents who had settled in England. He was a prolific
composer of pianoforte music, songs and hymn-tunes.
He died in 1817.

488—University College.

UNIVERSITY COLLEGE was written by Dr. Gauntlett
for *The Church Hymn and Tune-Book* (1852).

489—Grainger.

GRAINGER was composed by Dr. G. F. Brockless (see
No. 127) for the present (1933) edition of the *Methodist*

Hymn-Book. It is named in memory of the Rev. Grainger Hargreaves, father-in-law of the composer, and a well-known Methodist minister, who died in 1923.

490—Shepton-Beauchamp.

SHEPTON-BEAUCHAMP is an air from Cecil Sharpe's *Folk Songs from Somerset,* sung to the words 'Tarry Trousers' at Shepton-Beauchamp, Somerset, in 1904. There are various versions of the old song, one of them beginning :

> My mother wants me to wed with a tailor,
>   And not give me my heart's delight,
> But give me the man with the tarry trousers,
>   That shine to me like diamonds bright.

Charles Dickens was evidently acquainted with the song, for he makes Captain Cuttle quote the last two lines in greeting his friend, Captain John Bunsby.

491—Camberwell.

CAMBERWELL originally appeared in *The London Tune-Book* (1875). The composer, Joseph McMurdie, was born in 1792. He was a pupil of Dr. Crotch and took an active part in the various musical undertakings of his day. He was a director of the Philharmonic Society. He wrote glees and other part music, and compiled two collections of psalmody. He died in 1878.

492—Holy Rood.

HOLY ROOD, by A. H. Brown (see No. 302) was included in the first (1863) edition of the *Bristol Tune-Book.*

493—Ratisbon.

RATISBON (or JESU, MEINE ZUVERSICHT, ' Jesu, my confidence ') is from the same source as No. 10. The actual composer is unknown. The present form of the tune is much unlike the original.

494—Ein' Feste Burg.

EIN' FESTE BURG. The earliest available source of this melody is in Klug's *Gesangbuch* of 1535. Though not definitely stated there to be by Luther, he is generally acknowledged to be responsible for it. Schweitzer says that it is 'woven out of Gregorian reminiscences,' and one diligent German student has, so he says, traced the various phrases of the chorale to the Roman Gradual. Perhaps so, but whether it is original or not, there is no doubt that Luther is responsible for one of the finest of German chorales. The original form in Klug's Gesangbuch

has undergone modifications, and the form now used is nearly the same as that adopted by J. S. Bach in his cantata, 'Ein' feste Burg.' Luther is said to have composed the chorale at the most critical period of his life; the melody and its hymn spread rapidly throughout Germany, and became the war song of the country. It cheered the heart of Melancthon and his friends when, after Luther's death, they were driven into exile. It was sung a century later by the army of Gustavus Adolphus when he overcame the Catholic forces at

Leipzig (1631). It has now become the triumph song, not of any one nation only, but of the whole Protestant Church.

EIN' FESTE BURG may be said to have had an influence on the religious awakening in the English Church during the eighteenth century. In 1723 a number of persons belonging to the Moravian sect were assembled for worship in the house of one of their leaders, by name Ritchsmann. Those were the days of persecution, and the news of their meeting reached the ears of the authorities. An officer was sent to seize their books and dismiss the assembly; but when he entered the house the brethren all stood and sang 'Ein' feste Burg.' For this act twenty of them were arrested and imprisoned. After enduring great suffering some escaped from prison, and others were exiled. A few of these settled at Herrnhut, while one of them, with a little band of followers, reached England on the way to America. On leaving this country they were joined by the two Wesleys, and it was this contact with Moravian influence and doctrine that influenced John Wesley to commence and carry out the great Methodist revival.

This chorale has been made use of with considerable effect by various composers. It is suitably enshrined by Mendelssohn in the last movement of his *Reformation* symphony, and is introduced by Meyerbeer into his opera, *Les Huguenots;* but here it is decidedly out of its place, as this story of sixteenth-century Protestantism would in France be more correctly illustrated by one of the metrical psalm-tunes. The chorale receives its finest treatment in Wagner's 'Kaisermarsch,' written to celebrate the triumphal entry of the German soldiers into Berlin after the war of 1870. Throughout this fine march the theme of EIN' FESTE BURG is heard recurring at intervals, until towards the end a rushing semi-quaver passage heralds the final appearance of the chorale, thundered out by the whole orchestra with thrilling effect.

495—Walton.

WALTON was composed for the hymn ' Who puts his trust,' by Rev. W. F. Moulton (see No. 396) for *The People's Hymnary* (1906).

496—Invitation.

INVITATION is from Lampe's *Hymns on the Great Festivals* (1746). See under No. 411. The tune is also known as KENT and DEVONSHIRE. THE INVITATION is Lampe's own title.

497—St. Hilary.

ST. HILARY was composed by Dr. Dykes for the first edition of the *Bristol Tune-Book* (1863), set to Robert Seagrave's ' Rise my soul, and stretch thy wings.'

498—Redhead No. 76. See under No. 13.

499—Shelter.

SHELTER (or HIDING IN THEE) is from Ira D. Sankey's (see No. 171) *Welcome Tidings* (1877).

500—Leicester.

LEICESTER is from John Bishop's *Sett of New Psalm Tunes* (see No. 284).

501 (i)—Song 46. See No. 24.

501 (ii)—Pax Tecum.

PAX TECUM. There has always been a certain amount of mystery connected with the authorship of this tune. The story is rather complicated, but it appears that the melody, in a somewhat indefinite form, was supplied by G. T. Caldbeck to the Rev. E. H. Bickersteth when he was bringing out *The Hymnal Companion*. It was submitted to Dr. Charles Vincent, the music editor, who put the tune into its present form, and harmonized it.

To him, therefore, the tune should be credited. The whole story of PAX TECUM and its reputed composer is told in the *Choir* for December, 1934.

502—Laudate Dominum.

LAUDATE DOMINUM, by H. J. Gauntlett, first appeared in the revised edition (1875) of *Hymns Ancient and Modern*, where it was set to 'O Worship the King.'

503—Irish.

IRISH is one of the classic eighteenth-century tunes that has no definite history. Its earliest known appearance was in *Hymns and Sacred Poems*, published in Dublin in 1749 by S. Powell. This consists of hymns with a few tunes at the end, IRISH being amongst them, but not so named. The title of the book is similar to that used frequently by the Wesleys, but it has not yet been identified as their work. All that can be said is that John Wesley was in Dublin in the summer of 1749, and so was J. F. Lampe (see No. 411), who undoubtedly was associated with Wesley in musical work. Further identification is difficult owing to the scarcity of this book. Only one copy of *Hymns and Sacred Poems* has been known in recent years, and that was in the possession of John Dobson (see No. 68), a musical amateur of Manchester, who subsequently lived at Richmond, Surrey. He amassed a fine collection of psalmody, and on his death it was unfortunately dispersed, a good many of the books going to America, where many of them, the book under notice included, fell into the hands of James Warrington, who formed an extensive collection of tune-books. He died a few years ago, and all attempts to trace the book containing IRISH have hitherto failed.

Caleb Ashworth, a Rossendale Dissenting minister, was the first English editor to appreciate the tune, and he inserted it in his *Collection of Tunes* (c. 1760), christening it IRISH. In subsequent collections it was called DUBLIN, but Ashworth's name for it has prevailed. In the Dublin book it was headed ' Hymn cxci.' and set in two parts to a hymn by Dr. Watts, ' Time, what an empty vapour 'tis.'

In the preface to his *Jacobite Relics of Scotland*, the Scottish poet, James Hogg, says that he set about collecting the airs with great diligence and greater delight, but with very slender prospects of success, ' for I found that the people of every county in the eastern parts of Scotland sang them to their own favourite tunes. The Galloway people's music appears to be like themselves, a kind of Irish mixed with something else : nobody knows what it is.'

Hogg appears to have derived his collection from some manuscript volumes of songs lent him by a friend, wherein the name of a suitable air was affixed to nearly every one, and these he traced by referring to old collections of music; ' But,' he adds, ' the modern fashion of changing the name and style of these old tunes has been the cause of much perplexity and confusion of ideas to me. I look upon this as extremely reprehensible, if not disgraceful, in the collectors of our national airs.'

In the first volume of the *Collection* is a poem called ' The Cameronian Cat ' set to be sung to the tune IRISH. Here are the first two verses :

> There was a Cameronian Cat,
>   Was hunting for a prey,
> And in the house she catch'd a mouse
>   Upon the Sabbath day.
> The Whig being offended
>   At such on act profane,
> Laid by his book, the cat he took,
>   And bound her in a chain.

Hogg says of the air that ' it is very sweet, but has a strong resemblance to one of their popular psalm-tunes,' but he throws no further light on IRISH, nor does he suggest that he ever heard it in church. This,

however, is not surprising, as IRISH did not appear in a
Scotch tune-book till 1793, and in those days it took a
long time for a new tune to take a place in the music
of the kirk. It would seem, therefore, that we have
here a possible new theory for the origin of the tune in
question, though it does not appear that IRISH has any
features that would make it a folk-song of any nation.

504—Bremen.

BREMEN (or NEUMARK) was composed by George
Christian Neumark (1657) for the hymn to which it is
set. Bach makes use of the chorale in ' The Wedding
Cantata,' and in others, and Mendelssohn introduces it
into *St. Paul.* In *The Chorale Book for England* it is
in triple time.

George Neumark was born at Langensalza, Thuringia,
in 1621. He suffered much privation in his youth after
leaving the Gymnasium at Gotha, going from place to
place in search of work, but finding none. Once he was
attacked by robbers, who took away all his belongings
except his prayer-book and a small sum of money he
had concealed about his person. At last he found a
haven at Kiel, where he got employment as tutor in a
judge's family. He showed his gratitude by writing this
hymn (504) and probably composed the chorale at the
same time. From Kiel he went to Königsberg, where he
lost all his property, this time by fire. He soon resumed
his life of wandering till he obtained a court appointment at Weimar. Early in 1681 he became blind, and
his end came a few months later.

505—Psalm 8.

PSALM 8 (or WHITEHALL) is from the same source as
No. 467.

506—In Memoriam.

IN MEMORIAM is adapted from the opening movement
of Sullivan's *In Memoriam* overture, which he wrote in
memory of his father in 1866.

22

507 (i), 690—Franconia.

FRANCONIA was adapted by W. H. Havergal for his
Old Church Psalmody (1847), from a longer melody in
a 'Choral-Buch' edited by J. B. König (1738).

507 (ii)—Song 20.   See No. 24.

508—Christmas Carol.

CHRISTMAS CAROL, by Sir H. Walford Davies, was
composed for the hymn ' O little town of Bethlehem,' in
the Rev. Garrett Horder's *Worship Song* (1905).

509—St. Leonard's.

ST. LEONARD'S was written by Dr. H. Hiles for a
festival held at St. Mary's Church, Hulme, Manchester,
on September 19, 1867.   It was published the same
year in *Twelve Tunes to original or favourite Hymns,* set
to Miss Proctor's hymn, ' The shadows of the evening
hours.'

Henry Hiles was born at Shrewsbury in 1826.   During
the early years of his life he held organ appointments
at Shrewsbury (deputizing for his brother John), Bury,
Bishopwearmouth, Bowden (1861), and St. Paul's,
Manchester, from 1863 to 1867, when his organ
experiences ended.   He was a lecturer at Owens College
and also at the Victoria University, besides conducting
various musical societies in Lancashire and Yorkshire.
In 1893 he was appointed one of the professors at the
newly constituted Manchester College of Music.   It was
in 1870 that the members of the Methodist Church at
Cheetham Hill began to find that the old-fashioned tune-
books they were using were not adapted to modern
needs, and a small committee was appointed, with Hiles
as editor, to prepare a collection of tunes.   The result
was *The Wesley Tune-Book* (1872) a production which
bears testimony to the cultured tastes of the congregation.
Hiles also started and edited the *Quarterly Musical*

Review, which lasted from 1885-1888. He was a prolific composer, his published works including oratorios, cantatas, anthems and prize glees. He died in 1904.

510—Clifton.

CLIFTON is by James Brabham, and first appeared in a music edition of Watts's *Psalms and Hymns,* which he edited in 1840. He was music master at Dulwich College from 1870 to 1883.

511—Spetisbury.

SPETISBURY, by William Knapp (see No. 109), is found in his *Sett of New Psalm-Tunes and Anthems* (second edition 1741).

512—Wigtown.

WIGTOWN (or WIGTON) is one of thirty-one ' Common Tunes' in the *Scottish Psalter* of 1635 (see No. 37).

513—Green Hill.

GREEN HILL was composed by Dr. A. L. Peace (see No. 448) for the *Scottish Hymnal* (1885), of which he was editor.

514 (i)—Assurance.

ASSURANCE, by G. Baskeyfield, was composed for the present edition of the *Methodist Hymn-Book* (1933).

Mr. George Baskeyfield was born at Tunstall, Staffs., in 1878, and has been an organist since his boyhood. When sixteen years old he won a prize in a hymn-tune competition. His first organ appointment was at King Street Wesleyan Church, which he won in open competition. A year later (1912) he was invited to become organist and Musical Director at the Jubilee Methodist Church, Tunstall (the mother church of Primitive Methodism). He has also acted as organist to the North Staffordshire District Choral Society, a skilled body of singers which has competed successfully at five Welsh Eisteddfodau, winning the first prize on each occasion. He has had the advantage of studying under Sir Hugh Allen and Dr. Granville Bantock, and he has also been in recent years a lecturer in music to the Extra-mural Delegacy of Oxford University. He has also had charge of the music course at the summer schools held in Oxford. Elected a member of the Methodist Tune-Book Committee, he took an active part in its discussions, and showed an intimate knowledge of the essential demands of music worship in the Methodist Church. He has had considerable experience as an organ recitalist. He has also acted as organist at concerts given by the Hallé Orchestra under Sir Hamilton Harty.

514 (ii)—Dovedale.

DOVEDALE is from *The English Hymnal,* where it is called ST. HUGH. It is from Miss Broadwood's collection and is set to a ballad founded on the legend of St. Hugh of Lincoln.

515—Moab.

MOAB is by John Roberts, who is also known as Ieuan Gwyllt. In full this becomes Ieuan Gwyllt Gelltydd Melindwr, i.e. John of the Wild Woods near the Mill Tower. The reason is that there are so many John ' Roberts ' in a given Welsh locality that some distinctive pen name or appelation becomes essential for identification.

He was born at Tanrhiwfelen, near Aberystwyth. In his youth he tried various pursuits, being in turn schoolmaster, lawyer's clerk, and journalist. He then took to preaching and held pastorates at Pant-tywyll, near Merthyr Tydfil, and elsewhere. But his love of music prevailed, and the greater part of his life was devoted to musical propaganda.

In 1859 he published a collection called *Llyfr Tonau Cynulleidfaol*, a tune-book designed for congregational singing, which embodied his ideas of what church music should be. He believed that sacred music reached its pinnacle in the sixteenth and seventeenth centuries, and his aim was to revive both the style and the spirit of the past, and to some extent he succeeded. His best tunes are MOAB and LIVERPOOL, whilst SYRIA, BETHEL and RHEIDIOL are highly esteemed.

When his tune-book was published he brought into being the Cymanfaodd Canu, or singing festivals, which have had a great influence in Wales.

In the latter years of his life he edited the *Cerddor Cymreig* (The Welsh Musician). He also translated many of the Moody and Sankey hymns into Welsh and published a volume of them under the title of *Swn Y Jiwbili* in 1876. During these last years he was very much taken with the music of those evangelists, but probably found it difficult to reconcile it with the music of three centuries earlier, to which he was so much attached.

516—Trust and Obey.

TRUST AND OBEY is by Daniel Brink Towner, who was born in 1850 at Rome, Pennsylvania, and died in 1919 at Longwood, Missouri. He received his early musical training from his father, and later he studied under George F. Toot and Frederick Root. He became associated with Dwight L. Moody in 1885 in Cincinnati, where he conducted a chorus of one thousand voices for his evangelistic meetings. Then for twenty-six years he directed the music course of the Moody Bible Institute at Chicago, Illinois. He composed more than 2,000 gospel songs, and edited twenty-three hymnals. His TRUST AND OBEY was 'copyrighted' in 1887, and as it is number 59 in *Hymns, New and Old*, which was compiled and copyrighted the same year, it is probable that this was its first appearance.

517—Trusting Jesus.

TRUSTING JESUS is from Ira D. Sankey's (see No. 171) *Gospel Hymns*, No. 2 (1876).

518—Jesu, Meine Freude.

JESU, MEINE FREUDE was probably adapted from an earlier melody by Johann Crüger, and inserted in one of the editions of his *Praxis Pictatis* Melica (? 1653), set to the hymn of which 'Jesu, priceless treasure' is a translation (see No. 10).

519, 550—Abridge.

ABRIDGE, by Isaac Smith, is one of the classic eighteenth-century tunes which still find a place in every recognized hymnal. Little is known of the composer. He was clerk at a Nonconformist place of worship in Alie Street, Goodman's Fields, in the east of London, owned in former days by a farmer of that name who (according to the historian Stowe) used to retail his milk at three pints for a halfpenny. In or about 1770 Smith published *A Collection of Psalm-Tunes in three parts,* in which ABRIDGE first appeared. In a later edition (c. 1790), the new editor referred to Isaac Smith as 'a gentleman greatly admired for his fine taste, and to whom the public are much indebted for the pains he has taken to improve church music.'

Smith's suggestions are worth recording:

It is much to be wished that every congregation would appoint an hour or two some evening every week to practise such tunes as may be thought proper. By that means the mistakes of those who sing out of tune or out of time, will easily be corrected.

Here is the original form of ABRIDGE, from which it will be seen that the tune has come down to us unaltered, save that a few of the fancy trimmings have disappeared:

520—Carinthia.

CARINTHIA is taken from the ' Supplement ' to Booth's Psalmody. The original work was *The Wesleyan Psalmist*, a massive oblong quarto volume containing 284 tunes, published in 1857. A distinguishing feature was the metrical index, the first line of each tune being given, with the name of each. The ' Supplement ' was issued in 1873.

Edward Booth was born in Leeds about 1808. His parents were musical, and finding their son took after them they gave him every opportunity of advancing himself in the study of music. In 1828 he was appointed organist of Brunswick Wesleyan Chapel, Leeds, a position he held for over fifty years. He studied with Hummel, and also with Ferdinand Ries, who himself was a pupil at Beethoven. Booth certainly has a claim to being the first of Yorkshire's sons to make the county famous in the world of music. It was he who introduced the piano and organ works of Bach into Leeds and district, and so attractive was his organ playing at Brunswick, that other organists used to hurry off from their own places and congregate there to hear his recitals. It was a notable event when Paganini appeared at Leeds Music Hall in 1832 and played one of Hummel's concertos to Booth's accompaniment.

521 (i)—Eastergate.

EASTERGATE was contributed by John Ireland (see No. 144) to the *English Hymnal* (1906).

521 (ii)—Trust.

Trust is Part II (or chorus) of a tune called Urbane in *Songs of Grace and Glory,* edited by C. B. Snepp and F. R. Havergal (1876).

Frances Ridley Havergal was born at Astley, Worcestershire, in 1836. Her father, the Rev. W. H. Havergal (see No. 58) was a keen student of church music, and the daughter soon showed signs of musical ability. Her studies in music, however, received many interruptions owing to ill-health and other causes, but she found time for composition, and in 1866 submitted some songs to Ferdinand Hiller for his criticism. Responding to his invitation, she went to his house and found him 'a small, elderly man, quiet in manner, of handsome and peculiar Jewish physiognomy (he was a Jew) . . . and terribly clever-looking eyes; I think one would single him out as a genius among any number. He was in a double room full of musical litter, with a handsome grand piano in the middle. He received us very politely, and asked me a few questions (he is a man of few words), and then took my book of songs and sat down to read it through.' Conversation followed, and Hiller was much surprised to find she had had no systematic teaching. He found her melodies 'thoroughly English in character and type,' a remark he rather spoilt by saying that he did not think English melodies rank very high.

The interview led to little or no result. On returning home she had singing lessons and also took part in choral work. She continued her studies in harmony in order to prepare herself for editing her father's *Psalmody,* which was published in 1871. To this she contributed several new tunes, including Hermas (No. 820). Five years later she prepared an Appendix to the Rev. C. B. Snepp's *Songs of Grace and Glory,* and dispatched her MSS., only to learn shortly after that the printer's premises had been burnt down, and all the stereotypes of the music destroyed. As Miss Havergal had kept no copies, nor even a list of tunes, she had great difficulty in taking up the work again, but ultimately she was successful and the edition of the *Songs* was duly published. During the last few years of her life other work claimed her attention, and she had no opportunity of developing still further her undoubted musical abilities. Her gift of melody still lingers in her ' Ministry of Song '—in the hymns which have become an essential feature in the worship of the Church :

> Like the angelic choir, they cannot die,
> Preludes of triumph—songs of immortality !

522—Magdalena.

MAGDALENA was composed by Sir John Stainer for the second edition of *Hymns Ancient and Modern* (1868).

523—Tenax.

TENAX, by Alfred Beer (see No. 371 [ii]).

524—Wentworth.

WENTWORTH was contributed by F. C. Maker (see No. 206) to the 1881 edition of the *Bristol Tune-Book*.

525—Ar hyd y nos.

AR HYD Y NOS. This tune is probably of the eighteenth century, and is in Edward Jones's *Welsh Bards* (1784, p. 56). Bishop Heber's hymn, ' God that madest earth and heaven,' was written for it, and is set to it in the choir book which his sister Mary (afterwards Mrs. Cholmondeley) arranged, before 1822, for use at Hodnet Church. The story is that Heber was staying in a house where a harper was kept. One evening the harper played this melody in the hall, and Heber, retiring to a corner, wrote the hymn to be sung to it. In Baddeley's *North Wales* (1909, pt. ii, p. 87), it is said to have been written at Llangedwyn, on the Tanat, near Oswestry, where Heber often stayed with his friend, the Hon. C. W. W. Wynn. A more circumstantial account (quoted in the *Musical Times*, January, 1916, p. 17) says that Heber was 'staying in a house on the borders of Flintshire,' which rather suggests Bodryddan, near Rhuddlan, the house of his father-in-law, Dean Shipley. The tune has been put to a variety of uses, sacred and secular, and occasionally profane.

526 (i)—Norwick.

NORWICK, by B. E. Woods, was accepted by the Music Committee for the new *Methodist Hymn-Book* (1933).

The Rev. Bertram Ernest Woods has always been interested in music and made an early start as a composer. His first anthem was written when he was seventeen, and since then he has composed several songs and pianoforte solos. He is at present devoting himself to sacred music. During three years' residence in Shetland he 'improved each Sunday' by composing a new tune. Many of them were promptly suppressed, but NORWICK was one of the few that survived the composer's self-criticism. It is named after a beautiful little hamlet where he lived whilst in the Shetlands. It was originally designed for 'From Greenland's icy mountains.'

526 (ii)—Wolvercote.

WOLVERCOTE, by W. H. Ferguson, takes its name from a northern suburb of Oxford. It appeared anonymously in *The Public School Hymn-Book* (1919), of which the composer was one of the editors.

The Rev. W. H. Ferguson was born at Leeds in 1874. He was a chorister at Magdalen College, Oxford. In 1902 he was ordained and entered the scholastic profession, spending eleven years as organist and chaplain and assistant master at Lancing College, Sussex. He is now Warden of Radley College, near Oxford.

527—Petition.

PETITION. Though this tune is credited to Haydn, it is doubtful if that composer would either recognize or acknowledge it. It is adapted partly from the chorus ' God of light' in Haydn's *Seasons* (1801), and partly from an air ' Ere infancy's bud' in Méhul's *Joseph* (1807). The present combination is taken from the *Wesleyan Tune-Book* (1876).

528—Penlan.

PENLAN is by D. Jenkins, and is found in *Gemau Mawl Ail Attodiad* (1910).

Born of humble parentage at Trecastle, Breconshire, in 1849, David Jenkins presents a notable example of those who, unaided by the prestige of position or wealth, have attained to considerable eminence in the public life of the Principality. He entered Aberystwyth College in 1874, and studied under the tuition of Dr. Joseph Parry, who at that time filled the chair of music at the University. From Aberystwyth he went to Cambridge, graduating in 1879, being placed first on the list of successful candidates for the Mus.B. degree. He was much in evidence in the musical life of Wales as an adjudicator at the National Eisteddfod and the provincial Eisteddfodau. He also occupied a prominent place as a conductor of psalmody festivals, which are a characteristic of Welsh musical life. As a composer his pen was a prolific one. He wrote copiously from the hymn-tune to the oratorio, and much of his work is continuously in demand in Wales. Some of his more outstanding compositions (oratorios) are the following : *David and Saul, The Legend of St. David, The Psalm of Life, Job,* and *The Storm,* perhaps his *magnum opus,* produced with signal success by the Neath Choral Society. As a composer his forte lay in the writing of massive and descriptive choral music.

529, 675—Redhead No. 4.

REDHEAD No. 4 is from the same source as No. 13, where it is headed 'Ancient Melody.' Thus it is not an original tune, but appears to be founded on the plain-song theme VENI CREATOR. (See No. 779.)

530—Barnabas.

BARNABAS was in the Wesleyan Tune-Book of 1876, being taken from *Tunes New and Old* (1864), where it is assigned to a French Psalter of 1563. In the *Wesleyan Tune-Book* (1876) it is assigned to a similar source of date 1562, whilst in the Index it is said to be from 'Damantius' French Psalter, 1562.' The real source is a setting of Psalm lxxv. in the French Psalter of 1561, this being the original form:

531—Hull.

HULL was called OLD MELODY in the *Wesleyan Tune-Book* (1876), and this was a perfectly reliable statement. What little is known of its origin is thus stated by Cowan and Love in *The Music to the Church Hymnary*:

> The origin of this tune is very obscure, and it is quite uncertain whether it was originally the melody of a secular song or of a hymn-tune. In *The American Musical Miscellany* it appears as opposite, set to a song called 'The Indian Philosopher.'

This certainly seems a good foundation for HULL to rest on, and it is possible that its alternate name, GANGES, has some association with the title of the song. The connexion with Hull is not so clear.

532—St. Gregory.

ST. GREGORY is from the same source as ALL SAINTS (see No. 100).

533—Nox Præcessit. See No. 268.

534—St. Werbergh.

ST. WERBERGH was written by Dr. Dykes for Chope's *Congregational Hymn and Tune-Book* (1862).

535—Pavia.

PAVIA (or SOLDAU) is probably founded on some forgotten plain-song melody of pre-Reformation times. It is found in something like the present form in Walther's 'Gesangbuch' of 1524, where it is set to a Whitsuntide hymn by Martin Luther.

536 (i), 773—Memoria.

MEMORIA was written by S. S. Wesley (see No. 217) at the request of the editor of *The Hymnary* (1872).

536 (ii)—Southport.

SOUTHPORT is by George Lomas (see No. 451), who wrote it for *The Bristol Tune-Book* (1876).

537—Reverence.

REVERENCE was written for the hymn ' 'Tis not to ask for gifts alone,' by Dr. M. L. Wostenholm (see No. 256) for the *Methodist Hymn-Book* (1933).

538—What a Friend.

WHAT A FRIEND appeared in an American collection called *Silver Wings* (1870). The composer, Charles Crozat Converse (who wrote under the pen-name of Karl Redau) was born at Warren, Mass, in 1832. He developed a pronounced taste for music, and at the age of twenty-three he crossed to Europe to study at the Leipzig Conservatoire. On his return he decided to adopt the law as his profession, and settled at Eric, Pa. He has published overtures, quartets and cantatas, also the American National Hymn, ' God for us ' (1887). In 1859 he received the degree of LL.D. from Rutherford College. He was an inventor as well as a lawyer and musician. Of his numerous hymn-tunes only WHAT A FRIEND has survived. He died in 1918.

539—Farrant.

The anthem, ' Lord, for Thy tender mercies' sake,' from which the tune FARRANT is adapted, has become widely known since it appeared in the *Musical Times* in 1843. It first appeared in print in the *Cathedral Magazine*, a publication dating from the early part of George III's reign.

Richard Farrant was a gentleman of the Chapel Royal during the late Tudor period, but there is some doubt as to whether he is the composer of the anthem and tune. He died in 1580, and it was not until two centuries had elapsed that his name was associated with the music.

It is also assigned, but without any good reason, to the Elizabethan composer, William Mundy and to John Hilton of somewhat later date.

The words of the anthem are taken from a book of *Christian Prayers and Holy Meditations,* which was compiled and published in Elizabeth's reign.

It appears that its adaptation as a hymn-tune is due to Dr. Edward Hodges, of Bristol, who arranged it as a common metre, and sent it to the Rev. W. H. Havergal for inclusion in his *Old Church Psalmody* (1847) under the name FARRANT. It is also called GLOUCESTER by some editors. An addition is made to the puzzle by the existence of some music MSS. in Exeter Cathedral, amongst them being an anthem, ' Up, Lord, and help me, O my God.' It is marked as being ' by Mr. Tallis, adapted to these words by the Reverend Mr. John Hicks,' the music being identical with the FARRANT music.

540—Christ Chapel.

CHRIST CHAPEL, by Charles Steggall, is from his *Church Psalmody* (1849).

Dr. Steggall, who was born in 1826, entered the Royal Academy of Music in 1847, and a year later became organist of Christ Chapel, Maida Vale, N.W. In 1855 he was appointed organist of Christ Church, Lancaster Gate, where he remained for nine years. Here he played upon the old organ which was built for Winchester Cathedral by Avery in 1799, and removed to Lancaster Gate in 1851, when Henry Willis's Exhibition Organ took its place at Winchester under Dr. S. S. Wesley's direction. That organ is now in St. Peter's, Southsea. In 1864 Dr. Steggall became organist of Lincoln's Inn Chapel, and he retained this position until his death in 1905.

Steggall had interesting recollections of Mendelssohn's visit to this country in 1846. In the course of an interview some years ago, he said, ' I had the good fortune to be at Exeter Hall on the occasion of the rehearsal of *Elijah* under J. Surman. Soon after the rehearsal had commenced Mendelssohn entered the Hall. He was at once recognized, and received an uproarious greeting. After bowing his acknowledgements he walked up the centre passage and, to my delight, came and sat next to me. When one of the movements, " Hear, mighty God," was not going to his satisfaction, he ascended the orchestra and, Surman handing him the bâton, he took the chorus at about double the speed. I attended the subsequent performance when, between the parts, Mendelssohn played Handel's " Harmonious Blacksmith " with extempore variations. I shall never forget it. The finale was a marvel of execution. The manuals were, at that time, arranged so that the performer faced the audience, and as no book was on the desk, one could see the hands cross and recross each other with showers of arpeggios. I suppose the movement must have been somewhat in the style of the finale to the first organ sonata.'

Steggall took his Doctor's degree at Cambridge in 1851, his ' exercise ' being a setting of the thirty-third Psalm. T. Attwood Walmisley was then the University Professor of Music, and on his recommendation Steggall revised and re-scored the music, adding settings for an eight-part chorus. In those days the exercise had to be performed at the unfortunate and not infrequently impecunious candidate's expense, and Steggall found himself called upon to find £150 for the pleasure of hearing his composition. This took place in Trinity College Chapel, with Professor Walmisley conducting and the composer at the organ. Sterndale Bennett was present, and the chorus was composed of local choirs, who were assisted by young choristers from St. Paul's and the Temple Church. Amongst them was a youngster, John Stainer, who gave great satisfaction by his singing, ' including a long-sustained high B flat.'

Steggall was the first professor of the organ at the Royal Academy, and for some years he took his pupils at his own house in Notting Hill, where he had an instrument specially erected for the purpose. Amongst his pupils were G. J. Bennett (see No. 473) and Frank Idle.

Steggall wrote only a few anthems, but 'God came from Teman,' and 'Remember now thy Creator,' are still heard. The latter was composed on the day of the Duke of Wellington's funeral, when every shop was closed, and the doors were indeed 'shut in the streets.'

Steggall's best-known organ composition is, perhaps, his 'Postlude in C minor,' which introduces his tune, CHRIST CHAPEL. The tune holds a prominent place in modern psalmody, and is typical of the style which the composer continually advocated as being the one most suitable for use in church. He voiced his opinions on this subject in the preface to his *Church Psalmody* (1848) wherein he tried to impress on congregations the importance of their taking an active vocal part in church praise. Twenty years later he was invited by the Rev. Thomas Darling to act as musical editor for his *Hymns for the Church of England*. In this work Steggall carried out his definite opinions on the style of psalmody suitable for church use, and also the form in which it should be presented. Faithful to the old 'Proper Tune' theory, which gave each hymn its own melody, he made no attempt to distinguish them by names, maintaining that each tune should be known by the first line of its hymn, according to the custom adopted in Germany in distinguishing the various chorales. In this work Steggall included many chorales harmonized by Bach, and though he thought it advisable to simplify some of the more florid parts, he intimated that 'the incomparable harmonies of the great master have been scrupulously preserved.'

541—Bonar.

BONAR, by Charles Steggall (see No. 540) is from the same source as No. 653.

542—Leominster.

LEOMINSTER is adapted from a part-song by G. W. Martin (see No. 209), which originally appeared in *The Journal of Part Music* (1862), called ' The Pilgrim Song.' It was inserted in the *Wesleyan Tune-Book* (1876) as a hymn-tune, with the heading ' Author unknown.' But the author happened to be alive at the time and promptly sent in a claim for ten guineas for the use of his tune, threatening all kinds of legal penalties if his claim was not promptly met. The Rev. Dr. Jobson was at the head of the Methodist Publishing House in those days. He was an amiable old gentleman who had not had much to do with musicians. He had only just emerged from a very trying experience of the vagaries of Dr. Gauntlett, and he yielded without a murmur to Martin's claim, probably recognizing its justice. Five years previously Sullivan had got hold of the tune from some (to him) unknown source. It appealed to him, so he re-arranged it, adding his own harmonies here and there, christened it LEOMINSTER, and inserted it in *Church Hymns,* which he was then editing. What Martin did in this case has never been revealed.

543—Egypt.

EGYPT is by James Leach, who was born in 1762 at Wardle, a village near Rochdale. The only early training he had in music was from a local celebrity known as ' Owd Isaac,' who taught him the violin, but little else, for Leach himself states that when he began to write his tunes he was ignorant of the rules of composition. He early attained proficiency as an instrumentalist, and was appointed one of the performers in the King's Band. As a vocalist he rose to distinction both as a teacher and choir leader, and as a counter-tenor singer he was prominent in the great musical festivals held in Westminster Abbey and elsewhere. But it is as a composer of psalm and hymn-tunes that he best deserves to be remembered. Leach's first volume of sacred music was published in 1789. He was then twenty-seven years of age. In the preface to the volume, dated Rochdale, June 29, 1789, he says:

Having had a turn for music from my infancy, I have employed my leisure hours in cultivating the same. A few years ago I composed a few tunes, and without the least design of their being made public, being at the time ignorant of the rules of composition. These few tunes accordingly got handed about, and were introduced into many congregations, insomuch that I was called upon from all quarters for copies, so that I found myself under the disagreeable necessity of denying many requests of that kind. For, having a family to maintain with my hand labour, I had already spent more time than I could well spare; but a friend of mine, knowing my importunities of that kind, and wishing the tunes to be more generally known, advised me by all means to compose a few more to some select pieces, and let a number of them be struck off, as the price would be small, so that such as wished to have them might procure them at a small expense; and therefore I now submit them to the judgement of the public; I mean such as understand music.

A few years later (1797) Leach issued a second volume of his tunes. He now left Rochdale and went to live in Salford, as affording a wider sphere for his work. Here he remained till his death in 1798, which resulted from a coach accident as he was returning from a visit to Rochdale. He lies buried in the graveyard of Union Street Methodist Chapel, Rochdale. On his memorial stone is engraved his tune EGYPT.

544 (i)—Newcastle.

The hymn 'Eternal Light' was written by the Rev. Thomas Binney whilst he was minister at the Weigh House Chapel, near the Monument. It used to be sung

to NICOLAUS (formerly known as ST. GEORGE), by
Herman. The first tune written specially for the hymn
was ROYAL FORT, by E. J. Orchard. It appeared in the
Bristol Tune-Book (1863). In 1877 *The London Tune-
Book* was published, which contained a new setting
named NEWCASTLE, by H. L. Morley. Little is known
of this composer, except that at one time he was organist
at St. Paul's Church, Herne Hill, S.E. In 1883 he went
to America, and since then all trace of him has been lost.

544 (ii)—Royal Fort.

ROYAL FORT is by E. J. Orchard, who was born at
Bristol in 1834. He was greatly interested in the production of the *Bristol Tune-Book* in 1863, and on the
invitation of the Editor, Alfred Stone, contributed ROYAL
FORT for Binney's hymn. Moving to Salisbury, he
became organist of the Congregational Church, a position
he held for thirty-six years, resigning in 1906. He also
held the office of church treasurer. He died in 1915.

545—Arfon.

ARFON is a melody that has long been popular in
Wales, but whether it is an original tune, or derived from
a folk-song, is not known at present.

546—Wareham. See No. 109.

547—Aynhoe.

AYNHOE has been credited to Dr. Nares, but further
research has revealed that he cannot be definitely
associated with it. The tune was popular amongst
Methodists many years ago through being included in the
Companion to the Wesleyan Hymn-Book (1849).

548—Holy Faith.

HOLY FAITH was written by Sir George Martin (see
No. 31), for Faber's hymn, 'Faith of our fathers.' It
appeared in *Additional Hymns* (1894).

549—Simplicity. See No. 178.

550—Abridge. See No. 519.

551—Plymouth.

PLYMOUTH is from the *Manhattan Collection* (1837). The composer, Thomas Hastings, was born in 1784 at Washington, Conn. When he was twelve years old his father, a doctor, moved to Clinton, N.Y., where the boy joined the village choir, and at the age of eighteen became choir leader. His abilities as a leader led to an invitation to New York, where he acted as choirmaster for no less than twelve churches. His whole life was devoted to music, and his output was extraordinary. He is said to have written six hundred hymns, composed about a thousand hymn-tunes, and issued fifty volumes of music, besides contributing articles to numerous periodicals. He did not always put his own name to a tune. Some of them are headed Kl—ff, and others Zol—ffer. When asked the reason for this anonymity, he said, ' I have found that a foreigner's name goes a long way and that very ordinary tunes would be sung if " Palestrina " or " Pucilto " were placed over them, while a better tune by Hastings would pass unnoticed.' He and two of his brothers were albinos, his hair being entirely destitute of colour so that he looked old whilst still young. His devotion to his duty made him occasionally absent-minded; it is said that one evening he rode off to his work and then walked home, leaving his horse behind him. He was largely associated with Lowell Mason and W. B. Bradbury in editing and producing collections of psalmody.

552—Keine Schönheit hat die Welt.

KEINE SCHÖNHEIT HAT DIE WELT is the first line of a hymn by Scheffler in *Heilige Seelenlust* (see No. 689) for which Georg Joseph probably wrote the melody set to it.

553—Tarsus. See No. 65.

554—Huddersfield.

HUDDERSFIELD (or DURHAM or HAMPTON) is from
Aaron Williams' *Psalmody* (1770), and is probably by
Williams himself (see No. 591).

555—Pleyel.

PLEYEL (or GERMAN HYMN) is adapted from I. J.
Pleyel's *Quartet* No. 4, Op. 7, and was inserted as a
L.M. tune in *Arnold and Callcott's Psalms* (1791). (See
No. 390.)

556—Bangor.

BANGOR appeared in *A Compleat Melody* or *Harmony
of Zion* (1734), edited by William Tansur who, for some
reason best known to himself, persisted in calling himself Tans'ur, sometimes varying it in later life as Le
Tans'ur. He was born at Dunchurch, Warwickshire, in
1706, according to the parish registers, though he stated
in one of his books that 1700 was the date. He compiled
several books of psalmody, containing interesting autobiographical notices in the various prefaces. Psalmody
seems to have been his favourite pursuit from early
youth. When about thirty years old he made Ewell,
near Epsom, his headquarters, publishing here his
Melody of the Heart. This was the first of many
similar compilations. He was of a roving disposition,
going from place to place teaching music and doing his
best to improve the singing in the various places he
visited. He held psalmody classes, and he may possibly
be looked upon as the founder of 'community' singing.
After leading a wandering though busy life for several
years, he finally settled at St. Neots, where he died in
1783. Some of his tune-books passed through several
editions. One of the tunes from *A Compleat Melody*
was included by John Wesley in his 'Foundery Tune-
Book,' where it is called 'Tans'ur's Tune.'

557—Stafford.

Stafford is from the same source as St. Bride (see No. 81). It was originally called 'St. Clement's Tune' from the name of the church (St. Clement Danes, Strand), where the composer, Dr. Samuel Howard, was organist. It is also known as Lancaster.

558—St. Catherine.

St. Catherine is found in *The Crown of Jesus Music* (1864), the melody probably being by H. F. Hemy. The present arrangement was made by J. G. Walton in his *Plain Song Music for the Holy Communion Office* (1874).

559—Ballerma.

Ballerma. The history of this tune is the story of a curious development and also a remarkable instance of what adapters of melodies for hymn-tune purposes are capable of. The story centres round Robert Simpson (1790-1832), a weaver by trade, who led the psalmody at Dr. Wardlaw's Church in Glasgow. After a time he gave up weaving and took to teaching music, following his appointment as precentor at the East parish church of Greenock. He is said to have been a man of studious habits and generally respected. Shortly after his death in 1832 his library was examined, and amongst some music MSS. the tune Ballerma was discovered. The MS. passed into the possession of John Turnbull, who inserted it in Vol. 6 of Stevens' *Collection of Sacred Music,* which he was editing. There is no evidence to show that Simpson claimed the tune as his own, and subsequent investigations suggest that he adapted it from a song called 'Durante and Belerma,' a pathetic Scotch ballad, with an accompaniment for the harp, by F. H. Barthélémon. The words were by M. G. Lewis, and appeared in his story *The Monk.* He claimed his ballad to be of Spanish origin, and this led to Ballerma being designated as Spanish Air in the Wesleyan Tune-Book

(1876), but there seems no doubt that Barthélémon (see No. 931), was the composer. The only point that is ' Scotch ' in the tune is the fact that it is written in the Caledonian (or pentatonic) scale, in which the fourth and seventh notes do not appear (cf. ' The Campbells are coming '). As the heroine of Monk's song was named Belerma, this obviously ought to be the correct spelling of the name of the tune. But this is a minor detail.

560—Devizes.

DEVIZES is by Isaac Tucker, and comes from his *Sacred Music*, ' consisting of Psalm and Hymn-Tunes for three and four voices.' In order that there might be no mistake Tucker definitely announces on the title page that he is the ' author of the melodies.' The book is undated, but probably belongs to 1810. Tucker was a Wiltshire man, living at the time at Westbury Leigh.

561—Solomon.

SOLOMON is very much adapted from the air, ' What tho' I trace each herb and flower,' No. 10 in Handel's *Solomon* (1748).

562—Ombersley.

OMBERSLEY (the name of a beautiful village near Worcester) is by W. H. Gladstone, eldest son of W. E. Gladstone. The son was a good amateur musician. In his undergraduate days at Oxford the Musical Society possessed the greatest attraction for him. He not only could play the organ well—he often took the service at Hawarden Church—but he was a good singer, and a member of the Bach Choir and of one or two other similar institutions. He wrote several anthems, hymn-tunes, and chants, some of which are in use in St. Paul's Cathedral, and he was well versed in musical history, especially in that side which treated of compositions for the Church. He read an admirable paper at the Church

Congress at Carlisle in 1884, on 'Music as an Aid to Worship and Work.' He compiled a hymn-book, of which Sir Walter Parratt said, 'It is the only one I know in which there are no bad tunes.' The title was *A Selection of Hymns and Tunes, made and arranged by W. H. Gladstone* (1882). *Not for sale.* OMBERSLEY was included, but it originally appeared in *The Hymnary* (1872) set to ' Sun of my soul.'

563—Redhead No. 66. See No. 160.

564—Ripon.

RIPON (or DENNIS) is by Johann Georg Nägeli, who was born at Zurich in 1768. He was a strong supporter of Pestalozzi in the latter's efforts for developing the education of the people, and Nägeli wrote much in its favour. He composed many songs which he introduced in his business as a music publisher, and he also founded a school of music in his native town. Many of his manuscripts were bought by Lowell Mason, who discovered several hymn-tunes amongst them, including RIPON, which he included in one of his American collections of sacred music. Nägeli, who died in 1836, is one of several composers (including Mozart) to whom the once popular air, 'Life let us cherish,' has been ascribed.

565—Crediton.

CREDITON, by Thomas Clark, is from his *Second Sett of Psalm-Tunes* issued about 1810, and 'adapted to the use of country choirs.'

Thomas Clark was born in Canterbury in 1775 and spent practically the whole of his life in the city. He was brought up as a boot and shoe maker, but he was throughout his life devoted to music, and gave nearly all his spare time to it. He began to compose hymn-tunes at an early age, but he did not venture on publication till he reached his twenty-eighth year when, in 1805, he issued his first *Sett of Psalm and Hymn-*

Tunes. He had by this time achieved local renown as a trainer of country choirs, and it was to the members thereof that he dedicated his 'Setts.' Some of his tunes soon crossed the Atlantic, and appeared in early American tune-books.

Clark published other 'Setts' at intervals, and about 1830 he adopted a new title, and the *Sacred Gleaner* appeared which became a standard book.

In 1837 he edited, in association with B. F. Flint, the *Union Tune-Book,* destined for many years to be a popular publication.

Clark was held in great repute throughout the country, and the prefaces to various collections of tunes bear testimony to his reputation. For many years he was the leader of the Methodist Choir at Canterbury, and many special musical services were held there under his direction. As he grew older he fell under suspicion of holding opinions in sympathy with Unitarian teaching, though he never joined that body, but he found it necessary to resign his connexion with the Methodists. He died at his house in St. George's Street in 1859. That Clark's music was highly esteemed by his contemporaries is evident from a remark in the preface to *Lyra sacra* (1840) :

> Here are some of the best tunes by the best masters of music, and those by Clark of Canterbury, though last, are not the least in excellency of composition, and who has condescended to employ his musical talent in adapting some beautiful tunes to several pieces.

566—Benevento.

BENEVENTO is by Samuel Webbe. (See No. 75.)

567—St. Victor.

ST. VICTOR, by Richard Redhead (see No. 13) is from his *Ancient Hymn Melodies and other Church Tunes* (1859).

568—Crowland.

CROWLAND is from *Vierstimmiges Choralbuch* (1847), edited by F. Filitz. It was included in West and Sugden's *Wesleyan Hymn-Tune Book* (1871) and since then has percolated without interruption, but with altered harmonies, through various Methodist collections to the present day. It is ascribed to Johann Schop, a court musician of the seventeenth century, who achieved fame as a violinist. He wrote a number of hymn-tunes, and also instrumental music. He died in 1664.

569—Newington.

NEWINGTON is by William Dalrymple Maclagan, who was born at Edinburgh in 1826. From studying the law he passed to the army and served in India. Invalided home, he left the army for the Church, and held various livings till 1878, when he was created Bishop of Lichfield. Thirteen years later he became Archbishop of York, resigning in 1908. He died two years later.

Maclagan was both poet and musician, though as a composer he never got beyond the hymn-tune stage, except on one occasion. In a letter written whilst on his way to India in 1847, he refers to the music they had on board ship, and says that the band 'have just finished playing my polka, which their leader arranged for them.'

Maclagan composed several hymn-tunes during the period he spent as rector of Newington, in South London, and as vicar at St. Mary Abbott's, Kensington. At the latter church he had as his organist Henry R. Bird, who wrote thus of his vicar :

Mr. Maclagan was very fond of music, and proved himself a composer of several excellent hymn-tunes, but although he would play them either on his piano or harmonium, he found it difficult to write them down. He consequently often asked me to go to the vicarage—usually after the Sunday evening service—and I would then, after supper, take down the tunes and arrange them into four-part harmony, in doing which I never had to interfere with the harmony of his chords.

Some of these tunes appeared in the early edition of *Hymns Ancient and Modern,* and after he had been promoted to the bishopric of Lichfield, the composer gathered his tunes together into one small volume, which was published by Messrs. Novello in 1884. Here we find NEWINGTON written for the hymn, 'Thine for ever, God of love'; also PALMS OF GLORY and BREAD OF HEAVEN (see No. 621). In a preface Dr. Maclagen says that the tunes 'were chiefly composed to meet the requirements of the humbler classes, and they are for the most part very simple in their character.' It is rather difficult to understand exactly what he meant by this, but they are simple enough in form, and certainly do not in the slightest degree betray the fact that their composer had 'once composed a polka.'

Dr. Maclagan was a great believer in the efficacy of good, robust, congregational singing, and whilst at St. Mary's, Newington, he used to hold congregational practices after the weekly evening service. On such occasions he used to rehearse the hymns for the following Sunday, and always endeavoured to make the period thus spent one of real enjoyment as well as of practical utility. He carried out the same idea when he was appointed to Kensington. This was in 1875, when a new edition of *Hymns Ancient and Modern* had just been issued, and he held practices in order that the congregation might become acquainted with the new tunes. The happy results proved Maclagan's wisdom, and when the singing went well he was quite happy. Once, after preaching to a large congregation at a West London Church, he said to a friend, 'I feel so happy, for I knew they were in sympathy with me, and the singing was so good!'

570—Uffingham.

UFFINGHAM, by Jeremiah Clark (see No. 72), appeared in *The Divine Companion, or David's Harp New Tun'd* (1701). It was originally called ' An Evening Hymn ' and composed for a beautiful hymn of unknown authorship :

> Sleep, downey sleep, come close mine eyes
> Tired with beholding vanities.
> Welcome, sweet sleep, that driv'st away
> The toils and follies of the day.

571—Tichfield.

TICHFIELD, by John Richardson (see No. 408), is from Formby's *Collection of Catholic Hymns* (1853).

572—Mozart.

MOZART is an adaptation of the famous duet in the composer's *Il Flauto Magico* (1791). It is uncertain when it was first made into a hymn-tune.

Wolfgang Amadeus Mozart was born at Salzburg in 1756. In his eighth year his father, Leopold Mozart, himself a distinguished musician, took him and his sister on a concert tour, visiting London and other capitals. At fourteen he was made concert meister to the Archbishop of Salzburg. In 1781 he went to live in Vienna, and here it was that most of his famous operas were produced, but not always favourably. His *Marriage of Figaro* was received with indifference, but at Prague the contrary was the case, and the composer was enthusiastically received. For the Prague public Mozart wrote his *Don Giovanni,* and in appreciation the Emperor Joseph II made him court composer. His last great opera was *The Magic Flute,* and his last great work the *Requiem,* written under romantic and indeed mysterious circumstances. He died at the end of 1791, worn out with worry, anxiety and persecution. His vocal and instrumental works are too well known to call for detailed reference. About two years before his death

Mozart made the acquaintance of the works of J. S. Bach, and the result was a remarkable display of the treatment of *cantus firmus* in *The Magic Flute*. He had no difficulty in imitating other composers whilst retaining his own individuality. He is credited with the invention of the art form in songs, varying the melody according to the meaning of the text, the most striking example being his music to Goethe's 'Violet.'

573—Pater Omnium.

PATER OMNIUM is from *The Burnley Tune-Book* (1875). The composer, Henry James Ernest Holmes, was born at Burnley in 1852. He came of an old legal family, and after leaving Clitheroe Grammar School, he was educated for the legal profession, being admitted a solicitor of the High Court of Chancery in 1875. He has practised in his native town for about sixty years, and he is at present (1934) one of the oldest practising solicitors in Lancashire. From his earliest days he has been interested in music, especially in psalmody, and he has identified himself with the music of the Church Sunday-school in Sandygate. His work in composition dates from his seventeenth year, and his first book of fifty tunes was dedicated to the teachers and scholars of the school. One of the first tunes he composed was PATER OMNIUM, which has now become widely known. It it named from the first three words of the last verse of the hymn to which it was originally set :

> Onward through life Thy children stray,
> Groping at noon their silent way.
> Long is the road and fierce the sun,
> When will the dreary way be done.
> Footsore and faint, to Thee we cry,
> Father of all—be very nigh.

Mr. Holmes has been engaged in a number of charitable works, and needless to say he is held in high esteem in the town where he has spent a long and honourable life.

574—Wellspring. See No. 319.

575—St. James. See No. 307.

576, 670—Grosvenor.

GROSVENOR is by Edmund Harwood, and is found in his *Second Set of Psalm and Hymn-Tunes* (1786). The composer was born at Hoddesdon, near Darwen, in 1707. He was brought up as a hand-loom weaver, and also sang in the choir in the Higher Chapel at Darwen. He then went to Liverpool and took to music as a profession, being also an alto singer at St. Peter's. The following legend is told of one of Harwood's best-known settings. On one occasion he and a friend named A. Reed went up to London to have a look round. When they were about to return home they found they were at the end of their resources, so Harwood resolved to turn his musical talents to account. Finding a book of poetry in the sitting-room, he took it up, and turning over the leaves, found Pope's Ode, which he promptly set to music, and, taking his MS. to a publisher, sold the copyright for £40. (It must not be assumed from this that publishers are always as ready to accept MSS. and pay at sight.) 'Vital Spark' certainly had a long and prosperous run, and even now it is not quite extinct. Harwood issued two books of tunes, the first being published in London about 1777, and the second at Chester a year before his death, which took place in 1787. The former volume contained VITAL SPARK and several tunes named after places in or near Liverpool. In the second volume will be found the tunes now known as ST. PETER'S and GROSVENOR, the latter being originally called 'Christmas Hymn.'

577—Zu Meinem Herrn.

ZU MEINEM HERRN is one of about three hundred tunes written by J. G. Schicht for his *Allgemeines Choralbuch,* which he published in 1819.

Johann Gottfried Schicht was born at a village near Zittau, Saxony, in 1753. After leaving Leipzig University he became a solo clavier player, and in time was appointed head of the Thomas Schule. He wrote oratorios and other church music, and also edited an important edition of J. S. Bach's church motets.

578—Cambridge. See No. 234.

579—Something for Thee.

SOMETHING FOR THEE, by R. Lowry (see No. 211). It is uncertain in what American collection this tune first appeared.

580—Spohr.

SPOHR. In 1834 Spohr wrote an oratorio, *Das Heiland's letze Stunden* ('The last hours of the Saviour'), which was first heard in this country at the Norwich Festival of 1839. An English version, under the title of *The Crucifixion,* had been prepared by Edward Taylor, a Norwich musician, who was closely associated with the city festivals as organizer, soloist, and occasionally conductor. Both the title and the libretto of Spohr's new work were subjected to severe criticism, owing to religious prejudice, and one of the results was that the part of the Saviour was taken by the Apostle John. In the programme of the festival the oratorio was called *Calvary,* and Taylor's original title disappeared.

In Spohr's work there is a solo and chorus sung by Mary, 'Though all Thy friends prove faithless.' This was adapted to other words, 'As pants the hart,' by J. Stimpson, and its popularity as an anthem caused the opening strains to be adopted as the hymn-tune, SPOHR.

Born in 1784 at Brunswick, Louis Spohr displayed musical talent at an early age, and received an excellent education from his parents, both of whom were lovers of music. By dint of hard work he gradually gained a reputation both as violinist and composer, and in due time his great reputation induced the London Philharmonic Society to invite him to play at one of their concerts. His appearance here gave rise to a memorable incident which became one of the landmarks of the history of music. Up to the time of his coming the use of the baton was practically unknown, the conductor really being the first violin player, who gave the tempo and occasionally pulled his orchestra together by giving a sign with his bow. Spohr found this method so unsatisfactory that at his first concert he drew a baton from his pocket and gave the signal to begin. Astonishment at the innovation gave place to signs of approbation, and the use of the baton was thus sanctioned at its first appearance in England.

It was probably some time before the composer forgot his first experience of London. The morning after his arrival he had to meet the directors of the Philharmonic Society. Anxious to make a good impression, he arrayed himself in his best clothes, not forgetting ' a bright-red Turkish shawl-pattern waistcoat,' which formed part of his wardrobe, and which was at that time a highly fashionable article of men's attire. Scarcely had he appeared in the street than he found he was attracting much attention. Grown-up people gazed at him with looks of surprise, and the street urchins, amazed at the sight (Spohr was a tall man, and proportionately broad) formed a formidable tail in his rear. Spohr, greatly wondering at the unexpected attention he was receiving, at last reached a friend's house to which he had been directed, and then the mystery was explained. George III had just died, so official mourning was the order of the day, and the sight of the flaunting red waistcoat was too much for the London folk. Needless to say, Spohr quickly returned to his lodgings in Charlotte Street and selected a garment more in harmony with the occasion.

In 1830 Edward Taylor was on the look-out for new

works for the Norwich Festival. Hearing that Spohr
had just finished a new work, he obtained a copy, and
Sir G. Smart and Taylor were so impressed with the
work that it was produced at the Festival of 1831, Thus
was *The Last Judgement* introduced into England. His
other oratorios, *Calvary* and *The Fall of Babylon,* have
proved less successful. The cantata, *God, Thou art
great,* is still remembered. His other works include
operas, symphonies and chamber music. He ranks high
in history as a violinist. His long life came to a close
in 1859.

581—St. Ethelwald.

ST. ETHELWALD was written by W. H. Monk for the
first (1861) edition of *Hymns Ancient and Modern.*
(See No. 221.)

582—Let the Lower Lights.

LET THE LOWER LIGHTS, by P. Bliss, is from the
American *Gospel Hymns and Sacred Songs* (1875). This
was the first of the 'Gospel Hymns' series of six
numbers.

583—Beulah.

BEULAH (also known as WOOLWICH COMMON) is first
found in William Gawler's *Psalms and Hymns* (c. 1785).
Gawler was organist of the Royal Female Orphan
Asylum in Lambeth. He published three books of tunes
for the use of the children, the first of which contained
the famous 'Morning Hymn' by Barthélémon (see No.
931). This was published in 1784, and a succeeding
collection, issued possibly in the following year, contained BEULAH set as a L.M. with the name ST. MICHEL.
In the progress of years this long metre tune has been
elongated into an eight-line D.C.M., a decidedly unusual
process. Here is the original, in the unusual key of
B flat, but the setting was, of course, for girls' voices:

Cre - a - tor Spi - rit by whose aid

The world's found-a - tions first were laid,

Come, vi - sit ev - 'ry pi - ous mind,

Come, pour Thy joys on all man - kind.

584—Old 113th.

The OLD 113TH may be traced back to the *Strasburg Psalter* of 1542. The publication of these psalters began in this city about 1525, and in 1539 an edition was issued under the superintendence of Calvin, who took his edition to Geneva, where it underwent various additions, partly under the supervision of Louis Bourgeois until the whole psalter was completed in 1562. Some of the melodies have been assigned, on good authority, to the monk, Matthias Greiter, a chorister and perhaps organist at Strasburg Cathedral. It was formerly known as ' the Patriarch's tune.' In its original form it is one of the longest tunes in the Psalter, being set to a twelve-line eights. Early in the eighteenth century it was shortened to a six-line eights and in this form included in various hymnals. The tune had a great attraction for John Wesley, whose knowledge of it probably arose from having heard it in Epworth Church in his boyhood. He included it in his ' Foundery ' Tune Book (1742) in its full form to a hymn beginning:

> Ye priests of God, whose happy days
> Are spent in your Creator's praise.

It appeared in all his tune-books issued during his lifetime. It is said to have been the last tune he ever sang, and on the day before he died he employed what little strength remained to him in singing it to Watts's hymn, 'I'll praise my Maker while I've breath.'

585—Watchman.

WATCHMAN, by James Leach. See No. 543.

586—Unde et Memores.

UNDE ET MEMORES was written by W. H. Monk for the 1875 edition of *Hymns Ancient and Modern*. (See No. 221.)

587—Nicolaus.

NICOLAUS (or LOBT GOTT, also ST. GEORGE) is the English form of an old German melody ascribed to Nicolaus Hermann, which he set to his own Christmas hymn, 'Lobt Gott, ihr Christen alle gleich.' Both hymn and melody were published in 1560, but the tune itself had appeared in 1554 to a different hymn. This chorale is used by Bach in two of his cantatas, No. 151, and the *Wedding* Cantata.

588—Sheltered Dale.

SHELTERED DALE is a German volkslied introduced into England as 'The Millwheel.' Its German title is 'Das zerbrochene Ringlein' (The Broken Ring), the words for which are by Joseph von Eichendorff and the air from a melody by Johann Ludwig Friedrich Glück (1814).

589, 905—Grenoble.

GRENOBLE is taken from the *English Hymnal*, where it is called DEUS TUORUM MILITUM. These are the first words of an ancient Latin hymn of unknown origin, which have frequently been set to music (see No. 156). In the *English Hymnal* the air is said to be a 'Grenoble Church Melody,' but no definite information is forthcoming.

590—Antwerp. See No. 153.

591—St. Thomas.

St. Thomas is probably by Aaron Williams, an eighteenth-century musician who published several collections of psalm-tunes. The present tune is in his *Universal Psalmodist* (1770). He seems to have been a man of varied occupation—composer, teacher of music, and engraver of music, and on Sundays he was clerk to a Scottish church in London Wall.

592—Cripplegate.

Cripplegate, from the second edition of *Hymns Ancient and Modern* (1875), is by George Alexander Macfarren, who was born in London, March 2, 1813. His predilection for music was soon apparent, and at the age of fourteen he became a pupil of Charles Lucas, a sound theorist and accomplished violoncello player. Two years later he entered the Royal Academy, where he made harmony his chief, and the trombone his second, study. That he made good progress in his studies, and exhibited distinct ability, is evidenced by his appointment, at the early age of twenty-one, to a professorship in the Institution with which he was so intimately connected for the rest of his life. His first notable composition was the *Chevy Chase* overture, which had a long run both here and on the Continent. For the next few years he wrote a large number of operas, none of which achieved lasting success. Although his music was English in style, he had not the gift of easy flowing melody that distinguished the works of Balfe and Bishop. In 1843 he was appointed secretary of the newly-formed Handel Society, editing *Belshazzar* and two other oratorios for performance. In later years he edited others, providing valuable historical and analytical notes for each.

In 1875 he succeeded Sterndale Bennett as Principal of the Royal Academy of Music, and, thanks to his strong and beneficent rule, the Academy sailed out of stormy waters into the distinguished position it still occupies. Macfarren also succeeded his friend Bennett as Professor of Music at Cambridge University. In 1883, in company with Sullivan and George Grove, he received the honour of knighthood.

Although essentially a conservative in music, Macfarren was in the opposite camp in political matters. He held titles and degrees of little worth, and ever maintained that a man's value should be estimated by his works alone. One remarkable outcome of this feeling was the vigour with which he frequently denounced the Hanoverian family for their marked indifference to English music and musicians for over a century. He held that the Royal patronizing of foreigners had stopped progress, broken the continuity of our English school of music, and thus had prevented it from occupying in Europe its just position as an art. In 1873 Macfarren made an appearance in a new phase. He wrote for the Bristol Festival of that year his first oratorio, *St. John the Baptist.* This was so well received that it was suggested by many that a fresh departure in oratorio form had taken place. The composer was encouraged to persevere, but his subsequent works, *The Resurrection, Joseph* and *King David* failed to increase his reputation.

Macfarren had a wonderfully retentive memory. Even those brought into connexion with him, day by day, were amazed at his powers. He forgot nothing that he had once committed to the storehouse of his memory, from the details of the score of one of some great master's compositions, to the faults in the harmony exercises of his pupils, or some date in musical history. Considering that from the time of his youth to his ripened maturity he had witnessed a wonderful enlargement, and indeed, revolution in the art, this is saying much for any man; but not too much for Macfarren. On the production of Raff's *Leonora* symphony, at one of the Crystal Palace concerts, his attention was called to a peculiar melodic progression and attendant harmony as being strikingly original. ' Oh, no ! ' said Macfarren, ' I wrote a passage just like that in one of my symphonies forty-five years ago,' and he added, grimly, ' I don't like it.'

593—Retirement.

RETIREMENT was composed by Dr. G. F. Brockless (see No. 127) for the present (1933) edition of the *Methodist Hymn-Book*.

594—St. Michael. See No. 377.

595—Carlisle.

CARLISLE (originally called INVOCATION), by Charles Lockhart, is from the second edition (1792) of the ' Lock Hospital Collection ' (see No. 479). Blind from his birth in 1745, he led an active musical life, and held the post of organist at the Lock Hospital, Hyde Park, during the ministry of Rev. Martin Madan. From there he passed to the City Church of St. Katherine Cree from about 1775 to 1780, when he went to St. Mary's, Lambeth.

A short period at Orange Street Chapel followed, then he returned to the Lock Hospital. Besides hymn-tunes he wrote several songs. This tune does not take its name from the city of Carlisle, but from Carlisle Chapel, now Holy Trinity Church, W. Lockhart had the reputation of a skilful trainer of children's voices, and for this purpose he published, about 1810, *A Set of Hymn-Tunes and an Anthem* ' with chords inserted in small notes instead of figures for Juvenile Performers,' which he dedicated to William Wilberforce. He died in 1815.

596—Llanllyfni.

LLANLLYFNI is by John Jones, who, to distinguish him from others of the same name, is usually known as

John Jones of Tal-y-sarn, where he resided for the greater part of his life. He was born in 1796 at Tan-y-castell, Caernarvonshire. He was the eldest of a family of nine, and his father's death at an early age left him the chief supporter of the family. He obtained occupation in the quarries, where his musical abilities gained him the confidence and admiration of his fellow quarry-men.

One of the musicians into whose company the youth found his way was none other than the celebrated Ieuan Glan Geirionydd, whose knowledge of music was second to none in the Principality. He liked John and gave him a taste for worthy music, taught him the rudiments of learning and showed him how to walk boldly in the music world. He lent him not only works about music and musical books, but also books on theology. Such an opportunity was not to be missed by this young man. By hard work he became a Methodist preacher, and in 1820 entered the ministry. But he did not neglect his music, and during his life he composed about fifty hymn-tunes, of which the best known is LLANLLYFNI, which takes its name from the sacred spot where he was laid to rest on August 17, 1857.

There is a story to the effect that this tune is really by David Jenkins (No. 528) 'who based the tune on the remarkable intonation of the Rev. John Jones's voice in preaching.' Perhaps so, but as Jenkins was only eight years old when John Jones died, he must have been a very impressionable youth.

597—Sandys.

SANDYS is from the same source as No. 128.

598—Syria.

SYRIA first appeared in *The Union Tune-Book* (1842). Its composer is unknown.

599—Swabia.

The origin of SWABIA is usually attributed to *David's Harpffen Spiel* (1745), where it is set to the hymn, 'Ach, wachet, wachet,' by Johann Martin Spiess. But a much earlier source of the melody will be found in Lucas Lossius's *Psalmodia, hoc est, Cantica Sacra veteris Ecclesiae selecta*, published at Nuremberg by Gabriel Hayn, in 1553. In this rare book, of which a copy (not quite perfect, as it wants pp. xxvii-xxxiv) is in the British Museum, the tune appears set to the hymn, 'Festum nunc celebre.' As the title of the book sufficiently explains, the tunes are taken from pre-Reformation sources (*veteris Ecclesiae*), and the present hymn-tune is none other than a setting of 'Festum nunc celebre magnaque gaudia,' written by Rabanus Maurus (d. 856), and sung on the feast of the Ascension. This collection has an admirable preface by Melancthon.

The adaptation of the tune from Spiess's book of 1745 was made by W. H. Havergal for his *Old Church Psalmody* (1847).

600—Kettering.

KETTERING (or LONDON) originally appeared in *The Skylark* (c. 1720), which contained the hymns from Addison's *Spectator*, set to music by John Sheeles, who wrote it for 'The spacious firmament on high.' It was reproduced in *The Divine Musical Miscellany* (1754) and other Methodist tune-books in the eighteenth century, and then faded away. It was revived in the *Appendix* to the *Methodist Hymn-Book* (1904), and has now taken its rightful place. Nothing is known of the composer, except that in addition to *The Skylark*, he wrote some pieces for the harpsichord.

601—Everton.

EVERTON, by Henry Smart (see No. 12), is from *Psalms and Hymns for Divine Worship* (1867).

602 (i)—Arabia.

ARABIA. The history of this tune is not clearly defined. It is here stated to be by W. Wilson on the authority of Hawkes's *Collection of Tunes*, a massive volume published at Watchet, Somerset, in 1831. But this is not the first appearance of the tune, and there is considerable doubt as to who the composer really is.

602 (ii)—Lebanon.

LEBANON is arranged from the Andante in F of Spohr's *Quartet in A minor* (Op. 58, No. 2). It was originally adapted by H. J. Gauntlett for the *Comprehensive Tune-Book* (1851) as BEDFORD CHAPEL. The tune is also known as FLENSBURG.

603—Attercliffe. See No. 333.

604 (i)—St. Fulbert.

ST. FULBERT was contributed by H. J. Gauntlett (see No. 7) to W. J. Blew's *Church Hymn and Tune Book* (1852), where it is named ST. LEOFRED.

604 (ii)—Beatitudo.

BEATITUDO was written by Dr. J. B. Dykes (see No. 36) for *Hymns Ancient and Modern* (1875).

605—Colchester.

COLCHESTER is by S. S. Wesley, and appeared in his *European Psalmist* (1872).

606—Warsaw.

WARSAW is probably by Thomas Clark (see No. 565), and is taken from the Houldsworth edition of Chetham's *Psalmody* (1832).

607—Tallis' Ordinal. See No. 304.

608—Marienlyst.

MARIENLYST is from the 1876 edition of the *Wesleyan Tune-Book*. The composer, John W. David, was born in Guernsey in 1837. His musical talent was inherited, both his parents being musical. His first instruments were the fife and accordion, teaching himself to play by ear. He then passed on to a fiddle, and received his first lesson in his eighth year. On his twelfth birthday he was the proud recipient of a piano, on which he had lessons from W. A. Crousaz, organist of the town parish church. In 1852 David played the seraphim (a sort of harmonium) at the village chapel. The following year he was appointed organist at the French Wesleyan Chapel (Victoria Road). 'It was,' said Mr. David, 'very uphill work for a youngster to combat the prejudices of old men who thought they knew a great deal more about music than I did.' However, youth prevailed, and he remained twelve years at his post, and then resigned for an appointment in the Ebenezer English Wesleyan Chapel, where there was a two-manual organ. From there he passed on to St. Barnabas Church in 1874, where he was organist till his death in 1902. The only organ lessons he ever had were from Dr. Longhurst, organist of Canterbury Cathedral. Whilst he was at Ebenezer Chapel he was also organist at the afternoon service in the parish church, which at that time was in French. David is remembered as being the first to introduce a regular choral service in Guernsey.

609—Lewes.

LEWES, by John Randall (see No. 49), was originally published in leaflet form about 1774. It was written for the Rev. Robert Robinson's hymn:

> Mighty God, while angels bless Thee,
> May an infant lisp Thy name.

As both musician and hymnist were living in Cambridge at the time it is not unreasonable to suppose that they were associated in the production of the leaflet, perhaps for some special occasion.

610—Mount Beacon.

MOUNT BEACON, by Alfred Beer. See No. 371 (ii).

611—Mannheim.

MANNHEIM, CAPETOWN (No. 682), and CASWALL (No. 684), are all taken from *Vierstimmiges Choralbuch,* a collection of tunes formed and edited by F. Filitz in 1847. Born at Armstadt in 1804, he acquired fame as a critic and historian, and enjoyed the friendship of Baron von Bunsen.

612—Sandon.

SANDON first appeared in *The Church and Home Metrical Psalter,* edited by C. H. Purday, who wrote the tune. It was originally called LANDON. Purday was a music publisher and he also lectured on musical subjects. He was for some years precentor at the Church of Scotland in Crown Court, Drury Lane, during the ministry of the founder, Dr. John Cumming. Purday had a good deal of experience in church work. His selection of 101 tunes for one of his books was the result of practically illustrating his opinion that that number of tunes was sufficient for any tune-book. In one of his 'Introductions' he gives useful advice about the conduct of church music :

The Editor is of opinion that if every church were to be supplied with its tune-book in sufficient numbers for each individual of the congregation to have one, many more persons would join in singing the praises of the Great Redeemer of the World ; and there would be a greater amount of solemn and dignified praise uttered than is now generally found in our places of worship. And it is further suggested that, if every family would take the pains to have their children

taught to sing at sight, and use their tune-books at
home, we should have no lack of good congregational
singing in the church; and less complaint when the
precentor, choir, or organist introduces *new* tunes.
Singing should be made a necessary part of the education of all classes, that everybody might be enabled to
join in choral music, sacred and secular; and until
such is really the case, we shall never have good
congregational singing in our churches.

613—All Souls.

ALL SOULS is from *The English Hymnal,* which is
probably the first English collection in which it appeared.
The composer, John Yoakley, who died in 1932 in his
seventy-third year, was an organist of wide experience,
and played at various churches in the United States. He
was descended from a Yorkshire family who settled
in America.

614—Salvator.

SALVATOR originally appeared in the *Burnley Tune-
Book* (1875). It then passed into the *Bristol Tune-Book*
(1881) and thus became well known. The composer,
James Pentland Jewson, was born in Durham County in
1825. He received a musical education, showing a distinct
preference for the organ, and received his first appointment at Sedgfield. From there he went to the parish
church at Stockton-on-Tees, where he remained nearly
thirty years. He organized and conducted the Stockton
Orchestral Society. He had a large teaching connexion,
which he maintained till his death in 1889.

615 (i)—Cwm Rhondda.

John Hughes, the composer of CWM RHONDDA, was
born at Dowlais in 1873. In the following year his
parents removed to Llantwit Fardre, where he spent the
rest of his life. He started work as a door-boy at Glyn

Colliery at the age of twelve, and afterwards entered the service of the G.W. Railway as an official in the Traffic Department. He was a lifelong member of Salem Baptist Church, and succeeded his father as deacon and precentor, holding these positions till his death on May 14, 1932.

CWM RHONDDA (originally called RHONDDA) was composed for the annual Baptist Cymangfa Ganu (Singing Festival) at Pontypridd in 1905. By 1930 it had been heard in no less than 5,000 festivals. Hughes composed anthems and other music, but none of them has achieved success save CWM RHONDDA.

615 (ii)—Oriel.

ORIEL is set to the hymn ' Pange Lingua ' in *Cantica Sacra,* compiled by Kaspar (or Gaspard) Ett in 1840. He was born at Eresing in Bavaria in 1788. At the age of nine he became a chorister in a Benedictine Abbey, whence he passed to the Elector's School at Munich. In 1816 he was appointed organist at the church of St. Michael's in Munich, a position he occupied for thirty-one years till his death in 1847. He composed several masses and other music for the Catholic Church. There seems some uncertainty as to whether his Christian name was Caspar, Kaspar, or Gaspard. On the printed music it is Caspar, but Fétis calls him by the third name.

616 (i)—Ebenezer.

EBENEZER is by Thomas John Williams, who was born in 1869 at Rhos, Pontardawe, Glamorgan. The tune was composed under this name for a hymn by Rev. William Williams of Pantycelin (in *Llawlyfr Moliaint* 1890). Three years later it was included in the *Baptist Book of Praise,* where it was named ASSURANCE, owing to EBENEZER having been assigned to another tune in the book. After this the tune entered the realms of myth for a period owing to the mistaken enterprise of a

London daily paper. It was reproduced in four-part harmony and this explanation was added:

> A curious slurring dirge—half chant, half hymn-tune—has taken musical Wales by storm. It is popularly known as 'Ton-y-Botel,' which in plain English means 'The Tune in the Bottle,' for it is generally believed to have been picked up on the Welsh coast, sealed up in a bottle, cast ashore by the waves.

Thanks to the courtesy of Mr. W. Gwenlyn Evans, of Caernarvon, the owner of the copyright, we are able to reproduce the music, while the Welsh words have been rendered into English by the Rev. J. W. Wynne Jones, M.A., vicar of Caernarvon.

'I first heard it in Manchester,' said Mr. Evans, 'in October. There were hundreds of Welshmen there, and they struck up the quaint tune, with which I was very much struck at the time. Then I came home and heard people humming the tune, little boys in the street whistling it, and I thought it would take, so I made search for the author. After some delay I discovered that the tune had been composed as part of an anthem by Mr. T. J. Williams, Rhos, Pontardawe, in the Swansea Valley. The anthem was known as " Golen yn y Glyn " (" Light in the valley "). I secured and copyrighted it.'

The curious name was given to it at first in fun by a young man who rendered it at a private entertainment before it became widely known. When asked for the history of the tune, he laughingly told his friends that it had been picked up by a yokel on the coast of Lleyn, in a sealed bottle washed ashore. This touch of romance undoubtedly gave an impetus to the craze, for at that time Mr. Gwenlyn Evans had not discovered the composer, and the name clung to the tune, even after the publisher had rechristened it EBENEZER.

The progress of 'Ton-y-Botel,' for it will ever remain to be known as such, has been phenomenal. It marched from one Welsh village to another long before printed copies of it were to be obtained. It was learnt by ear. One day a congregation in one town sang it; next day it would be heard more inland; and the next in the very wilds of the snow-covered mountain fastnesses. Then there came the rush for printed copies, especially in North Wales; and though one half the population had not seen the music, almost every child could sing the tune correctly, and parties could render the four parts.

Arrangements are now being made for its production at half-a-dozen musical festivals. It is not improbable that before long it will be hawked round the London streets, and its soul-stirring strains rendered on barrel organs.

The tune came unscathed through these curious experiences, and finds a place in most modern hymnals.

616 (ii)—Marching.

MARCHING, by Martin Shaw, was included in a collection of 'Additional Tunes' he published for use at St. Mary's Church, Primrose Hill, N.W., in 1915.

Dr. Martin Shaw was born in London. He inherited his musical instincts from his father, who was organist at various places of worship, including Bedford Chapel, Bloomsbury, and Hampstead parish church. At the Royal College of Music he studied under Stanford, Parry, and Walford Davies. After leaving he was associated in various operatic enterprises, showing a marked preference for Purcell and for folk-song. About 1906 he was associated with Dr. Vaughan Williams in the production of the *English Hymnal*, and he 'used to spend hours at the British Museum finding and copying tunes.' He accepted Dr. Dearmer's invitation to be his organist at St. Mary's, Primrose Hill, and in 1913 he edited *The English Carol Book*. Four years later he announced in *To-Day* his schemes to place England 'on its own feet as a musical nation ':

SCHEME No. 1.—DESTRUCTIVE.

1.—The abolition of all schools, colleges, and academies of music.

2.—The giving up of the concert habit.

3.—A bonfire of pianos, classical music, and drawing-room songs.

4.—The painless extinction of all concert ' artistes.'

SCHEME No. 2.—CONSTRUCTIVE.

1.—The singing of English nursery-rhymes to all children in the nursery, as part of their upbringing.

2.—The teaching of folk-song and new music, written in the English manner or idiom, in universities and schools, public, private, and elementary.

3.—The establishment of civic music guilds in every town and village.

In recent years Dr. Shaw has written some important choral works, and his *Up to Now* is one of the most entertaining and clearly-written autobiographies ever published.

617—Armageddon.

ARMAGEDDON is from the Appendix to Mercer's *Church Psalter and Hymn-Book* (1872), set to ' Onward, Christian soldiers.' The tune is thought to be an adaptation by Sir J. Goss of a German melody, but there is a good deal more of Goss than of the German melody in the tune.

618—Knecht.

KNECHT is named after its composer, Justin Heinrich Knecht, who included it amongst his contributions to the Stuttgart *Vollständige Sammlung* (1799), which he edited in association with J. F. Christmann.

25

J. H. Knecht was born at Biberach, Swabia, in 1752. He was director of music in his native town, and for a time director of the opera at Stuttgart. However, he proved unequal to the task, and returned to Biberach, where he obtained a great reputation as an organist. He died in 1817.

619—Forward! be our Watchword.

FORWARD! BE OUR WATCHWORD was composed by Henry Alford, who was created Dean of Canterbury in 1857. There was in existence at that time a Canterbury Diocesan Choral Festival, the original leader having been H. L. Jenner (No. 677). On his being appointed Bishop of Dunedin he was succeeded by the famous naturalist, J. G. Wood, who made a great success of the first festival for which he was responsible. He had noticed on previous occasions that the procession of the singers into the cathedral was distinctly straggly, so he decided to remedy this. Dr. Alford had some reputation as a hymnist, so Wood asked him to write a suitable hymn for processional use. The Dean didn't see the use of it. Wood did, and gradually brought the Dean round. His first attempt failed to satisfy Wood, as it did not possess the necessary 'marching' rhythm. He suggested that the Dean should go into the cathedral, walk slowly along the course the procession would take, and compose another hymn as he did so. The Dean, not in the least offended, did as he was bid, and the result was the hymn, 'Forward! be our watchword.' The MS. reached the precentor with a humorous little note to the effect that the Dean had written the hymn and put it into its hat and boots, and that Mr. Wood might add the coat and trousers for himself. On looking at the music Wood found that only the treble and bass had been supplied by the composer, the alto and tenor being subsequently added by Mrs. Worthington Bliss, better known in those days as 'Miss Lindsay,' composer of many ballads of great but fleeting popularity.

J. G. Wood's son says, in his biography of the great naturalist: 'The effect of the hymn, when sung by the vast body of choristers, was almost overwhelming. From the time when the leaders of the procession emerged from the cloisters into the north aisle to that in which the last of the long stream ascended the steps of the choir, nearly half-an-hour elapsed. And throughout the whole of this time the glorious strains of Dean Alford's hymn were taken up again and again by fresh bodies of voices, each pair of choristers joining in the chorus as they reached a specified spot, and ceasing as they set foot on the last step of the ascent to the choir. Such were the conditions under which FORWARD! BE OUR WATCHWORD was first heard.' Alford's tune was inserted in the 1875 edition of *Hymns Ancient and Modern,* but dropped subsequently. Its revival is an interesting experiment.

620—Monks Gate.

MONKS GATE has become associated (through *The English Hymnal*) with Bunyan's verses beginning, 'Who would true valour see.'

It was adapted by R. Vaughan Williams from a folk-song he collected, 'Our captain calls all hands on board to-morrow.' The singer came from Monks Gate, near Horsham, Sussex, hence its name:

> Our captain calls all hands on board to-morrow,
> Leaving my dear to mourn in grief and sorrow.
> Dry up those briny tears and leave off weeping,
> So happy may we be . . . at our next meeting.

It has been suggested that MONKS GATE is the tune to which Bunyan's verses were intended to be sung. This is wholly erroneous. Hymns were unknown at Elstow Church, and only metrical psalms were used. According to the records of the meeting-house he attended in Bedford, there was no singing of any kind till two years after Bunyan's death.

621—Bread of Heaven.

BREAD OF HEAVEN was originally composed by Archbishop Maclagan for Josiah Conder's hymn, 'Bread of heaven on Thee we feed.' See No. 569.

622—Cords of Love.

CORDS OF LOVE was written by J. Barnby (see No. 105) for the *Congregational Church Hymnal* (1887).

623—Nachtlied.

NACHTLIED, by Henry Smart (see No. 12), was written for *The Hymnary* (1872).

624—Spire.

SPIRE is one of several names given to this tune, others being SEELENBRAUTIGAM, from the first word of the German hymn to which it was written, also ARNSTADT, HAARLEM, THURINGIA, DARMSTADT, ZINZENDORF. Of all these the most inappropriate is SPIRE, as the composer, Adam Drese, had no connexion with the place. The tune originally began :

Drese is said to have been born at Weinral, in Thuringia. He was trained as a musician. He held office at Kapell-meister, and also became Town Mayor, at Jena. He joined the sect of Pietists, and wrote hymns with tunes for their use at services held at his house, SPIRES, with its hymn, being one of them. It was published in the *Darmstadt Gesangbuch* (1698). Drese died in 1701 in his eighty-second year. In 1657 he contributed some tunes to G. Neumark's *Lustwald*.

625, 749—Dundee.

DUNDEE (also known as FRENCH) is from *The CL. Psalmes of David in Prose and Meeter with their whole usuall Notes and Tunes,* which was published with the melodies only by Andro Hart, Edinburgh, in 1615. In this book the tune is called FRENCH. When Ravenscroft published his Psalter (see No. 45), in 1621, he inserted FRENCH amongst his Scottish tunes, but changed the name to DUNDY, evidently thinking it a more appropriate one. But this was an unfortunate choice, since there was a tune called DUNDIE in Hart's *CL. Psalmes* already referred to. This DUNDIE (or DUNDEE) is the name now given in Scotland to WINDSOR (see No. 237). Thus the English WINDSOR is known in Scotland as DUNDEE, and south of the Tweed the Scotch tune, FRENCH, is also called DUNDEE by some, and FRENCH by others.

The metrical version of the Scottish Psalms is very dear to those who have been brought up on them, and equally dear are their melodies, some of which Burns mentions in his 'Cottar's Saturday Night.' Here is a modern testimony from a distinguished officer :

I have heard the Metrical Psalms, set to these grand old tunes, sung in quiet churches in Highland glens, often with the waves beating an accompaniment on the rocks; I have heard them sung—frequently in Gaelic—at open-air Communion services—among the heather hills; I have heard them sung (when serving with a famous Highland regiment) on the plains of Flanders, with the guns booming their diapason in the distance. The glorious, resonant phrases rising and falling to the stately strains of FRENCH always, always filled one with a sense of peace, contentment and solemnity.

626—Albano.

ALBANO, by Vincent Novello, first appeared in the Appendix (1868) to *Hymns Ancient and Modern.*

Vincent Novello, son of an Italian, Guiseppe Novello, was born in 1781 in a house in Oxford Street, London, now replaced by the Marble Arch Tube Station. Music was born in him, and he became a chorister in the Sardinian Chapel under Samuel Webbe, for whom the boy frequently officiated at the organ. His first appointment was to the Portuguese Embassy's Chapel in South Street, W., where he and his friend, S. Wesley, used to have great times at the organ. In after years he was organist at Moorfields R.C. Chapel, E.C., and he also presided at the organ during the Westminster Abbey Festival of 1834. His house in Oxford Street was the resort of many famous men of the day, and Charles Lamb, Keats, Leigh Hunt and Shelley frequently visited him there. Lamb wrote an amusing note to Novello's son-in-law, Cowden Clarke, about the Abbey Festival :

> We heard the music in the Abbey at Winchmore Hill ! and the notes were incomparably softened by the distance. Novello's chromatics were distinctly audible. Clara was faulty in B flat. Otherwise she sang like an angel. The trombone and Beethoven's waltzes were the best. Who played the oboe?

' Clara ' was Novello's daughter, and one of the most famous singers of the time.

Novello led a wonderfully industrious life. He composed, edited, copied voluminously at Cambridge and York, and found time in 1832 to compete for the Manchester Prize for a cheerful glee ('Old May Morning') and win it. In 1830 Novello moved with his family into Frith Street, and here his son Alfred commenced the music publishing business which has long since acquired world-wide fame. Here Mendelssohn and Malibran visited him, and the home was the scene of much music making. Novello was actively associated with Samuel Wesley in the latter's persistent advocacy of J. S. Bach's music, and the visit they paid to Dr. Burney with a view to making him a convert was indeed a memorable one. Novello's long and active life came to an end in 1861. There is a memorial window to him in the north transept of Westminster Abbey.

627—Spes Celestis.

SPES CELESTIS is by W. A. Smith, a musician living at Brighton in the seventies of last century. The tune was heard at Brighton by the Rev. Dr. Young, who introduced it to the notice of the committee engaged in preparing the *Wesleyan Tune-Book* (1876). It was accepted by them and set to the hymn to which it is now restored.

628—Truro.

TRURO is from *David's Harp*, edited in 1805 by Dr. E. Miller (No. 182) and his son, the Rev. W. E. Miller.

One of the first Methodist ministers to distinguish himself in the musical line was the Rev. W. E. Miller, son of the celebrated Dr. Miller of Doncaster. He inherited his father's love of music, and was brought up to the profession, being a pupil first with his father and then under Cramer. He spent six years in India, and on his return to England settled in Sheffield as a professional musician. He was an excellent fiddle-player, and possessed a fine instrument, in reference to which we are told that when in India he heard that in the court of Tippoo Sahib there was a musician—a member of the Sultan's band—who had the use of a very fine violin. Accordingly he went to Seringapatam, and having been introduced to the Sultan, he so charmed him with his playing that Tippoo Sahib gave the coveted instrument to Miller.

When living in Sheffield he took to attending Norfolk Street Chapel, to which he had been attracted by the excellent singing, for which it was famous even in those remote times. He then commenced preaching, and also wrote several hymns and tunes, the latter being specially composed for use at a great revival which took place in the Sheffield district about 1796. In 1799 he entered the Wesleyan ministry, and from this time he put his violin on one side and never touched it again. When stationed in Sheffield he frequently had to make long journeys into the country, and a difficulty arose owing to his objecting to use a horse when his divine Master had used an ass; so minister and Wesleyan officials argued the point, with the result that the matter was compromised and a mule procured for Miller's use. This, however, did not turn out a very satisfactory arrangement, and although the young preacher had no difficulty with the animal, his superintendent, the Rev. W. Griffiths, had, the result being that on one occasion the animal stuck in the road, and would neither go forward nor backward, so the congregation was left without a minister that morning. This powerful argument entirely overcame Miller's scruples, and the ' circuit ' horse was reinstated.

W. E. Miller's chief musical work was the editing, in association with his father, a large collection of tunes called *David's Harp* (1805). It contained about 300 tunes ' adapted to Mr. Wesley's Selection of Hymns.'

629—St. Austin.

ST. AUSTIN is from *The English Hymnal* (1906) where it is said to be an English traditional melody. It is a form of the old CHEVY CHASE tune.

630—Alstone.

ALSTONE first appeared in the Appendix to *Hymns Ancient and Modern* (1868) set to Mrs. Alexander's hymn, ' We are but little children weak.' The composer, C. E. Willing, was born in 1830, his father being an alto singer who frequently joined the Chapel Royal choir. At the age of eight young Willing entered the Westminster Abbey choir under Turle (see No. 73). Even then he was able to play the organ, and on one occasion, when Turle was ill, the youngster walked down the nave and past the congregation to the west end of the Abbey, where the organ then stood, climbed on to the stool, and finished the service. When he was fourteen young Willing became deputy organist and Turle would frequently go away, leaving his pupil in sole charge.

In 1848 Willing was elected organist of the Foundling Hospital, where he stayed for thirty-one years. During part of this time he held three other appointments, driving at full speed from one to another. His services at the Foundling were greatly appreciated, and when he left the little ones subscribed their pennies and gave him a set of gold studs. Willing did not confine himself to church music, being ready for any adventure, and so when the organist at the opera was suddenly taken ill, Balfe, at Turle's suggestion, fetched Willing to his help. This was the beginning of a long association with Costa, and it is interesting to remember that up to that time Willing was the first Englishman to hold the post of 'master of the piano' at Covent Garden.

When the Sacred Harmonic Society was dissolved in 1882 Willing got a body of singers together, and under the name of 'Willing's Choir,' a successful series of concerts was given at St. James's Hall. One of his latest appointments was to act as organist at the Rev. H. R. Haweis's church in Westminster Place, Marylebone, not far from Charles Wesley's London home. Willing, who died in 1904, compiled a collection of tunes which contained several of his own compositions.

631—Tiltey Abbey.

TILTEY ABBEY, by A. H. Brown. See No. 302.

632—Slane.

SLANE is adapted from a traditional Irish air, ' With my love on the road,' which is found as No. 323 in Joyce's *Old Irish Folk Music*. The present arrangement is by Sir Charles Stanford.

633—St. Cyril.

ST. CYRIL was written for *The Hymnal Companion* (1894) by Dr. Charles Vincent. See No. 243.

634—Will Your Anchor Hold?

WILL YOUR ANCHOR HOLD? is by W. J. Kirkpatrick. See No. 316.

635—Potsdam.

POTSDAM is from Mercer's *Church Psalter and Hymnal* (1854). It appears to be an adaptation of the subject of Bach's second fugue in E major in the *Forty-Eight Preludes and Fugues* (Book II, No. 9) which opens thus :

636—Barton.

BARTON was composed for Mrs. Ormiston Chant's hymn, ' Light of the world,' by J. T. Lightwood (see No. 27) at the request of some who thought that SANDON might have a well-deserved rest. It received its present title in order that the name of the Rev. Edgar C. Barton, Secretary of the Tune-Book Committee, might be perpetuated in the present edition of the *Methodist Hymn-Book*. The tune, composed in 1904, and circulated in MS. for some years, was included in the *New People's Hymnary* (1922).

637—Rutherford.

The melody of RUTHERFORD first appeared in *Chants Chrétiens,* a collection of French Protestant hymns with music published in Paris in 1834. Amongst the contributors to this work was Chrétien Urhan, who in his young days was a veritable musical prodigy. Born near Aix-la-Chapelle in 1790, the infant proceeded to invert the usual order of things by beginning to compose before he learnt any music. In after life he attained great proficiency on the violin, and became a noted concert performer. Meyerbeer wrote a special obligato solo to one of the airs in his *Huguenots* for Urhan's special benefit. Although he played in the theatre orchestra he had a pronounced objection to operatic performances, and it is said that during the whole of his career he never once allowed his eyes to stray towards the stage. He was for some time organist of St. Vincent de Paul in Paris, and this association with the church may have led to his being invited to contribute to *Chants Chrétiens*. This is the original form :

In its modern form the melody has been slightly compressed, and the unexpected A flat in the last line has disappeared. The original tune was, of course, set to French words. It was introduced into England by E. F. Rimbault in *Psalms and Hymns for Divine Worship* (1867).

The tune takes its name from Samuel Rutherford, a seventeenth-century Scottish divine whose life story had a great attraction for Mrs. Cousin, author of the hymn.

638—St. Augustine.

ST. AUGUSTINE (also known as AUGUSTINE, BEVERLEY, GILDAS) is found in Michael Weisse's *Ein Neu Gesengbuchlen* (1531). This was the first hymn-book of the Bohemian Brethren, and it is probable that the melodies it contains are of pre-Reformation origin (see Introduction, p. vii). It later appeared in J. S. Bach's *Choralgesänge* (1769).

639—Cambridge.

CAMBRIDGE, by Charles Wood, is from the 1925 edition of *Songs of Praise*.

Dr. Charles Wood was born at Armagh in 1866. He commenced music under Dr. Marks, the Cathedral organist, and in 1883 was successful in obtaining the Morley Scholarship at the R.C.M., where he continued his studies with Stanford. He was appointed organist-scholar at Caius College, Cambridge, in 1889, and five years later was made a Fellow. In 1924 he succeeded Stanford as professor of music at the University. His compositions include choral works (' Ode to the West Wind,' ' Ode on Time,' &c), composed during his earlier years, and also some instrumental works. He made several contributions to church music. He died in 1926.

640—Crossing the Bar.

CROSSING THE BAR was composed by Sir J. F. Bridge (see No. 122) for Lord Tennyson's funeral at Westminster Abbey, October 12, 1892.

641—Annue Christe.

ANNUE CHRISTE (also called THURE FUNANTES) is from La Feillée's *Plaine Chant* (1808, p. 143). La Feillée was connected with the choir in Chartres Cathedral towards the middle of the eighteenth century. The first edition of his *Method* for learning the rules of Plain-Song and Psalmody was published in 1745. Several later editions were printed, some authorized and some pirate.

642—Gifford.

GIFFORD was composed for Whittier's hymn, 'When on my day of life the night is falling' for *The Church Hymnary* (1927). The composer, T. C. L. Pritchard, was born at Glasgow in 1885. He is a graduate in music of Trinity College, Dublin. He has been organist of various churches in and around Glasgow, and since 1913 he has been organist at Belhaven U.F. Church, Glasgow. He represented the Glasgow Society of Organists on the Committee for revising the *Church Hymnary*.

643—Pressburg.

PRESSBURG is from Freylinghausen's *Gesangbuch* (1714). See No. 89.

644—Dinbych.

DINBYCH, by Dr. Joseph Parry, is from the same source as MERTHYR TYDFIL (No. 195).

645—Llef.

LLEF is from David Jenkins' *Gemau Mawl* (1890). The composer, Griffith Hugh Jones, known as Gutyn Argon, was born in 1849 at Ty Du, Llanberis. He was the youngest of four children. His father was precentor at Capel Coch, Llanberis, for over sixty years, and it was in helping his father that the boy developed an interest in music. When Ieuan Gwyllt (see No. 515) became pastor of Capel Coch he formed a class for teaching Tonic Sol-Fa, and young Jones was one of the pupils, gaining knowledge that was afterwards to prove invaluable.

He then became a pupil teacher at Dolbadarn. Afterwards he became assistant master at the British School, Aberystwyth, where he became attached to a group of musicians who were mutually helpful.

In February, 1869, he moved to the Elementary School of Rhiwddolion, a small place between Bettws-y-coed and Dolwyddelen, where he remained to the end in 1919.

At Rhiwddolion he started Sol-fa classes, which were popular for decades. Every Friday evening he walked five miles to Capel Curig for a class. From the outset at this village he became the inspirer of anything that was musical. Beyond the village he was conductor at Cymanfaoedd Ganu and adjudicator at Eisteddfodau. In the village he formed and conducted choirs; taught the children operettas; had two brass bands at one time or another. He was known throughout the Principality as a poet of some merit, being master of the intricate Welsh metres.

He wrote many anthems and tunes, some of his children's tunes being very popular. LLEF is the tune that has won world-wide popularity. It was written in memory of his brother, the late Rev. D. H. Jones (Dewi Arfon). It was first sung at the Cymanfa at Dolwyddelen, the conductor being Prof. D. Jenkins (see No. 528). Soon afterwards the tune was published in *Gemau Mawl*. Hugh Jones was the first to introduce a musical instrument to any Methodist chapel in Caernarvonshire. He was school-master at Rhiwddolion for just over fifty years. In 1918 he was presented with a National Testimonial of £65. He died in the following year.

646—Dies Irae.

DIES IRAE was composed by A. H. Brown (see No.

302) for use at Brentwood parish church, where he was organist. It was originally printed in leaflet form.

647—Cheshire. See No. 461.

648—Hymn of Eve.

HYMN OF EVE is taken from Dr. Arne's oratorio, *The Death of Abel,* where it is set to the words:

> How cheerful along the gay mead
> The daisy and cowslip appear,
> The flocks as they carelessly feed,
> Rejoice in the spring of the year.
> The myrtles that shade the gay bowers,
> The herbage that springs from the sod;
> Trees, plants, cooling fruits and sweet flowers,
> All rise to the praise of my God.

The oratorio was first heard in Dublin. It was never published, and no manuscript copy is known to exist. But the song just quoted became very popular, and was in such request that Arne inserted it at the beginning of Act III of his oratorio *Judith* (1761). John Wesley heard the oratorio three years later, and he would then become acquainted with the HYMN OF EVE. This is what he said of the oratorio:

> Some parts of it were exceedingly fine, but there are two things in all modern pieces of music which I could never reconcile to common sense. One is singing the same words ten times over; the other, singing different words by different persons at one and the same time. And this, in the most solemn addresses to God, whether by way of prayer or of thanksgiving. This can never be defended by all the musicians in Europe, till reason is quite out of date.

Under its new title THE HYMN OF EVE went forth to do its duty as a hymn-tune. Both Methodist and Anglican books made good use of it for over a century. It was in the *Methodist Hymn-Book* of 1876, omitted in

1904, and now it is restored to favour once more. In 1904 it was inserted in the revised edition of *Hymns Ancient and Modern*. As regards metre, the HYMN OF EVE has had a double duty to perform, appearing both as eight-eights (anapaestic) and as 7-6-7-6 (double) Iambic measure. In the *Primitive Methodist Hymnal* Supplement a new name, UXBRIDGE was found for it.

649—Beulah.

BEULAH, by G. M. Garrett, first appeared in the 1889 edition of *Hymns Ancient and Modern*.

650—Jerusalem.

JERUSALEM, by S. Grosvenor. See No. 77.

651 (i)—La Suissesse.

LA SUISSESSE is adapted from an old-time famous French song, 'O ma patrie,' the composition of Jacques Nicolas Goulé ' (or Goulley). He was born about 1774 at St. Jean du Cardonnay, and died at Rouen in 1818. As a boy he had a beautiful voice and decided aptitude for music, and this brought him under the notice of the Marquis d'Herbouville. Thus he became a chorister at Rouen Cathedral, where he had Boieldieu as a fellow-student. At the age of fifteen he blossomed forth as a composer, and his ' Grand Mass ' was performed with full orchestral accompaniment. He wrote other choral works, but his success was achieved in songs, and the ' O ma patrie, O mon bonheur,' became very popular. It reached England and was arranged for various instruments. Goulé remained at Rouen, and occupied a prominent position in music. One of his pupils was Godefroi, one of the most famous organists of Rouen.

Here is the original air :

La Suissesse au Bord du Lac.

L'en-cens des fleurs em - bau - me cet a-

zi - le la nuit des - cend à

pas si - len - ci - eux le lac est

pur, l'air est frais et tran-quil - le

la paix du soir se re-pand en ces

lieux ô ma Pa - tri - e

ô mon bon-heur! tou - jours ché-

- ri - e tu rem - pli - ras mon coeur.

The tune was probably adapted in this country for some Roman Catholic tune-book. Being deemed suitable for children, it found its way into various Sunday-school collections, and has even been thought worthy of a place in the *English Hymnal*.

Sir F. A. G. Ouseley had very decided opinions about the adaptation of secular airs, such as the music of love-songs and sentimental ditties, for use as hymn-tunes. In an address he delivered at the Church Congress in Leeds in 1872 he instanced as an appropriate example the once popular air 'La Suissesse au Bord du lac,' and asked,

' How can such tunes—in 6-8 time, in tripping measure, in secular style, with associations of secular and even amorous and questionable words—how can such tunes conduce to devotion. . . . How can they result in aught but the disgust and discouragement of all musical churchmen, the misleading of the unlearned, the abasement of sacred song, the falsification of public taste and (last, but not least) the dishonour of God and His worship?'

651 (ii)—Pilgrims.

PILGRIMS was composed by Henry Smart (see No. 12) for the *Appendix to Hymns Ancient and Modern* (1868).

652 (i)—Ewing.

EWING, by A. Ewing, was originally printed on single sheets about 1853. The first tune-book to contain it was Grey's *Manual of Psalms and Hymn-Tunes* (1857) where it appeared in triple time, as originally intended by the composer :

The rhythm, however, did not meet the approval of W. H. Monk, who, like others of his race, had a penchant for altering other people's tunes, and reduced the tune to 7-6's common time as it is now printed. The composer strongly disapproved of the change, maintaining that it made his tune sound like a polka. Dr. Neale, the translator of St. Bernard's hymn, said of this tune, 'I have so often been asked to what tune the words of Bernard may be sung, that I may here mention that of Mr. Ewing, the earliest written, the best known, and with children the most popular; no small proof, in my estimation, of the goodness of church music.'

Alexander Ewing was born in Aberdeen in 1830, and as a youth he achieved distinction as an amateur musician.

He did not sing (says one who knew him well), but in the instrumental line he was gifted in exceeding measure. He could perform well on the violin, 'cello, and cornet, while his brilliant tone and execution on the piano were more those of a professional of great ability rather than of a young amateur simply playing for amusement. For some time he took a prominent part in the management of the 'Haydn Society' in Aberdeen, of which the conductor was Henry Baker, organist of St. Andrew's Church.

Ewing was connected with another musical society in Aberdeen which was known as 'The Harmonic Choir,' and which made a special study of madrigal and anthem singing. The members met weekly in a room known as Western's Hall, opposite the Royal Hotel, and under the skilful guidance of Mr. William Carnie, one of Aberdeen's most distinguished musicians, the young society made excellent progress. The doings of the choir excited much interest and discussion in local musical circles, and one of the most regular attendants at the rehearsals was 'Alick' Ewing, who was only too glad to leave his legal studies for the greater attractions that music offered.

One evening, after the practice was ended, Ewing approached the conductor and confessed that he had tried his hand at hymn-tune composing, and would be so glad if Mr. Carnie would allow the 'Harmonic Choir' to sing it over. The young composer had taken the precaution to bring copies of the voice parts, and so on that eventful evening the new hymn-tune, EWING, was launched on what has proved to be a long and successful voyage.

Alexander Ewing left Aberdeen about 1853, and rarely visited his northern home again. When the Crimean War broke out he joined the Commissariat Department and was stationed at Constantinople, where his abilities as a linguist rendered his services of great value. After a period of foreign service extending over a dozen years he returned to England, and in 1867 married Juliana Horatia Gatty, whose stories for children have become classics. After another lengthened period of official work in far distant lands he finally settled in England in 1883, taking up his abode at Taunton. His wife died two years later, and was buried in the churchyard of the little village of Trull, some two miles or so from Taunton, and here, ten years later, the soldier husband was laid to rest in the same churchyard.

652 (ii)—St. Alphege.

ST. ALPHEGE was written by Dr. Gauntlett for *The Church Hymn and Tune-Book* (1851). The tune has been put to hymns of such varying sentiment as : ' The voice that breathed o'er Eden,' and ' Brief life is here our portion.' It was written for another hymn altogether. One day, during the compilation of *The Church Hymn and Tune-Book,* Dr. Gauntlett was sitting at dinner, when a messenger came to say that the printers could not find the tune assigned to the words, ' The hymn of glory sing we.' ' Give me some paper,' he said, pushing aside his plate, and in a few minutes the well-known melody was composed. It subsequently appeared in two or three hymnals set as a C.M., but probably without the composer's sanction. (See No. 7.)

653—Christchurch.

CHRISTCHURCH, by Charles Steggall (see No. 540), is from *Hymns for the Church of England* (1865), edited by the Rev. T. Darling.

654—Homeland.

HOMELAND was composed by Arthur Sullivan (see No. 18) at the request of the editor of *Good Words,* and appeared in that magazine in 1867.

655 (i)—Bocking.

BOCKING, by the Rev. F. Luke Wiseman (see No. 5), first appeared in the *New People's Hymnary* (1922).

655 (ii)—Diana.

DIANA is the same as the old English air, ' Rogero,' and there are references to the tune under this name in late sixteenth-century playwrights, the air being made to do duty for several ballads. This appears to be the first time that ROGERO has appeared in a modern tune-book. Why it has been christened DIANA is uncertain. This is not the first time ROGERO has been fitted to a moral song, for in the Roxburgh Collection of Ballads there is one called ' A right Godly and Christian A.B.C. showing the duty of every degree,' to the tune of ROGERO. This ' godly ' song consists of thirty verses, each beginning with a letter of the alphabet, with a few added by way of exhortation.

656—Glory.

GLORY is from *The Tune-Book* edited by John Curwen in 1842. Nothing is known of the origin or history of the tune.

657—Meyer. See No. 266.

658—Nearer Home.

NEARER HOME, also known as WOODBURY, FOR EVER
WITH THE LORD, or MONTGOMERY, is from *The Choral
Advocate,* a musical journal published in America in
1852. The tune originally had a refrain, and in this
form it appeared in the *Wesleyan Tune-Book* (1876).
The refrain has now dropped out of use.

Isaac Baker Woodbury was born in Beverley, Mass.,
in 1819. At the age of thirteen he went to Boston to
study music, and six years later he crossed the Atlantic
to study in London and Paris. A year of foreign travel
proved sufficient for him, and he returned to Boston to
enter the musical profession. His next adventure was
to travel as the conductor of the Bay State Glee Club,
an organization that travelled through New England
giving concerts. He next settled in Vermont and founded
a Musical Association in the district. Back in New
York, he directed the music at Rudgers Street Church.
Ill-health compelled him to resign this work, and he
crossed to Europe once more, partly in search of health,
and also to gather material for a musical journal he had
started. Failing in the former object, he returned home
once more and died on a journey to South Carolina.

In his youth Woodbury was full of energy, and
thought nothing of walking from Boston to Beverley,
fifteen miles, to direct a singing school at his native
town. His compositions were confined almost entirely
to psalmody, and he edited a large number of tune-books.
After his death it was found that he had left the considerable fortune he had accumulated to found a Music
School, but the law intervened and changed the deposi-
tion of his fortune to the advantage of his family. His
friend, G. F. Root, said of him, ' Mr. Woodbury was a
genial, pleasant gentleman, and because he wrote only
simple music, never was credited, by those who did not
know him, with the musical ability and culture he really
possessed.'

659—Munich.

MUNICH is stated at the heading of the tune to be from Storl's *Gesangbuch* (1710). This is quite correct (except that the date should be 1711), but it really belongs to an earlier period. According to Zahn it is constructed out of bits of melodies found in J. L. Prasch's *Lobsingende Harffe* (1682) and MUNICH first appeared in concrete form in the *Meiningisches Gesangbuch* (1693). It is introduced by Mendelssohn in 'Cast thy burden upon the Lord' (*Elijah*).

660—Dulwich College.

DULWICH COLLEGE is by Edward Davey Rendall, who was born in 1858. After passing through Cambridge, where he came out as a Wrangler in the Mathematical Tripos, he decided to adopt music as a profession, and studied music for a time in Berlin. In 1883 he was appointed music master at Dulwich College, where he had a wonderful influence on the school music. Perhaps his most notable achievement in composition at this period was a cantata called *The Compleat Angler; an Idyll in two days, after Isaak Walton,* wherein a series of recitations formed a somewhat unusual feature. The musical portion consisted of settings of the poems. In 1901 Mr. Rendall accepted a similar position at Charterhouse School, where he remained till within a year of his death, which took place in 1920. His tune DULWICH COLLEGE was written for the *Public School Hymnal.* His other compositions include many glees, part-songs, and choral works. He wrote the music for the Charterhouse School Song, sung at the Tercentenary in 1911, and also for the Charterhouse Masque, 1919.

661—Plymouth Dock.

PLYMOUTH DOCK originally appeared in *Sacred Harmony* (1780) set to C. Wesley's hymn, 'Blow ye the trumpet, blow,' and was consequently named TRUMPET. Edward Booth, in his *Wesleyan Psalmist,* renamed it

Portsmouth, without any apparent reason, and the same may be said for its most recent name of Plymouth Dock. The tune has sometimes been ascribed to Handel, but it is certainly not an example of his idea of a hymn-tune. The only original tune he wrote to this metre is Gopsal (No. 247).

662—Woolmer's.

Woolmer's, by F. A. G. Ouseley, appeared in the first edition (1861) of *Hymns Ancient and Modern*.

Sir Frederick Arthur Gore Ouseley was born in London in 1825, his father (from whom he inherited his baronetcy) being a distinguished member of the diplomatic service. After leaving Oxford he took Holy Orders and was appointed curate at St. Paul's, Knightsbridge, where he had special charge of the choristers. A change of régime led to the disbanding of the choir, but Ouseley took his choir boys to a house near Slough, putting them in charge of a friend, and then proceeded to carry out a scheme that he had long entertained. He was anxious that there should be an institution specially devoted to the training of choir boys, and he built a choral school, now known as St. Michael's, at Tenbury, Worcestershire, and it stands to-day as a worthy memorial of its founder. Ouseley succeeded Sir Henry Bishop as Professor of Music at Oxford, and he was successful in raising the standard and position of music to a height till then unknown in the University. Under his exacting rule candidates had really to earn their degree, and some of them did not like it. One disappointed aspirant wrote :

Your rejection of my exercise confirms the opinion I have long entertained of your utter incompetence to hold the office.

Ouseley's command of the theory and practice of music has rarely been equalled. As an extempore fugue-player he displayed wonderful skill, and the writing of the most intricate forms of music was child's play to him. He was a voluminous composer, and his works include organ music, anthems, part-songs, all of which are practically forgotten to-day. His oratorio, *The Martyrdom of St. Polycarp*, had a spell of popularity. He wrote learned—perhaps too learned—treatises on music, but they are forgotten. Whether there will ever be a revival of his music is doubtful, but his College at Tenbury will perpetuate his memory. He died in 1889, and was interred in the chancel of his collegiate church.

Many are the tales that are told of Ouseley's goodness. His life was one of self-sacrifice; he was never so happy as when doing a kindness, and his greatest pleasure seems to have been to think for and help others. His devotion to his various duties and to his art was indeed remarkable. No work appeared to be too much for him; the tasks he set himself to do he invariably accomplished, and that right well.

663—Lüneburg.

LÜNEBURG was taken from the *Methodist Free Church Tunes* (1892). It is found in C. P. E. Bach's edition of J. S. Bach's *Chorales*, published in four parts, 1784-1787, and was there taken from a Lüneburg *Gesangbuch* (1686), set to the hymn, ' Meinen Jesum lass ich nicht,' also by B. Schmolk (author of ' Light of light ').

664—St. Oswald.

ST. OSWALD was written by Dr. Dykes for Grey's *Manual of Psalm and Hymn-Tunes used in the parish church of St. Michael, Houghton-le-Spring* (1857), set to the anonymous hymn, ' Praise the Lord ! ye heavens, adore Him,' with the name ST. BERNARD. This was changed to ST. OSWALD in *Hymns Ancient and Modern* (1875).

665—Eignbrook.

EIGNBROOK is from the 1854 edition of *The Hallelujah*. The Preface is dated 1851.

666—Norwood.

Norwood is by W. H. Hart, who wrote the tune for 'Sun of my soul' in the *London Tune-Book* (1875). Thence it was taken for the *Wesleyan Tune-Book* (1876), and also appeared in the *Primitive Methodist Hymnal* (1889). No details about the composer are available.

667 (i)—Radford.

Radford was composed by S. S. Wesley (see No. 217) for *Church Hymns* (1874).

667 (ii)—St. Clement.

St. Clement, by the Rev. C. C. Scholefield, first appeared in *Church Hymns* (1874). The composer, who was born at Edgbaston, Birmingham, in 1839, was the youngest son of William Scholefield, who was for twenty years M.P. for Birmingham. He was educated at Pocklington Grammar School, and after three years at Cambridge he took orders in the Church of England. His appointments included Hove parish church, and Holy Trinity, Knightsbridge. He was also chaplain at Eton College. In 1895 he retired from clerical work and devoted his time to various pursuits. He was extremely fond of music, though he had no systematic education in the art, but as a pianist he was far above the average player. He wrote several songs, but it is by his tunes St. Clement and Irene (No. 975) that he is remembered. After his death his estate was administered by the Court of Chancery, and pending an order being made the executors were for some time obliged to refuse all applications for the use of St. Clement.

667 (iii)—Les Commandemens de Dieu.

Les Commandemens de Dieu is taken from the *French Psalter* of 1540, which was compiled and edited by Louis Bourgeois. He belongs to the first half of the sixteenth century, but his actual dates are unknown. For any information about him we are indebted to the researches of MM. Douen and Bovet, who, in their *History of the French Psalters*, have examined all sources of information about them.

The tune's first appearance in an English work was in *One and Fiftie Psalms* (1556 edition). It is also known in another form—as a long metre—under the name COMMANDMENTS.

668 (i)—Eide.

EIDE, by Alfred Beer. See No. 371 (ii).

668 (ii)—Angel Voices.

ANGEL VOICES was written for an organ opening at Winwick, Lancashire, in 1861, and frequently appeared in Festival books and on anniversary hymn-sheets after that date. The composer, Dr. E. G. Monk, was born at Frome in 1819. After receiving lessons in Bath, and also in London from G. A. Macfarren for theory and Henry Phillips for singing, he became organist at Midsomer Norton church, proceeding from there to Christ Church, Frome. In 1844 he became organist at Rathfarnham, Dublin, and three years later organist and music director at Radley College. In 1858 he was appointed to York Minster. After twenty-five years' service here he resigned and returned to Radley, where he died in 1900. A new organ in the Radley parish church was dedicated to his memory, bearing an inscription testifying to the high respect in which he was held. To E. G. Monk (who was no relation to W. H. Monk) is due the credit of having suggested to J. Alfred Novello the publication of a series of part-songs, which resulted in the issue of ' Novello's Part-Song Book.'

669—Georgia.

GEORGIA was composed by C. W. Jordan for insertion in the *Methodist Tune-Book* (1904).

Dr. Charles Warwick Jordan was born at Clifton in

1840, and at the age of eight was admitted as a chorister
in Bristol Cathedral, where he remained till the family
removed to London. His next step was his enrolment
in the choir of St. Paul's, having John Stainer and
Henry Gadsby as fellow choristers. His next move was
to the Forest of Dean, where he exercised himself on
the organ in Mitcheldean Church. All this time he never
had a lesson, his only instructor being a lady who showed
him how to finger his scales.

Another removal to London followed, and here he
remained for the rest of his life. He made the
acquaintance of George Cooper, organist at St.
Sepulchre's, and very attractive he found the famous
player's recitals after the Sunday evening services. A
few years at business proved enough for young Jordan,
for he could not keep away from the organ, and after
holding three minor appointments, he was invited to be
organist at St. Stephen's, Lewisham. This was in 1866,
and he remained here till his unfortunate death in 1909.
Jordan became deeply interested in Gregorian music,
and maintained that the tones were specially suitable for
the Psalms on account of their elasticity and close
relation to speech.

Jordan made a special feature of the great church
festivals, and he was a pioneer in the modern introduction of trumpets and drums as an addition to the organ.
His compositions were limited to church music, and
proved of a somewhat ephemeral character. They are
rarely heard now. A popular and effective anthem is
'Come unto Me, ye weary.' An interesting episode in
Jordan's career was his intercourse with Gounod some
thirty-nine years ago, during the Franco-German war.
Gounod, when he came to England, took a furnished
house in Morden Road, Blackheath, which was near to
St. Stephen's, Lewisham, and to Jordan's home, and the
two musicians becoming acquainted, saw much of one
another. Dr. Jordan used to recall, among other things,
Gounod's admiration for much of the English church

music, which he introduced to his notice. As to Gounod's own music, the composer's injunction, when he heard it played, was almost invariably, ' Slower, slower; not so fast.'

670—Grosvenor.

GROSVENOR is by E. Harwood. See No. 576.

671—Alleluia Perenne.

ALLELUIA PERENNE was composed by W. H. Monk (see No. 221) for the 1868 Supplement to *Hymns Ancient and Modern.*

672—Norfolk Park.

NORFOLK PARK, by Henry Coward. See No. 332.

673—Ruth.

RUTH, by Samuel Smith, was originally published in 1865 for private circulation. The first public appearance was in *Church Hymns* (1874). The composer was born at Eton in 1821, and belonged to a musical family, both his brothers, Alfred and George, being connected with St. George's Chapel, Windsor, where he himself received music lessons from Sir George Elvey, singing as a choir boy at the coronation of William IV and Queen Adelaide. He held several positions as church organist, his longest tenure of office being at Windsor parish church, where he had charge of the music from 1861 till 1895. He lived in retirement to a good old age till his death in his ninety-seventh year in 1917.

674—Boston.

BOSTON, by Lowell Mason (see No. 238), is founded on a Gregorian chant. It first appeared in the Boston Handel and Haydn Societies' Collection, 1824 (or 1828) with the heading ' Gregorian Chant BENEDICTUS, see Novello's Evening Service.'

675—Redhead No. 4. See No. 529.

676—St. George. See No. 248.

677—Quam Dilecta.

QUAM DILECTA is by H. Lascelles Jenner, who was born at Chislehurst in 1820. After leaving Cambridge he held various curacies, and in 1866 was consecrated Bishop of Dunedin, N.Z. He later returned to England and resumed charge of the parish church of Preston, Kent. He always took a great interest in music, and was a strong advocate for the restoration of plain-song in church worship. His tune was included in the original edition of *Hymns Ancient and Modern* (1861).

678—Darwall's 148th.

DARWALL'S 148TH was first printed in Aaron Williams' *New Universal Psalmodist* (1770). The tune originally began on the dominant (or fifth) note.

The Rev. John Darwall was born at Haughton, Staffs., in 1731, and educated at Manchester Grammar School. At the early age of fourteen he went to Brazenose College, Oxford. After leaving college he was ordained curate at St. Matthew's, Walsall, of which church he afterwards became vicar. He was a good amateur musician, and amongst his other accomplishments, wrote a tune for each of the Psalms, but of these only that to the 148th has lived. It is said to have been specially written for the opening of the new organ in Walsall parish church. The following account of the ceremony, and the introduction of the tune is thus told in the *Gentleman's Magazine* for 1800 :

In Whit Week, 1773, some anthems were performed by the Walsall singers in the Parish Church. Admittance that day was paid for, and the organ was opened by Dr. Alcock, of Lichfield, who then declared that it was a good instrument. And on the next

Sunday, in the afternoon, it was first played in full congregation by Mr. Balam, our then organist (who was blind, and had been a pupil of the celebrated Stanley). The first psalm was part of the 30th, New Version, UXBRIDGE tune; and Mr. Darwall, our vicar (who was himself a musical man), preached a sermon from Psalm cl.: ' Praise Him with stringed instruments and organs.' In this discourse the preacher, among other things, recommended psalmtunes in quicker time than common; as, he said, ' six verses might be sung in the same space of time that four generally are.' After the sermon the entire 150th[1] Psalm, New Version, was sung, to a new tune of the vicar's composing; and the whole concluded with appropriate prayer and the blessing.

Darwall died in 1789.

679—Maidstone.

MAIDSTONE, by Gilbert, was composed at Maidstone, and inserted in *Church Hymns* (1874).

W. B. Gilbert was born at Exeter in 1829. A move to Birmingham found him at King Edward's School, but a return to his native place became a necessity, and here he pursued his studies in music in spite of home opposition. The vicar of St. Thomas's Church took an interest in the boy, and allowed him to practice on his organ. He became so competent that he was engaged by J. W. Walker to open their new organ in St. Olave's Church. He was then articled to the Cathedral organist, Alfred Angel, for five years, and after this period he received further instruction from S. S. Wesley at Winchester, and also Sir H. Bishop.

Thus equipped he embarked on a musical career, and after a few brief appointments he went to the Old Collegiate Church at Maidstone. Whilst he was here he

[1] The scribe obviously meant the 148th.

wrote a tune to an 'eight-line sevens' metre, never dreaming that it would interest anybody. However, Archbishop Sumner heard it sung, and when the compilers of *Church Hymns* were at their work he called their attention to it, and it was fitted to Montgomery's hymn, 'Songs of praise the angels sang,' but subsequently transferred to Lyte's 'Pleasant are Thy courts above.' This was in 1874. In 1867 Gilbert was appointed to Boston parish church, but two years later he accepted a position at Trinity Chapel, New York, where he remained till 1897, when he retired on a pension.

It is not often that an American church organist retains his position as long as Gilbert did, but the reasons for this success were faithfully recorded by a writer in these words:

> Mr. W. B. Gilbert, Mus.B. (Oxon.), the organist of Trinity Chapel, is one of the most successful choirmasters in the country, and possesses a remarkable talent for keeping out of scrapes; we mean by this that he has rare gifts of order, system, regularity, punctuality, and discipline—and that with a daily service too—everything in the chapel ran smoothly, without trouble and without engendering any bad feeling amongst his numerous choristers.

Gilbert's compositions were confined almost entirely to church music. His 'Service in F' is well known, and he has many anthems and hymn-tunes to his credit. His two oratorios, *The Restoration of Israel* and *St. John*, are at rest with hundreds of similar compositions of the Victorian period.

Gilbert was perhaps the first to make the music at a public school a live affair. Whilst boys of other schools —Harrow, Eton, &c.—were singing by ear the popular songs of the day and other ditties, Gilbert formed his class at Tonbridge School into a complete choir of some fifty boys, who sang glees and part-songs in full harmony and with great delight. He died in 1910.

680, 709—Falcon Street.

FALCON STREET (also known as SILVER STREET) is by Isaac Smith, and from the same source as ABRIDGE (No. 519).

681—Dix.

DIX is by Conrad Kocher, who inserted it in his collection of tunes, *Stimmen aus dem Reiche Gottes,* published at Stuttgart (1838), where the composer was for nearly forty years organist of the Stiftskirche. After a visit to Italy Kocher became imbued with the spirit of Palestrina's music, and he founded a school for the study and propagation of a high type of church choral music. Another of his collections of chorales, *Zionsharfe,* contained many that have come into use, notably ELLACOMBE (No. 208), the exact origin of which is doubtful.

682 (i)—Huddersfield.

HUDDERSFIELD, by Sir Walter Parratt (see No. 444), was composed at the request of the editors of the *English Hymnal* for the hymn, 'Holy Father, cheer our way.'

682 (ii)—Capetown.   See No. 611.

683, 723—Vater Unser.

VATER UNSER first appeared in its present form in *Geistliche Lieder* (1539), set to Luther's metrical version of the Lord's Prayer. It passed into the Anglo-Genevan Psalter of 1561 and thence into the English Psalter the following year, set to Kethe's version of Psalm cxii, and thus it received its alternate name of OLD 112TH. It was a favourite with John Wesley, who placed it in his 'Foundery' Tune-Book, calling it PLAYFORD'S TUNE (1742). There is a story that he once said to some friends, 'If you want to hear pure psalmody you must go to Fulneck and hear the Moravians sing,' and

27

he quoted a hymn which they sang to the OLD 112TH.
VATER UNSER is used extensively by Bach, and it also
forms the foundation of Mendelssohn's Sixth Organ
Sonata.

684—Caswall.

CASWALL (also known as FILITZ and WEM IN
LEIDENSTAGEN). See No. 611.

685—Doncaster.

DONCASTER (or BETHLEHEM), by S. Wesley (see No.
410), is from Sale's *Psalms and Hymns* (1837).

686 (i)—Birmingham.

BIRMINGHAM is found in a *Selection of Psalm-Tunes*
formed by Rev. F. Cunningham in 1834 (2nd edition).
It is set to the hymn:

> Come gracious Spirit, heavenly Dove,
> With light and comfort from above.

686 (ii)—Woodlands.

WOODLANDS is by Walter Greatorex. He was born at
Mansfield in 1877, and educated at Derby School. He
is now Director of Music at Gresham's School, Holt,
Norfolk.

687—Erskine.

ERSKINE is from a collection of tunes published by
W. H. Gladstone in 1882 (see under OMBERSLEY, No.
562). In the preface Gladstone said:

My main purpose in making this collection was
to suggest suitable hymns for some of the tunes,
original and other, comprised in Dr. Wesley's
European Psalmist, a work published a few years
before his death in 1876, but in such a form as to have
little chance of obtaining attention. For this project
Dr. Wesley was kind enough to give me his sanction.

I have, however, gone further afield and included tunes from various other sources. Fitness for congregational use, dignity of character, and soundness of construction have been the qualities for which I have sought in the selection of both hymns and tunes.

688—Morecambe.

F. C. Atkinson, the composer of MORECAMBE, was born at Norwich in 1841. He was a pupil of Dr. Buck's, for whom he frequently deputized at the cathedral services. For some years he was organist at St. Luke's, Manningham, Bradford, returning to Norwich in 1881 to became the cathedral organist. After five years' service there he went to St. Mary's Church, Lewisham. He died at East Dereham in 1897.

MORECAMBE was composed by Atkinson whilst he was organist at Manningham, and published as a leaflet in 1870 for use in the church. It was originally called HELLESPONT.

689—Angelus.

ANGELUS is a tune that has undergone a considerable amount of editing and consequent alteration. It is originally traceable to this melody :

and set to a hymn beginning :

> Du meiner seelen güldne ziehr
> Du Freude die dein Vater mir,

in *Heilege Seelen-Lust, oder Geistliche Hirten-Lieder der in ihren Jesum verliebten Psyche. Gefungen von*

Johann Angelo Silesio und von Herren Georgio Josepho mit aussbundig schönen Melodeyen geziert . . . Breslau (1657).

It will be noticed that only the first line and part of the second bear any resemblance to ANGELUS. This phrase next appears in *Cantica Spiritualia* with additions, bringing the whole tune to its present form.

Heilige Seelenlust is a collection of hymns formed by Johann Scheffler, who was born at Breslau (in Silesia) in 1624. Brought up as a strict Lutheran, he went through various phases of faith until in 1652 he came under the influence of the Jesuits, and a year later joined the Roman Catholic Church, taking the name of Angelus, to which he added the epithet ' Silesius ' (i.e. the Silesian) to avoid confusion with another Angelus, of the Lutheran faith. The collection referred to appeared in 1657, and associated with Angelus was Georg Joseph, who supplied the music, and also contributed original compositions. He was a musician in the service of the Bishop of Breslau during the seventeenth century.

690—Franconia. See No. 507.

691 (i)—Ellers.

ELLERS, by E. J. Hopkins, first appeared (with Goss's PRAISE, MY SOUL, No. 12) in R. Brown-Borthwick's *Supplemental Hymn and Tune-Book* (1869). The tune is written in one of the old church modes to which the composer closely adhered, save in the penultimate note of the second line. It was originally written for unison singing, with varied accompaniments for each verse.

691 (ii)—Adoro Te. See No. 184 (i).

692—St. Matthias.

ST. MATTHIAS was written by W. H. Monk for the first (1861) edition of *Hymns Ancient and Modern.* (See No. 221.)

693—Dismissal.

DISMISSAL is by William Letton Viner, who was a native of Bath and organist for some years at St. Michael's Church. His family were very friendly with the sons of the Rev. Charles Wesley, and both Charles and Samuel Wesley and their mother used to stay at the Viners' on their visits to Bath. From Bath Viner moved, in 1838, to Penzance, where he was organist at St. Mary's Chapel for some years before going to America in 1859, where he died in 1867 at the age of seventy-seven. Whilst at Penzance he published, in 1838, *One Hundred Psalm and Hymn-Tunes in score for one voice only*. In the preface he referred to himself as ' professor and organist.' DISMISSAL is not in this collection, but it is in an old volume of manuscript tunes formerly in use at the Wesleyan Chapel in Penzance, where it is called VINER'S DISMISSAL. In E. Flood's *Psalmodist* (1845) it appears as a long-metre tune. Viner also compiled *The Organists' Library, Multum in Parvo* (easy pieces for the organ) and *Wesley's Psalms and Hymns arranged for the English organ with Pedals.*

694—Dettingen.

DETTINGEN. The German hymn with which this choral is associated is by Speratus (1484-1551) :

Es ist das Heil uns kommen her,

and first occurs (as far as is at present known) in *Etlich Christliche Lieder* (1524) (' Some Christian Songs '), a copy of which is preserved in the British Museum. It is set to Luther's version of Psalm xii. The composer of DETTINGEN is unknown, but it is supposed to be of pre-Reformation origin.

695—Mainzer. See No. 362.

696 (i)—Trull.

TRULL is by C. L. Wiseman, who thus describes its birth :

> I think a man is standing on a high hill overlooking a green plain stretching eastward to the sunrise. It gradually fills up with pilgrims, the sun shining in their faces and on their white robes, until the sound of their singing comes from everywhere in a great volume of sound.

The tune takes its name from a village near Taunton.

696 (ii)—Melling.

MELLING is taken from J. Fawcett's *New Sett of Sacred Music,* published about 1820-22.

John Fawcett, born in 1789 at the village of Wennington, in North Lancashire, was brought up as a shoemaker, but a natural taste for music led him to adopt it as a profession. He was entirely self-taught, and the proficiency he attained was owing entirely to his wonderful diligence. In order to become acquainted with the principles of harmony he would spend days and nights in copying out hymn-tunes, comparing their harmonies, and noting the correct progression of chords. From these he proceeded to more complicated music, such as anthems, part-songs and choruses.

Nor did he neglect instrumental music, and he joined the militia in order to study the various band instruments, taking his place as a clarinet player, and being subsequently appointed bandmaster. The organ also attracted his attention, and having attained some proficiency on it he accepted an appointment in Kendal, whence he removed from Bolton. Returning to Bolton, he settled down there and accepted the post of organist at the Wesleyan Chapel in Bridge Street.

The conscientious way in which he performed his duties is very evident from this letter, which he wrote to the trustees of the chapel in January, 1836 :

Gentlemen,—You will doubtless expect me to look after the Books and Instruments belonging to Bridge Street Chaple, and see that all are kept in proper order, but as I have not as yet been authorized to get anything done that is or might be wanting I thought it best for some plan to be laid down by you for me to act upon, perhaps it would if you think best for me to get the repairs done, or Strings, &c., which are or might be wanting, and give in a quarterly account. There is one violincello now in a state not likely for use, and if it remains unrepaired it will soon be in pieces. There is also a string wanting to one of the violincellos.

I have now a favour to beg respecting the Hymn-Books, there are a many of them incorrect, which makes confusion amongst the Singers. I shall be greatly obliged, if you will take away those and replace them with correct ones.

I remain, your obedient st.,

JOHN FAWCETT.

N.B.—As a Funeral Sermon will be preached on Sunday night next I thought you perhaps might wish the old Funeral Ode ('Vital Spark') sung, as I had the Singers practising it at my house on Monday night after preaching. I practised them with the above piece supposing it might be desired. I think should it be desired we can go thro' it desantly; I do not state this thro' any particular desire of my own, only I always think it best to have proper notice when anything particular is wanted.

Fawcett wrote a large number of hymn-tunes which he published in collections bearing the names of *Melodia Divina, Voice of Devotion, Harp of Zion,* and similar titles. He has also to his credit an oratorio called *Paradise,* published in 1865, which he composed 'For the special purpose of meeting the requirements of those societies whose members are not sufficiently numerous to do justice to the compositions of Handel, Haydn and Mendelssohn.' John Fawcett died in 1867, having reached his seventy-eighth year.

697—Abney.

ABNEY, by the Rev. F. Luke Wiseman (see No. 5), first appeared in the present (1933) edition of the *Methodist Hymn-Book*.

698—Abbey.

ABBEY is from the *Scottish Psalter* of 1615 (see No. 37), where it is included amongst the 'common' tunes, i.e. not identified with any particular psalm.

699—Josiah.

JOSIAH, SARAH (A.T.2) and JOB (A.T. 14) are all from *Original Psalms and Hymn-Tunes* by William Arnold, published about 1801. He was a shipwright in H.M. Dockyard at Portsmouth, and also choirmaster at the Daniel Street Wesleyan Chapel. Many of his tunes were composed whilst he was at work, and he used to note them down with his carpenter's pencil on a piece of board. He got practical help in the publication of his tunes from his friend, Mr. Johnson. SARAH and JOSIAH were subsequently sanctified by being called ST. SARA and ST. JOSIAH, an honour that has not yet been conferred on JOB.

700—Ishmael.

ISHMAEL, by Dr. C. Vincent, was written by him for *The Hymnal Companion* (1894). (See No. 243.)

701—Aurelia.

AURELIA. Dr. J. Kendrick Pyne, formerly organist of Manchester Cathedral, has recorded how, when he was an articled pupil of Wesley's, he was once sitting in the composer's drawing-room in the Close at

Winchester, when Wesley entered abruptly and said, ' I *think* I have written a tune for " The voice that breathed o'er Eden," which will be popular.' He played it over many times ' and,' says Dr. Pyne, ' we all agreed with him.'

This was in 1864, and Wesley does not appear to have realized that he had chosen a hymn of four-line stanzas for his new tune. In the same year the Rev. Charles Kemble engaged Wesley to edit the music edition of his *Selection of Psalms and Hymns,* containing 150 tunes, of which Wesley composed at least thirty-three. He included the tune under notice, but transferred it from his first choice to the three sections of St. Bernard's hymn :

> Brief life is here our portion.
> For thee, O dear, dear country.
> Jerusalem the golden,

and it is from the last word (Latin *aurum,* gold), that the name AURELIA is derived. Curiously enough this association has rarely been maintained, and the tune has been mated to various hymns, especially Stone's ' The Church's one foundation.'

AURELIA received a great advertisement in 1872, when it was one of the tunes sung at the service in St. Paul's Cathedral and elsewhere to commemorate the recovery of the Prince of Wales on February 27. This particular choice greatly annoyed Dr. Gauntlett, who wrote to *The Choir* denouncing the tune as being ' inartistic, and not fulfilling the conditions of a hymn-tune.' He even called it ' secular twaddle ' ! A fierce correspondence ensued, from which AURELIA emerged unscathed.

702—Harewood.

HAREWOOD, by S. S. Wesley (see No. 217), first appeared in C. D. Hackett's *National Psalmist* (1839).

703 (i)—Richmond. See No. 1.

703 (ii)—Bristol. See No. 82.

704—Sleepers, Wake.

Sleepers, wake.   See No. 255.

705—Lasus.

Lasus is from a set of *Twelve Popular Hymns,* by Dr. A. H. Mann (see No. 168) published in 1874.

706—Lux Eoi.

Lux Eoi was originally composed by Sir A. Sullivan (see No. 18) for the second edition of *Hymns for the Church of England* (1875), but the tune appeared the previous year in *Church Hymns,* edited by Sullivan.

707—Old 120th.

Old 120th is here credited to Este's *Psalter* (see No. 461), but it is a slightly altered form of a melody that supplanted the original setting of Psalm cxx. in Sternhold and Hopkins. The present Old 120th is found in *Damon's Psalmes* (1759) (see No. 239), and is also traceable in earlier psalters back to 1570. Este settled the standard form of the tune, giving the name of Giles Farnaby as the arranger.

708—St. Giles.

St. Giles is by John Montgomerie Bell, professor of conveyancing at Edinburgh University. He was an amateur musician of great ability, and was deeply interested in the production of the *Church Hymnary*, edited by Sir John Stainer in 1898. St. Giles was set to Bishop How's hymn, 'We give Thee but Thine own' in the *Scottish Hymnal* (1885).

709—Falcon Street.

Falcon Street is by Isaac Smith.   See No. 680.

710—Otterbourne.

Otterbourne is adapted from the slow movement in one of Haydn's symphonies.

711—Nicomachus.

Nicomachus is from a set of *Twelve Popular Hymns* (1874) by Dr. A. H. Mann. See No. 168.

712—Tiverton.

Tiverton, by J. Grigg. See No. 460.

713—Love-Feast.

Love-Feast is from the 'Foundery' Tune-Book (1742), but how it got in there is uncertain. It appears to be founded on the following melody by J. G. Hille, Cantor in Glaucha, near Halle, 1739. According to the Rev. W. Cairns, the tune was known in Herrnhut when John Wesley visited the Moravian Settlement there, but how it got into England, and who arranged and changed it for the 'Foundery' Tune-Book is a story that has not yet been fully told :

O ihr auserwählten kinder.　　　　　J. G. Hille.

714—O Jesu mi Dulcissime.

O Jesu mi dulcissime is said to be derived from the *Clausener Gesangbuch* (1653).

715—Mountain Christians.

MOUNTAIN CHRISTIANS. The late Sylvester Horne heard this tune, it took his fancy, and he decided that it might serve a useful purpose. Failing to find words to suit it he wrote the hymn, 'For the might of Thine arm we bless Thee,' and the combination was inserted in the revised edition of *The Fellowship Hymn-Book* (1933). In the *Methodist Hymn-Book* it is attributed to J. Mannin, but this reference is doubtful.

716—St. Godric. See No. 269.

717—Lunenburg.

LUNENBURG is adapted from the air ' Non vi Piacque ' in Handel's opera, *Siroe* (1728).

718—Reuben.

REUBEN is by Samuel Wakeley. When it first appeared is doubtful, but in *The Village Harmony*, which he published in 1846, he calls himself ' author of the well-known tunes called REUBEN and NAVARINO. The latter name is probably associated with the Battle of Navarino, October 20, 1827.

719—Bishopthorpe.

BISHOPTHORPE, by Jeremiah Clark. See No. 107.

720—Vienna.

VIENNA (or RAVENNA), by J. H. Knecht, is from the same source as No. 618.

721—St. David.

ST. DAVID is from T. Ravenscroft's *Psalter* (see No. 45), where it is called a Welsh tune.

722—Chimes.

CHIMES comes to us from the eighteenth century, but is of somewhat uncertain origin. As far as is known the tune first appeared in *Harmonia Sacra,* or *A Choice Collection of Psalm and Hymn-Tunes, &c., in two and three Parts for the Voice, Harpsichord and Organ.* This was compiled by Thomas Butts, who unfortunately omitted to date his work. There are at least three different editions, and the earliest, in which CHIMES appears was published certainly not later than 1757.

This is the work John Wesley refers to in the Preface to his *Select Hymns with Tunes Annext* (dated 1761) where he wrote :

1. Some years ago a Collection of Tunes was published, under the title of *Harmonia Sacra.* I believe all unprejudiced persons who understand music allow, that it exceeds beyond all degrees of comparison, anything of the kind which has appeared in *England* before ; the tunes being admirably well chosen, and accurately engraven, not only for the voice, but likewise for the organ or harpsichord.

2. But this, tho' it is excellent in its kind, is not the thing which I want. I want the people called *Methodists* to sing true, the tunes which are in *common use* among them. At the same time I want them to have in one volume, the *best Hymns* which we have printed : and that, in a *small* and *portable* volume, and one of an *easy price.*

But although Wesley did not approve of the *Harmonia Sacra* as a whole, he certainly welcomed some of the new tunes therein of which CHIMES was one, and it was included in his *Select Hymns with Tunes Annext.*

In *Harmonia Sacra* CHIMES, which, however, does not bear that name, is headed :

Psalm CL. By King James.

But although it would be very pleasing to have a tune by James I in the *Methodist Hymn-Book,* the reference is not to the music, but to the king's metrical version of the Psalms. But the fact is that he only got as far as

Psalm xxx, the rest of the version being finished by another hand. Chimes has maintained its popularity. It suffered an eclipse during the middle of last century, but again found a place in the *Wesleyan Tune-Book* (1876). Dropped in 1904, it has now been restored to favour. The composer has never been traced.

Curiously enough, no attempt to 'edit' it has ever been made (a fate that few tunes escape), and it has come down unscathed and unaltered through the years since its first appearance about 1757.

723—Vater Unser. See No. 683.

724—Jordan.

Jordan is from a book of Welsh tunes edited by R. H. Pritchard in 1857. It is an old melody, but its origin is unknown. It is said to be founded on the air ' Dewch i'r Brwydr ' (come to battle).

725—St. Philip.

St. Philip was written by W. H. Monk for the first (1861) edition of *Hymns Ancient and Modern*. See No. 221.

726—Aberystwyth.

Aberystwyth, by Dr. Joseph Parry (see No. 195), first appeared in a new (1879) edition of Stephen and Jones's *Ail Lyfr Tonau ac Emynau* (second book of Hymns and Tunes) set to the Welsh hymn, ' Beth sydd i mi yn y byd.' At the time of its composition Dr. Parry was professor of music at University College, Aberystwyth. He placed the tune (setting it to ' Jesu, lover of my soul ') as the concluding number of his cantata, *Ceridwen*, but it proved a rather abrupt ending to a purely Druidical story.

727—Agapé.

Agape is the refrain of a song by Mrs. Barnard called ' Children's Voices.' The composer, who published under the name of 'Claribel,' was a popular song-writer of the mid-Victorian period, but her compositions are now practically forgotten. AGAPÉ is taken from a book of 'Kyries' written by George Herbert, at one time choir director at Farm Street Church, W. This tune is also known as PILGRIMAGE.

728—Amor Dei.

AMOR DEI is from the *Church Hymnary* (1898). It was adapted for that collection by the editor, Sir John Stainer, from a Bremen *Kirchen Gesänge* (1707).

729—Cloisters.

CLOISTERS was composed by Sir Joseph Barnby for the 1868 edition of *Hymns Ancient and Modern,* where it is set to the hymn, 'Lord of our life, and God of our salvation.'

730—Stamford.

STAMFORD was written by S. Reay at the request of Mr. John Dobson, of Richmond, when preparing his *Tunes New and Old* in 1863. Mr. Dobson's tastes inclined strongly towards the early English school of psalmody, and he drew largely on the Old and New Versions of the Psalms for his tunes. Those of the curly type, sometimes known as Old Methodist tunes, had no attraction for him, and, greatly daring, he omitted such tunes as ASHLEY (to 'Salvation! O the Joyful Sound') from his collection.

In his day the inevitable tune to what was known as 6 lines 8's (second metre) was MONMOUTH, but this was on Dobson's *Index Expurgatorius,* so he applied to his friend, Samuel Reay, for a new tune to that metre. STAMFORD was the result.

Samuel Reay was born in the north country in 1822. His father was living at Hexham, and from here the

boy passed on to Durham, where he became a cathedral
chorister under William Henshaw, who was organist for
fifty-one years. During his reign the music at Durham
underwent considerable improvement, especially during
his later years, when Dr. Dykes was associated with him
as precentor. On leaving Durham young Reay held
several positions as organist in the North of England.
He appears to have had somewhat eclectic tastes, for his
appointments included both Roman Catholic and
Anglican churches. In after years his most important
appointments were at Bury and Newark-on-Trent. It
was whilst he was at Bury that he became acquainted
with John Dobson, who was living in Manchester, and
who was then busy preparing his *Tunes New and Old*.
Reay wrote several new tunes for this work besides
STAMFORD, and due acknowledgement of his services is
made in the preface. Whilst living at Tiverton, Reay
wrote his famous part-song, 'The Dawn of Day,' which
was at one time in the *repertoire* of every glee and
choral society in the country.

Reay has another claim to fame, for he used to
maintain that he was the first musician to play
Mendelssohn's 'Wedding March' at a nuptial festival.
This question of priority was discussed some years ago
in *The Musical Times*. It seems that early in 1847,
Ewer and Co. published a pianoforte duet arrangement
of the *Midsummer Night's Dream* music. Reay secured
a copy and made a manuscript organ transcription of
the 'Wedding March,' at the foot of which he wrote:

'Arranged for the organ by Samuel Reay, and
played for the first time on such an occasion at the
marriage of Mr. Tom Daniel and Miss Dorothea
Carew, at St. Peter's Church, Tiverton, June 2,
1847.'

731—Cœna Domini.

CŒNA DOMINI, by Sir A. Sullivan, is from *Church
Hymns with Tunes* (1874).

732—Southport.

SOUTHPORT is taken from *The Primitive Methodist Hymnal* (1889), where it is ascribed to the Rev. J. Davies. He may have contributed it to that work, but no acknowledgement is made to him in the Preface, nor is anything at present known about him.

733—Lux Prima.

LUX PRIMA was contributed by Sir G. A. Macfarren (see No. 592) to the *Songs of Praise* (1876).

734—St. Constantine.

ST. CONSTANTINE, by W. H. Monk, was written for the first (1861) edition of *Hymns Ancient and Modern*. See No. 215.

735—Intercession.

INTERCESSION was composed in 1865 by W. H. Callcott, and inserted in *Psalms and Hymns for Divine Worship* (1867). The last two lines are from the prayer for rain in Mendelssohn's *Elijah*.

William Hutchins Callcott, son of Dr. J. W. Callcott, was born at Kensington in 1807. He studied music under his father, and also under William Horsley. He composed much for the pianoforte; also glees, songs and anthems. He was for a time organist at Ely Place Chapel. He died in 1882.

736, 762—Arnold's.

ARNOLD'S is by Dr. Samuel Arnold (see No. 465), and is taken from *Arnold and Calcott's Psalms* (1791), where it is set to Psalm xv (N.V.).

737—Cheshunt College.

CHESHUNT COLLEGE was contributed by J. Barnby (see No. 105) to the *Congregational Church Hymnary* (1887).

738—Revive Thy Work, O Lord.

REVIVE THY WORK, O LORD is by W. H. Doane (see No. 161) from his *Songs of Devotion* (1870).

739—Aberdeen.

ABERDEEN (or ST. PAUL'S) is from the second edition (1762) of Bremner's *Rudiments of Music,* but it is said to have been in use at an earlier period, though there is no definite proof of this.

Robert Bremner opened a music shop in Edinburgh about 1748 under the sign of the ' Harp and Hautboy,' where he sold all kinds of musical instruments from bass violin and harpsichord to bagpipes, pitch-pipes and tabors, and indeed all the essentials of the trade. In 1756 he published the first edition of his *Rudiments of Music* ' revised and approved by the directors of the Music Society.' In 1762 Bremner went to London and opened a branch in the Strand, also under the ' Harp and Hautboy opposite Somerset House.' Bremner did nothing more in the way of music for church use, but the various collections he made of Scotch melodies must certainly have had far-reaching effects.

740—Bevan.

BEVAN was written by John Goss (see No. 12) for Rev. Peter Maurice's *Choral Harmony* (1854). The tune is dated 1853.

741—Credo.

CREDO was written by Sir J. Stainer (see No. 20) for Gurney's hymn, ' We saw Thee not when Thou didst come ' in *Hymns Ancient and Modern* (1875).

742—Blackburn.

BLACKBURN (or BLACKBOURNE) is first found in Harrison's *Sacred Harmony* (1784). It has been variously ascribed to a mysterious John Fish, of Blackburn, and also to a certain William Defesch, a

Dutch organist of the first half of the eighteenth century. He wrote two oratorios, *Joseph* and *Judith*, and also a mass and a variety of instrumental works. A careful search through all these might possibly reveal BLACKBURN.

743—Frilford.

FRILFORD was composed by the Rev. Dr. W. H. Ferguson for the *Public School Hymn-Book* (1919). See No. 526.

744—Happy Day.

HAPPY DAY. The earliest known printed copy of this tune is in the *Wesleyan Sacred Harp* (1855), no composer's name being given. It is very probable that the tune was current before that date.

745—Lucius.

LUCIUS and WILLIAMS (No. 968), are said to be from an American collection known as *Templi Carmina*, published in 1829, but they are not found in any available copies of the book.

746—Draw Me Nearer.

DRAW ME NEARER is by W. H. Doane (see No. 161), and was composed for an American collection called *Brightest and Best* (1875).

747—St. Ignatius.

ST. IGNATIUS is by the Rev. John Beaumont, and is taken from his *New Harmonic Magazine* (1801).

John Beaumont, who was born in 1762, had the advantage of a musical home, for his father, who possessed a farm near Holmfirth, in the West Riding, had a considerable local reputation for his skill in music. When his young son was in his fourth year his father took him in hand and began to teach him his notes, and proud enough the youngster was when he could sing the OLD HUNDREDTH without assistance. He made such

good progress that in his seventh year he made his first
public appearance, taking one of the solos in an oratorio.
This success induced his father to take the boy on a
tour as a sort of musical prodigy, and his beautiful
treble voice gained him a host of admirers at Lancaster,
Kendal and other places in the North of England.

A long spell of home life followed, during which the
boy became a proficient performer on the bass viol, and
he often conducted the band of singers at the church
when his father was away.   Now it was that his
upbringing in the school of Croft, Green, and Kent—
names to conjure with in those days—stood him in good
stead, and he spent much of his time in preparing for
rehearsals and in practising and performing vocal and
instrumental music.

When he was about sixteen years of age, Beaumont
accompanied a party of musicians to Mexboro', near
Barnsley.   Here he heard for the first time a Methodist
preacher, and was much struck by the sermon.   Soon
afterwards some Methodists settled in the neighbourhood of his home, but the elder Beaumont was a strong
Churchman, and would have nothing to do with the new
preachers.   The boy, however, persisted in going to the
Methodist meetings, and at last his father told him he
must either give up attending them or else he would
have him in the house no longer.   The fact really was
that the father was afraid lest 'the new religion,' as he
called it, might keep his son from his music and so
spoil his future outlook.   However, young Beaumont had
made up his mind, and went forth to seek his fortune
in the cloth weaving trade.   This occupation he subsequently abandoned on qualifying as a Methodist preacher.

In 1801 he published his psalmody efforts in a thick
oblong volume under the title :

*The New Harmonic Magazine, or Compendium
Repository of Sacred Music in Full Score.*

The work was originally issued in ten monthly
numbers at half a crown each, and these formed a

complete volume which cost a guinea. The tunes also seemed to have been issued in single sheets, price threepence each. In his 'Preface' Beaumont issues a warning to those people who think they can improve his music. 'If any person,' he says, 'chooses to alter my composition, let them remember, it is not with my consent.' But he has no objection to any one altering the pitch of his tunes, in case they find the range too high. This was a kindly and gracious concession, for in some of his tunes he takes the treble up to B and B flat above the line, whilst ST. CHRISTOPHER starts on the top F sharp. Beaumont apologizes for these lofty notes, and explains it is due to 'my being able to feign my voice to any tolerable height . . . not sufficiently considering those voices not able to do so.'

The *New Harmonic Magazine* contains upwards of sixty tunes, and also several 'set pieces,' a convenient term that was in use when the very word 'anthem' aroused suspicion and resentment in certain minds. It appears to have been Beaumont's last musical production. For twenty more years he continued his ministerial work at important places in Cheshire and the North of England, and whilst at Nantwich he wrote his auto-biography, which gives us a true and faithful picture of the trials and troubles of a Methodist preacher's life at the beginning of the last century. His early upbringing on a moorland farm had made him a lover of horses, and his tastes 'for a blood horse and a fine psalm-tune' were a matter of common knowledge amongst the friends of his later years. To the end of his life he found comfort and solace in the pursuit of music, and his love for the art, and his proficiency therein, gave him welcome relief from the usual routine of a preacher's life. His last appointment was at Driffield, but the work there proved too much for him, and he removed to Macclesfield, where he passed away in 1822. His son, Dr. Joseph Beaumont, attained great fame as a Methodist preacher. He died with tragic suddenness at Waltham

Street Chapel, Hull, whilst giving out the second verse
of Dr. Watts's hymn:

> Eternal Power, whose high abode
> Becomes the grandeur of a God.

748—Harts.

HARTS is a reduced form of a tune by Benjamin
Milgrove from the same source as HARWICH (No. 66).

749—Dundee (French). See No. 625.

750—Eaton.

EATON, by Zerubbabel Wyvill, is from his *Anthem,
Two Hymns, and two dismissions selected and composed
for the General Thanksgiving.* This event took place
on June 1, 1802, in celebration of the Treaty of Amiens.
Wyvill, born in 1763, was a music teacher at Maidenhead,
also organist at the Episcopal Chapel of S.S. Mary and
Andrew. He is spoken of as a man of excellent
character, and was highly esteemed. EATON was
originally designed as a L.M., the last two lines being
repeated.

751—Dublin.

DUBLIN, by J. A. Stevenson, is from *The Chorale Book*
(Bemrose and Adlington, 1861).

Sir John Stevenson was the son of a violinist in the
State Band at Dublin. Born about 1762 he was brought
up as a chorister in the cathedrals of Christ Church and
St. Patrick, of which he was after vicar choral. His
association with Thomas Moon brought him considerable
fame at one time, his accompaniments to the poet's
'Irish Melodies' having a wide and continued
circulation.

752—St. Mark.

ST. MARK is one of the many variants of a choral by
J. R. Ahle. It is better known by the name LIEBSTER
JESU, the first words of the German hymn to which it

was written. Ahle was born at Mulhausen in 1625, and was for some years organist at the Church of St. Blasius in that town. He took a prominent part in public affairs, and served as a town councillor and as burgomaster.

753—Ffigysbren.

FFIGYSBREN is found in *Y Caniedydd Cynulleidfaol Newydd* (1921), where it is called CLÔD (Welsh for 'Praise'). It originally appeared in *Caniadau Scion* (1840) ascribed to R. Mills.

754—Kerry.

KERRY is from *A Manual of Parochial Psalmody* (1825), edited by the Rev. Joseph Jowett, M.A., rector of Silk Willoughby (near Sleaford). KERRY is at p. 42, with the initials 'J.J.' at the foot, showing it to be an original tune by the compiler. Jowett also published in 1823 *Musae Solitariae,* 'included as a help to devotion: in the closet or the domestic circle.' It is in two volumes, all the melodies being Jowett's own compositions. He also published *Verses on Various Occasions for Friends,* a volume of short poems chiefly on musical subjects. It was printed for private circulation, and is rarely met with.

755—St. Chrysostom.

ST. CHRYSOSTOM is by J. Barnby. See No. 438.

756—Rendez à Dieu.

RENDEZ A DIEU is the tune set to a metrical version of Psalm cxviii in the *Genevan Psalter* of 1543, probably composed or adapted by Louis Bourgeois.

757—Culbach.

CULBACH is found in J. Scheffler's *Heilige Seelenlust* (1657) (see No. 689), where it is said to be a 'well-known melody.' This is the original form of the tune (on p. 3 of the work referred to) :

758—Leicester.

LEICESTER was contributed by William Hurst to the 1875 edition of *Hymns Ancient and Modern*. The composer was born at Leicester in 1849, but spent the greater part of his life at Coalville, where for many years he took an active part in the musical life of the district. Though entirely self-taught he was an able organist and accompanist. He never held any permanent position, but he was always ready to place his services at the disposal of any place of worship, regardless of the denomination. He had considerable experience as a conductor, and directed the massed bands of the district at Queen Victoria's Jubilee. His compositions were limited to organ music and hymn-tunes. His last effort was a tune to ' How sweet the name of Jesus sounds,' which he wrote the day before his death, expressing the wish that it might be sung at his funeral, a request which was faithfully observed. He died in 1934.

759—Unde et Memores. See. No. 586.

760—Devotion.

DEVOTION was contributed by Clarkson Garbutt to the *Methodist Hymn-Book* of 1904. He was connected with the Methodist Church at Holly Park, N., where C. J. Dale (see No. 169) was choirmaster.

761—St. Augustine. See No. 638.

762—Arnold's. See No. 736.

763—Abbey. See Nos. 37 and 698.

764—Wesley.

The source of WESLEY is unknown. There is a tune
NASEBY in *The Psalmist*, 'Arranged by V. Novello,' of
which the first line is identical with WESLEY, but no
composer's name or source is added. Why it has been
christened WESLEY is also a mystery, as no member of
that family appears to have any connexion with it. It
is very probable that WESLEY has developed from the
same original source as DAVID (No. 973), which is
adapted from an opera by Handel.

765—Sicilian Mariners.

It is very doubtful if SICILIAN MARINERS has anything to do with Sicily, or whether the mariners of that
island ever included it amongst their sea shanties. An
early—if not the first—public appearance in this country
was in the Rev. W. D. Tattersall's *Psalmody* (1794),
where it is called SICILIAN HYMN. Between that year
and 1805, when Dr. E. Miller included it in his *Watts'
Psalms and Hymns, set to music,* it was issued in leaflet
form, set to :

> O sanctissima
> O piissima
> Dulcis Virgo Maria!
> Mater amata
> In temerata
> Ora pro nobis!

The first line of the hymn gave a name to the tune
in some books. The melody has never been definitely
traced, and nothing is known of its history.

766—Belmont.

The first known appearance of BELMONT in its present
form was in the *Psalms and Hymn-Tunes,* issued in 1854
for the use of St. Mary's Church, Islington. The

editor of the work was Charles Severn, who was born in 1805. He adopted music as a profession, and was a Court musician when Queen Victoria ascended the throne. He was one of the principal performers in the music in connexion with the coronation ceremony, his special instruments being the violoncello and double bass. He also took part in the first performance of the *Elijah* at Birmingham in 1846. He was organist of Islington Parish Church for forty-six years, whilst he played in the opera orchestra for over half a century. His long and honourable career came to a close in December, 1894. Charles Severn was a brother of the Severn who was a friend of Keats, and he was the uncle of Mr. Arthur Severn, the friend and biographer of Ruskin.

BELMONT always has been, and still is, a somewhat elusive melody. Many have sought, but none has succeeded in discovering its origin. Some suggest that it occurs somewhere in Mozart's works, but no one has hitherto succeeded in locating it there. It has been assigned to Samuel Webbe, Jr., but up to now the verdict is against him, as it is not to be found in any book that can be associated with him. In the *Handbook to the Church Hymnary* the source, as originally suggested in Love's *Scottish Church Music* is still adhered to. This gives it as an adaptation from a melody in William Gardiner's *Sacred Melodies,* consisting of eight lines, the first four furnishing the suggested origin of BELMONT.

No name of composer is given, but in a catalogue appended to his *Music and Friends* (1838) Gardiner claims it as his own composition.

In *Hymn-Tunes and their Story* (p. 354) reference is made to the fact that as the result of inquiries, two correspondents stated that the tune was adapted from a song called 'O sing again that melody.' No such song appeared in the British Museum catalogue, but after many years search a copy was found in a bound volume of old songs exposed for sale in an old furniture shop in Croydon. It was published by Dale Cockerell and Co., 19 Poultry, the words being by Charles Jefferys. It was 'Composed for Mr. H. Phillips, and dedicated to Miss T. Sandmann, by S. Nelson.' Here is the opening phrase:

Oh, sing a-gain the me - lo - dy We lov'd in o-ther years; It

may not bring re - turn of joy, But still can banish tears.

and there we may have BELMONT.

767—Hampstead. See No. 433.

768—Passion Chorale. See No. 202.

769—Spanish Chant. See No. 306.

770—Tyholland.

TYHOLLAND is said to be of German origin, perhaps an old carol, but it is so ancient that its origin is lost in the mists of antiquity. It has appeared in varying forms. The present version has been put into shape by the Rev. D. F. R. Wilson, canon and precentor of St. Patrick's Cathedral, Dublin. He was formerly Master of the Cathedral Choir School. He acted as one of the editors of the *Irish Church Hymnal.*

771—Euphony. See No. 173.

772—St. Agnes.

ST. AGNES, by J. Langran, was originally composed
and published in leaflet form in 1861 for the hymn ' Abide
with me.'

James Langran was born in the St. Pancras district
of London in 1835. Three years later his parents
removed to Tottenham, where he spent the rest of his
life. He received organ lessons from the organist at
St. James's Church, Edmonton, and in 1856 obtained
his first appointment at St. Michael's, Wood Green.
This was the successful result of a competition in which
the fifty-three candidates had to play two voluntaries
selected by themselves, and two or three hymn-tunes,
together with an arrangement of ' The heavens are
telling.' This was rather a difficult task, as the organ,
though of excellent tone, was a one-manual instrument.
The choir under his control consisted of half-a-dozen
school children and some elderly ladies. Some members
of the congregation from the Printers' Almshouses in
the neighbourhood also used to attend the practices and
contribute what help they could.

Two years at an instrument of such limited scope
proved sufficient, and the young organist passed on to
Holy Trinity Church, Tottenham, where he had a good
instrument by Henry Willis. Here the choir consisted
of eight schoolgirls arrayed in green frocks and caps and
tippets, supported by several ladies and gentlemen who
sat promiscuously round the organ. Their efforts were
occasionally supplemented at the evening service by two
or three boys from the St. Paul's Cathedral choir.

Langran's final move was to the Tottenham parish
church in 1870, and there he remained in harness till his
death in 1909. During his early career the only lessons
he received were from J. Baptiste Calkin (see No. 268),
of whom he used to speak in cordial terms ' of the
benefits he received from his painstaking and thoroughly

onscientious method. Every bar was carefully
examined, and much benefit derived from Mr. Calkin's
polished and artistic performance of the music in hand.'

773 (i)—Memoria.

Memoria, by S. S. Wesley. See No. 536.

773 (ii)—Willenhall.

Willenhall was written by John Cluley (see No.
94) for the *Methodist Hymn-Book* (1904).

774—Saffron Walden.

Saffron Walden, by A. H. Brown. See No. 302.

775—St. Alphege.

St. Alphege, by Dr. Gauntlett. See No. 652.

776—Day of Rest.

Day of Rest was originally composed by J. W. Elliott
see No. 196) for the hymn ' O day of rest and gladness.'
t appeared in *Church Hymns* (1874).

777—O Perfect Love.

O Perfect Love is adapted from an anthem written
y Sir Joseph Barnby for the marriage of H.R.H.
Princess Louise with the Duke of Fife, July 27, 1889.

778—Day of Praise.

Day of Praise, by Charles Steggall (see No. 540), is
rom the *Supplemental Hymn and Tune Book* (1869),
dited by R. Brown-Borthwick.

779—Veni Creator. See No. 184.

780 (i)—St. Leonard.

St. Leonard (also known as Liebe die du mich) is
scribed, on doubtful authority, to John Christopher

Bach, a second cousin of J. S. Bach. Born in 1643 he was court and town organist at Eisenach. Forkel says that 'he was particularly happy in the invention of beautiful melodies,' and also points out that he was somewhat of an adventurer in the harmonic resources of his day, in that 'he ventured to make use of the extreme (or, as it is now called, the augmented) sixth, which in his day was considered as an extremely bold attempt.' J. C. Bach was a prolific composer, rarely content unless he was writing in a multiplicity of parts, even up to twenty-two. ST. LEONARD is from a Meiningen *Gesangbuch* of 1693, where it is set to a hymn by Scheffler, translated by Miss Frances E. Cox as:

> Love, who in the first beginning,
> Man in Thine own likeness made.

Definite proof that J. C. Bach composed the tune is wanting.

780 (ii)—Ottawa.

OTTAWA. It is uncertain in which of the numerous collections that Lowell Mason (see No. 238) was responsible for, this tune occurs.

781—Galilee.

GALILEE, by Dr. Armes, appeared in the 1875 edition of *Hymns Ancient and Modern,* set to the hymn 'Jesus shall reign where'er the sun.'

Philip Armes was born at Norwich in 1836. His father, who was a schoolmaster at a village some four miles from the centre of the city, was a noted bass singer, and used to visit the city regularly to take his part in glee clubs. When the boy was nine years old he became a chorister at the Cathedral under the famous Dr. Zechariah Buck, and became one of the doctor's 'show' boys. When Jenny Lind was staying at the Bishop's Palace in 1847, the Cathedral choir received an invitation to sing before her. The old doctor evidently thought that Philip was as good as the

Swedish Nightingale, for he made him sing ' Where the bee sucks,' to the great delight of the famous singer.

When Armes was at the Cathedral the music was rendered very differently from the way in which it is now. Then everything was done in the most florid style, viz. grace-notes, cadenzas, shakes (single, double, and triple), while time was not much considered. Indeed, some of the treble solos were nearly sung *ad libitum*. In the anthems, three boys would make ' shakes ' simultaneously; and not only the boys, but the lay clerks used to ' shake ' most extensively. There was one lay clerk—Mr. William Smith—who had so good a shake that he was requested not to forget it at the service, as the ladies so much admired it! He would begin a solo with an elaborate shake, and end with one, besides introducing two or three in the middle of an anthem. In fact, shakes were so numerous that, as someone once remarked, the Cathedral must on occasion have been shaken to its very foundations.

But there is no doubt that Buck was a great trainer, and young Armes profited greatly under his teaching. He was a strict disciplinarian, and everything had to give way for the daily singing lessons. These would last from 8.30 a.m. till 5, when the boys went off to a rudimentary sort of education imparted by a teacher who was already so worn out by his day's work that he would sometimes fall asleep in his chair. Dr. Buck would pay particular attention to the diet of his boys. If he thought they were underfed he would feed them himself even to a quarter of a pint of stout and some bread and butter, with an occasional taste of three or four oysters as a special treat. In this connexion A. N. Gaul used to recall a touching story of his own experiences, as related in F. G. Kitton's *Memoirs* of Dr. Buck :

> I can fully corroborate the statement that Dr. Buck was exceedingly particular regarding the diet of those boys whose voices were eminently serviceable in solo-

singing. I recall an instance of this in my own experience. A Norfolk clergyman (well known in musical circles of that day) desired to favour a party of friends at his own house with a rendering of Mendelssohn's *Elijah*, and he asked Dr. Buck if he would lend him a boy to assist in the solos. The wish was complied with, and I was the boy selected for the occasion, *àpropos* of which I vividly remember, as though it happened yesterday, an incident which covered me with confusion. The dinner came before the music, and the guests had taken their seats, a place being found for me at a small side-table; presently, while the first course was being served, a note arrived for the host, who, observing its nature, proclaimed his intention of reading it aloud to those assembled around the festive board, and, amid breathless silence, he announced the contents of the brief missive, which ran thus :

'Dear Sir,—Please don't let little Gaul have any pudding.

'Yours faithfully,

'Z. Buck.'

Such spartan conditions as these produced excellent results, for Philip Armes was only one of many of 'Buck's boys' who gained distinction in after life.

After leaving Norwich Armes became a chorister at Rochester Cathedral, where he had J. F. Bridge as a companion. Armes distinguished himself greatly as a soloist, and such satisfaction did his performance give that on leaving the choir he was presented with a handsome Broadwood piano, subscribed for by those who had enjoyed his singing.

In 1854 Armes gained his first organ appointment at Milton, near Gravesend, and three years later he was appointed, on the recommendation of Sir George Elvey, to St. Andrew's, Wells Street, W., where the music was of the cathedral type. Whilst in London he was a member of the renowned choir formed by Henry Leslie and thus gained an invaluable knowledge of part music and how to conduct it.

From Wells Street, Armes went to Chichester Cathedral in 1861, and about a year later he competed for the post at Durham Cathedral, which he was successful in obtaining, the adjudicator being the Rev. J. B. Dykes. Here he spent the remainder of his life fulfilling his cathedral duties, composing oratorios and other music, and examining candidates for their Durham degree in Music. He retired from full work in 1906, being then made Honorary Organist. In 1897 he was appointed the first Professor of Music at Durham University, and this position he held till his death in 1908.

782—Supplication.

SUPPLICATION, by G. F. Vincent, is from *The Hymnal Companion* (1890).

George Frederick Vincent was the son of an organ-builder at Sunderland. He was born at Houghton-le-Spring, in 1855. After private study at home he went to Leipzig Conservatoire for three years and was then appointed organist of Sunderland parish church, subsequently passing to St. Thomas in the same town. In 1900 he became organist at St. Michael's, Cornhill, and here he instituted the custom of week-day organ recitals, which have since become a recognized feature of City life. His compositions were confined chiefly to organ music. He died in 1928.

783—Birstal.

BIRSTAL is by Accepted Widdop. See No. 63.

784—Duke Street.

DUKE STREET is by John Hatton, of whom nothing is known except that he lived at St. Helens, where he died in 1793. The tune is also known as WINDLE, from the district where he lived, whilst DUKE STREET more exactly locates his habitation. The tune has been traced to Henry Boyd's *Select Collection of Psalm and Hymn-Tunes* (1793).

785—Old 44th.

OLD 44TH is a survival from a collection of fifty-one Psalms published at Geneva in 1556. The full title of the book is:

> 'One and Fiftie Psalmes of David in English metre whereof 37 were made by Thomas Sternholde and the rest by others. Coferred with the hebrew and in certayn places corrected as the text and sens of the Prophet required.'

786—Lothian.

LOTHIAN was written by Sir J. F. Bridge as a special setting of the Rev. T. B. Stephenson's hymn, ' Lord, grant us, ' like the watching five,' in the 1904 *Methodist Hymn-Book*.

787—Avon.

AVON is taken from the festival book of the Bath and Wells Diocesan Choral Association. The composer and the original source of the tune are both unknown. It was introduced by the late A. H. Peppin, music master at Rugby School, and subsequently at Clifton College, who was one of the committee appointed to draw up the Festival Booklet referred to.

788—St. Merryn.

ST. MERRYN, by Dr. H. A. Harding. See No. 420.

789—Fritwell.

FRITWELL was composed by Dr. G. F. Brockless (see No. 127) for the present (1933) edition of the *Methodist Hymn-Book*.

790—Fulda. See No. 323.

791—Elim (Hesperus).

Elim (Hesperus), by Henry Baker. See No. 325.

792—Mount Ephraim.

Mount Ephraim, by B. Milgrove. See No. 424.

793—Herrnhut.

Herrnhut, by J. Crüger. See No. 245.

794—St. Pancras.

St. Pancras is by J. Battishill. It first appeared in Riley's *Parochial Psalmody* (1762), for which it was composed.

Born in London in 1738, Jonathan Battishill was placed in the choir of St. Paul's in his tenth year, and he soon gave proof of his keen appreciation of the music in which he took part, so that visitors to the cathedral used to inquire who the boy with the beautiful voice was. When his voice broke he took up the study of the organ, and his abilities attracted the attention of such famous musicians as Drs. Arne, Worgan and Boyce, and the last-named frequently entrusted the young musician with the services at the Chapel Royal, St. James's. In due course he applied for, and obtained, the post of organist at St. Clement, Eastcheap, E.C., which he resigned in 1767 for a similar position at Christ Church, Newgate Street. Nor did he confine his attention entirely to church music. He played the harpsichord at Covent Garden Theatre, and also composed incidental music for the stage. After the death of his wife, Battishill seems to have retired from public life, and to have devoted himself to the arrangement of his library, though he continued to give a certain amount of time to private tuition. It was during this period of retirement that he made the acquaintance of the Rev. Charles Wesley, and his eldest son Charles, and took part in the concerts arranged by Charles and Sam in their father's house in Marylebone. Samuel Wesley, when recording his reminiscences, wrote this about him:

> Among the first-rate musicians I have been acquainted with may be justly reckoned the late Jonathan Battishill, to whom my dear father was very partial, and who composed a valuable set of beautiful tunes to sundry of his hymns. His talents were versatile, as he excelled in the Church, Chamber and Theatrical styles. His glorious anthem, 'Call to remembrance' will remain a perpetual monument to his fame as an ecclesiastical composer, and his Operas, Glees, Canons and secular productions will be always prized among real competent judges of musical Art and Science.
>
> He was a perfect master of the Organ, and his extemporaneous performance on that instrument was in all respects attractive and commanding. His singing was very engaging, energetic and commanding, and it was a high treat to hear him take part in a Duet of Handel's or a Canzonet of Travers', or sing any of Purcell's Songs or Anthems.

His friendship with Charles Wesley led him to set some of the poet's hymns to music, and they were published under the title:

> *Twelve Hymns: the Words by the Rev. Charles Wesley, M.A., late Student at Christ Church, Oxford: set to Musick by Jonathan Battishill.*

The tunes are distinctly florid in form, and it is doubtful if they were ever used in public worship in their original form.

The following anecdote seems to suggest that Battishill had not a high opinion of some of his contemporaries. Hearing that Dr. Nares (see No. 463), the master of the children at the Chapel Royal, was indisposed, he inquired what his complaint was. Being told that it arose from a consistent singing in the doctor's head, Battishill remarked, 'Then that's a favourable symptom, for if there be singing in his head now, who knows but that some time or other there may be music there!'

795—Kingsland.

KINGSLAND comes from an eighteenth-century collection of tunes with a very long title, which may be briefly set down as *The Psalms of David in Metre*. The collection, which is not dated (probably 1791-3) was made by Hugh Bond, who described himself as ' Lay Vicar of Exeter Cathedral.' This would be in the days when W. Jackson, of ' Te Deum ' fame, was organist.

Bond ascribes KINGSLAND (also another tune in his collection) to Dr. Boyce (No. 868), but as he had been dead some years it is quite possible that it is by his son, William Boyce.

796—Contemplation.

CONTEMPLATION is an original chorale by Mendelssohn in his setting of Psalm xiii.

There is a very interesting history connected with this setting. In a letter written by Moscheles to his wife in 1841 he says :

A Mr. B., one of my most zealous pupils, came to me to-day with the request that Spohr, Mendelssohn and I would each write for him a psalm with orchestral accompaniments, and he offers to pay £20 for each. Mendelssohn chose the 13th, I the 93rd Psalm, and Mr. B. wishes them to be published with the utmost care.

This ' Mr. B.' was the Rev. Charles Bayles Broadley, who, in 1840, was deputy professor of Civil Law at Cambridge.

Mendelssohn finished his music for this Psalm and dispatched the MS. on December 20, 1840, to the librettist with this covering letter :

Enclosed you will find an anthem which I have composed to the given words on the recommendation of Moscheles. Play it through if it doesn't bore you, and give it to Moscheles with the enclosed letter.

Broadley received the music in due course, but on finding that there were only three separate numbers he does not appear to have been quite satisfied. Perhaps he did not think he was getting full value for his £20; at any rate, he communicated with Mendelssohn, suggesting that he might write a short instrumental prelude, but the composer declined the suggestion. The psalm was first performed at the Hanover Square Rooms, London, on May 30, 1848.

797—Staples.

STAPLES is taken from an anthem by H. J. Staples, ' God the Father, be Thou near,' which in turn is founded on a melody which is No. 158 of the ' Virginal Book,' now preserved in the Fitzwilliam Museum at Cambridge. It was formerly supposed to have belonged to Queen Elizabeth, but there appears to be no foundation for the suggestion. The melody bears W. Byrd's name in the ' Virginal Book,' but only as the arranger of it, not the composer. Reference is made to the tune in Shakespeare's *Henry V*. In Act IV, Pistol has got hold of a French soldier:

PISTOL.—Yield, cur!

SOLDIER.—Je pense que vous estes gentilhomme de bonne qualité.

PISTOL.—Qualtitie? Calmie custure me!

There are various readings of the last three words, Boswell giving the version, ' Callino castor me,' which is the nearest to the ' Callino casturame ' in the ' Virginal Book.'

Boswell explains that ' Callino, castore me,' ' is an old song still preserved in Playford's *Musical Companion*

(1673),' and that the words mean 'Little girl of my heart for ever and ever.' He may be right, but further proof of the latter statement is wanting.

Callino Casturame.   WILLIAM BYRD.

Malone says that the words are the burden of an old song—'A sonnet of a Lover in the praise of his Lady,' which may be found in Clement Robinson's *Handful of Pleasant Delights* (1584).

The question was discussed in a number of *T.P.'s Weekly* (September 24, 1927) when three or four anonymous writers combined to say that 'Caleno custere me' is an Anglicized version of 'Cailinog a stuaire,' signifying 'young girl, my treasure,' and corresponding to the more modern 'Colleen asthore.'

It is probable that it would be more correct to include STAPLES amongst the Irish traditional airs rather than those of English origin.

798—Parting.

PARTING, by Jane Rhodes, first appeared in the *Methodist Sunday-school Hymnal* (1889). It was originally composed for a Sunday-school Anniversary in Bradford.

Miss Jane Rhodes was born at Bradford in 1835. Her father, a Bradford merchant, was an accomplished amateur musician. The year after his death in 1847 a selection of his original hymn-tunes was published, one of which, MORNING FLOWERS, was included in the

Wesleyan Tune-Book (1876). Miss Rhodes inherited her father's musical gifts. For upwards of fifteen years she was a member of the Bradford Choral Society, and for a time acted as deputy organist at Eastbrook Chapel. In 1873 she accepted the position of organist at Richmond Terrace Chapel, where she remained for twenty-three years. For over half a century Miss Rhodes was librarian to the Bradford Library (now the Bradford Library and Literary Society), entering on her duties in 1854, first as assistant, whilst in 1881 she succeeded Miss Mason as the head librarian. She held the post with much distinction till 1910. After living for a few years in retirement she died in 1917.

799—Colvend.

COLVEND, by the Rev. F. Luke Wiseman (see No. 5), first appeared in the *Methodist School Hymnal* (1910).

800—Bethany.

BETHANY, by Henry Smart (see No. 12) is from *Psalms and Hymns for Divine Worship* (1867).

801—Missionary.

MISSIONARY (or HEBER) by Lowell Mason (see No. 238), appeared in *The Handel and Haydn Society's Collection* (1829). The collection was really made by Mason, but 'fathered' by the Society (see under No. 238). It is said that a lady in Savannah was greatly taken with the beauty of Bishop Heber's missionary hymn, and could not find a tune for it to satisfy her. Remembering that there was a young clerk, Lowell Mason, at the bank who had a reputation for his musical gifts, she sent her son to ask him to write a suitable tune for the hymn. In half an hour the boy was back with the music, which has since been the recognized, or 'proper' tune for the hymn.

802—New Sabbath.

NEW SABBATH is the composition of Thomas Phillips, of Bristol. Its earliest known appearance was in *Tunes to Watts' Psalms and Hymns,* edited by W. E. Miller and his son, the Rev. E. Miller. An obituary notice that appeared in Farley's *Bristol Journal* (June 20, 1807) supplies the following information, which is all that is known about him :

> June 15th.—Mr. [Henry] Phillips, of this city, brushmaker, known among the lovers of psalmody, for nearly half a century, by the familiarly distinctive appellation of 'Doctor.' As a specimen of his unassuming attempts at musical composition, the tune called 'New Sabbath,' in score for four voices (which has been heard in almost every place of public worship throughout the United Kingdom) will perpetuate his memory, while any taste for the truly devotional style of praise remains.

803—Malvern.

MALVERN is a very much altered form of the melody (called DORCHESTER) in *The Hallelujah* (1849) :

The original tune is by H. J. Gauntlett, and what he would say to this perversion of it is very doubtful, but he was given to express himself on the subject with much freedom at times, forgetting, perhaps, that he himself did not hesitate to alter a melody to meet his taste. See No. 257.

804—Dent Dale.

Dent Dale is called a 'traditional English melody' in the *English Hymnal* (1906), from which it is taken. It belongs to the old shepherd song, 'Tarry Woo,' and is familiar in wool-raising districts in the north of England, south of Scotland, and Lake District. The ancient village of Dent in Yorkshire, where this version was obtained, used to be famous for its wool and knitters.

805 (i)—Doxford.

Doxford was written by Sir Richard R. Terry (see No. 254) for the hymn 'Christ for the world, we sing,' and makes its first appearance in the *Methodist Hymn-Book* (1933).

805 (ii)—Edinburgh.

Edinburgh was contributed by Edmund S. Lamplough to the *Methodist School Hymnal* (1910). The composer was born at Islington, London, in 1860. He was privately educated at a school at Tulse Hill, where he received the only instruction in music that he has had. He has, however, always taken a deep interest in it, especially in sacred music, and in 1904 was a member of the Committee that produced the *Methodist Hymn-Book*. At the invitation of Sir Frederick Bridge, he formed one of the choir at the Abbey during the Coronation of King George V. In 1910 he assisted in the compilation of the *Methodist School Hymnal*, and acted on the committees in connexion with the production of the present *Methodist Hymn-Book*.

806—Heaven.

Heaven was written for the 1904 edition of *Hymns Ancient and Modern*. The composer, Bertram Luard-Selby, was born at Ightham, Kent, in 1853. After studying at Leipzig Conservatoire under Reinecke and Jadassohn, he became organist at St. Barnabas, Marylebone, going from there to Salisbury Cathedral for two years. His next appointment was at St. John's, Torquay, and then at St. Barnabas, Pimlico. In 1900 he succeeded John Hopkins as organist at Rochester Cathedral till 1916, when he resigned. He composed organ music, anthems, songs and chamber music. He was the editor of the Supplement (1916) to *Hymns Ancient and Modern.*

807 (i)—Bethlehem.

BETHLEHEM (DONCASTER), by S. Wesley. See No. 685.

807 (ii)—Canada.

CANADA, by W. Mather, is from the same source as No. 333.

808—St. Thomas.

ST. THOMAS is from the same manuscript volume as ADESTE FIDELES (No. 118), where it is set to the Latin hymn, ' Tantum ergo sacramentum.'

809—Londonderry Air.

LONDONDERRY AIR. The late Mr. F. E. Weatherly thus explained how his setting of ' the Londonderry Air ' came into existence. In 1912 he received a copy of the air, which greatly attracted him. He had on hand some verses called ' Danny Boy,' and :

> By lucky chance it only required a few alterations to make it fit that beautiful melody. After my song had been accepted by a publisher I got to know that Alfred Percival Graves had written two sets of words to the same melody, ' Emir's Farewell,' and ' Erin's Apple-blossom,' and I wrote to tell him what I had done. He took up a strange attitude and said that there was no reason why I should not write a new set of words to ' The Minstrel Boy,' but he did not suppose that I should do so ! The answer, of course,

is that Moore's words, 'The Minstrel Boy,' are so 'perfect a fit' to the melody, that I certainly should not try to compete with Moore. But beautiful as Graves's words are, they do not, to my fancy, suit the LONDONDERRY AIR. They seem to have none of the human interest which the melody demands. . . . However, 'Danny Boy' is accepted as an accomplished fact and is sung all over the world by Sinn Feiners and Ulstermen alike, by English as well as Irish, in America as well as in the homeland . . .

The LONDONDERRY AIR has no history, and has not been traced earlier than Petrie's *Ancient Music of Ireland* (1855).

810—Da Christus Geboren War.

DA CHRISTUS GEBOREN WAR. These are the first four words of a hymn unknown in English hymnals, but which deal with the birth of Christ. The tune, which is from *Vierstimmiges Choralbuch,* a collection formed by J. F. Doles in 1785, is probably founded on an old German melody.

Johann Friedrich Doles, born in 1715, studied music under J. S. Bach, but seems to have been more interested in secular than in sacred music. However, he was content to accept the position of cantor at the Thomasschule, Leipzig, where he certainly did little, if anything, to perpetuate the music or the fame of Bach, save on one occasion. In 1789 Mozart visited Leipzig and played the organ at St. Thomas's Church whilst Doles arranged the stops for him. He was so delighted with Mozart's playing that he caused his choir to sing Bach's eight-part motet, 'Singet dem Herrn,' which caused Mozart to say, 'Here is music from which all may still learn.'

811—St. Cecilia.

ST. CECILIA, by L. G. Hayne. See No. 140.

812 (i)—Medak.

MEDAK, by the Rev. F. Luke Wiseman (see No. 5), first appeared in the present *Methodist Hymn-Book* (1933).

812 (ii)—Purpose.

PURPOSE was composed by Martin Shaw (see No. 616) for Canon Ainger's hymn, ' God is working His purpose out,' and inserted in *Songs of Praise* (enlarged edition 1931).

813—Gräfenberg.

GRAFENBERG is stated to be from *Praxis Pietatis Melica,* an important collection of German chorales, of which a very large number of editions were issued during the seventeenth century.

814—Doversdale.

DOVERSDALE, originally STONEFIELD, by Samuel Stanley, is from the same source as SIMEON (No. 301).

815—Little Cornard.

LITTLE CORNARD, by Martin Shaw, is from the same collection as MARCHING (No. 616). It takes its name from a village in Suffolk where the composer spent his honeymoon.

816—Fight of Faith.

FIGHT OF FAITH is by Dr. A. L. Peace (see No. 448). It was composed for the *Scottish Hymnal* (1885), of which he was editor.

817—Pentecost.

PENTECOST, by W. Boyd, was written for a collection named *Thirty-two Hymn-Tunes composed by Members of the University of Oxford* (1868). This contains tunes from fourteen contributors, including Henry Hiles, J. F. Bridge and W. Boyd. Only the last-named contributor's tune has survived the test of time, this being PENTECOST, here set to the hymn :

> Come, Holy Ghost, our hearts inspire,
> And lighten with celestial fire.

As this is a six-line hymn, the composer directed the last two lines of the tune to be repeated in order to make it fit properly. Sullivan, when he was preparing the music for *Church Hymns,* took a fancy to the tune, and obtained Boyd's consent to use it, but he did not obtain the composer's permission to change the original setting to ' Fight the good fight,' an alteration which did not meet with Boyd's approval.

William Boyd was born in Jamaica in 1847, and was educated at Hurstpierpoint and at Worcester College, Oxford, where he was organ student. Whilst here he joined in publishing the collection referred to above. This was not his first appearance in print, for this seems to have been in association with his friend Baring-Gould who, during his tour in Iceland in 1862, noted down some church melodies, which he sent home to Boyd to harmonize. Three of them appeared in the traveller's account of his adventures, headed with the initials W.B.

Mr. Boyd was vicar of All Saints, Norfolk Square, W., for twenty-five years, and he had at least three organists during his tenure of office who have long been famous. E. C. Bairstow, the present organist of York Minster, was with him for four years before going to Wigan parish church. He was succeeded by Hamilton Harty, who came fresh from Ireland, but, as Mr. Boyd once said, ' we both of us soon discovered that his métier lay in a direction other than that of organ playing, and he left to ascend the ladder of accompanists—and I am told that he has no superior in London.' This was over twenty years ago, and the former All Saints' organist has ascended many more steps on the ladder of fame.

The next organist engaged by Mr. Boyd was the most famous of the lot in his own special department. Mr.

Boyd used to wax enthusiastic over the wonderful gifts that William Wolstenholme displayed. 'To listen to him,' he once said, 'every week as I do is to listen to a fresh spring charged with the sparkle and the gaiety of clear rushing water. He never tires or wearies one—there is always the unexpected, the possibility, the potentiality—and just when you think he may be getting a little volatile there comes a phrase, a chord, a suggestion of an old-time memory which carries you back to Gregorian times, and induces a picture of tonsured monks with their violoncellos rolling out the music which befits the great "Amen."' Here, indeed, we have evidence of Mr. Boyd's love of music, and his ability to estimate it at its true value. At first, the vicar hesitated to engage Mr. Wolstenholme, as he was not quite sure 'that he knew his Psalms as well as I do.' Mr. Boyd subsequently confessed that his new organist knew them even better!

Boyd left Norfolk Square in 1918 and lived in retirement till his death in 1928.

818—St. Leonard.

ST. LEONARD, by Henry Smart (see No. 12), is from *Psalms and Hymns for Divine Worship* (1867).

819—Jericho Tune.

JERICHO TUNE appeared in the 'Foundery' Tune Book (1742) to the hymn, 'Commit thou all thy griefs.' It is adapted from the march in Handel's *Riccardo Primo*. The opera was short-lived, but the march had a long run of popularity. Wesley, who seems to have availed himself of various sources for his tunes, doubtless realized that it was a popular air and included it in his collection, but inserted a first violin part of the march, which took the tune to the D above the treble stave!

820—Hermas.

HERMAS, by Frances R. Havergal (see No. 521), is from *Havergal's Psalmody* (1871). Composed in 1870, it is her chief contribution to psalmody, and was reprinted in the memorial volume issued after her death, set to Mrs. Walker's hymn, ' Jesus I will trust Thee.'

821—Morning Light.

MORNING LIGHT is by George James Webb, who was born at Rushmore Lodge, near Salisbury in 1803. In 1830 he emigrated to America, where he taught pianoforte and singing. He was one of the first founders of the Boston Academy of Music (1836), and acted for some years as the conductor of its oratorio and symphony concerts. In 1876 he settled in New York as a teacher of music. He became associated with Lowell Mason, and assisted him in his church music, besides publishing five collections edited by himself. MORNING LIGHT first appeared in an American collection of children's songs called The Odeon (1837), set to ' 'Tis dawn, the lark is singing.' It has had various names, including WEBB, MILLENIAL DAWN and GOODWIN.

822—St. Gertrude.

ST. GERTRUDE, by Arthur Sullivan, first appeared in The Musical Times for 1871, and the next year it was included in The Hymnary. Its immediate origin is related in the following letter from a lady friend of the composer's which appeared in The Musical Times (1902) :

In answer to your letter regarding the composition of Sir Arthur Sullivan's tune to ' Onward, Christian soldiers,' which he dedicated to me, I can tell you that I believe the tune was written at Hanford, my home in Dorsetshire, while Sir Arthur was staying there, but it is so long ago I cannot be quite sure; what I do remember, however, is that we sang it in the private chapel attached to the house, Sir Arthur playing the harmonium, and having taught us the tune, as we had not the music. Therefore it was certainly not published then, but I think we may assume that it was written there. Sir Arthur often stayed with us for several weeks at a time, and composed several songs, &c., while at Hanford, after which place he named another of his hymn-tunes, but not one of such striking merit as 'Onward, Christian soldiers,' which has now a world-wide reputation, and of which I am proud to be the sponsor.

823—St. Lawrence.

St. Lawrence is one of several tunes contributed by R. A. Smith (see No. 54) to *Devotional Music Original and Selected*, which he edited in 1810.

824—St. Matthew.

St. Matthew, by Dr. W. Croft, is from the same source as Hanover (No. 8), and St. Anne (No. 878), namely *A Supplement to the New Version of the Psalms*, sixth edition (1708).

825—Rest.

Rest was composed by Sir John Stainer (see No. 433) for a festival of London Church Choirs held at St. Paul's Cathedral in 1873. It was originally set to 'Thou hidden love of God.'

826—St. Justin.

St. Justin is from the *St. Alban's Tune-Book* (1865), whence it passed into the *Primitive Methodist Hymnal* (1889). No composer has been assigned to it, but it rather suggests an adaptation from the slow movement of one of the classic sonatas.

827—Frogmore.

FROGMORE is by Sir W. Parratt, who originally wrote
it to 'I need Thee every hour' in the *Methodist Hymn-
Book* (1904), calling it 'a tunelet for a hymnlet.' See
No. 444.

828—Alford.

ALFORD, by J. B. Dykes (see No. 36), was written for
Hymns Ancient and Modern (1875).

829—Thanksgiving.

THANKSGIVING, by W. B. Gilbert (see No. 679), was
originally included in *Songs of Praise and ten other
Hymns* (1862).

830—Deerhurst.

DEERHURST was composed by James Langran (see No.
772) for the hymn, 'Lord, dismiss us with Thy blessing,'
and published in leaflet form in 1859. In this, the
original form of the tune, bars nine and also ten, thirteen
and fourteen ran thus :

These bars were altered to the present form when the
tune was included in John Foster's *Psalms and Hymns*
(1863). The tune is named from a beautiful old village
near Tewkesbury.

831—Mylon.

MYLON is found in *The Family Choir, or Psalms,
Hymns and Spiritual Songs for Social Worship* (1849),
where it is called PARADISE and attributed to J. A.
Naumann. Whether there is an earlier appearance of
the tune is uncertain. This is the original melody in
the work mentioned :

There is an hour of peace-ful rest, To
mourning wand'rers giv'n; There is a joy for souls dis-
-tress'd, A balm for ev - 'ry wounded breast,
'Tis found a - bove in heav'n.

The hymn is by W. B. Tappan (1794-1849) an
American writer who was actively engaged in Sunday-
school work. In his *Gems of Sacred Poetry* Tappan
says that the hymn was published ' at Philadelphia in
1819, and soon after was set to music by A. P. Heinrich,
Esq., in the same city.' MYLON may possibly be the
music referred to.

J. A. Naumann is not easily identified by these initials,
but they are probably a combination of his German and
Italian Christian names, Johann Gottlieb and Giovanni
Amadeo. He was ' a prolific composer of church music;
thirteen oratorios and twenty-one masses, with Te
Deums and smaller church pieces, being preserved in
Dresden ' (Grove). If MYLON is buried in all that music
it scarcely seems worth while to journey to Dresden to
disinter it.

832 (i)—Sine Nomine.

SINE NOMINE was specially written by Dr. Vaughan
Williams for the *English Hymnal* (1906), and it appears
in that book as number 641, to Bishop How's words, ' For
all the saints.' For a long time certain musicians had felt
that Barnby's popular tune known as ST. PHILIP, was
scarcely worthy of the words, and now SINE NOMINE is
gradually displacing it. Many of us cling to old

associations, perhaps a little too long sometimes, and with many people even yet the older tune remains the more popular. It is said that a certain bishop, on hearing Vaughan Williams' tune for the first time, exclaimed, 'Good gracious, they will change the tune of "God Save the King" next!'

When Sine nomine is sung as a processional hymn, the unisonal verses are helped considerably by the moving bass part of the accompaniment. The tune moves about a good deal, but yet is stately, and the florid nature of the end provides a good contrast to the more solid beginning. A point worthy of notice is the group of four descending notes in the last 'Alleluia,' a figure which is often used to express this word.

The irregular arrangement for the various verses of this hymn has proved a stumbling block. Thus the first verse begins on the second beat of the bar, while the second verse begins on the first beat, with consequently a longer note. Many such variations occur throughout the hymn, and although a little careful study on the part of choristers and congregations might overcome any difficulties, yet these same variations in time values are found to be a continual source of annoyance and misfits. In recent hymnals the composer has arranged the tune to begin throughout on the second beat of the bar.

832 (ii)—For All the Saints.

For all the saints (originally called St. Philip) was composed by Sir Joseph Barnby for Bishop How's hymn, and first appeared in *The Sarum Hymnal* (1869), edited by T. E. Aylward. See No. 398.

833—Benevento.

Benevento is by Samuel Webbe. See No. 75.

834—Children's Voices.

Children's Voices was written by E. J. Hopkins (see No. 103) for *Church Hymns* (1874).

835—Tours.

Tours receives its name from the composer, Berthold Tours, a musician of considerable attainments, whose name will be found in most tune-books. Born at Rotterdam in 1838, he received his musical education at the Brussels Conservatoire, whence he subsequently proceeded to Leipsic, where he had Arthur Sullivan, John Francis Barnett, and Sidney Smith as fellow students. After fulfilling several engagements on the Continent, he came to this country in 1861, and he made England his home until his death in 1897. For a time he had some difficulty in making his way—but two anthems, ' Blessed are they that dwell in Thy house,' and ' To Thee, O Lord,' attracted the notice of Joseph Barnby, who was at that time musical adviser to Messrs. Novello. This recognition of his merits soon bore fruit, and his skill as a violinist led to the publication of his *Violin Primer,* which has achieved a great success, whilst the same may be said of his *Thirty Easy Melodies* for the violin, each of which is a gem in itself. In 1875 Stainer succeeded Barnby as musical adviser to Messrs. Novello, but a few months later he resigned, and Tours was appointed to that responsible position. Amongst the important works he accomplished for the firm were pianoforte arrangements of several great choral works, including *Elijah, Redemption,* and Schubert's Masses, whilst his original compositions included a large amount of church music. In addition to those already mentioned, his anthems, ' God hath appointed a day,' and ' Sing, O heavens,' are in frequent use, whilst his service in C is widely known. His chief hymn-tunes were written for *The Hymnary* (1872), and in these, as in his other works, he showed how readily he could adapt himself to what is an essentially English form of composition.

836—Ellacombe.

Ellacombe.   See No. 208.

837—Infant Praise.

INFANT PRAISE (also called CHILDREN OF JERUSALEM) is from John Curwen's *The Tune-Book* (1842), where it is ' anonymous,' nor has the composer ever been revealed.

838—Glenfinlas.

GLENFINLAS, by K. G. Finlay, is taken from *Songs of Praise* (1925).

Kenneth George Finlay, though of Aberdeen parentage, was born in London in 1882. After receiving his education at Aberdeen, he had a year at the Royal College of Music and then adopted music as a profession. He has had considerable success as a choral conductor and as a teacher of class singing in schools in Glasgow and Greenock. He has been conductor of the Harland and Wolff Male Voice Choir. His compositions include hymn-tunes and several part-songs. GLENFINLAS, originally composed for a four-line arrangement of ' Summer suns are glowing,' first appeared set to a different hymn in *Songs of Praise*. It was one of the items at the Festival of English Church Music held at the Crystal Palace in 1933.

839—In Memoriam.

IN MEMORIAM. When the *Hymns Ancient and Modern* Committee were preparing the enlarged 1875 edition they had under consideration suitable music for Midlane's hymn, ' There's a Friend for little children.' As no tune appeared to be available someone suggested that Dr. Stainer, who was present, should be asked to set the hymn. Accordingly he retired into an adjoining room and soon returned with a freshly-written manuscript, which was at once accepted, the name IN MEMORIAM being bestowed on it in memory of the composer's young son Frederick, who had died the previous year at the age of three.

840—Peacefield.

PEACEFIELD is an old Irish lullaby, the origin of which is unknown. The Rev. David Wilson (see No. 770), of Dublin, had recalled it from his boyhood days, and is responsible for it in its present form. The first strain belongs to an old Irish cradle-song, ' Husho, my lannah,' No. 1016 in the *Complete Petrie Collection* of Irish folk-songs :

Cradle Song (Hush, oh my Lanna).

Hush, oh my Lanna, Hush, oh my Lanna, Hush,

oh my Lan-na, my Lanna Machree.

841 (i)—Westridge.

WESTRIDGE, by Martin Shaw (see No. 616), appeared in *Songs of Praise for Boys and Girls* (1930).

841 (ii)—Derwent.

DERWENT was composed by C. L. Naylor for the *Methodist School Hymnal* (1910).

Charles Legh Naylor was born at Scarborough in 1869. He was educated at St. Peter's School, York, receiving his training in music from his father, Dr. John Naylor, organist of York Minster (1883-1897). From school he passed to Emmanuel College, Cambridge, where he took his Mus.B. degree in 1892, and his M.A. four years later. After leaving the University he took up his residence in Harrogate, where he has held several important musical posts. He conducted the Harrogate Choral Society for many years, and was conductor of the

Kursaal Orchestra from 1902-1906. He was organist and choirmaster of St. Peter's Church from 1892 to 1902, when he resigned, to take up the position again from 1917 to the present time. He was editor of *The Methodist School Hymnal* (1910), and has established a wide reputation as a successful music master at most of the important schools in Harrogate.

842 (i)—Innocents.

Iɴɴᴏᴄᴇɴᴛs first appeared in its present form in *The Parish Choir* (1850). This magazine was the organ of the ' Society for promoting Church Music,' but its aims did not appeal to the churchgoer of the day, and it only lived for three years. W. H. Monk (see No. 221) was for a time the musical editor.

The origin of Iɴɴᴏᴄᴇɴᴛs is lost in obscurity. Attempts have been made to trace its origin from various sources, ranging from a Handel theme in his opera *Siroe* (on which Lᴜɴᴇɴʙᴜʀɢ [No. 717] is founded) to an unpublished song called ' The Sun,' by Joseph Smith, of uncertain date (probably about 1850).

842 (ii)—Gentle Jesus.

Gᴇɴᴛʟᴇ Jᴇsᴜs, by Martin Shaw, is from the same collection as Mᴀʀᴄʜɪɴɢ (No. 616).

843—Castle Eden.

Cᴀsᴛʟᴇ Eᴅᴇɴ, by R. W. Dixon, is from the *Burnley Tune-Book* (1875).

844—Evening Prayer.

Eᴠᴇɴɪɴɢ Pʀᴀʏᴇʀ was composed by Sir J. Stainer for Mary Duncan's hymn—' an ideal evening hymn for a wee bairnie on the verge of slumberland '—and first appeared in the *Church Hymnary,* edited by Stainer in 1898. The composer told F. G. Edwards (a former editor of *The Musical Times*) that the air was founded on the opening theme of Beethoven's ' Andante in F.'

845—Capel.

CAPEL is the old carol tune known as ' King Pharaoh and the cock ' :

> King Pharaoh sat a-musing
> A-musing all alone,
> There came the blessed Saviour
> And all to him unknown.

The tune is named from the village near Horsham where the tune was noted from the singing of three gypsies named Goby.

846—This Endris Nyght.

THIS ENDRIS NYGHT (' The other night ') dates from the fifteenth or sixteenth century. It was originally found in a MS. preserved in the British Museum (Royal Appendix 58) set for three voices with the melody in the tenor.

847—Solothurn.

SOLOTHURN is from *The English Hymnal* (1906), where it is said to be a ' Swiss traditional melody,' and that appears to be all that is known about it.

848—Samuel.

SAMUEL (or HUSHED WAS THE EVENING HYMN) was written by Sir Arthur Sullivan (see No. 18) for *Church Hymns* (1874).

849—Supplication.

SUPPLICATION, by J. B. Calkin (see No. 268) first appeared in *The Hymnary* (1872).

850—Excelsior.

EXCELSIOR was written by J. Booth for the *Congregational Church Hymnal* (1887).

Josiah Booth was born at Coventry, and at an early age he was finding a lively interest in music. He was practically self-taught, but gained sufficient confidence in himself to apply for the post of organist at West

Orchard Congregational Church, Coventry, though at the time he had never touched an organ. Naturally he was not successful. But his opportunity came during a visit to Banbury, where he was called out of his uncle's pew one Sunday morning to take the organ as substitute for the regular player, who was ill. He now took a few lessons from Sims, organist at Coventry parish church, and then accepted an invitation to return to Banbury as the regular organist at the Wesleyan chapel. But he was ambitious, and decided to try his luck in London, where he became a student at the Royal Academy of Music. He also joined Leslie's famous choir, two of his part-songs being given at the concerts. Eager to get a regular appointment, he heard of and applied for a vacancy at Park Chapel, N. (Congregational). He entered the competition, and though not successful at the time, he was afterwards appointed to the post. He had a difficult job here at first, for the choir was as poor musically as the organ. A very different state of affairs prevailed when Mr. Booth retired in 1918, when he celebrated his jubilee as an organist and his retirement was made the occasion for a presentation to him by his very numerous friends of an annuity of £75, and a sum of money. His influence on the music of his church was very great, and he was ever willing to expend his gifts and his time to the best interests of his art. When Dr. E. J. Hopkins was editing the *Congregational Church Hymnary* (1886) he entrusted Mr. Booth with the task of selecting and editing the music to the chants and anthems, and he was also responsible for the printing of the Psalms. When the *New Congregational Hymnary* (1916) was being prepared, Mr. Booth acted as musical adviser to the committee. He had a wide circle of friends, and was universally respected. He died in 1930.

851 (i)—All Things Bright and Beautiful.

ALL THINGS BRIGHT AND BEAUTIFUL was written by W. H. Monk for Mrs. Alexander's hymn in the second edition (1887) of the *Home Hymn-Book*. The name was, for some unknown reason, changed to KEATS in the *Primitive Methodist Supplement* (1912), but there is no authority for the name, and the poet certainly had nothing to do with either hymn or tune. (See No. 215).

851 (ii)—Royal Oak.

ROYAL OAK is from *Songs of Praise*. It is taken from an English seventeenth-century melody, 'The Twenty-Ninth of May,' a loyal song on the restoration of Charles II, May 29. The tune was also used as a country-dance air, and is found in *The Dancing Master* from 1686 onwards. It was also known as 'The Jovial Crew.' The original is in Vol. II of Chappell's *Popular Music of the Olden Time*.

852—Rodmell.

RODMELL is from the *English Hymnal* (1906), where it is said to be a 'traditional English melody.' It belongs to the folk-song class, and was noted by Dr. R. Vaughan Williams.

853—Newland.

NEWLAND. In 1862 appeared the *Congregational Psalmist,* edited by Dr. H. Allon and H. J. Gauntlett, the latter having charge of the music. NEWLAND was one of the tunes written by Gauntlett for the book.

854—Herongate.

HERONGATE is an old folk-song tune known as DIED FOR LOVE. This version was noted in Essex.

855—Newbury. See No. 136.

856—Angels' Story.

ANGELS' STORY, by Dr. A. H. Mann (see No. 168), was contributed by him to the *Methodist Sunday-school Tune-Book* (1881).

857—The Story of Jesus.

THE STORY OF JESUS was contributed by C. B. Jutson
to *School Worship* (1926).

The Rev. Charles Bentley Jutson was born in 1870.
he was trained at the Countess of Huntingdon's College
at Cheshunt and entered the Congregational ministry in
1901. He held pastorates at Forest Hill (London),
Claremont, Brighton, and Reigate, where he remained
until he had finished his course in 1930. He took a great
interest in hymnology and church music generally, and
was a member of the committee appointed by the
Congregational Union to compile *School Worship*. He
also served on the committee which prepared the *Book
of Congregational Worship*.

858—Stories of Jesus.

STORIES OF JESUS is by F. A. Challinor, and was
written for one of the publications of the National
Sunday-school Union.

Frederic Arthur Challinor was born in Staffordshire
in 1866. His father was a miner, and the boy had to
commence the battle of life at an early age. In his
tenth year he commenced work in a brickfield, where
hours were long and the labour exhausting, and two
years later found him working in a coal-mine. When
he reached the age of fifteen he obtained a situation in
a china manufactory, and during this period part of a
legacy to the family was a cottage piano, which greatly
stimulated the boy, whose career meant more to him than
being just a potter; in fact, he worked at lessons on
harmony whilst taking his meals at the factory.

After gaining the A.R.C.M. diploma he took fresh
courage and set to work for the Mus.B. degree—passing
the Arts section in March, 1896, and gaining the final
distinction in the early part of the following year. From
that period to 1903 he was very successful in the field
of composition—this is very adequately proved by such
cantatas as *Judah in Babylon, The Gardens of the Lord,*

and *Bethany,* all being distinctive on account of their varied harmonies, and vitality in melodic structure and idiom. His music is attractive, partly because of the simplicity and truly expressive qualities it contains, but especially for its originality and directness—he speaks through his music and in language all can understand.

In the year 1903 by sheer hard work he took the Mus.D. degree, and he has never since departed from that standard; even the music he has written for children's choirs confirms this statement, and at the time he was reading for the final degree he had about four hundred published compositions to his name, all of a type worth singing.

It is only possible in such a concise account as this to mention Dr. Challinor's work in outline, but one fact must not be overlooked. Seldom do we find a composer of music who has been so successful in providing his own lyrics, and here again one finds, upon looking through some of Challinor's words, not only clear rhythm, but true expression, as characteristic in every way as the music to which it is wedded.

859—Irby.

In the British Museum is a little-known work called *Christmas Carols, four numbers* (1849). One of the four is called 'Once in royal David's city,' and the melody is the tune now known as IRBY. It is set for voice with piano accompaniment, the voice part on a separate line. The other three carols in this 1849 booklet are 'As Joseph was a-walking,' 'Upon the snow-clad earth without,' and 'There were shepherds once abiding.'

The tune next appeared in *Hymns for Little Children* (1858) with music by Gauntlett. It was inserted in a harmonized form in the *Appendix to Hymns Ancient and Modern* (1868) and was now first called IRBY, possibly from a village in Lincolnshire.

860—Away in a Manger.

AWAY IN A MANGER (also called CRADLE SONG) is by W. J. Kirkpatrick. See No. 316.

861—Temple Fortune.

TEMPLE FORTUNE was composed by Dr. G. F. Brockless (see No. 127) for the present (1933) edition of the *Methodist Hymn-Book*.

862—Worship.

WORSHIP, by Dr. A. H. Mann (see No. 168) was written for the *Methodist School Hymnal* (1910).

863—Christina.

CHRISTINA, by the Rev. F. Luke Wiseman (see No. 5), first appeared in the *Methodist School Hymnal* (1910).

864—Holmbridge.

HOLMBRIDGE was composed by J. T. Lightwood (see No. 27) for the *Methodist School Hymnal* (1910).

865—Athens.

ATHENS is an example of a tune coming first and a hymn being written to suit it. In 1841 Miss Jemima Thompson was a lady student at the Manual College, Gray's Inn Road, London. She happened to hear the air of a Greek march which greatly pleased her, and she decided it would be very suitable for Sunday-school purposes. Being unable to find any poetry for the purpose, she wrote the first two verses of this hymn whilst in a coach on her way to her home at Blagdon, Somerset. Both hymn and tune ultimately appeared in the *Sunday-school Teachers' Magazine* for March, 1841. Miss Thompson married the Rev. Samuel Luke, a Congregational minister. Her long and useful life came to a close in 1906.

866—Salem.

SALEM, which is said to be a ' German students' song,'
appeared in A. Methfessel's *Liederund Commersbuch*
(1818), called CRAMBAMBULI. Its earliest appearance in
this country appears to have been in a translation of Dr.
Cornelius' *Student-Life in Germany* (1841). We are
there told that the students had very definite and
stringent rules for the proper management of their
convivial meetings, and this particular song was
appointed to be sung on returning to Heidelberg after
merry-making in the country. Returning by boat in
the evening, they would make for their headquarters and
finish the proceedings by imbibing a variety of liquids,
including ' Crambambuli.' In order to prepare this
liquid an earthenware dish was used, into which a certain
amount of sugar was put, and it was then filled up with
spirit. The mixture was then set on fire, and the
company sang :

The Crambambuli Song.

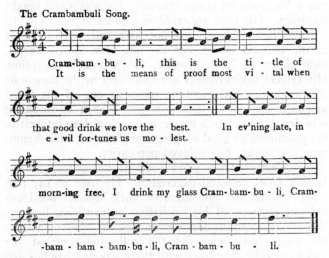

Cram-bam - bu - li,   this   is   the   ti - tle of
It   is   the   means of proof most vi - tal when

that good drink we love the   best.   In ev'ning late, in
e - vil for-tunes us   mo - lest.

morn-ing free, I   drink my glass Cram- bam- bu - li, Cram-

-bam - bam - bam- bu - li, Cram - bam - bu - li.

The tune fell (how, we know not) into the hands of
William Medlen Hutchings, a native of Devonport, who

migrated to Wigan. He wrote a hymn, 'Mothers of Salem' for a Sunday-school anniversary at St. Paul's Church, Wigan, and it met with such approval that the author trimmed it up for missionary purposes and sent it with the music to the editor of the *Juvenile Missionary Magazine*. Both hymn and tune appeared in the issue for June, 1850. The poet's attempt to give a missionary touch to the hymn resulted in the unfortunate couplet:

> And oh, how we pity
> Those poor deluded creatures;

but it lacked inspiration, and was soon abandoned.

867—Slingsby.

SLINGSBY (or DAY BY DAY) is by the Rev. E. S. Carter, who was born in 1845 at New Malton, Yorks, and educated at Durham Grammar School and Worcester College, Oxford. He held various benefices in York, and was a Vicar-choral at the Minster. He was a self-taught musician. His tune appeared in *Church Hymns* (1874).

First-class cricketers are not, as a rule, shining lights in the musical world, but the late Rev. E. S. Carter, vicar-choral of York Minster, was a notable exception. His cricket achievements are enshrined in the annals of the Yorkshire C.C., and he ranks as one of the finest amateurs the county has ever had. As a musician he was devoted to church music, and took a deep interest in the promotion of good congregational singing. His hymn-tune, SLINGSBY, has enjoyed popularity.

Mr. Carter had a good fund of anecdotes, derived largely from personal experience. He used to say that when he was first appointed to York Minster the Dean did not approve of his cricketing propensities, but one Sunday morning, as Mr. Carter took the alms dish from the choir boys who did the collecting, one of the awkward collecting bags with three wooden handles fell off. Mr. Carter instinctively 'fielded' it, catching it neatly with his left hand, while he held the heavy alms dish in his right. After the service the Dean said, with a smile, 'Well, Mr. Carter, I see there are some advantages in being able to play cricket.'

The tune, which is also known as WREFORD, was composed at Slingsby, E. Yorks., in 1865.

868—Boyce.

BOYCE (or SHARON or HALTON HOLGATE) is from *A Collection of Melodies* (1765), by William Boyce (see No. 795). The tunes were set to the metrical version of the Psalms by Christopher Smart.

William Boyce was born in London (within the precincts of the City) in 1710. According to Burney his birth took place 'at Joyners' Hall in the City of which his father was Housekeeper.' He entered St. Paul's Cathedral as a chorister under Dr. Greene, and pursued his studies under him for some years. His first organ appointment was at Oxford Chapel (now St. Peter's, Vere Street), and he also secured a good teaching connexion at ladies' schools (or 'seminaries,' as they were then called). Boyce also obtained the important position of organist to the Chapels Royal. He was ever on the look out for an opportunity of improving his position, and when his old master, Dr. Greene, of St. Paul's, was sick unto death, Boyce anticipated his decease by putting in an application for the position of Master of the King's Band in succession to Greene. He was successful, but was not officially appointed to that post till eighteen months after Greene's death. He also held two City organ appointments concurrently with his position at the Chapels Royal, and this inevitably led to neglect of duty, with the result that he was dismissed from Allhallows, Thames Street, after being its organist for twenty years. (This church was destroyed in 1894.)

Dr. Boyce was acquainted with the two musical sons of the Rev. Charles Wesley, and thought very highly of their abilities. In 1765 he visited Charles Wesley at

31

Bristol and said, 'Sir, I hear you have got an English Mozart in your house.' Wesley called young Sam to answer for himself, and he brought his oratorio *Ruth* (written when he was eight years old) for Boyce to see. 'The Doctor looked it over very carefully and seemed highly pleased with the performance. Some of his words were, "These airs are some of the prettiest I have seen. This boy writes by nature as true a bass as I can do by rule and study."' When Sam had put the finishing touch to his *Ruth* he sent a copy to Dr. Boyce, who acknowledged the gift with 'thanks to his very ingenious brother-composer, Mr. Samuel Wesley.' Dr. Boyce was a voluminous composer, upwards of seventy anthems standing to his credit. His dramatic output was not so extensive, but with many people his name lives to-day chiefly through his famous song, 'Hearts of oak,' which occurs in his last composition for the stage, a pantomime called *Harlequin's Invasion*. Of his anthems, 'Wherewithal shall a young man,' 'O where shall wisdom be found,' and 'Give the King Thy judgements,' are amongst a few that still survive. Boyce's death in 1779 was commemorated by Charles Wesley in a noble hymn beginning :

> Father of harmony, farewell!
> Farewell for a few fleeting years!
> Translated from the mournful vale,
> Jehovah's flaming ministers
> Have borne thee to thy place above,
> Where all is harmony and love.

869—Bede.

BEDE first appeared as a hymn-tune in Mercer's *Church Psalter and Hymn-Book* (1864). It is an arrangement by John Goss from the duet, 'Cease thy anguish,' in Handel's oratorio, *Athalia* (1733).

870 (i)—Pilgrimage.

PILGRIMAGE was composed by Sir G. J. Elvey (see No.

11) for the Appendix to *Hymns Ancient and Modern* (1868).

870 (ii)—Tonbridge School.

TONBRIDGE SCHOOL has not been traced to any definite composer. The melody was heard by Mr. Maurice Besley at Tonbridge, and transferred by him to a collection of tunes (chiefly melodies only) he prepared for use at the Queen's College, Oxford.

871—Ashburton.

ASHBURTON was contributed by Robert Jackson (see No. 297) to *The Bristol Tune-Book* (second edition 1881).

872—Chilton Foliat.

CHILTON FOLIAT, by Sir G. C. Martin (see No. 31), was written for the *Westminster Abbey Hymn-Book* (music edition) edited by Sir J. F. Bridge in 1894.

873—Wendell.

WENDELL was composed by S. H. Gregory for the *Methodist Hymn-Book* (1933).

The Rev. Stephen Herbert Gregory was born at Howden, Yorks., in 1869, and educated at Kingswood School, Bath. Whilst he was there he was for three years a member of the choir at Walcot Street Wesleyan Chapel. Deciding to enter the Wesleyan ministry, he entered Didsbury College, and in 1892 went as a missionary to India, being stationed in the Lucknow and Benares District. During his stay he did a good deal of work as military chaplain. In 1915 he returned to this country, and has since been engaged in English circuits. He comes of a musical family, his mother being the daughter of Sidney Stead, once organist of St. Peter's Chapel, Leeds. Two of his relations, A. S. Gregory and T. C. Gregory, are prominent musicians in the Methodist Church. Mr. Gregory never had the opportunity of learning music, but he is very fond of it, and a strong believer in the gracious influence it exerts.

874—Builth.

BUILTH is, as far as is at present known, first found in *The Divine Musical Miscellany* (1754), where it is called BEVELTH (also BEUELTH) Tune, and is in this rather more sedate form than that given in the present *Methodist Hymn-Book,* which is a later form found in *Sacred Melody* (1761).

875—Strength and Stay.

STRENGTH AND STAY was written by Dr. Dykes for Ellerton's translation, ' O Strength and Stay, upholding all creation,' in *Hymns Ancient and Modern* (revised edition 1875).

876—Benevento.

BENEVENTO is by Samuel Webbe (see No. 75).

877—Saxby.

SAXBY, by the Rev. T. R. Matthews (see No. 150),

was composed for a prize competition for a setting of
'Sun of my soul,' but was unsuccessful, being placed
fourth in order of merit. It was first published in the
composer's *Twenty-four Hymn-Tunes* (1867).

878—St. Anne.

In the *Wesleyan Tune-Book* (1876) St. Anne was
ascribed to Barber's *Psalm-Tunes* (1686). The book
there referred to is :

> The Psalm Tunes in Four Parts, viz.: Treble,
> Counter Tenor, Tenor and Base. The Fourth Edition
> Corrected and Revised. By A. Barber.
> Licensed February 14, 1686(7) and entered
> according to Order. Rob. Medgley.
> York. Printed by John White, for Abraham Barber,
> Bookseller; and sold by him at his shop in Wakefield,
> and by J. Penrose in Leeds, and by Eben. Tracy at the
> 'Three Bibles' on London Bridge, London, 1700.

Now, although this book was 'licensed' in 1687, the
earliest known edition of it (1700) does not contain the
St. Anne's tune, nor does it make its appearance therein
till the issue of the seventh edition in 1715.

Meanwhile an important collection of tunes had been
issued in 1708 under the title of *A Supplement to the
New Version of Psalms, by Dr. Brady and Mr. Tate,*
which was the sixth edition, 'corrected and much
enlarged,' of a collection originally issued in 1700. This
1708 book contains 'near thirty new tunes, composed by
the best Masters,' and these are indicated in the index
by an asterisk. Amongst those 'starred' as new tunes
are St. Anne, St. Matthew, and a third which is
unnamed, but is now generally known as Hanover.
Although no composer's name is given to any of them,
the authorship is generally ascribed to Dr. Croft, who
is considered to have been the editor of the book, and
who was at the time organist of the church of St. Anne,
Soho. Testimony to Croft's authorship is borne by

some of his contemporaries, notably Philip Hart and John Church, both of whom attach his name to the tune in question.

These three tunes soon achieved popularity, which may account for the fact that Abraham Barber included them in the seventh edition of his collection as already stated, but why he attached Denby's name to them, or who that gentleman was, has never been ascertained. As, however, it appears from the title-page of his book that Barber lived in Wakefield, it is possible that Denby was a friend of his who resided either in that town or in Leeds. The latter supposition would account for the name given to the tune in Barber's book.

The opening phrase of ST. ANNE is used by both Bach and Handel, by the former in the Fugue in E flat (known as the ' St. Anne's Fugue ') and by Handel in the opening vocal phrase of the Chandos anthem, ' O praise the Lord.' The rhythm Handel uses is precisely that found in modern hymnals, and therefore different from that used by Bach, where the initial note is a long one, on an accented beat, and where the two top E flats are blended in one and syncopated. It is not a little singular that these two great contemporaries, born within a month or two of each other, yet never coming into contact, should each select for treatment a theme practically the same. That the working out of the theme is entirely different goes without saying. Bach uses it as a fugue subject, while Handel uses it as a kind of opening phrase, and then discards it for a florid fugal theme of quite a different character. One point in common, however, is the fact that neither composer has used more than the first out of the four phrases of which the tune is composed.

The following is the original version of ST. ANNE'S TUNE, set to Psalm xlii (N.V.). It is a pity that the passing notes in the last line have now disappeared. The composer's indifference to consecutive fifths will be noticed :

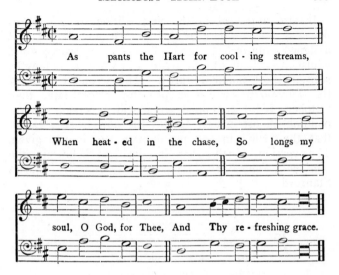

As pants the Hart for cool-ing streams,
When heat-ed in the chase, So longs my
soul, O God, for Thee, And Thy re-freshing grace.

879—The National Anthem.

THE NATIONAL ANTHEM. The earliest definite date when this appeared in print was in the number of *The Gentleman's Magazine,* Vol. xv., p. 522 (October 1745), where it is given in this form:

God save great George, our King; Long live our no - ble King;
God save the King! Send him vic - to - ri - ous,
Hap - py and glo - ri - ous, Long to reign
o - ver us: God save the King!

It also appeared in the first edition of *Thesaurus Musicus*, but the date of this is uncertain, though it is assigned tentatively to 1743. This is a very scarce work, whilst the volume of *The Gentleman's Magazine* may be seen in most public libraries. The second edition of the *Thesaurus* (which is probably rather later than October, 1745) contained an amended version corresponding almost exactly to the one now in use, except that the 'run' in the penultimate bar is not given. The version of this bar is given as below in the *National Song-Book*, 1906, edited by Sir Charles Stanford :

God   save   the King !

The composer of the National Anthem has never been discovered, and probably never will be. It appears to have developed from various sources, without any very definite fountain head. Many variations on the theme have been written by various composers, and Beethoven, Weber, and Wagner have all treated it in various ways.

880—Moscow.

Moscow. The name of Felice Giardini is familiar to the present generation as the composer of this tune, which is found in most hymnals; but to the musical historian he is famous as being the first of a long line of foreign violin-players who have made this country their home, and who have exercised no small amount of influence on native musical talent. Like many other famous musicians, Giardini, who was born at Turin in 1716, commenced his musical career as a cathedral chorister. Showing a decided partiality for the violin, he was allowed to study the instrument, and began to earn his living as an orchestral player. Being blessed with more than the ordinary amount of youthful 'cheek,' he began making free with the violin parts put before him, interpolating impromptu flourishes and turns *ad libitum*. This proceeding brought its own reward, the occasion being a performance at the opera house at Naples, under the direction of Jomelli. Here is Giardini's own account, as related by himself to Dr. Burney: 'I acquired great reputation among the ignorant for my impertinence, yet, one night, during the opera, Jomelli, who had composed it, came into the orchestra and, seating himself close by me, I determined to give the *maestro di capelli* a touch of my taste and execution, and in the symphony of the next song, which was in the pathetic style, I gave loose to my fingers and fancy, for which I was rewarded by the composer with a violent slap in the face—the best lesson I ever received from a great master in my life.'

Giardini arrived in England about 1750, and soon took a foremost place as a violinist, his execution exceeding anything that had hitherto been heard. He maintained his supremacy for over thirty years, and besides his concert work, he earned a considerable income by giving lessons. His reputation opened the doors of the aristocracy to him, and amongst those who befriended him was the famous Countess of Huntingdon, and it was through her influence that Giardini consented to write some hymn-tunes for a compilation that was being made by the Rev. Martin Madan. This was published in 1769 under the title of *A Collection of Psalm and Hymn-Tunes*. It was sold for the benefit of the Lock Hospital, of which Madan was chaplain, and is now known as 'The Lock Collection.' Giardini contributed four tunes, one of them having had a long career of usefulness :

HYMN TO THE TRINITY.

Come, Thou Al-migh-ty King, Help us Thy

Name to sing, Help us to praise!

Fa-ther All glor-i-ous, O'er All Vic-tor-i-ous!

Come and reign o-ver us, An-tient of Days.

The above is the original of the tune, and it will be noticed that it has not escaped the zeal of the editorial fraternity. Not only has the melody been altered, but a comparison with the original score shows that the harmony has been interfered with, while some editors have actually harmonized the fine unison passage in the third line, in spite of the composer's 'tasto solo,' which is 'a direction to play the part without accompanying chords.' The writer of the hymn to which it is set is unknown.

PELHAM (No. 191) from the same collection is another of the tunes supplied by Giardini.

The composer left England in 1784, but six years later he returned with the object of settling once more in this country. However, he found he had ceased to be a popular favourite, for it was soon discovered that he no longer possessed the skill that had made him famous. So he set out once more on his travels, finally settling at Moscow, where he died in great poverty at the age of eighty. For many years the tune has been known as

Moscow from the place of his death, but it still retains the name TRINITY in some hymnals.

881—Lincoln. See No. 367.

882—Gonfalon Royal.

GONFALON ROYAL was written for the use of Harrow School, whilst the composer was music master there. It was intended as a setting for the Latin hymn, ' Vexilla Regis Prodeunt ' (' The royal banners forward go '). It is taken from the *Public School Hymnal*, where it is set to O. W. Holmes's hymn, ' Lord of all being, throned afar.'

The career of Dr. Percy C. Buck affords an interesting example of rapid development in music science and technique. Born in 1871, he knew little of music till he was twelve years of age. Educated at Merchant Taylors' School, he was a chorister in West Ham parish church. He now began to teach himself to play, and at the age of fifteen he was sufficiently skilled to obtain an appointment as organist at Plaistow parish church. His progress thenceforth was rapid. He became a student at the Guildhall School of Music, and from there he proceeded to the Royal College of Music, where he obtained an organ scholarship, and studied the instrument under Sir Walter Parratt. His next success was an organ scholarship at Worcester College, Oxford, where in due course he obtained his M.A. degree. Such a series of successes promised well for his future, and in 1894 he was appointed music master at Rugby School. This post he only occupied a short time, as in 1895 he became organist at Wells Cathedral. Four years later he moved to Bristol Cathedral, where he succeeded Mr. Riseley. Here he stayed only a brief period, for he soon went to Harrow as music master at the school. Ten years as Professor of Music at Trinity College, Dublin, followed, and in 1925 he proceeded to a similar position at London University. He is now musical adviser to the London County Council.

883—Rhuddlan.

Rhuddlan is a traditional Welsh melody found in Edward Jones's *Musical and Poetical Relicks of the Welsh Bards* (1784-1802). The present arrangement is from *The English Hymnal* (1906).

884—Strasburg. See No. 33.

885—Gloria in Excelsis.

Gloria in Excelsis, by J. W. Elliott (see No. 196) was written for Godfrey Thring's hymn for the consecration of an organ :

Hark ! hark ! the organ loudly peals.

The tune first appeared in *Church Hymns* (1874).

886—Gratitude. See No. 209.

887—Sannox.

Sannox was abridged and adapted by Sir Richard R. Terry (see No. 254), from an air in the *Landshut Gesangbuch* (1777). The name of the tune commemorates the memory and work of the late Mr. W. E. Potts, who was an active member of the Committee of the *Methodist Hymn-Book*, but who died during its sittings. Sannox is the name of a favourite holiday resort of Mr. Potts in the Isle of Skye.

888—Rex Regum.

Rex Regum. The late Rev. Dr. Burton, the author of the hymn, has thus recorded the origin of this tune : ' In the celebration of the Queen's Jubilee in 1887, Dr. Stephenson requested me to write a Jubilee Ode, which was set to music by Sir John Stainer, and sung at a Children's Home Festival in the Royal Albert Hall, London. After the Festival Sir John wrote me, " I was very much delighted with your words, and can only regret that they will cease to be ' current coin ' in a few month's time." ' Stainer went on to suggest that Dr. Burton might write another ' set of words ' so that both might live a little longer than a year only. The hymn-writer fell in with the suggestion, and so ' in this case the words were set to the music, and not the music to the words.'

889—Lest we Forget.

LEST WE FORGET was originally written by G. F. Blanchard in July, 1898, as a baritone solo. It was then harmonized in four parts for the Christmas number of the *People's Friend*, in 1905. It was subsequently included in the *Methodist School Hymnal* (1910). The composer, who was for some years an organist in Weston-super-Mare, died in 1926 in his fifty-ninth year.

890—Marazion.

MARAZION was composed by Dr. Wostenholm (see No. 256) at the special request of the committee for the *Methodist Hymn-Book* (1933).

891—Urbis Rex.

URBIS REX is by J. A. Benson, and first appeared in the *Methodist School Hymnal* (1910).

J. Allanson Benson, who was born at Ripley, Yorks., was connected with a family of farmers, ' The Bensons of Nidderdale,' who had resided in those parts some five or six hundred years. He was thus related to the late Archbishop Benson. His parents removed to Harrogate in 1857, where his father, in addition to farming, carried on building and contracting. In 1859 young Benson joined the choir of the Church of St. John's, Bilton, thus beginning his forty years' association with the musical life of the town. On leaving school it was intended that he should become an architect, but the project fell through and he took service with his father, remaining with him in a rather uncongenial occupation for the next ten years. In 1876 he adopted

music as a profession and took the positions of organist
at the Methodist Free Church, Harrogate, and music
master at Ashville College, a denominational school for
the sons of ministers. Prior to this he had already done
a good deal as an amateur musician. He had sung,
played and conducted in a number of performances, and
was quite well known locally as a composer. In 1869 he
became choirmaster at the Congregational Church,
Harrogate, an appointment he held for some years,
during which period he worked hard to produce good
amateur performances of *Messiah, The Creation,
Hear My Prayer,* &c. In 1867-68 a Philharmonic
Society was formed. It came to an early end, but another
society was started in 1872, and of this latter society
Benson was conductor, although, as he said himself, he
was too inexperienced for the office. All this
miscellaneous work was, however, good preparation for
his professional career. He realized that there were in
those days comparatively few good easy choral works
suitable for small amateur choirs and musical societies.
When he turned his attention to composition, he had this
in mind and endeavoured to write accordingly. He
retired from public life in 1906 and went to live at
Bromley (Kent), where he died in 1931. He was a
member of the music committee for the *Methodist
School Hymnal* (1910).

892—Song 1.

SONG 1, by Orlando Gibbons. See No. 458.

893—Delhi.

DELHI, by E. F. Rimbault (see No. 219), is from the
enlarged edition of Maurice's *Choral Harmony* (1858).

894—Quem Pastores Laudavere.

QUEM PASTORES LAUDAVERE is an old German carol of
uncertain origin. Sir Richard R. Terry has found it in

an old mediaeval MS. of the fifteenth century, and it is found in collections in the sixteenth and succeeding centuries.

895—St. Bartholomew.

ST. BARTHOLOMEW is by Henry Duncalf, who contributed the tune to Riley's *Parochial Psalmody* (1762). Nothing is known of the composer except that he was organist of St. Bartholomew-the-little-by-the-Exchange. This church was restored after the Great Fire of 1666, and finally destroyed in 1841. Duncalf was also organist at St. Mary-at-Hill in Love Lane (off Eastcheap), which is to-day the City Church of the Church Army.

896—Brynhyfryd.

BRYNHYFRYD is by John Williams of Dolgelly (1740-1821). In the course of a speech delivered at a concert of the Criccieth Choral Society, Mr. Lloyd George said that he regarded this tune as 'the most beautiful he knew,' and added that the composer was 'a farmer who lived a couple of miles from Criccieth.'

BRYNHYFRYD probably made its first appearance in *Peroriaeth Hyfryd* ('Cheerful Melody') edited by John Parry and published at Caerlleon in 1837.

897—Forest Green.

FOREST GREEN is an old tune called THE PLOUGHBOY'S DREAM which was noted by Dr. R. Vaughan Williams at Forest Green, Surrey, in 1903. It appears to be a variant of GOSTERWOOD in *The Church Hymnary* and *The English Hymnal*.

898—Adrian.

ADRIAN was sent by the composer, Sir R. P. Stewart (see No. 354) at Dr. A. H. Mann's request as a contribution to the *Church of England Hymnal* (1895), of which Mann was editor. It was composed some years previously.

899—Land of our Birth.

LAND OF OUR BIRTH, by Dr. A. E. Floyd (see No. 174), was written for the 1910 edition of the *Methodist School Hymnal.*

900—Thaxted.

THAXTED is an adaptation of a melody from Gustav Holst's orchestral work, *The Planets.* It is the *Andante Maestoso* in the section headed, ' Jupiter, the bringer of Jollity.' The composer resided for some time at Thaxted, in Essex. (See No. 30.)

901—Russia.

RUSSIA is by Alexis Feodorovich Lvov, who has given this account of its origin in his *Memoirs* :

> In 1833 I accompanied the Emperor Nicholas on his journeys to Prussia and Austria. On returning I heard that the Emperor had expressed regret that Russia had no national hymn, and as he was tired of the English tune that had been used, I was asked to write a national anthem for Russia.

After long consideration he composed a tune which seemed to him to be suitable, but he had no words to fit them. He consulted a Russian poet, who could not for some time adapt his lines to the minor close at the end of the second line. At last he was successful, and Lvov announced that the ' anthem ' was ready. At the Emperor's command Lvov got the choir and orchestra of the Court Chapel together, and supplementing their efforts with a second orchestra, the hymn was played. The Emperor asked for several repetitions, and finally expressed his approval by saying ' It is superb.' The hymn was officially adopted for the Russian army in 1833, and was first publicly performed at the Grand Theatre, Moscow, at the end of the year.

Lvov was born at Reval in 1799. His father was director of the Court Chapel at St. Petersburg, and the son thus gained a musical education which was unusual in those days. He wrote several operas and some church music, but his compositions have not survived. He was a skilful violin player, and Schumann, in one of his magazine articles, speaks highly of his playing. But his fame now rests on the Russian National Anthem, and its future depends entirely on its duration as a hymn-tune in English hymnals. He died in 1871.

902—St. Cyprian.

ST. CYPRIAN, by Sir John Goss (see No. 12), is from *Tunes New and Old* (enlarged edition, 1876), though it was probably composed some years earlier.

903—Erhalt' Uns, Herr.

ERHALT' UNS, HERR. This title, although doubtless the correct one originally, disguises what was formerly known as the POPE AND TURK TUNE. Luther wrote (probably in 1541) a hymn beginning ' Erhalt uns, Herr, hei deinens Wort,' as a special prayer for protection against the Turks at a time when Turkish power and influence was spreading over Europe. A folk-song sort of tune, or at any rate one derived from a popular source, was fitted on to the hymn and inserted in Klug's *Geistliche Lieder* (1543-4), where it was called ' a hymn for the children to sing against the two arch-enemies of Christ and his Holy Church, the Pope and the Turks.' Both tune and hymn (or at any rate the sentiment) soon found their way to England, where the hymn was translated by Robert Wisdom, beginning

> Preserve us, Lord, by Thy deare word,
> From Turk and Pope defend us Lord,

and both were included in the early editions of Day's Psalter (1561-2). The hymn is not included in modern collections, but the tune is coming to the front again. The present arrangement is J. S. Bach's.

904—Glasgow.

GLASGOW is from T. Moore's *Psalm-singer's Pocket Companion* (1756).

About the middle of the eighteenth century Thomas Moore was living in Manchester, where he devoted much of his time to teaching psalmody. In order to provide his pupils with what he considered a suitable selection of tunes, he published a volume called *The Psalm-singer's Divine Companion,* containing 'a collection of curious psalm-tunes,' the word ' curious ' being here used in its eighteenth-century meaning of excellent, or ingenious. Even in those days choirmasters seemed to have appreciated the fact that church choirs occasionally wanted something stronger than a simple hymn-tune to satisfy their musical cravings, so Mr. Moore included in his book a carefully selected set of ' grand anthems in four parts, abounding with the most beautiful fugues that are to be met with in any musick of this kind '— at any rate, that is what he says in his preface.

This was at a time when the church authorities in Glasgow began to be concerned about their music. A movement for the improvement of psalmody had found favour in and about Aberdeen, and stories about the success of the venture encouraged the Town Council of Glasgow to take steps to deal with the matter. It would appear that in these days one of the duties of the Town Council was the nomination of the precentor of any church built on land owned by the Corporation, and as this office had not yet been filled in a church recently erected on town property, the Councillors proceeded to give a practical turn to their new burst of musical enthusiasm by looking out for a suitable man to carry out their plans.

Their choice fell on Thomas Moore, and in June, 1755, he was duly nominated ' to be precentor in the new church at Bellsyeard, and to be teacher of psalmody and church music in the Town Hospital of Glasgow,' at a salary of £20 yearly.

Thus did Thomas Moore pack up his goods and chattels and hie him across the border to the banks of the Clyde. Probably he soon got to work at 'the new church at Bellsyeard,' but it was not till the end of 1756 that he began teaching classes at the Hospital. So popular did the new psalmody teacher become that the Council in 1756 nominated him a burgess of the borough, but with Scots caution they did not actually admit him till three years later. In this same year (1756) Moore was commissioned to arrange and publish a collection of tunes, which he called the *Psalm-singer's Pocket Companion.*

After a time enthusiasm began to wane, and the Town Council brought the waverers to book by compelling all the precentors in the town to attend Moore's classes. Then opposition appeared in the person of John Girvan, precentor at the Tron Church. He issued his own tune-book, which Moore countered by publishing *The Psalm-singer's Delightful Pocket Companion,* attacking his enemy in the Preface as 'Mr. Marmusic.' Girvan soon retired, leaving Moore in full possession. In 1787 he resigned his appointment, and died five years later.

905—Grenoble. See No. 589.

906—Elberfeld.

ELBERFELD is generally supposed to have been built up out of an old untraceable melody by Nicholaus Decius, who wanted a chorale to fit his metrical version of the ' Gloria in Excelsis.'

Allein Gott in der Höh' sei Ehr'.

The hymn and chorale were used by Mendelssohn in *St. Paul.* The libretto was originally in German. The translator, William Ball, thus rendered the first line :

To God on high be thanks and praise.

Little is known about Decius. He is first heard of about 1519 when he became a monk, and three years later, having become influenced by the teachings of Luther, he became a schoolmaster at Brunswick. From there he went to Stettin (which is one of the names of this tune) and became a pastor at St. Nicholas Church. He died in 1541 'with some suspicion of being poisoned by his enemies of the Roman Catholic faction.' This tune is also known by the first line of its German hymn, and also as DECIUS, but there seems no reason for calling it ELBERFELD, a place with which Decius had no associations.

907—Vermont.

VERMONT, by Dr. A. E. Floyd (see No. 174) makes its first appearance in the present (1933) edition of the *Methodist Hymn-Book*.

908—Brandenburg.

The actual source of BRANDENBURG is not known. It appeared in its present form in the *Supplement of Samuel Dyer's Third Edition of Sacred Music,* published at Baltimore about 1826 (but it is quite possible there was an earlier appearance in 1823). In Dyer's work it is called GERMAN SET, and that is the only suggestion as to its real origin. Lowell Mason altered it slightly, at the same time calling it MENDON, and it was often thought to be his composition. Originally a L.M., it appeared in the *Wesleyan Tune-Book* (1876) as a four-sevens. It was dropped in 1904, and now re-appears in the present work in the same guise.

Samuel Dyer was of English origin, born in Hampshire in 1785. He received musical instruction from Thomas Walker, who formed a 'Collection' of tunes as a supplement to Dr. Rippon's tune-book. Walker was a noted singer in his time—'a fine counter-tenor, of extraordinary compass and power, and his style animated and expressive.'

In 1811 Dyer went to New York, and except for one return visit, spent the rest of his life in the States. He found serious fault (and rightly so) with the bad printing and paper used in American psalmody books, and also condemned the alteration and mutilation of tunes. In the face of much opposition he strove to bring about reforms, and was to some extent successful. He died at Hoboken, N.J., in 1835.

909—Commonwealth.

COMMONWEALTH, which has been one of Josiah Booth's most popular tunes, was contributed by him to the *Congregational Church Hymnary* (1887). It obtained great popularity in the palmy days of the P.S.A. movement. Mr. Lloyd George once declared that he had heard it sung ' with great effect by many thousands and tens of thousands at Liberal gatherings throughout the country.'

Mr. Booth (see No. 850) once related the origin of this well-known tune.

I was seated at the breakfast-table one morning and I opened a letter which had just come from Dr. Barrett, of Norwich, who, writing with reference to the hymnal, said he desired to include the hymn which he enclosed and wanted a good tune for it. He mentioned that he was sending the words to two other composers. I read through the verses, wheeled my chair to the piano and played the now familiar COMMONWEALTH, and directly afterwards I wrote the tune just as it afterwards appeared in print.

910—Arizona.

ARIZONA, by R. H. Earnshaw, was originally written for a hymn for travellers by the Rev. Dr. Henry Burton, and circulated largely in transatlantic steamers. The composer, Dr. Robert Henry Earnshaw, was born at Todmorden in 1856. He studied music under various masters in London, and on returning north he became organist at Morecambe parish church for three years. After a year at St. Philip's, Southport, he went to reside in Preston, where he was for some years organist at Christ Church. On retiring from active work he went to live at Southport, where he served on the Town Council. Later he became interested in cinemas, and finally retired to Blackpool, where he died in 1929.

911—Intercessor.

INTERCESSOR was contributed to *Hymns Ancient and Modern* by Sir C. H. H. Parry for Miss Greenaway's hymn, ' O word of pity for our pardon pleading ' (No. 240).

912—Old 124th.

THE OLD 124TH is from the Genevan Psalter of 1551. This Psalter was gradually developed from a collection of thirty tunes in 1542 to a complete edition of all the Psalms in 1562. The 1542 book was probably made up by Calvin, who used as his foundation a collection of thirty psalms formed three years earlier by Clement Marot. In 1551 Calvin requested Beza to continue the versification of the psalms, and thirty-four more were added with music, including the OLD 124TH. Only the melody of each tune was given, and no suggestion was made as to the composer or the source of any of the tunes.

The tune receives its name from its being set to Psalm cxxiv. in the Old Version (Sternhold and Hopkins) of the Psalms. It was set to a five-line verse in accordance with the original form of the melody, the version of the Psalm being the work of W. Whittingham.

Now Is-ra-el may say and that tru-ly

If that the Lord had not our cause main-tained,

If that the Lord had not our right sus-tain'd,

When all the world a-gainst us fu-rious-ly

Made their up-roars and said, We should all die.

The melody has, in its four-line adapted form, long been familiar as TOULON. The introduction into the hymn-book of Clifford Bax's hymn with its somewhat unusual metre (5-10's) afforded an opportunity for introducing the historic OLD 124TH in what is practically its original form.

913—Verbum Pacis.

VERBUM PACIS is by George Lomas. It first appeared in *The Bristol Tune-Book* (1876). (See No. 451.)

914—Randolph.

RANDOLPH, by R. Vaughan Williams (see No. 273), is from the *English Hymnal* (1906).

915—Ings.

INGS, by J. W. Allen North, makes its first appearance in the present *Methodist Hymn-Book*. It was composed during the Great War and frequently sung to the hymn,

' To Thee, O God, we fly,' in various places where it got known. The composer suggests that it is of a more contemplative character than the tune set to the same hymn in the *Methodist Hymn-Book* of 1904.

J. W. Allen North, who was born at Southport in 1869, was formerly head of a well-known firm of solicitors in Liverpool. He retired from business a few years ago. He has held most of the offices open to laymen in the Trinity Methodist Circuit in Southport, and has, in addition, been deputy organist at Trinity Church for about forty-five years. He is a past president of the Southport District Organists' Association, and also a vice-president of the Southport Orchestral Society. His compositions have been chiefly in the department of church music, and include works for piano and organ, morning and evening services (two of which have been frequently rendered in past years at Liverpool Cathedral), also settings of the Te Deum and Benedicite. Mr. North is well known in West Lancashire for his various compositions.

916—St. Helen's.

St. Helen's was written by Sir R. P. Stewart (see No. 354) for the *Irish Church Hymnal* (1874), of which he was editor.

917—Melita.

Melita was composed by Dr. Dykes (see No. 36) for *Hymns Ancient and Modern* (1861), and is a perfect setting of the hymn. ' In the last line but one of each verse the inflected note (F sharp) gives to the word "cry" a piercing and plantive emphasis, and yet its introduction seems both natural and unrestrained ' (F. G. Edwards).

918—St. Petrox.

St. Petrox is by Reginald F. Dale, who took an active interest in church music during his college days and joined with a friend in publishing *Twenty-two Original Hymn-Tunes, by two Oxford Graduates,* which was issued by subscription from an Oxford press in 1867. This book contained ST. PETROX, which is signed ' F,' but was later acknowledged by Dale to be his own composition. One of the tunes, signed ' J,' is a curiosity, being constructed on the melody of EIN FESTE BURG, which forms the bass part. Dale also composed songs and pianoforte music. He joined with the Rev. J. Troutbeck in writing a Music Primer, and he arranged a service of song called *Elijah,* the music of which was selected chiefly from *The Hymnary.*

919—St. Matthew.

ST. MATTHEW, by W. Croft. See No. 824.

920—Evensong.

EVENSONG, by J. Summers, appeared in the first edition (1863) of the *Bristol Tune-Book.*

Dr. Joseph Summers was born at Charlton, Somerset. He was a boy chorister at Wells Cathedral, and after leaving he proceeded to London, studying music under Sterndale Bennett and Gauntlett. After being organist at Bradfield College, Weston-super-Mare parish church, and St. Peter's, Notley Hill, he went to Melbourne and spent the rest of his life in Australia, where his work was largely of an educational nature. He died in 1916.

921—Land of Rest.

LAND OF REST is from R. S. Newman's book of original tunes (see No. 310). It originally had the heading, COME UNTO ME—I WILL GIVE YOU REST, and set to Bonar's ' I heard the voice of Jesus say.'

922—Komm, Seele.

KOMM, SEELE are the first words of a hymn for which the music was written by J. F. Franck. Little is known of him except that he wrote a number of *Geistliche Lieder* ('Spiritual Songs') amongst which this is included.

923—Windermere.

WINDERMERE was composed for How's hymn, ' We give Thee but Thine own,' for the *English Hymnal* (1906).

Sir Arthur Somervell, a member of an old Westmorland family, was born at Windermere in 1863. After leaving Uppingham, he went to King's College, Cambridge, studying music under Stanford, at that time organist at Trinity College. After further study under Parry, Sir Arthur, in 1901, commenced his work as an inspector of schools, afterwards becoming Principal Inspector of Music in succession to Sir John Stainer. He has composed cantatas, instrumental music and songs, his *Powers of Sound,* produced at Kendal in 1895 being a notable work.

924—Heathlands.

HEATHLANDS, by Henry Smart (see No. 12), is taken from *Psalms and Hymns for Divine Worship* (1867).

925—Moseley.

MOSELEY, by Henry Smart (see No. 12), was written about 1876 for the *Book of Common Praise.*

926—St. Timothy.

ST. TIMOTHY was contributed by Sir H. W. Baker to the 1875 edition of *Hymns Ancient and Modern.* See No. 320.

927—Melcombe.

MELCOMBE is by Samuel Webbe. See No. 75.

928—Gounod.

GOUNOD first appeared in the *Hymnary* (1872). Charles Gounod, the composer, was born in Paris in 1818. He was the son of a painter, his mother being a skilful musician, and it was to her that he was indebted for his early musical training. He has recorded how, when a boy, he was so impressed with hearing Mozart's

Don Giovanni, that he determined that he, too, would be a composer. He then commenced the study of music, and the winning of the Grand Prix de Rome at the Paris Conservatoire marks the next milestone in his musical career. This success meant a sojourn in Rome, and here he made the acquaintance both of Schumann and Mendelssohn. His early compositions met with but slight success, and, discouraged thereat, he thought of abandoning music and entering the Church. Wiser counsels prevailed, and on his return to France he added his name to the long list of composers who have also served as organists, his first appointment being to the Church of Foreign Missions in Paris. His decision to enter the Church was soon abandoned, and he took to writing operas, *Faust* being produced in 1859.

The sixties of last century saw the production of several of Gounod's smaller compositions which have since had an enormous popularity. The ' Meditation ' on Bach's first Prelude belongs to this period, so also do the famous song ' Nazareth,' and the anthem, ' Send out Thy Light.' The history of this piece is remarkable. Gounod wrote music for three female voices to a ' Hymn to the Virgin.' This made its first appearance in England as a solo arranged for the harmonium. In this form it attracted the notice of Henry Farnie, a skilful adapter of words to music, who realized that the harmonium piece would work up very nicely as an anthem. Accordingly, he dressed it up in its present well-known form, and ' Send out Thy light ' has proved one of the most popular anthems of modern times. For a time Gounod lived in England, and here he wrote his cantata *Gallia,* which was first heard at the opening of the International Exhibition of 1871. His oratorios, *The Redemption* and *Mors et Vita* were written for the Birmingham Festivals of 1882 and 1885. The subject of the former had occupied his attention for a long time. The composer's last years were spent in his native country, and he died at St. Cloud in 1893.

929—Meine Armuth.

MEINE ARMUTH are the first words of C. F. Richter's
hymn, ' Meine armuth macht mich schreien,' to which this
tune is set on p. 1031 in Freylinghausen's *Gesangbuch*
(1704) (see No. 89). It appears here practically unaltered.
It is such a merry tune that it is a wonder John Wesley
did not discover it in his copy of Freylinghausen which
is now preserved in the library at Richmond College. The
composer is unknown.

930—Dorking.

DORKING is the modern name for an old melody of
uncertain date. In Chappell's *Popular Music* it is
quoted thus :

It is also known as QUEEN ELEANOR'S CONFESSION. It
is a somewhat sedate version of a more sprightly form
of the air as found in Dunstan and Bygott's *Sight Singing
through Song.*

931—Morning Hymn.

MORNING HYMN appeared in a collection of *Hymns and Psalms* selected by W. Gawler for the use of the Female Orphan Asylum, about 1788-9. Barthélémon composed it specially for use in the orphanage at the request of the Chaplain, the Rev. J. Duché. The tune was 'published by permission of Mr. Barthélémon.'

François Hippolyte Barthélémon was born in 1741 at Bordeaux. Little is known of his early life, except that he was an officer in the Irish brigade, but his love of music induced him to take it up as a profession. Having become an expert violin player, he came to England, and was engaged as leader of the opera band. His professional engagements took him to Dublin, France, Italy and Germany. He also conducted the orchestras at Vauxhall and Marylebone Gardens. He was engaged to teach singing at the Orphan Asylum, at that time in Westminster Bridge Road (removed some years ago to Beddington, near Croydon), but after a few months he retired, as the committee would not increase his salary. As a violinist he was undoubtedly highly esteemed. He died in 1808.

932 (i)—St. Venantius.

ST. VENANTIUS is from the *English Hymnal* (1907), where it is said to be a 'Rouen Church Melody,' but beyond this indefinite statement nothing further appears to be known about its origin.

932 (ii)—Deventer.

DEVENTER (also known as O HAPPY DAY) was composed by Berthold Tours (see No. 835) for *The Hymnary* (1872).

933—St. John.

ST. JOHN is by the Rev. Richard Cecil (1748-1810), whose fame rests chiefly on his simple anthem 'I will arise and go to my Father.' In his early days Cecil was something of a scapegrace. When his thoughts took a serious turn, he decided for the Church—the Church expressly so-called—for his father told him that if he connected himself with the Dissenters he would have nothing to do with him, 'living or dying.' He had become proficient on the violin, but he now destroyed his instrument, lest it should interfere with his theological studies. He became minister of St. John's Chapel, Bedford Row, long since demolished. Here he had Dr. Worgan for his organist, who was succeeded by Cecil's daughter, Theophania. After taking orders his interest in music was confined to improving the singing at the various churches he was connected with, and he wrote some hymn-tunes designed to supersede the florid specimens then prevalent. His compositions were subsequently collected and published by his daughter in a volume called *The Psalm and Hymn-Tunes used at St. John's Chapel, Bedford Row,* in which St. John was included. Theophania seems to have flourished on music, for she was within a few months of being a centenarian.

Richard Cecil seems to have led a gay life in his early days. When quite a youth he took a trip to France to see the galleries, and would have gone to Rome if his cash had held out. Everybody was idolizing Voltaire in those days; and Cecil, as became a youth of aesthetic taste, declared himself an unbeliever. Presently he became a convert and took to moping. His father feared that he might join the Methodists, and so he sent him to Queen's College, Oxford, where he graduated after taking orders—an inversion of the usual process. One is almost amused by his simple trust. He was once nearly killed by his horse throwing him in Oxford Street. The wheel of a passing wagon crushed the hat he wore and escaped his head literally by a hair's breadth. Ever after the dilapidated head-gear used to hang in his bedroom as a gentle reminder of 'God's Good Providence.'

934—Epworth.

EPWORTH (or LAUGHTON) is by Charles Wesley. See No. 366.

935—Motherland.

MOTHERLAND, by T. Hutchinson, is from the Supplement (1912) to the *Primitive Methodist Hymnal.* It was originally written for the Festival of the Stockton and Darlington Primitive Methodist Psalmody Association at the request of the conductor, Mr. W. Heslop.

Dr. T. Hutchinson was born at Sunderland in 1854. He studied music under Dr. Philip Armes (see No. 781), organist at Durham Cathedral. In 1896 he was elected organist at Darlington parish church, an office he held for twenty years, gaining a great reputation as a voice trainer and also as a lecturer. He died in 1917.

936—Brindley.

BRINDLEY, by C. T. Groves, made its first appearance in the *Methodist Hymn-Book* (1933). (See No. 76.)

937—Sebaste.

SEBASTE first appeared in the 1875 edition of *Hymns Ancient and Modern.* The city of Samaria was renamed Sebaste after the time of Herod the Great.

938—Evening Hymn.

EVENING HYMN is by William Jackson, who wrote it for *The Bradford Tune-Book* (1863).

Jackson of Masham—as he is called, to distinguish him from his namesake of Exeter—was born in 1815. The little village was the centre of great musical activity, and young Jackson soon showed a deep interest in all things pertaining to music. His grandfather was a leading singer and also a bell-ringer at the parish church, while his father belonged to the church choir, besides being a fife player in the village band. In those days there was a barrel-organ in the west gallery of

Masham church, and when the doors of the instrument were thrown open behind to let out the sound more fully into the building, young Jackson's amazement and joy were complete. There revealed to view were all the inner works of the mysterious instrument—pipes, sliders, barrels, and all kinds of regulators and accessories, the various uses of which he carefully investigated when he got the chance.

The result of these investigations was that he succeeded in making a barrel-organ for himself. It played ten tunes, and became the wonder of the neighbourhood. From this he went on to construct a four-stop pipe organ, and having thus got his instrument he proceeded to the study of harmony by means of Callcott's *Thorough Bass*—a standard work in those days—and having mastered its contents, he then made further explorations in the mysteries of harmony and counterpoint by means of books and musical scores which he borrowed from Swallow's book-shop in Leeds. In order to increase his practical knowledge he joined a military band in Masham, and became acquainted with the peculiarities of all the brass and reed instruments he could get hold of. Subsequently he gained an acquaintance with the various members of the violin family.

In 1839 he wrote his first anthem, 'For joy let fertile valleys sing,' and the following year he gained the first prize offered by the Huddersfield Glee Club with his part-song, 'The sisters of the lea.' When we remember that amongst the competitors were such distinguished composers as Horsley, S. Webbe, Jun., Bishop, and Tom Cooke, it must be owned that the success of the self-taught village musician redounded greatly to his credit. His next two choral works were of a more ambitious character, his music to the 103rd Psalm being laid out for double chorus and orchestra.

Two oratorios, *The Deliverance of Israel from Babylon* and *Isaiah,* were his next achievements. Whilst writing the former he also composed a *Mass in E.* In 1852 he left Masham for Bradford, where he became organist at St. John's Church, and subsequently at the Congregational (formerly the Independent) Church in Horton Lane. There was an influential layman and enthusiastic musician connected with this place, named Samuel Smith, and he and Jackson were associated in the production of a tune-book to which they gave the name of *Congregational Psalmody.* In 1853 Jackson acted as chorus-master at the first Bradford Festival, at which Sir Michael Costa conducted, and so successful was it that a clear profit of over £1,000 resulted. For the next festival the Yorkshire composer revised his setting of the 103rd Psalm, which was given under Costa's conductorship. The Bradford Festival Choral Society was the outcome of all this music, and some of the members took part in the first Handel Festival. This was in 1857, and in the next year the fame of the Yorkshire singers reached the ears of Queen Victoria, with the result that a 'command' performance was given at Buckingham Palace. A number of choruses and part-songs were given, including a delightfully fresh and tuneful number, 'O the flowery month of June,' specially written by the Yorkshireman for the occasion, and which afforded great delight to the Queen.

Jackson died in 1866, and there is no doubt that his death was a great loss to native music.

939—St. Columba.

St. Columba, by H. S. Irons, is from the same source as No. 111.

940—St. Gabriel.

St. Gabriel was composed by Sir F. A. G. Ouseley (see No. 662) for the Appendix (1868) to *Hymns Ancient and Modern.*

941—Companion. See No. 310.

33

942 (i)—Hursley.

Hursley was chosen by the editors of *Hymns Ancient and Modern* (1861) as the tune for Keble's 'Sun of my soul,' the name being derived from the village where he was vicar from 1836 till his death in 1866. For the origin of the tune we go back to a melody in *Katholisches Gesangbuch*, published at Vienna between 1744 and 1780, which contains a melody somewhat similar to the modern tune, but in 6-8 time. From Vienna it passed into France, and appeared in 1824 in a book called *Choix de Cantiques*.

About this time, also, it came into England, as it occurs in some old manuscript books belonging to this period. The earliest known appearance of it in print is in a book entitled *A Sequel to Melodia Sacra*, by David Weyman, who was assisted in his work by John Smith, Mus.D., and R. W. Beatty; the last-named being musical instructor at Christ Church Cathedral, Dublin. The work is in two volumes, the second containing Hursley (under the name of Stillorgan), set to 'Jesus, and shall it ever be.'

Hursley first appeared in America under the name Framlingham, in the Boston Handel and Haydn Society's *Collection* in 1829-30.

942 (ii)—Abends.

Abends, by Sir Herbert Oakeley (see No. 441), was written for the *Irish Church Hymnal* (1874). The composer told a correspondent that he was impelled to set Keble's words ('Sun of my soul') to music in consequence of the 'inadequacy' of the tune (Hursley) that was popular at the time. 'One of my reasons for disliking it,' wrote Oakeley, 'is the resemblance it bears to a drinking song, "Se vuol ballare," in Mozart's *Nozze di Figaro*. As Mozart produced that opera in 1786 he is responsible for the opening strain which suits his Bacchanalian words very well. But to hear "Sun of my soul, Thou Saviour dear" sung to a lively tune unsuitable

to sacred words often had the effect of driving me out
of church.' HURSLEY has certainly not maintained the
character for liveliness that Oakeley gave it. A friend
of the Rev. J. Keble said that both the poet and his
wife selected HURSLEY as the most suitable setting for
the hymn, and it was so used in the first edition (1861)
of *Hymns Ancient and Modern.*

943—Tallis' Canon.

TALLIS' CANON. Towards the close of Queen Mary's
reign Matthew Parker, Archbishop of Canterbury completed his versification of the Psalms. It was printed, but
promptly suppressed, a few copies only being probably
distributed amongst the Archbishop's friends. Of these
only some five or six are still in existence. At the end
of the book there are nine tunes, one in each of the
eight modes, and one set to the hymn ' Veni Creator,'
composed by Thomas Tallis. The tunes are syllabic, and
in plain counterpoint. He gave an explanation of each
mode, and the eighth, which, he said, ' goeth wilde : in
modest pace,' is the tune long known as TALLIS' CANON.
It was originally twice as long as its present form, every
section being repeated before proceeding to the next.
It is written in strict canon form. In the original the
tenor leads in the canon, but this is reversed in the
modern arrangement. It was reduced to a four-line L.M.
tune by Ravenscroft (see No. 45) in his Psalter (1621).
The tune underwent several alterations in the eighteenth
century, a specially popular but singularly corrupt form
being inserted as the alternative in *Methodist Hymn-Book*
(1904). The tune has had various names during its long
life, starting with CANNON TUNE, in the ' Foundery '
Tune-Book, then BERWICK, BRENTWOOD, SUFFOLK, MAG-
DALEN, EVENING HYMN to TALLIS'S CANON and plain
CANON.

944—Eudoxia.

EUDOXIA, by S. Baring-Gould, was said by him to be

founded on a German air he had heard in his early days. When he adapted it to his hymn, ' Now the day is over,' he was under the impression that it was entirely original.

The Rev. Sabine Baring-Gould was born at Exeter in 1834. He graduated at Cambridge in 1850, and took holy orders in 1864. Three years later he became incumbent at Horbury Bridge, whence he went to the rectory of East Mersea, in Essex. In 1881 he became rector and squire at Lew Trenchard, where he died in 1924 in his ninetieth year. His versatility was truly remarkable, and he wrote with equal—some would say with fatal—ease on an infinite variety of subjects. He was specially versed in antiquarian lore, and he did the student of folk-songs a good service when he went out to search for treasures in the West Country. He has told of the difficulties he had at first in getting some of the old people to sing to him, more especially as they had not sung their old ballads for a long time, and the words did not return very readily. When, however, they found that the parson was in earnest, and that he was going to make a book about them, they became quite interested, and their interest developed into astonishment when they found that Mr. Sheppard, who was helping his friend, could actually take the music down on paper as they sang.

One old enthusiast promised to find out some old songs whilst Mr. Baring-Gould was away on holiday. So he went hobbling about the district, searching out all his old acquaintances and manfully learning by heart all their songs. Unhappily, before the spring came the old man died, and with him Mr. Baring-Gould lost what might have proved a valuable addition to his collection of West Country ballads.

During the summer of 1894 Mr. Baring-Gould traversed Cornwall, and subsequently he gave an interviewer the following interesting account of his adventures :

Amongst the places I visited in search of songs was Fowey, where I met with much kindness from Mr. Quiller-Couch. Mr. Bussell and I had been putting up for many nights at inns in all sorts of out-of-the-way places, and, as you may suppose, our quarters were not always very comfortable. So we thought that, for a change, we would stay at the Fowey Hotel. But it was, of course, of no use looking for songs there, so I went down to a delightful old-fashioned hostelry called the 'Lugger,' where I enlisted the landlord in my service. He told me of two or three men working on the railway near who were reputed to be great singers. But it was impossible to get them to come and see me at the 'Lugger'—they were far too shy of the 'strange gentleman.' So I went to the stationmaster, and as soon as he heard my name he exclaimed that he would be delighted to do anything he could for me. It appeared that he was father of a schoolmaster we had at Lew Trenchard, who went off suddenly one night in a demented condition. I rode after him, succeeded in bringing him back, and took charge of him for the time. For this the stationmaster was anxious to show his gratitude, and so he gave me the use of a shed for about half an hour, and got the 'song men' to come to me there. Once with me, they soon lost their shyness, and sang with a vigour which brought to the shed in admiration and surprise a small crowd of other workmen on the line.

Whilst in Yorkshire he took a deep interest in the quaint legends and stories of a past generation with which the county abounds, and some of these he re-wrote and published as *Yorkshire Oddities and Strange Events*. Herein he included the interesting story of David Turton, the famous Horbury musician, also the creepy experience of a piper who, after being hung for his misdeeds, came to life again and lived honestly ever afterwards. Here, too, and told at great length, is the story of John Martin, the madman who set York Minster ablaze in 1829, when the fine old organ erected by Dallam in the reign of Charles the First was totally destroyed.

945—The Blessed Rest.

THE BLESSED REST was written by Sir Joseph Barnby (see No. 105) for *Home and School Hymnal* (1892).

946—Innsbruck.

Few tunes have so curious and romantic history as INNSBRUCK. A song of unknown origin, it came into notice during the fifteenth century, a song of farewell to the Tyrol city of Innsbruck. Dr. H. Betts thus renders the first verse :

> Innsbruck, I must depart from thee,
> And take my journey—woe is me!
>   To strange lands far away.
> Fled is my happiness; nor smile
> Nor song will cheer my sad heart, while
>   In foreign realms I stray.

This song was first printed at Nurnberg in 1539 in Försters *Ein ausszug guterteutscher liedlein,* set to a melody by Heinrich Isaak. Little is known about him. He was probably born at Prague during the latter half of the fifteenth century. He was for some years Kapell-meister to the Emperor Maximilian I. The popularity of Isaak's song led Johann Hesse, pastor of St. Mary Magdalene in Breslau, to write a parody on the song beginning ' O Welt, ich muss dich lassen ' (' O world, I now must leave thee '). This hymn was adapted to Isaak's tune, and so the melody found its way into the Church. Its popularity was increased when

Paul Gerhardt wrote a similar hymn to Hesse's, and in
the same metre, beginning, ' O Welt, sieh hier dein
Leben.' Bach used three verses of this hymn in adapting
the chorale in his ' Passion Music ' (St. Matthew and
St. John). Mendelssohn also introduces INNSBRUCK in
St. Paul. The following is the earliest known form of
this famous melody :

In the memoirs of Baron Bunsen there is a letter to
his wife written on March 10, 1828, in which he says :

> I understand from Poelchau that many of our
> hymn-tunes originated in popular songs; for instance
> that of the evening hymn ' Nun ruhen alle Wälder '
> (' Now all the woods are sleeping ') can be traced up to
> the year 1840 as being in use among travelling work-
> men. It was composed or adapted to the hymn by the
> *maître de Chapelle* of Maximilian I, a pupil of the
> celebrated Josquin.

947—Evensong.

EVENSONG was contributed by O. J. Stimpson to *The
National Book of Hymn-Tunes, Chants and Kyries,*
edited by W. A. Jefferson in 1884. Orlando John

Stimpson was born at Durham in 1835. He was a
son of James Stimpson, organist of Birmingham
Town Hall from 1842 to 1886. He was a chorister at
Durham Cathedral, and afterwards music master at
Durham Diocesan Training College. He was a graduate
of music both at Oxford and Durham.

948—Eventide.

EVENTIDE was written for the first (1861) edition of
Hymns Ancient and Modern (see No. 221). In response
to a letter of inquiry about the tune, Dr. Monk's widow
wrote, ' The tune was written at a time of great sorrow
—when together we watched, as we did daily, the glories
of the setting sun. As the last golden ray faded he took
up some paper and pencilled that tune, which has gone
all over the world.'

949—St. Bernard. See No. 408.

950—Egham.

EGHAM is by William Turner, who was born at Oxford
in 1651. He learnt his music as a chorister at Christ
Church, and afterwards in London at the Chapel Royal.
He edited, in 1728, an edition of Ravenscroft's *Psalter*,
and wrote operas and songs.

951 (i)—St. Anatolius. See No. 302.

951 (ii)—St. Anatolius.

ST. ANATOLIUS was composed by Dr. Dykes for
Chope's *Congregational Hymn and Tune-Book* (1862).
It takes its name from a supposed association of the
verses with the Greek hymn-writer Anatolius.

952—Palestine.

PALESTINE, by C. H. Lovett, is found in *The Family Choir,* a collection of ' Psalms, Hymns, and Spiritual Songs,' published in 1849.

No records are obtainable of the composer.

953—Toulon.

TOULON. See OLD 124TH (No. 912).

954 (i)—Another Year.

ANOTHER YEAR was composed by Dr. G. F. Brockless (see No. 127) for the present (1933) edition of the *Methodist Hymn-Book.*

954 (ii)—Cherry Tree Carol.

CHERRY TREE CAROL. This is the version given in Husk's *Songs of the Nativity* of a wrongly-barred tune in Sandys' *Christmas Carols* (1833). There is little doubt that the carol was actually sung in triple time, like almost all of the other traditional ' Cherry Tree' tunes. Sandys also barred the triple-time VIRGIN MOST PURE as if in duple time, but that error has been corrected, while this tune has never been restored, though Husk made sense of the supposed C in the version here used. Re-barred, without alteration of a note, from Sandys' copy, the tune would run thus :

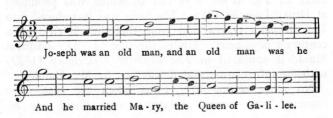

Jo-seph was an old man, and an old man was he
And he married Ma-ry, the Queen of Ga-li-lee.

Sandys' Version.

955—Fylde.

FYLDE was composed by J. T. Lightwood (see No. 27) to the hymn 'Forward! be our watchword,' for a Sunday-school Anniversary at St. Annes-on-Sea in 1898. The tune is named from a district on the Lancashire coast, and is an old form of 'field.'

956—Derbe. See No. 262.

957—Dedication.

DEDICATION was contributed by Sir G. Macfarren (see No. 592) to the 1875 edition of *Hymns Ancient and Modern*, where the name of the tune is 'Father, let me dedicate.'

958—Heber.

Heber's original MS. of his hymn, 'From Greenland's icy mountains,' is preserved in the Rylands Library, Manchester. It bears an interesting suggestion by Heber as to the tune he thought most suitable for his new verses, for at the top he has written, ''Twas when the seas were roaring.' This song is in Gay's farce of *The What d'ye call it*, which was produced at Drury Lane in 1715. The song was introduced into *The Beggar's Opera*, and from that time it enjoyed a century's popularity. Under the title of 'The Faithful Maid' it appeared in *The Musical Miscellany* (1729) with the information that it was 'set by Mr. Handel.'

No other setting of ''Twas when the seas were roaring' was current except a very florid one by

William Jackson, and there is no doubt that it was to Handel's music that Heber wanted his tune to be sung, being apparently quite indifferent to its secular origin.

This tune HEBER, as given at No. 958, has nothing to do with Bishop Heber. It comes from a combination of recitative and music arranged by Thomas Moore, which he published with the title a 'Melologue.' He thus explains the word, 'I thought that an unintelligible word of the kind would not be without its attraction for the multitude.' The poetry is his own, and he illustrates it with this tune:

and adds 'For this pretty Greek melody I am indebted to Mr. Gell, who brought it with him from Athens.' Heber died before this tune was published, and he did not compose it, nor certainly had he anything to do with its adoption. All that is known about the tune is that it is a 'Greek Air.'

959—Northrop.

NORTHROP, by the composer of that name, first appeared in Pitman's *Sacred Melodist* (c. 1882). It was written to 'While shepherds watched,' and the following is the original form:

BETHLEHEM.   A. NORTHROP.

And glo-ry shone a-round,   And glo-ry shone a-

And glo-ry shone a - round,   And

- round,   And glo - ry shone a - round.

glo-ry shone around, And glo-ry shone a - round.

The tune soon achieved popularity, and mangled forms
of it got about, probably through manuscript copies, until

at last it found its way into the hands of the editor of *Songs of Praise,* who, as the composer says, ' has re-arranged it to suit his purpose.'

Mr. Abraham Northrop, who was born in West Hartlepool, has been organist and choirmaster at Burbank Methodist Church in that town for over forty years; whilst as organist alone he has attained his jubilee this year (1934). He inherited his musical talent from his father, who was a well-known local musician and choir leader. His first experience was at Belle Vue Chapel, where he played the harmonium whilst yet a boy. In later years it was on the invitation of Lord Furness (then Mr. Christopher Furness) that he entered on his duties at Burbank Church as honorary organist. He is the composer of several anthems, cantatas and hymn-tunes, some of which have obtained a wide popularity. His musical work is not confined to the church, and he has rendered valuable assistance in musical services in the Hartlepools and district.

960—Winchester Old. See No. 129.

961—The Golden Chain.

THE GOLDEN CHAIN, by Sir J. Barnby (see No. 105), first appeared in the *Congregational Church Hymnal* (1887).

962—St, George's, Windsor. See No. 263.

963—Wir Pflügen.

WIR PFLÜGEN is assigned to Johann Abraham Peter Schulz, a native of Lüneburg, in Saxony, and a decidedly prolific composer. He has to his credit numerous songs, besides operas and much church music. He also made excursions in literary fields, and wrote an elaborate treatise on a new way of writing music. He is recognized as being the first to invest the Volkslied with an artistic interest, and was equally careful in the selection of suitable words.

The earliest appearance of WIR PFLÜGEN hitherto discovered is in the second edition of Hoppenstedt's *Lieder für Volksschulen,* published in 1800. In this the tune is anonymous, but is set to a hymn, ' Wir pflügen und wir streuen.' In 1812 Lindner's *Jugenfreund* was published, and here the tune is assigned to Schulz. Its first appearance in England was in the November, 1854, number of the *Bible Class Magazine.* From thence it progressed through the Rev. C. S. Beye's *Garland of Song* (1863) to the Appendix to *Hymns Ancient and Modern* (1868). In the 1904 edition of *Hymns Ancient and Modern* the hand of the editor fell heavily on the unfortunate WIR PFLÜGEN, employment of modern progressions and harsh discords, and the removal of all the unison passages alike displaying a singular disregard for simplicity and effect.

964 (i)—Golden Sheaves.

GOLDEN SHEAVES, by Sir Arthur Sullivan, was written for *Church Hymns,* which he edited in 1874. (See No. 18.)

964 (ii)—Bishopgarth.

BISHOPGARTH was composed for Bishop How's hymn, ' O King of kings, whose reign of old,' written to celebrate the Diamond Jubilee of Queen Victoria in 1897. Here is the story of its origin :

At Eastertide, 1897, Bishop How received this letter from the Prince of Wales :

It is proposed that a special hymn should be composed to be sung in all our churches, both at home and abroad, on June 20, the day on which the Queen attains the sixtieth year of her reign. I write these lines to ask whether you will kindly consent to compose this hymn. Sir Arthur Sullivan has consented to compose the music, and is also most anxious that the hymn should be sent to all the colonies.

Sullivan expressed himself delighted with the words, and wrote a tune which he said was ' *not* a part song, or an exercise in harmony.' He also expressed a wish that the profits, if any, should be given to the Prince of Wales' Hospital Fund.

BISHOPGARTH is probably a good second to ST. GERTRUDE, but the somewhat unusual metre has, perhaps, militated against any extended popularity. It is, however, a fine melody well adapted for congregational singing, and consequently some choirmasters have tried to adapt it to other metres, as, for instance, ' Head of Thy church triumphant,' which it certainly does not fit. Probably the first collection of tunes in which it appeared was the *Methodist Hymn-Book* (1904). The melody of the first line was originally :

965—Sandys.

SANDYS is an old carol tune, A CHILD THIS DAY IS BORN, named after William Sandys, who included it in his *Christmas Carols, Ancient and Modern* (1833).

966—Princethorpe.

PRINCETHORPE is by William Pitts, who was born in 1829 at Oundle. His father, who was an organ builder, trained the boy in music, and on going to London he was appointed organist on the opening of the Brompton Oratory, holding the office for over half a century. In 1871 he edited *Oratory Hymn-Tunes,* which was ' published in compliance with a desire expressed by many persons to possess the hymn-tunes which have stood the practical test of daily use in the services at the Oratory.' This collection contains his tune A DAILY HYMN TO MARY, later known as PRINCETHORPE.

967—Morgenlied. See No. 206.

968 (i)—Daniel.

DANIEL is from *Songs of Praise for Boys and Girls* (1930), where it is said to be an 'Irish traditional melody.' In the preface to *Irish Folk Songs,* arranged by Charles Wood (see No. 639), the tune is called DANIEL THE WORTHY. It has, however, a strong likeness to a folk-tune known as 'ONE NIGHT AS I LAY ON MY BED' (a song of mariners and a mermaid), sung by W. Bartlett at Wimborne, Dorset, and noted in 1905 by H. E. D. Hammond in the *Folk Song Journal,* III, p. 50.

968 (ii)—Williams.   See No. 745.

969—Almsgiving.

ALMSGIVING, by J. B. Dykes (see No. 36), was written for Dr. C. Wordsworth's *Holy Year* (1865), the music edited by W. H. Monk.

970—Peel Castle.

PEEL CASTLE is a traditional Manx ballad-tune from Dr. Clague's collection. It was not connected with any hymn sung by Manx fishermen till W. H. Gill wrote the 'Harvest of the Sea,' now called 'The Manx Fishermen's Evening Hymn,' to the melody. It is a variant of a stock ballad-tune widely spread over Great Britain and Ireland, best recognized as 'The Banks of Sweet Dundee.' It was also sung in the Isle of Man to 'Sweet Water in the Common,' and in Ireland to various ballads, including the 'Enniskillen Dragoon.' The PEEL CASTLE form belongs to a Manx-Gaelic folk-song beginning 'Eaisht oo as clash-tyn' (properly 'Eaisht shin as clasht shin') 'Listen and hear'—a common opening address— of which Dr. Clague only preserved a fragment.

Mr. W. H. Gill, though of Manx nationality, was born in Sicily in 1839. When his parents returned home he went to King William's College, Isle of Man. He spent most of his life in Government offices, but was able to devote much time to music, of which he was very fond. He was greatly interested in the traditional music of Manxland. In his young days the science of folk-song collecting was comparatively unknown, and he was one of the earliest workers in the field. Associated with him were his brother, Deemster Gill, and the late Dr. Clague, and it was whilst he was engaged in this search that Mr. Gill came upon the melody which has now achieved a world-wide fame.

During his long and busy life he had many strings to his bow, and the occupations of his leisure hours were varied and interesting. As he himself said, 'I have ridden so many hobbies—music, painting, literature—that commercially at least they have all succeeded more or less in cutting each other's throats.' Amongst his early musical experiences he was called upon to play a one-manual church organ, and when he came to look for voluntaries adapted to such an instrument, he found that there was a singular lack of such works. He at once made up his mind to supply the deficiency as far as he was able, and the result was the issue of several books of voluntaries selected from *Judas Maccabaeus, Messiah, The Creation, Elijah* and *St. Paul.* The venture proved highly successful, and Gill's *Easy Voluntaries* became the happy refuge of thousands of organists. Belonging to an earlier period are his *Easy Anthems for Village Choirs,* which, as the title suggests, were written to supply a similar want. W. H. Monk thought so highly of these that he selected three of them for insertion in the book of *Anthems* which he edited in 1875 for the General Assembly of the Church of Scotland.

In the early seventies, Mr. Gill wrote several songs, such as 'Elixir Vitae,' 'The Miller's Daughter,' 'The Legend of the Forget-me-not.' His other musical works include a volume of 'Cradle Songs,' and one of original 'Hymns and Carols.' Amongst his purely literary works may be mentioned a small volume of poems entitled *A*

34

Manx Wedding and other Songs. He spent the last years of his life at Angmering, where he died in 1923.

971—The Blessed Name.

THE BLESSED NAME was composed by Sir Joseph Barnby (see No. 105) for the *Congregational Sunday-school Hymnal* (1891).

972—Springfield.

SPRINGFIELD is from *Choral Harmony*, edited in 1852 by the Rev. Peter Maurice. It is anonymous, but the suggestion that it is by Dr. Gauntlett is quite plausible.

973—David.

DAVID is adapted from the aria, 'Rendi il sereno al ciglio,' in Handel's opera, *Sosarme* (1732), in which a devoted daughter soothes a mother's grief. The song was one of the special items at the great Handel Festival of 1784. Shortly after it was adapted as an anthem (probably by Dr. S. Arnold) beginning ' Lord, remember David.'

974—God of the Living. See. No. 186.

975—Irene.

IRENE, by the Rev. C. C. Scholefield (see No. 667), was written for *Church Hymns* (1874).

976—Requiescat.

REQUIESCAT was written by Dr. Dykes (see No. 36) for *Hymns Ancient and Modern* (1875).

977—Safe Home.

SAFE HOME was written by Arthur Sullivan (see No. 18) for *The Hymnary* (1872).

978—Redhead No. 47. See No. 358.

979—Meirionydd.

MEIRIONYDD is from *Caniadau Seion* (1840). It is ascribed to William Lloyd of Rhosgoch, Caernarvon (1786-1852), and should not in any case be called a 'Welsh Traditional Melody.' It is found in *Y caniedydd Cynulleidfaol* (1921) and other modern Welsh tune-books.

980—St. Francis Xavier.

ST. FRANCIS XAVIER, by Sir J. Stainer (see No. 20), first appeared in the 1875 edition of *Hymns Ancient and Modern*. The tune received its name from a supposed association of the original hymn, for which it was written (No. 446), with St. Francis.

981—Goshen.

GOSHEN is adapted from a song 'Childhood's happy hours,' by Miss Marcel Davis, published in Dublin about 1857. It was made into a hymn-tune and inserted in the *Bible Class Magazine* (1860). No details of the composer are available.

982—Exeter.

EXETER is by William Jackson, who was born in Exeter in 1730. During his childhood he had few musical advantages till a violinist from London gave him lessons in music. He proved an apt pupil and his father, hopeful of his future, sent him to London, where he studied under John Travers, organist of the Chapel Royal. He now began to try his hand at composition, and in 1760 his first set of ' Elegies ' was published, and also, by subscription, a set of songs by which he made about £300. At this time painting occupied as much of his attention as music, being greatly encouraged by his friend, Gainsborough, but he found song-writing more profitable, and also published some sonatas for violin and harpsichord, calling himself ' Jackson of Exeter,' to distinguish himself from a certain ' Jackson of Oxford,' long since forgotten. In 1777 he was appointed organist of Exeter Cathedral, though what training he had had for the post is not clear. In his 'autobiography' he thus describes his early experiences, and also the writing of his famous 'Te Deum in F':

> Cathedral duty was not new to me. I found a bad choir, which I was determined, if possible, to make a good one. By degrees I succeeded, and it is now (1801) and has been for many years, the best in the kingdom. Some time previous to this I had been in correspondence with Dr. Lowth, Bishop of London, on the subject of the 'Te Deum.' We both agreed as to the proper division of the parts of that hymn, and having my own opinion aided by so very respectable a critic, I executed our joint ideas by composing my service in F. It is all in plain counterpoint from the beginning to the end. The same plan was continued throughout the Jubilate, Sanctus, Commandments and Creed, and in the evening service as well. The effect was in all respects superior to my expectation . . .

> The first time of performance, besides the usual congregation, the church was full of soldiers, who are always talkative and noisy. However, by degrees, the noise abated and they were all attention.

> Many years after I recomposed this service for five parts, when the alto was added.—*Leisure Hour,* June 1882.

The MS. was formerly in the possession of William Elmisley, Q.C., County Court Judge of Derbyshire, who received it from William Jackson, son of the composer. He married one of the daughters of Charles Barry, of Exeter.

In 1785 he went for a continental tour, of which he has left a lovely account, and his sketch of Gainsborough's life throws much light on the painter's career. He retained his position at Exeter Cathedral until his death in 1803.

983—Winchester New. See No. 274.

984—Jubilate.

JUBILATE, by Sir C. H. H. Parry, first appeared in *The Hymnal Companion*. (See No. 145.)

A.T. 1—Rhodes.

RHODES (also known as CANA) was contributed to the *London Tune-Book* (1875), by Dr. C. W. Jordan (see No. 669). It was composed for the marriage of Canon Rhodes Bristow at St. Stephen's, Lewisham, where Dr. Jordan was organist, and was originally named WEDDING HYMN.

A.T. 2—Sarah.

SARAH, by William Arnold. See No. 699.

A.T. 3—Trentham.

TRENTHAM was originally written for Baker's hymn, ' O perfect life of love,' and appeared in 1888 in *Fifty Sacred Leaflets*.

Robert Jackson, born at Oldham in 1842, received his musical education at the Royal Academy of Music, whence he passed on to become organist at St. Mark's, Grosvenor Square, London. In 1868 he returned to Oldham to succeed his father as organist at St. Peter's church, who had been in office there since 1821. He died at Royton in 1914, and it is a notable fact that father and son had held the organist's place at St. Peter's between them for ninety-two years.

A.T. 4—Vigil.

VIGIL is from a set of hymns, published about 1852, composed by Thomas Bairstow. The last tune in the collection is VIGIL, under the name of THE LAST WISH, and set to a hymn by the Rev. Thomas Taylor, of Bradford :

Saviour and Lord of all,
We lift our souls to Thee;
Guide us and guard us,
Guide us and guard us,
Whate'er our lot may be.

Little is known about Bairstow. He was a tailor by trade, and spent most of his life in Bingley. He was an officer at the Independent Chapel in the town, and also leader of the singing. The tune came to him one Sunday evening whilst calling at a friend's house, and having no paper available he chalked the melody on an oven tin.

A.T. 5—Covenanters.

COVENANTERS. This is an unfortunate misnomer, as the tune has not the slightest connexion with the seventeenth-century Scottish Covenanters. When they sang at all they sang the old psalm-tunes, and not adaptations of secular airs. This tune appears to be an adaptation of an American song, ' O what can you tell, little pebble? ' in a collection of hymns and tunes for Sabbath schools called *Clariona,* formed by W. B. Bradbury (see No. 321) in 1867:

From 'Clariona,' 1867.

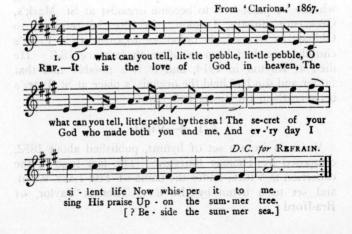

1. O what can you tell, lit-tle pebble, lit-tle pebble, O
REF.—It   is   the   love   of   God in   heaven, The

what can you tell, little pebble by the sea! The se-cret of your
God who made both you and me, And ev-'ry day I

D.C. for REFRAIN.

si-lent life Now whis-per   it   to   me.
sing His praise Up-on   the   sum-mer tree.
[? Be-side the sum-mer sea.]

From this it will be seen that LITTLE PEBBLE would have been a more appropriate name for this tune than COVENANTERS.

Miss Gilchrist, a well-known authority on folk-song, is of the opinion that COVENANTERS is an old ballad tune of the Scottish border, taken out to America two or three centuries ago.

The tune first appeared in print in America in the *Christian Lyre*, Vol. I, 1838, called PISGAH, and set to a revival or camp-meeting hymn, 'Jesus, Thou art the sinner's Friend,' with a refrain, 'Lord, remember me.' It was from this source that Bradbury got it for his 'little pebble' song in *Clariona*.

It is possible that COVENANTERS is a lineal descendant of the old song, 'Little Musgrave and Lady Barnard,' which is thus quoted in Chappell's *Old English Minstrelsy*.

LITTLE MUSGRAVE & LADY BARNARD.

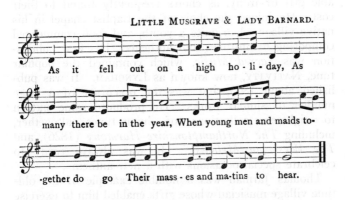

As it fell out on a high ho-li-day, As many there be in the year, When young men and maids to-gether do go Their mass-es and ma-tins to hear.

A.T. 6—Diadem.

DIADEM was first printed in leaflet form for a Sunday-school Anniversary at Droylsden, near Manchester. It was the birthplace of the composer, James Ellor, a self-taught musician who worked in a hat factory in his native town on week-days, and on Sunday led the choir at the Wesleyan chapel. In 1843 he conducted his last anniversary and went to America, where he died in 1899.

A.T. 7—Jazer.

JAZER, by A. E. Tozer, is from *Catholic Church Hymns*. (See No. 402.)

A.T. 8—Lyngham.

LYNGHAM is by Thomas Jarman, who was born in 1776 at Clipstone, a small village near the northern border of Northamptonshire. His father was a tailor, and he was brought up to the same trade; but his natural taste for music considerably interfered with his work, and he was frequently reduced to dire straits, from which only the extreme liberality of his publishers relieved him. He was a man of fine, commanding presence, but self-willed, and endowed with a considerable gift of irony, as choirs frequently found to their cost. He joined the choir of the Baptist chapel in his native village when quite a youth, and soon commenced composing hymn-tunes and anthems. His first publication was *Sacred Music,* which contained the popular tune, NATIVITY, now known as LYNGHAM. It was published about 1803, and was the precursor of a large number of similar works. He produced some sixteen to eighteen collections of hymn-tunes altogether, including *The Northamptonshire Harmony* (1826), and *The Wesleyan Melodist.* He was always ready to celebrate special occasions with a new anthem.

Thomas Jarman was a notable example of the old-time village musician whose gifts enabled him to exercise a great influence for good in the praise worship of the church. Many are represented in the present hymn-book, and their music lives to remind us of what they have accomplished in the past. Jarman was also a successful choir-trainer, and the village choir festival held under his direction at Naseby (of battle celebrity) in 1837, was the talk of the district for long after. He spent some six or seven years at Leamington, during which time he enjoyed the friendship of C. Rider, a wealthy Methodist who did much for psalmody in Lancashire and elsewhere some fifty or sixty years ago. Jarman died at Clipstone in 1861, and was buried in the grounds of the Baptist chapel. On his tombstone was the verse:

> Sweet son of song,
> Though humble was thy lot;
> Thy honoured memory
> Ne'er shall be forgot.

A.T. 9—Sawley.

SAWLEY has had a long run of popularity, and it is still a useful stand-by for a would-be precentor whose stock of C.M. tunes is limited. Its composer, James Walch, was born at Egerton, near Bolton, in 1837. Educated by his father, he attained proficiency on the organ, and at the age of fourteen was appointed organist of Duke's Alley Congregational Church, Bolton. Two years later he went to Bridge Street Wesleyan Chapel, where he remained five years, leaving there for an appointment at St. George's Church. He was appointed conductor of the Bolton Philharmonic Society, a position he held for four years. About 1877 he went to live in Barrow-in-Furness, where he commenced a music business and also acted as honorary organist of the parish church. He died in 1901.

SAWLEY was written for a Sunday-school Anniversary in 1857, and printed for private circulation. It became well known, and manuscript copies were made of it in which the name of the composer was not always given, and it gradually completely disappeared. When the tune once more appeared in print it was credited to ' Anon.' and subsequently, by the editor of the *Hymnal Companion,* to the Rev. F. Pigou, an ascription which must have greatly delighted that humour-loving dean. Ultimately Walch wrote to the editor, claiming the tune and giving full credentials, and he has ever since been recognized as the composer. Walch wrote several other tunes, including EAGLEY, and numerous fugitive piano pieces.

A.T. 10—Castle Rising.

CASTLE RISING is by Canon F. A. J. Hervey, and was written whilst he was an undergraduate at Cambridge. Whilst on a visit to Castle Rising (a beautiful village near King's Lynn) he was looking through *Hymns Ancient and Modern,* and on coming to Mrs. Alexander's hymn, ' The roseate hues of early dawn,' it occurred to him that he could improve on the tune to which it was set (the OLD 44TH in the 1861 edition). He wrote out a new melody, instinctively changing the rhythm at the fifth line. He showed it to Barnby, who thought he could improve on one of the lines, and then the tune came round to Brown-Borthwick, who inserted it in his *Supplemental Hymn and Tune-Book* (1867).

In discussing the tune the composer once said, ' My old master, Dr. Garrett, discovered a likeness between the second part of my tune and a song then in vogue called, I think, " The Mousetrap Man." I am bound to admit that there is a certain justification for the gibe, though I emphatically declare I had never heard the ditty in question when I wrote CASTLE RISING.'

A.T. 11—Norseman.

NORSEMAN. The original edition of the melody is headed ' The hardy Norseman's House of Yore, a Norse National Song,' and this note is added by R. L. Pearsall, who arranged it in four parts :

The following melody was given to me by the late Joseph Ponny of Vienna, who heard it at a family festival in the interior of Norway and noted it on the spot. It was there described to him as a very ancient popular song, referable to the times of the Kempions or Sea-Kings, and as being always sung with the greatest enthusiasm. The words, for want of a better, are my own, founded on a rough guess at what the original Norse might mean; for being able to make out but a word or two here and there I could not pretend to translate it.

A.T. 12—Athlone.

ATHLONE appeared in John Wesley's *Sacred Harmony* (1780). It is evidently an adaptation of the air ROISIN DUBH, or MY LITTLE BLACK ROSE, which is one of the many allegorical names for Ireland. This is recognized as the composition of Turlogh O'Carolan and, as will be seen, the hymn-tune follows the air very closely (from a MS. 1756).

O'Carolan was born in 1670. Losing his sight soon after birth he devoted himself to music, and became an accomplished harpist. Here is an example of his wonderful memory. Being a guest at the house of an Irish nobleman, where Geminiani was present, Carolan challenged that eminent composer to a trial of skill. The musician played over on his violin the Fifth Concerto of Vivaldi; it was instantly repeated by Carolan on his harp, although he had never heard it before. The surprise of the company was increased when Carolan asserted that he would compose a Concerto himself, and did then and there invent a piece that has since gone by his name. He composed upon the buttons of his coat, the buttons serving for the purpose of the lines, the intervals between them for the spaces. Another story about Carolan is adduced in amusing proof of his amazing musical memory. He was about to perform one evening at a patron's house in competition with another minstrel whom he had overheard a little previously practising what was evidently intended to be his show piece on the occasion. When the trial came off, Carolan, as the more distinguished harper, was called upon to play first, and, to the mingled rage and astonishment of his rival, played, as his own, the very piece which he was about to perform, but with a feeling and finish he could never have approached. Carolan had received his education and professional outfit in the family of MacDermot Roe, of Alderford House, in the county of Roscommon, and here he was always welcome.

Carolan was of a roving disposition with a love of excitement and a distinct tendency to dissipation, but he had a wonderful talent for improvisation, and his skill as a composer is shown in the music bearing his name that has been preserved. He died in 1738.

A.T. 13—Castle Street.

CASTLE STREET (or LUTHER'S CHANT) is from *The American Harp*, a collection of tunes edited by Zeuner in 1832-34.

This tune-book contains several tunes written in a form which Zeuner appears to have introduced, and which he designates 'hymn-chants,' two examples being LUTHER'S CHANT and MISSIONARY CHANT. The former, which, it is scarcely necessary to state, has no connexion whatever with Luther, was introduced into the *Wesleyan Tune-Book* of 1876, and has had a long run of popularity. When the new *Methodist Hymn-Book* appeared in 1904, LUTHER'S CHANT seemed to have been left out, whereat those who had had enough of it rejoiced openly, whilst those who still hankered after its simple strains mourned in secret. Finally it was discovered under the new name of CASTLE STREET.

Zeuner was born at Eisleben, in Saxony, in 1795, his baptismal names being Heinrich Christopher, for which he substituted the simpler one of Charles when he left his native country for America. Settling in Boston, he achieved much renown as an organ player. In addition to *The American Harp*, he published a second collection, which he called *The Ancient Lyre*.

But Zeuner did not confine his attention entirely to composing hymn-tunes. About 1838 he completed an oratorio which he called *The Feast of Tabernacles*, and then entered into negotiations with the Handel and Haydn Society for its production, suggesting that they should bring it out and give him 3,000 dollars for it. This they were quite unable to do, for they could buy all the oratorios in the world for that amount of money at that time. They told him that they would bring it out, and take all risks of its proving a financial success, and that he should consider the fame that it would bring him as a sufficient remuneration on his part. Zeuner declined this offer, remarking that he did not 'write music for fame but for money.'

After further argument the rehearsals were commenced with Zeuner as conductor and G. J. Webb (see No. 821) as organist. The chorus found it impossible to get along with Zeuner's conducting, owing to his violent temper and impatience, so after two rehearsals he gave up the baton to Mr. Webb and played the organ instead.

In 1854 Zeuner left Boston and took up his residence in Philadelphia, where he acted as organist at two or three churches. His way of giving up one appointment was quite characteristic of the man. During his voluntary one Sunday he astonished and delighted the few musical members of the congregation with a masterly performance of an impromptu fugue. The remainder of his audience, including, of course, the church officials, were equally shocked to hear music which they utterly failed to comprehend. When Zeuner had finished one of the officials went up to him and said, ' Pray, Mr. Zeuner, is our organ out of order? There was such an unaccountable jolting and rumbling in the pedals this morning that altogether it sounded very strangely indeed.' This was too much for the eccentric and outraged performer, and with a contemptuous remark at such ignorance, he rushed away from the church and never went near it again.

It is not surprising to find that the life of this eccentric gentleman terminated in a fit of insanity. He disappeared from the boarding-house where he was staying, and put an end to his life in some woods that border on the river Delaware. This sad event took place in 1857.

A.T. 14—Job.

JOB is by William Arnold. See No. 699.

A.T. 15—Rimington.

RIMINGTON takes its name from the Yorkshire village in Ribblesdale where the composer, Francis Duckworth, was born in 1862. When he was five years old the family removed to the adjacent village of Stopper Lane, and here he had his first and only music lessons. He soon became skilful enough to take the organ at the services in the local chapel. In 1882 he left to take up business in Colne, where he has resided until the present time. He was appointed deputy organist, then organist, at Albert Road Wesleyan Chapel, where he continued in office till 1929. For many years he has had a Mustel organ in his home, which has frequently been a source of inspiration to him. RIMINGTON came to him in early life, but it was not printed till 1904, when it appeared in leaflet form. Since then its success has been remarkable. It has been sung everywhere—in Manchester Cathedral, the Albert Hall, London, on Mount Calvary, and on the lonely Pitcairn Island. It has also appeared in a dozen English hymnals, and the Salvation Army literature has taken it all over the world.

A.T. 16—Trinity.

TRINITY (with five other tunes) was originally published in full music size, being printed in Italy about 1866. The tune came to the notice of Dr. Bowden, a member of the 1876 *Wesleyan Tune-Book* committee, and it was introduced into that collection. The composer, Emilio Vincenzio Pieraccini, was born in Italy in 1833. He came to this country about 1866, and settled in Bath, where he practised as a teacher of singing, visiting Clifton and other places in the west of England. He had a large and fashionable connexion, and was held in high repute in his profession. He was also known as a composer of songs and cantatas, as well as church music. His cantata *Dorcas* was produced by a special choir at Bath in 1885. In 1902 he proposed to return to his native country, but illness prevented him carrying out his intention. He died in Bath in 1902.

A.T. 17—Trumpet.

TRUMPET is by Lewis Edson, who was descended from one of the early settlers in Salem, Massachusetts, who afterwards drifted to Bridgewater, where Lewis was born January 22, 1748. He was a blacksmith by trade, and during the difficulties with England he and his family, being Tories, found it desirable to remove to the sparsely-settled section of western Massachusetts. Here he found names for two of his best-known tunes, GREENFIELD and LENOX. Another of his tunes was called BRIDGEWATER, from the town of his birth. These three tunes were first printed in *The Chorister's Companion,* a book of various classes of church music, where they are marked as 'never before printed.' The

date of this book is probably 1782 or 1783, there being
a copy of it in the Library of Congress, in which the
original owner had placed the date, 1783. It was printed
for and sold by Simeon Jocelin and Amos Doolittle in
New Haven, Connecticut. Lewis Edson was called 'the
great singer,' and taught music throughout the section of
Western Massachusetts, New York, and Connecticut.
He married in 1770, removed to New York in 1776,
moved again in 1817 to Woodstock, Connecticut, where
he died in the spring of 1820.

A.T. 18—Warrenne No. 5.

Warrenne No. 5. (or Peveril) is by the Rev. Dr.
Olinthus R. Barnicott (see No. 218). Warrenne was a
family name, adopted by the composer owing to the
difficulty of finding names for his rapidly accumulating
number of original hymn-tunes.

Writing about this time the composer said 'Peveril
belongs to "Songs in the night." It was composed
wholly in the dark. As I retired to rest, one verse of
the hymn to which it is set ("Jerusalem on high"), was
running in my mind—"Ah me, ah me, that I," &c.
When in bed I began constructing the tune to these
words, taking phrase by phrase, and setting them to
appropriate notes, until the whole was finished, which
occupied the greater part of the night. In the morning
I wrote it down. This is the only tune I have composed
in this way.'

A.T. 19—Nottingham.

Nottingham is from the Kyrie of the *Twelfth Mass,*
which was for many years credited to Mozart, but, as
Ernest Newman says, in his Introduction to Holmes's
biography of the composer, 'its spuriousness is now
universally recognized.'

The standard authority on the subject of Mozart's
compositions is Köchel's *Chronological Thematic
Catalogue of Mozart's Complete Works,* and in this the

compiler treats the Twelfth Mass as a spurious work, ending up his argument by this statement: 'By all connoisseurs this mass is definitely declared to be *untergeschoben'* (spurious).

This *Catalogue* was issued in 1862, and some thirty years later, when Messrs. Breitkopf and Hartel were issuing their monumental edition of Mozart's compositions, the editors, after again studying its claims, declined to admit the mass as one of Mozart's compositions.

A further proof is given by the writer of the notice of Mozart in Grove's *Dictionary*, where we are told that the violinist, Leopold Jansa, who was born in 1795, recognized this Twelfth Mass as one in which he used to sing as a boy at school in his native village, where it was known as 'Müller's Mass,' but who this particular Müller was has never been definitely ascertained.

A.T. 20—Paraclete.

PARACLETE was written by Mrs. Barker for the second series of *Hymns chiefly of the Eastern Church,* translated by J. M. Neale. These were published in a small quarto pamphlet which contained eight hymns. No. 5 was 'Taste of myrrh He deign'd to know,' for which the tune was written. It was introduced into the *Wesleyan Tune-Book* (1876) for the hymn, 'Gracious Spirit, dwell with me,' hence the name PARACLETE.

Mrs. Elizabeth Barker was the daughter of Mr. William Halkett, of Aylestone Hall, Leicester. Born in 1829 she studied music under G. A. Löhr. In 1853 she married the Rev. F. Barker, of Oriel College, and through him became acquainted with Dr. Neale, who greatly appreciated her musical talent. In 1867 Mrs. Barker joined the Roman Catholic Church. She died about 1916.

A.T. 21—Bullinger.

BULLINGER. Born in 1837, E. W. Bullinger was a choir boy in Canterbury Cathedral, and subsequently studied for the ministry at King's College. He was an able Greek and Hebrew scholar, and received the Lambeth D.D. for his critical work in 1881. He composed several hymn-tunes, some of which were published in booklet form. BULLINGER is the only one that has survived.

A.T. 22—Sacred Rest.

SACRED REST first appeared in the *Primitive Methodist Hymnal* (1889). It is by John Barrass Birkbeck, a Durham musician who took a great interest in psalmody. Born in 1831 at Shiney Row, Co. Durham, he taught himself music from books, which were rather scarce in his early days. He also studied the clarinet, but gave it up in favour of the violin. At the age of seventeen he was appointed choirmaster at the Primitive Methodist Church, Pittington, where he had a string orchestra to support the singers. During his long life he composed and published a large number of song-services and hymn-tunes. He also wrote a life of Thomas Jarman (see A.T. 8), which is still in manuscript.

A.T. 23—Rest.

REST was written by F. C. Maker (see No. 206) for the *Congregational Hymnary* (1887).

A.T. 24—Grace.

GRACE is associated with the early days of Primitive Methodism, but this is its only claim to be called ' traditional.' The hymn to which it is set comes from the *Large Hymn-Book for the use of the Primitive Methodists* (1824). Both hymn and tune were used at open-air processions, and came to be known as THE PRIMITIVE METHODIST GRAND MARCH. For some years the tune suffered a temporary eclipse, and it only just managed to find a place in the Appendix to the *Primitive Methodist Hymnal* of 1889, having been supplanted in the earlier part of the hymnal by ROUSSEAU (or ROUSSEAU'S DREAM). GRACE occupies a similar position in the present hymn-book. The composer is unknown.

A.T. 25—Leipsic.

LEIPSIC is from the first edition (1542) of the Genevan *Psalter,* edited (probably) by Louis Bourgeois. J. S. Bach uses the tune in five of his cantatas in common time, and in two cantatas in triple time. The harmonies given at A.T. 25 are not his. In the *Chorale Book for England* (1863) the tune is incorrectly ascribed to Goudimel, and it is also suggested that LEIPSIC may originally have been adapted from a secular tune, which is possible. It is also found in the French *Psalter* (1565).

A.T. 26—Rousseau.

ROUSSEAU. The connexion between J. J. Rousseau, the Swiss-French philosopher, and the tune bearing his name is of the slightest. In 1752 he wrote an opera, *Le Divin du Village* (The Village Doctor) wherein this air is found:

Out of this J. B. Cramer evolved the tune he called ROUSSEAU'S DREAM, and published it with variations about 1818. In its new form the tune was included by Thomas Walker in his *Companion to Dr. Rippon's Tune-Book* (c. 1825), and since then it has had a prosperous career. Why it was ever christened ROUSSEAU'S DREAM is not known. A more suitable designation would have been PANTOMIME, thus retaining the original name in *Le Divin du Village.*

A.T. 27—Agnus Dei.

AGNUS DEI, by Rev. W. Blow, is from the enlarged 1881 edition of the *Bristol Tune-Book.*

A.T. 28—Crucifixion.

CRUCIFIXION is by Samuel Akeroyd. It appeared in *The Divine Companion* (1701 &c.). It is No. 31 in John Wesley's 'Foundery' Tune-Book (1742), and there is every reason to believe that it is the one sung by Wesley and his friends on the night of his conversion, May 24, 1738. Wesley set it to the hymn, 'And can it be that I should gain.'

Little is known of the composer. He is said to have been born in Yorkshire, and composed various pieces which have long since had their day. He is now remembered only by his tune CRUCIFIXION.

A.T. 29—Lloyd.

LLOYD, by Cuthbert Howard, originally appeared in leaflet form. The composer was born in 1856. He was for some years an organist at various churches in Manchester and the suburbs, including Oakfield Union Church, Sale, during the ministry of the Rev. Carey Bonner. In later years he put his skill as an accompanist to good use by playing at various concerts, at which he was associated with many well-known singers. For a time he kept a music shop, but it did not prove a success. He died in 1927.

A.T. 30—Wonderful Love.

WONDERFUL LOVE, by Adam Watson, was originally published in leaflet form. The composer was born at Stretford, Manchester, in 1845. He entered the scholastic profession and began as a schoolmaster in Padiham. After a brief stay here he was appointed to the vacant headmastership of the Sale Township Schools (now the Springfield Council Schools), which he retained for thirty-five years. He studied music under George Oakey, and did good service in advancing the cause of Tonic Sol-Fa. He acted as choirmaster at Sale Congregational Church, and later at Stretford Congregational Church. He conducted the Sale Amateur Orchestral Society and also the Stretford Choral Society. He wrote several prize hymn-tunes for Sunday-school Festivals in Lancashire and Yorkshire, one of them being WONDERFUL LOVE. He died at Pinner in 1912.

A.T. 31—Epiphany.

EPIPHANY was contributed by E. J. Hopkins (see No. 103) to R. R. Chope's *Congregational Hymn and Tune-Book* (1862).

A.T. 32—Marylebone.

MARYLEBONE was composed by Sir H. H. Parry (see No. 145) at the request of the committee of the *Methodist Hymn-Book* (1904) for Charles Wesley's ' swan-song '—his last composition, ' In age and feebleness extreme.'

Other words were subsequently written for the music by T. B. Stephenson in order to make it better known.

COMPOSERS, ARRANGERS, AND SOURCES
OF TUNES

Denotes an arrangement by the person named. When the Composer's dates are unknown the year of the first appearance of the tune is given.

The figures in this index refer to the numbers of the tunes, not to the pages.

526

Steggall, Charles, 1826-1905:
Bonar . . . 541
Christ Chapel . . 540
Christchurch . . 653
Day of Praise . . 778
Stevenson, John Andrew, 1762-1833:
Dublin . . . 378, 751
Stewart, Robert Prescott, 1825-94:
Adrian . . . 898
St. Helen's . . 916
St. Werburgh . . 354
Stimpson, O. J., 1835:
Evensong . . . 947
Storl's *Gesangbuch*, 1710:
Munich . . . 659
Stralsund Gesangbuch, 1665:
Lobe den Herren . 64
Strasburg Psalter, 1525-42:
Old 113th . . 584
Strasburg . . 33, 884
Students' Hymnal, 1923:
Childhood . . . 166
Sullivan, Arthur Seymour, 1842-1900:
Bishopgarth . . 964
Cœna Domini . . 731
Constance . . 423
Ever faithful . . 18
Golden Sheaves . 964
Homeland . . 654
In Memoriam . . 506
*Leominster . . 542
Lux Eoi . . . 706
*Nearer Home . . 658
*Noel . . . 130
St. Gertrude . . 822
Safe Home . . 977
Samuel . . . 848
Valete . . . 346
Summers, Joseph, 1843-1916:
Evensong . . . 920
Swift, James Frederick, 1847-1931:
Te laudant omnia . 29
Swiss Traditional Melody:
Solothurn . . . 847

Tallis, Thomas, c. 1510-85:
Tallis' Canon . . 943
Tallis' Ordinal . 304, 607
Tansur, William, 1706-83:
Bangor . . . 556
Templi Carmina, 1829:
Lucius . . . 745
Williams . . . 968
Terry, Richard Runciman, 1865- :
Doxford . . . 805
Highwood . . 254
*Sannox . . . 887
Teschner, Melchior, c. 1615:
St. Theodulph . . 84
The Tune-Book, 1842:
Glory . . . 656
Infant Praise . . 837
Thommen's Gesangbuch, 1745:
Cassel . . . 291

Thompson, Robert George, 1862- :
Blairgowrie . . 231
Thrupp, Joseph Francis, 1827-67:
Epiphany Hymn . 122
Tiddeman, Maria, 1837- :
Ibstone . . . 462
Tours, Berthold, 1838-97:
Deventer . . . 932
Tours . . . 835
Towner, Daniel Brink, 1850-1919:
Trust and obey . . 516
Tozer, Augustus Edmonds, 1857-1910:
Faith of our fathers . 402
Jazer . . . A.T. 7
Trotter, George, 1866-1917:
Howcroft . . . 394
Tucker, Isaac, 1761-1825:
Devizes . . . 560
Turle, James, 1802-82:
*Atonement . . 181
Westminster . . 73
Turner, William, 1651-1740:
Egham . . . 950
Turton, Thomas, 1780-1864:
Ely 373

'University of Wales' (*Students' Hymnal*), 1923:
Childhood . . . 166
Union Tune-Book, 1842:
Syria . . . 598
Urhan, Chrétien, 1790-1845:
Rutherford . . 637

Vetter, Daniel, c. 1713:
Nunhead . . . 379
Vierstimmiges Choralbuch, 1785:
Da Christus geboren war . 810
Vincent, Charles, 1852-1934:
Ishmael . . 243, 700
St. Cyril . . . 633
St. Dorothea . . 459
Vincent, George Frederick, 1855-1928:
Supplication . . 782
Viner, William Letton, 1790-1867:
Dismissal . . . 693
Vulpius' Gesangbuch, 1609:
Jena . . . 343
Vulpius, Melchior, 1560-1616:
Pastor . . . 466

Wade's, J. F., MS. Book, 1751:
Adeste fideles . . 118
St. Thomas . . 808
Wainwright, John, 1723-68:
Yorkshire . . 120
Wainwright, Richard, 1758-1825:
Liverpool (Newmarket) . 326
Wainwright, Robert, 1748-82:
Manchester . . 172, 292
Wakeley, Samuel, 1820-c. 1882:
Reuben . . . 718

36

INDEX OF TUNES

DEAD MAN'S GRIP

Also by Peter James

DEAD LETTER DROP

ATOM BOMB ANGEL

BILLIONAIRE

POSSESSION

DREAMER

SWEET HEART

TWILIGHT

PROPHECY

ALCHEMIST

HOST

THE TRUTH

DENIAL

FAITH

Children's Novel

GETTING WIRED!

The Roy Grace Series

DEAD SIMPLE

LOOKING GOOD DEAD

NOT DEAD ENOUGH

DEAD MAN'S FOOTSTEPS

DEAD TOMORROW

DEAD LIKE YOU

DEAD MAN'S GRIP

PETER JAMES

MACMILLAN

First published 2011 by Macmillan
an imprint of Pan Macmillan, a division of Macmillan Publishers Limited
Pan Macmillan, 20 New Wharf Road, London N1 9RR
Basingstoke and Oxford
Associated companies throughout the world
www.panmacmillan.com

ISBN 978-0-230-74725-8 HB
ISBN 978-0-230-74724-1 TPB

1 3 5 7 9 8 6 4 2

A CIP catalogue record for this book is available from
the British Library.

Typeset by SetSystems Limited, Saffron Walden, Essex
Printed in the UK by CPI Mackays, Chatham ME5 8TD

Visit www.panmacmillan.com to read more about all our books
and to buy them. You will also find features, author interviews and
news of any author events, and you can sign up for e-newsletters
so that you're always first to hear about our new releases.

TO EVA KLAESSON-LINDEBLAD

DEAD MAN'S GRIP

1

On the morning of the accident, Carly had forgotten to set the alarm and overslept. She woke with a bad hangover, a damp dog crushing her and the demented pounding of drums and cymbals coming from her son's bedroom. To add to her gloom, it was pelting with rain outside.

She lay still for a moment, gathering her thoughts. She had a chiropody appointment for a painful corn and a client she loathed would be in her office in just over two hours. It was going to be one of those days, she had the feeling, when things just kept on getting worse. Like the drumming.

'Tyler!' she yelled. 'For Christ's sake, stop that. Are you ready?'

Otis leapt off the bed and began barking furiously at his reflection in the mirror on the wall.

The drumming fell silent.

She staggered to the bathroom, found the paracetamols and gulped two down. I am so not a good example to my son, she thought. I'm not even a good example to my dog.

As if on cue, Otis padded into the bathroom, holding his lead in his mouth expectantly.

'What's for breakfast, Mum?' Tyler called out.

She stared at herself in the bathroom mirror. Mercifully, most of her forty-one-year-old – and this morning going on 241-year-old – face was shrouded in a tangle of blonde hair that looked, at this moment, like matted straw.

'Arsenic!' she shouted back, her throat raw from too many cigarettes last night. 'Laced with cyanide and rat poison.'

Otis stamped his paw on the bathroom tiles.

'Sorry, no walkies. Not this morning. Later. OK?'

'I had that yesterday!' Tyler shouted back.

'Well, it didn't sodding work, did it?'

She switched on the shower, waited for it to warm up, then stepped inside.

2

Stuart Ferguson, in jeans, Totectors boots and company overalls on top of his uniform polo shirt, sat high up in his cab, waiting impatiently for the lights to change. The wipers clunked away the rain. Rush-hour traffic sluiced across Brighton's Old Shoreham Road below him. The engine of his sixteen-wheel, twenty-four-ton Volvo fridge-box artic chuntered away, a steady stream of warm air toasting his legs. April already, but winter had still not relaxed its grip, and he'd driven through snow at the start of his journey. No one was going to sell him global warming.

He yawned, staring blearily at the vile morning, then took a long swig of Red Bull. He put the can into the cup-holder, ran his clammy, meaty hands across his shaven head, then drummed them on the steering wheel to the beat of 'Bat Out of Hell', which was playing loud enough to wake the dead fish behind him. It was the fifth or maybe the sixth can he had drunk in the past few hours and he was shaking from the caffeine overdose. But that and the music were the only things that were keeping him awake right now.

He had started his journey yesterday afternoon and driven through the night from Aberdeen, in Scotland. There were 603 miles on the clock so far. He'd been on the road for eighteen hours, with barely a break other than a stop for food at Newport Pagnell Services and a brief kip in a lay-by a couple of hours earlier. If it hadn't been for an accident at the M1/M6 interchange, he'd have been here an hour ago, at 8 a.m. as scheduled.

But saying *if it hadn't been for an accident* was pointless. There were always accidents, all the time. Too many people on the roads, too many cars, too many lorries, too many idiots, too many distractions, too many people in a hurry. He'd seen it all over the years. But he was proud of his record. Nineteen years and not one scrape – or even a ticket.

As he glanced routinely at the dashboard, checking the oil

2

pressure, then the temperature gauge, the traffic lights changed. He rammed the gear lever of the four-over-four splitter box forward and steadily picked up speed as he crossed the junction into Carlton Terrace, then headed down the hill towards the sea, which was under a mile away. After an earlier stop at Springs, the salmon smokery a few miles north in the Sussex Downs, he now had one final delivery to make to offload his cargo. It was to the Tesco supermarket in the Holmbush Centre on the outskirts of the city. Then he would drive to the port of Newhaven, load up with frozen New Zealand lamb, snatch a few hours' sleep on the quay and head back up to Scotland.

To Jessie.

He was missing her a lot. He glanced down at her photograph on the dashboard, next to the pictures of his two kids, Donal and Logan. He missed them badly, too. His bitch ex-wife, Maddie, was giving him a hard time over contact. But at least sweet Jessie was helping him get his life back together.

She was four months pregnant with their child. Finally, after three hellish years, he had a future to focus on again, instead of just a past full of bitterness and recrimination.

Ordinarily on this run he would have taken a few hours out to get some proper kip – and comply with the law on driver hours. But the refrigeration was on the blink, with the temperature rising steadily, and he couldn't take the risk of ruining the valuable cargo of scallops, shrimps, prawns and salmon. So he just had to keep going.

So long as he was careful, he would be fine. He knew where the vehicle check locations were, and by listening to CB radio he'd get warned of any active ones. That was why he was detouring through the city now, rather than taking the main road around it.

Then he cursed.

Ahead of him he could see red flashing lights, then barriers descending. The level crossing at Portslade Station. Brake lights came on one by one as the vehicles in front slowed to a halt. With a sharp hiss of his brakes, he pulled up, too. On his left he saw a fair-haired man bowed against the rain, his hair batted by the wind, unlocking the front door of an estate agency called Rand & Co.

He wondered what it would be like to have that sort of job. To be able to get up in the morning, go to an office and then come home in the evening to your family, rather than spend endless days and nights driving, alone, eating in service station cafés or munching a burger in front of the crappy telly in the back of his cab. Maybe he would still be married if he had a job like that. Still see his kids every night and every weekend.

Except, he knew, he'd never be content if he was stuck in one place. He liked the freedom of the road. Needed it. He wondered if the guy turning the lock of the estate agency door had ever looked at a rig like his and thought to himself, I wish I was twisting the ignition key of one of those instead.

Other pastures always looked greener. The one certainty he'd learned in life was that no matter who you were or what you did, shit happened. And one day you would tread in it.

3

Tony nicknamed her Santa because the first time they made love, that snowy December afternoon in his parents' house in the Hamptons, Suzy had been wearing dark red satin underwear. He told her that all his Christmases had come at once.

She, grinning, gave him the cheesy reply that she was glad that was the only thing that had come at once.

They had been smitten with each other since that day. So much so that Tony Revere had abandoned his plans to study for a business degree at Harvard and instead had followed her from New York to England, much to the dismay of his control-freak mother, and joined her at the University of Brighton.

'Lazybones!' he said. 'You goddamn lazybones.'

'So, I don't have any lectures today, OK?'

'It's half eight, right?'

'Yep, I know. I heard you at eight o'clock. Then eight fifteen. Then eight twenty-five. I need my beauty sleep.'

He looked down at her and said, 'You're beautiful enough. And you know what? We haven't made love since midnight.'

'Are you going off me?'

'I guess.'

'I'll have to get the old black book out.'

'Oh yeah?'

She raised a hand and gripped him, firmly but gently, below his belt buckle, then grinned as he gasped. 'Come back to bed.'

'I have to see my tutor, then I have a lecture.'

'On what?'

'Galbraithian challenges in today's workforce.'

'Wow. Lucky you.'

'Yeah. Faced with that or a morning in bed with you, it's a no-brainer.'

'Good. Come back to bed.'

'I am so not coming back to bed. You know what's going to happen if I don't get good grades this semester?'

'Back to the States to Mummy.'

'You know my mom.'

'Uh huh, I do. Scary lady.'

'You said it.'

'So, you're afraid of her?'

'Everyone's afraid of my mom.'

Suzy sat up a little and scooped some of her long dark hair back. 'More afraid of her than you are of me? Is that the real reason why you came here? I'm just the excuse for you to escape from her?'

He leaned down and kissed her, tasted her sleepy breath and inhaled it deeply, loving it. 'You're gorgeous, did I tell you that?'

'About a thousand times. You're gorgeous, too. Did I tell you that?'

'About ten thousand times. You're like a record that got stuck in a groove,' he said, hitching the straps of his lightweight rucksack over his shoulders.

She looked at him. He was tall and lean, his short dark hair gelled in uneven spikes, with several days' growth of stubble, which she liked to feel against her face. He was dressed in a padded anorak over two layers of T-shirt, jeans and trainers, and smelled of the Abercrombie & Fitch cologne she really liked.

There was an air of confidence about him that had captivated her the first time they had spoken, down in the dark basement bar of Pravda, in Greenwich Village, when she'd been in New York on holiday with her best friend, Katie. Poor Katie had ended up flying back to England on her own, while she had stayed on with Tony.

'When will you be back?' she said.

'As soon as I can.'

'That's not soon enough!'

He kissed her again. 'I love you. I adore you.'

She windmilled her hands. 'More.'

'You're the most stunning, beautiful, lovely creature on the planet.'

'More!'

'Every second I'm away from you, I miss you so much it hurts.'

She windmilled her hands again. 'More!'

'Now you're being greedy.'

'You make me greedy.'

'And you make me horny as hell. I'm going before I have to do something about it!'

'You're really going to leave me like this?'

'Yep.'

He kissed her again, tugged a baseball cap on to his head, then wheeled his mountain bike out of the apartment, down the stairs, through the front door and into the cold, blustery April morning. As he closed the front door behind him, he breathed in the salty tang of the Brighton sea air, then looked at his watch.

Shit.

He was due to see his tutor in twenty minutes. If he pedalled like hell, he might just make it.

4

Click. Beeehhh . . . gleeep . . . uhuhuhurrr . . . gleep . . . grawwwwwp . . . biff, heh, heh, heh. warrrup, haha . . .

'That noise is driving me nuts,' Carly said.

Tyler, in the passenger seat of her Audi convertible, was bent over his iPhone playing some bloody game he was hooked on called Angry Birds. Why did everything he did involve noise?

The phone now emitted a sound like crashing glass.

'We're late,' he said, without looking up and without stopping playing.

Twang-greep-heh, heh, heh . . .

'Tyler, please. I have a headache.'

'So?' He grinned. 'You shouldn't have got pissed last night. Again.'

She winced at his use of adult language.

Twang . . . heh, heh, heh, grawwwwpppp . . .

In a moment she was going to grab the sodding phone and throw it out of the window.

'Yep, well, you'd have got *pissed* last night, too, if you'd had to put up with that prat.'

'Serves you right for going on blind dates.'

'Thanks.'

'You're welcome. I'm late for school. I'm going to get stick for that.' He was still peering intently through his oval wire-framed glasses.

Click-click-beep-beep-beep.

'I'll phone and tell them,' she offered.

'You're always phoning and telling them. You're irresponsible. Maybe I should get taken into care.'

'I've been begging them to take you, for years.'

She stared through the windscreen at the red light and the steady stream of traffic crossing in front of them, and then at the

8

clock: 8.56 a.m. With luck, she'd drop him off at school and get to her chiropody appointment on time. Great, a double-pain morning! First the corn removal, then her client, Mr Misery. No wonder his wife had left him. Carly reckoned she'd probably have topped herself if she'd been married to him. But hey, she wasn't paid to sit in judgement. She was paid to stop Mrs Misery from walking off with both of her husband's testicles, as well as everything else of his – correction, *theirs* – that she was after.

'It really hurts, still, Mum.'

'What does? Oh, right, your brace.'

Tyler touched the front of his mouth. 'It's too tight.'

'I'll call the orthodontist and get you an appointment with him.'

Tyler nodded and focused back on his game.

The lights changed. She moved her right foot from the brake pedal and accelerated. The news was coming up and she leaned forward, turning up the radio.

'I'm going to the *old people* this weekend, right?'

'I'd rather you didn't call them that, OK? They're your *grand-parents.*'

A couple of times a year Tyler spent a day with her late husband's parents. They doted on him, but he found them deadly dull.

Tyler shrugged. 'Do I have to go?'

'Yes, you have to go.'

'Why?'

'It's called *servicing the will.*'

He frowned. 'What?'

She grinned. 'Just a joke – don't repeat that.'

'Servicing the will?' he echoed.

'Forget I said it. Bad taste. I'll miss you.'

'You're a lousy liar. You might say that with more feeling.' He studiously drew his finger across the iPhone screen, then lifted it.

Twang . . . eeeeeekkkk . . . greeeep . . . heh, heh, heh . . .

She caught the next lights and swung right into New Church Road, cutting across the front of a skip lorry, which blared its horn at her.

'You trying to get us killed or something?' Tyler said.

'Not us, just you.' She grinned.

9

'There are agencies to protect children from parents like you,' he said.

She reached out her left arm and ran her fingers through his tousled brown hair.

He jerked his head away. 'Hey, don't mess it up!'

She glanced fondly at him for an instant. He was growing up fast and looked handsome in his shirt and tie, red blazer and grey trousers. Not quite thirteen years old and girls were already chasing him. He was growing more like his late father every day, and there were some expressions he had which reminded her of Kes too much, and in unguarded moments that could make her tearful, even five years on.

Moments later, at a few minutes past nine, she pulled up outside the red gates of St Christopher's School. Tyler clicked off his seat belt and reached behind him to pick up his rucksack.

'Is Friend Mapper on?'

He gave her a 'duh' look. 'Yes, it's on. I'm not a baby, you know.'

Friend Mapper was a GPS app on the iPhone that enabled her to track exactly where he was at any moment on her own iPhone.

'So long as I pay your bill, you keep it on. That's the deal.'

'You're overprotective. I might turn out to be emotionally retarded.'

'That's a risk I'll have to take.'

He climbed out of the car into the rain, then held the door hesitantly. 'You should get a life.'

'I had one before you were born.'

He smiled before slamming the door.

She watched him walk in through the gates into the empty play area – all the other pupils had already gone inside. Every time he went out of her sight, she was scared for him. Worried about him. The only reassurance that he was OK was when she checked her own iPhone and watched his pulsing purple dot and could see where he was. Tyler was right, she was overprotective, but she couldn't help it. She loved him desperately and, despite some of his maddening attitudes and behaviour, she knew that he loved her back, just as much.

She headed up towards Portland Road, driving faster than she should, anxious not to be late for her chiropodist. The corn was giving her grief and she did not want to miss the appointment. Nor did she want to get delayed there. She badly needed to be in the office ahead of Mr Misery and, with luck, have a few minutes to catch up with some urgent paperwork on a forthcoming hearing.

Her phone pinged with an incoming text. When she reached the junction with the main road, she glanced down at it.

I had a great time last night – wld love to see you again XXX

In your dreams, sweetheart. She shuddered at the thought of him. Dave from Preston, Lancashire. Preston Dave, she'd called him. At least she had been honest with the photograph of herself she'd put up on the dating website – well, reasonably honest! And she wasn't looking for a Mr Universe. Just a nice guy who wasn't 100 pounds heavier and ten years older than his photograph, and who didn't want to spend the entire evening telling her how wonderful he was, and what a great shag women thought he was. Was that too much to ask?

Just to put the icing on the cake, the tight bastard had invited her out to dinner, to a far more expensive restaurant than she would have chosen for a first encounter, and at the end had suggested they split the bill.

Keeping her foot on the brake and leaning forward, she deleted the text, decisively, returning the phone to the hands-free cradle with no small amount of satisfaction.

Then she made a left turn, pulling out in front of a white van, and accelerated.

The van hooted and flashing its lights angrily, closed up right behind her and began tailgating her. She held up two fingers.

There were to be many times, in the days and weeks ahead, when she bitterly regretted reading and deleting that text. If she hadn't waited at that junction for those precious seconds, fiddling with her phone, if she had made that left turn just thirty seconds earlier, everything might have been very different.

5

'Black,' Glenn Branson said, holding the large golf umbrella over their heads.

Detective Superintendent Roy Grace looked up at him.

'It's the only colour!'

At five foot, ten inches, Roy Grace was a good four inches shorter than his junior colleague and friend, and considerably less sharply dressed. Approaching his fortieth birthday, Grace was not handsome in a conventional sense. He had a kind face with a slightly misshapen nose that gave him a rugged appearance. It had been broken three times – once in a fight and twice on the rugby pitch. His fair hair was cropped short and he had clear blue eyes that his long-missing wife, Sandy, used to tell him resembled those of the actor Paul Newman.

Feeling like a child in a sweet shop, the Detective Superintendent, hands dug deeply into his anorak pockets, ran his eyes over the rows of vehicles on the Frosts' used-car forecourt, all gleaming with polish and rainwater, and kept returning to the two-door Alfa Romeo. 'I like silver, and dark red, and navy.' His voice was almost drowned out by the sound of a lorry passing on the main road behind them, its air horns blaring.

He was taking advantage of the quiet week, so far, to nip out of the office. A car he'd liked the look of on the *Autotrader* website was at this local dealer.

Detective Sergeant Branson, wearing a cream Burberry mackintosh and shiny brown loafers, shook his head. 'Black's best. The most desirable colour. You'll find that useful when you come to sell it – unless you're planning to drive it over a cliff, like your last one.'

'Very funny.'

Roy Grace's previous car, his beloved maroon Alfa Romeo 147 sports saloon, had been wrecked during a police pursuit the previous autumn, and he had been wrangling with the insurance company ever since. Finally they had agreed a miserly settlement figure.

'You need to think about these things, old-timer. Getting near retirement, you need to look after the pennies.'

'I'm thirty-nine.'

'Forty's looming.'

'Thanks for reminding me.'

'Yeah, well, the old brain starts going at your age.'

'Sod off! Anyhow, black's the wrong colour for an Italian sports car.'

'It's the best colour for everything.' Branson tapped his chest. 'Look at me.'

Roy Grace stared at him. 'Yes?'

'What do you see?'

'A tall, bald bloke with rubbish taste in ties.'

'It's Paul Smith,' he said, looking hurt. 'What about my colour?'

'I'm not allowed to mention it under the Racial Equality Act.'

Branson raised his eyes. 'Black is the colour of the future.'

'Yep, well, as I'm so old I won't live long enough to see it – especially standing here in the pissing rain. I'm freezing. Look, I like that one,' he said, pointing at a red two-seater convertible.

'In your dreams. You're about to become a father, remember? What you need is one of those.' Glenn Branson pointed across at a Renault Espace.

'Thanks, I'm not into people carriers.'

'You might be if you have enough kids.'

'Well, so far it's just one on the way. Anyhow, I'm not choosing anything without Cleo's approval.'

'Got you under her thumb, has she?'

Grace blushed coyly. 'No.'

He took a step towards a sleek silver two-door Alfa Brera and stared at it covetously.

'Don't go there,' Branson said, stepping along with him, keeping him covered with the umbrella. 'Unless you're a contortionist!'

'These are really gorgeous!'

'Two doors. How are you going to get the baby in and out of the back?' He shook his head sadly. 'You have to get something more practical now you're going to be a family man.'

Grace stared at the Brera. It was one of the most beautiful cars he'd ever seen. The price tag was £9,999. Within his range – although with rather high mileage. As he took a further step towards it, his mobile phone rang.

Out of the corner of his eye, he saw a salesman in a sharp suit, holding up an umbrella, scurrying towards them. He glanced at his watch as he answered the phone, mindful of the time, because he was due for a meeting with his boss, the Assistant Chief Constable, in an hour's time, at 10 a.m.

'Roy Grace,' he said.

It was Cleo, twenty-six weeks pregnant with their child, and she sounded terrible, as if she could barely speak.

'Roy,' she gasped. 'I'm in hospital.'

6

He'd had enough of Meat Loaf. Just as the railway-crossing barrier began to rise, Stuart Ferguson switched to an Elkie Brooks album. 'Pearl's a Singer' began to play. That song had been on in the pub the first time he'd gone out with Jessie.

Some women on a first date tried to distance themselves from you, until they knew you better. But they'd had six months of getting to know each other over the phone and the Internet. Jessie had been waiting tables in a truck stop just north of Edinburgh when they'd first met, late at night, and chatted for over an hour. They were both going through marriage bust-ups at the time. She'd scrawled her phone number on the back of the receipt and hadn't expected to hear from him again.

When they'd settled into the quiet side booth, on their first proper date, she'd snuggled up to him. As the song started playing, he'd slipped an arm around her shoulder, fully expecting her to flinch or pull away. Instead she'd snuggled even closer and turned her face towards him, and they'd kissed. They continued kissing, without a break, for the entire duration of the song.

He smiled as he drove forward, bumping over the rail tracks, mindful of a wobbly moped rider just in front of him, the wipers clunking. His heart was heavy with longing for Jessie, the song both beautiful and painful for him at the same time. Tonight he would be back in her arms.

'In one hundred yards turn left,' commanded the female voice of his satnav.

'Yes, boss,' he grunted, and glanced down at the left-angled arrow on the screen, directing him off Station Road and into Portland Road.

He indicated and changed down a gear, braking well in advance,

15

careful to get the weighting of the heavy lorry stabilized before making the sharp turn on the wet road.

In the distance he saw flashing headlights. A white van, tailgating a car. Tosser, he thought.

7

'Tosser,' Carly said, watching the white van that filled her rear-view mirror. She kept carefully to the 30mph speed limit as she drove along the wide street, heading towards Station Road. She passed dozens of small shops, then a post office, a curry house, a halal butcher, a large red-brick church to the right, a used-car showroom.

Immediately ahead of her was a van parked outside a kitchen appliance shop, with two men unloading a crate from the rear. It was blocking her view of a side road just beyond. She clocked a lorry that was coming towards her, a few hundred yards away, but she had plenty of space. Just as she started pulling out, her phone rang.

She glanced down at the display and saw to her irritation that it was Preston Dave calling. For an instant she was tempted to answer and tell him she was surprised he hadn't reversed the charge. But she was in no mood to speak to him. Then, as she looked back up at the road, a cyclist going hell for leather suddenly appeared out of nowhere, coming straight at her, over a pedestrian crossing on her side of the road, just as the lights turned red.

For an instant, in panic, she thought it must be her who was on the wrong side of the road. She swung the steering wheel hard to the left, stamping on the brake pedal, thumping over the kerb, missing him by inches, and skidded, wheels locked, across the wet surface.

Empty chairs and tables outside a café raced towards her as if she was on a scary funfair ride. She stared, frozen in horror, gripping the wheel, just a helpless observer as the wall of the café loomed nearer. For an instant, as she splintered a table, she thought she was going to die.

'Oh shitttttttttttt!' she screamed as the nose of her car smashed into the wall beneath the café window and a massive explosion numbed her ears. She felt a terrible jolt on her shoulder, saw a blur of white and smelled something that reminded her of gunpowder.

Then she saw glass crashing down in front of the buckled bonnet of the car.

There was a muffled *barrrrrrrrrrrppppppppp*, accompanied by a slightly less muffled banshee siren.

'Jesus!' she said, panting in shock. 'Oh, God! Oh, Jesus!'

Her ears popped and the sounds became much louder.

Cars could catch fire, she'd seen that in films. She had to get out. In wild panic, she hit the seat-belt buckle and tried to open her door. But it would not move. She tried again, harder. A baggy white cushion lay on her lap. The airbag, she realized. She wrenched the door handle, her panic increasing, and shoved the door as hard as she could. It opened and she tumbled out, her feet catching in the seat belt, tripping her, sending her sprawling painfully on to the wet pavement.

As she lay there for an instant she heard the banshee wail continue above her head. A burglar alarm. Then she could hear another wailing sound. This time it was human. A scream.

Had she hit someone? Injured someone?

Her knee and right hand were stinging like hell, but she barely noticed hauling herself to her feet, looking first at the wreckage of the café and then across the road.

She froze.

A lorry had stopped on the opposite side. A huge artic, slewed at a strange angle. The driver was clambering down from the cab. People were running into the road right behind it. Running past a mountain bike that had been twisted into an ugly shape, like an abstract sculpture, past a baseball cap and tiny bits of debris, towards what she thought at first was a roll of carpet lying further back, leaking dark fluid from one end on to the rain-lashed black tarmac.

All the traffic had stopped, and the people who had been running stopped too, suddenly, as if they had become statues. She felt she was staring at a tableau. Then she walked, stumbling, out into the road, in front of a stationary car, the high-pitched howl of the siren almost drowned out by the screams of a young woman holding an umbrella, who was standing on the far pavement, staring at that roll of carpet.

Fighting her brain, which wanted to tell her it was something different, Carly saw the laced-up trainer that was attached to one end.

And realized it wasn't a roll of carpet. It was a severed human leg.

She vomited, the world spinning around her.

8

At 9 a.m. Phil Davidson and Vicky Donoghue, dressed in their green paramedic uniforms, sat chatting in the cab of the Mercedes Sprinter Ambulance. They were parked on a police bay opposite the taxi rank at Brighton's Clock Tower, where they had been positioned by the dispatcher.

Government targets required that ambulances reached Category-A emergencies within eight minutes, and from this location, with a bit of aggressive driving, they could normally reach anywhere in the city of Brighton and Hove well within that time.

Ninety minutes into their twelve-hour shift, the rush-hour world passed by in front of them, blurred by the film of rain on the windscreen. Every few minutes Vicky flicked the wipers to clear their view. They watched taxis, buses, goods vehicles passing by, streams of people trudging to work, some huddled beneath umbrellas, others looking sodden and gloomy. This part of the city didn't look great even on a sunny day; in the wet it was plain depressing.

The ambulance service was the most constantly busy of all the emergency services and they'd already attended their first call-out, a Category-B emergency shout to attend an elderly lady who had fallen in the street outside her home in Rottingdean.

The first life lesson Phil Davidson had learned, from his eight years as a paramedic, was very simple: *Don't grow old. If you have to, don't grow old alone.*

Around 90 per cent of the work of the paramedics was attending the elderly. People who had fallen, people who were having palpitations, or strokes or suspected heart attacks, people who were too frail to get a taxi to hospital. And there were plenty of wily old birds who knew how to exploit the system. Half the time, much to their irritation, the paramedics were nothing more than a free big taxi service for lazy, smelly and often grossly overweight people.

They'd delivered this particular lady, who was a sweetie, into the care of Accident and Emergency at the Royal Sussex County Hospital and were now on standby, waiting for the next call. That was the thing Phil Davidson most liked about this job, you never knew what was going to happen. The siren would sound inside the ambulance and trip that squirt of adrenalin inside him. Was it going to be a routine job or the one he would remember for years? The job's category of emergency, ranging from A to C would appear on the screen on the console, together with the location and known facts, which would then be updated as further information came in.

He glanced down at the screen now, as if willing the next job to appear. A rainy rush hour like today often produced accidents, particularly traffic *collisions*, as they were now known. They were not called *accidents* any more, because it was always someone's fault; they were known as Road Traffic Collisions.

Phil liked attending trauma cases best. The ambulance's lockers were packed with the latest trauma technology. Critical haemorrhage kits, Israeli military dressings, a combat application tourniquet, an ACS – Asherman Chest Seal – standard equipment for the British and US military. The benefits of war, he often thought cynically. Little did some victims of terrible accidents, who recovered thanks to the paramedics' work at the scene, realize they owed their lives to the medical advances that came out of battlegrounds.

Vicky nipped out to have a quick pee in the Starbucks just beside them. She'd learned always to grab the opportunity to use a loo, because in this job you never knew when you were going to get busy and there might not be another chance for hours.

As she climbed back behind the wheel, her crewmate for the day was talking on his phone to his wife. This was only her second time out with Phil and she had enjoyed working with him a lot the last time. A lean wiry man in his late thirties, with his hair shaven to stubble, long sideburns and several days' growth of beard, he had the air of a movie bad guy about him, although he was anything but. He was a big-hearted softy who doted on his family. He had a reassuring manner, a kind word for everyone he treated and a true passion for this work, which she shared with him.

Finishing his call, he looked down at the screen again.

'Unusually quiet, so far.'

'Not for long, I don't expect.'

They sat in silence for a moment as the rain pattered down. During her time with the ambulance service, she'd discovered that every paramedic had his or her own particular favourite field of work and seemed by some quirk of fate to attract that particular call-out. One of her colleagues always got mentally ill patients. She herself had delivered fifteen babies over the past three years, while Phil, in all his career, had yet to deliver one.

However, in her two years since qualifying, Vicky had only attended one serious road accident, and that had been on her first ever shift, when a couple of teenage boys had accepted a lift home in Brighton from a drunk driver. He'd hit a parked car, at 80mph in the centre of town. One boy had been killed outright and another had died at the roadside. Despite the horror of that incident, she found her work incredibly rewarding.

'You know, Phil,' she said. 'It's strange, but I haven't been to a road fatality in almost two years.'

He unscrewed the cap from a bottle of water. 'Stay with this job long enough and you will. In time you get everything.'

'You've never had to deliver a baby.'

He smiled sardonically at her. 'One day—'

He was interrupted by the high-pitched *whup-whup-whup* siren inside the ambulance. It was a sound that could dement you sometimes, especially during the quiet of the night. The sound of a call-out.

Instantly he looked down at the screen mounted between their seats and read the Incident Review information:

Emergency Inc: 00521. CatB Emergency

Portland Road, Hove.

Gender unknown.

Three vehicle RTC. Bicycle involved.

He tapped the button to acknowledge the call. It automatically loaded the address into the satnav system.

The target response time for a CatB was eighteen minutes – ten minutes longer than for a CatA, but it still called for emergency action. Vicky started the engine, switched on the blue lights and siren, and pushed her way carefully out over a red traffic light. She turned right and accelerated up the hill, past St Nicholas's Church, pulling out into the right-hand lane and forcing oncoming traffic to brake. She switched between the four different tones of the ambulance's sirens to get maximum attention from the vehicles and pedestrians ahead.

Moments later, peering hard at the incident screen, Phil updated her. 'Situation confused,' he read out. 'Several calls. Upgraded to CatA. A car crashed into a shop. Oh shit, cyclist in collision with a lorry. Control not sure of situation, backup requested.'

He leaned through the bulkhead for his fluorescent jacket and Vicky felt a tightening in her gullet.

Screaming down towards the clogged-up Seven Dials round-about, concentrating hard on her driving, she said nothing. A taxi driver sensibly pulled over on to the pavement to let them through. Fuck me, Phil thought, a cabbie who was actually awake! He unclipped his seat belt, hoping Vicky didn't choose this moment to crash, and began wriggling into his jacket. At the same time he continued watching the screen keenly.

'Age unknown, gender unknown,' he updated her. 'Breathing status unknown. Unknown number of patients involved. Oh shit – high mechanism. SIMCAS en route.'

That meant the Accident and Emergency doctor had been summoned from the hospital to the scene.

Which meant the status of the incident was worsening by the minute.

That was confirmed by the next update on the screen. 'Limb amputation,' Phil read out. 'Ouch! Bad day for someone.' Then he turned to her and said, 'Sounds like you might be getting your wish.'

9

Hospitals gave Roy Grace the heebie-jeebies and particularly this one. The Royal Sussex County Hospital was where both his parents, at a few years' interval, had spent most of the last days of their life. His father had died first, at just fifty-five, from bowel cancer. Two years later, when she was only fifty-six, his mother had succumbed to secondaries following breast cancer.

The front façade, a grand Victorian neoclassical edifice with an ugly black metal and glass portico, used to give him the impression of an asylum whose portals you entered once, never to leave.

Stretching out beside it, and up the hill behind the front entrance, was a massive, messy complex of buildings, new and old, low- and high-rise, joined by a seemingly never-ending labyrinth of corridors.

His stomach knotted, he drove his unmarked silver police Ford Focus estate up the hill to the east of the complex and turned into the small parking and turning area for ambulances. Strictly speaking, this area was for emergency vehicles and taxis only, but at this moment he did not care. He pulled the car up to one side, where he wasn't causing an obstruction, and climbed out into the rain.

He used to pray as a child, but since his late teens Roy had never had any religious convictions. But he found himself praying now, silently, that his darling Cleo and their unborn child were OK.

He ran past a couple of ambulances backed up to the entrance to Accident and Emergency, nodding greetings to a paramedic he knew who was standing beside a NO SMOKING IN HOSPITAL GROUNDS sign, grabbing a cigarette under the awning. Then, bypassing the public entrance, he went in via the paramedics' emergency doors.

Early in the day it was always quiet in here, in his experience. He saw a youth sitting in a chair, in handcuffs, a thick bandage on his forehead. A woman police officer stood by him, chatting to a

24

nurse. A long-haired man, his face the colour of alabaster, lay on a trolley, staring vacantly at the ceiling. A teenage girl sat on a chair, crying. There was a strong hospital smell of disinfectant and floor polish. Two more paramedics he knew wheeled an empty trolley out past him.

He hurried along to the admittance desk, behind which were several harassed-looking people, most of them on phones, urgently reading forms or tapping at computer terminals. A male orderly with a thin fuzz of blond hair and wearing blue scrubs, was writing on a large whiteboard on the wall. Grace leaned over the desk, desperately trying to catch someone's attention.

After an agonizingly long minute the orderly turned to him.

Grace flashed his warrant card, not caring that he was on a personal matter. 'I think you've just admitted Cleo Morey?'

'Cleo Morey?' The man looked down at a list, then at the whiteboard on the wall. 'Yes, she's here.'

'How do I find her?'

'She's been taken to the labour ward. Do you know your way around here?'

'A little.'

'Thomas Kent Tower.' He pointed. 'Down there and follow the signs – they'll take you to the lift.'

Grace thanked him and ran along the corridor, following it left, then right, passing a sign that read X-RAY & ULTRASOUND. ALL OTHER BUILDINGS. He stopped for a moment and pulled his phone out of his pocket, his heart a lead weight in his chest, his shoes feeling like they had glue on them. It was 9.15 a.m. He dialled his boss, ACC Rigg, to warn him he would be late for his 10 a.m. meeting. Rigg's MSA – his Management Support Assistant – answered and told him not to worry, the ACC had a clear morning.

He passed a WRVS Coffee Shop, then ran on along a corridor lined with a mural of swimming fish, following more signs, then reached two lifts with a parked mobility scooter near them. He stabbed the button for a lift, debating whether to take the stairs, but the doors opened and he stepped in.

It climbed agonizingly slowly, so slowly he wasn't even sure if it was moving. Finally he stepped out, his heart in his mouth, and opened a door directly in front of him labelled LABOUR WARD. He went through into a bright reception area filled with rows of pink and lilac chairs. There was a fine view out from its windows across the rooftops of Kemp Town and down to the sea. A photocopier sat in one corner and in another there were several food and drink vending machines. Racks full of leaflets had been fixed to the walls. On a modern television screen was the gaily coloured word KIDDICARE.

A pleasant-looking woman in a blue smock sat behind the large reception counter. 'Ah yes, Detective Superintendent Grace. They phoned from downstairs to say you were on your way.' She pointed along a corridor with yellow walls. 'She's in Room 7. Fourth door on the left.'

Grace was too churned up to say anything beyond a mumbled thank you.

10

The traffic ahead of them was braking and further along Portland Road Vicky Donoghue could see that it had come to a complete halt in both directions. Phil Davidson pulled on his surgical gloves, mentally preparing himself for the task ahead.

A lorry was facing them, the driver's door open, and several people were gathered towards its rear offside. On the other side of the road a black Audi convertible had ploughed into the side of a café. The driver's door of that was open, too, and a woman was standing near it, looking dazed. There was no sign of any other emergency vehicles here yet.

She raced the ambulance past the line of vehicles, on the wrong side of the road, keeping her eyes peeled for anyone who hadn't heard them coming. Then she braked, slowing to a crawl, killing the siren, and halted in front of the lorry. Her stomach tightened and her mouth felt suddenly dry.

The digital display read six minutes, twenty seconds – the length of time taken to get here from when the call came in. Comfortably inside the CatA eight-minute target. That was some small relief. Phil Davidson switched the emergency lights to stationary mode. Before jumping down from the vehicle, both of them briefly absorbed the scene.

The woman standing near the Audi, who had wavy blonde hair and was wearing a smart raincoat, was holding a mobile phone some distance away from her head, as if it was a ball she was about to throw to a batsman. Smashed and upturned tables and chairs lay around the car, but there was no immediate sign of any casualties there, and no one, apart from a youth in a cagoule, who was photographing the scene with his mobile phone, seemed to be taking any notice. The concentration seemed to be around the rear wheels of the lorry.

The two paramedics climbed out, looking around carefully,

continuing to take in as much as they could and making sure there was no danger from any passing traffic. But everything had very definitely stopped.

A short, stubby man in his mid-forties, in jeans and overalls, holding a mobile phone, hurried towards them. From his pallid face, wide staring eyes and quavering voice, Vicky could see he was in shock.

'Under my lorry,' he said. 'He's under my lorry.' He turned and pointed.

Vicky noticed, a short distance further along, a bicycle lamp, a saddle and a reflector lying in the road. Then, near them, was what looked at first like a length of denim tubing with a trainer attached. Her gullet constricted and she felt a rush of bile, which she swallowed back down. She and Phil hurried through the rain towards the rear of the sixteen-wheel articulated lorry, gently edging back the crowd to give them space.

A young woman was kneeling under the truck, but moved out the way for them. 'He has a pulse,' she said.

Nodding thanks, both paramedics knelt down and peered under the vehicle.

The light was poor. There was a stench of vomit from somewhere nearby, mixed with the smells of engine oil and hot metal, but there was something else too, that sour, coppery tang of blood that always reminded Phil Davidson of going into butcher's shops with his mother, when he was a kid.

Vicky saw a young man with short, dark hair streaked with blood and a lacerated face, his body contorted. His eyes were closed. He was wearing a ripped anorak and jeans, and one leg was wrapped around the wheel arch. The other was just a stump of white bone above the knee surrounded by jagged denim.

The anorak and layers of T-shirt around his midriff were ripped open and a coil of his intestines lay in a pool of fluid on the road.

Followed by her colleague, Vicky, who was smaller, crawled forward, beneath the lorry, smelling oil and rubber, and seized the young man's wrist, feeling for a pulse. There was a very faint one. The two paramedics were getting covered in oil, road grime and blood, which was soaking into their trousers and elbows and coating their gloves, turning them from blue surgical coverings into bloody, grimy gauntlets.

'*Fubar Bundy*,' Phil Davidson whispered grimly.

She nodded, swallowing acrid bile. It was a term she had heard before, at the fatal accident she had attended previously, only a short distance from this location. The gallows humour of the paramedics – one of their mental survival mechanisms for coping with horrific sights. It stood for: *Fucked Up Beyond All Recovery But Unfortunately Not Dead Yet.*

With internal organs exposed and on the tarmac, there was very little chance of the victim's survival. Even if they got him to hospital still technically alive, infections would finish him off. She turned to her more experienced colleague for his guidance.

'Pulse?' he asked.

'Faint radial,' she replied. A radial pulse meant that he had enough blood pressure to maintain some of his organs.

'*Stay and play*,' he mouthed back, knowing they had no option, as they couldn't move him because his leg was trapped in the wheel. 'I'll get the kit.'

Stay and play was one step above *Scoop and run*. It meant that although the victim's chances were slim, they would do all they could – try their best until he was dead and they could stop. Going through the motions, if nothing else.

She was aware of the scream of an approaching siren getting louder. Then she heard Phil radioing for the fire brigade to bring lifting gear. She squeezed the young man's hand. 'Hang on in,' she said. 'Can you hear me? What's your name?'

There was no response. The pulse was weakening. The siren was getting louder still. She looked at the stump of his severed leg. Almost no blood. That was the only positive at this moment. Human bodies were good at dealing with trauma. Capillaries shut down. It was like the accident she had attended two years ago, when one of the young lads was dying but was hardly bleeding at all. The body goes into shock. If they could get a tourniquet applied, and if she was careful with his intestines, then maybe there was a chance.

She kept her fingers pressed hard on his radial artery. It was weakening by the second.

'Hang in there,' she said. 'Just hang in there.' She looked at his face. He was a good-looking kid. But he was turning increasingly paler by the second. 'Please stay with me. You're going to be OK.'

The pulse was continuing to weaken.

She moved her fingers, desperately searching for a beat. 'You can make it,' she whispered. 'You can! Go for it! Go on, go for it!'

It was personal now.

For Phil he might be a *Fubar Bundy*, but for her he was a challenge. She wanted to visit him in hospital in two weeks' time and see him sitting up, surrounded by cards and flowers. 'Come on!' she urged, glancing up at the dark underbelly of the lorry, at the mud-encrusted wheel arch, at the grimy girders of the chassis. 'Hang on in there!'

Phil was crawling back under the lorry with his red bag and his critical haemorrhage kit. Between them, they covered everything that modern medical technology could throw at a trauma victim. But even as Phil tugged the red bag open, displaying pockets filled with vials of life-saving drugs, apparatus and monitoring equipment, Vicky realized, in this particular situation, it was mere cosmetics. Window-dressing.

The young man's pulse was barely detectable now.

She heard the whine of the EZ-10 bone drill, the fastest way to get the emergency cannula in. Every second was critical. She assisted Phil, locating the bone inside the flesh of the good leg, just below the knee, the professional in her kicking in, pushing all emotion aside. They had to keep trying. They *would* keep trying.

'Stay with us!' she urged.

It was clear that the poor young man had been dragged right around the wheel arch after the wheel had gone over his midriff, crushing him and splitting him open. Phil Davidson was calculating the likely damage to his internal organs and bones as he worked. It looked as if one of the wheels had shattered his pelvis, which in itself was usually sufficient to cause massive internal bleeding and almost certain death – on top of everything else that was probably going on in there.

This lad's best hope, he thought grimly as he worked on, would be to die quickly.

11

Roy Grace was shocked to see how pale Cleo looked. She lay in a high bed, in a room with pale blue walls that was cluttered with electrical sockets and apparatus. A tall man in his early thirties, with short, thinning brown hair, dressed in blue medical pyjamas and plimsolls, was standing beside her, writing a measurement on a graph on his pad as Roy entered.

She was wearing a blue hospital gown, and her blonde hair, cascading round her face, had lost some of its usual lustre. She gave Roy a wan, hesitant smile, as if she was happy he had come, but at the same time embarrassed that he was seeing her like this. A forest of electrode pads were attached to her chest and a monitor, like a thimble, covered her thumb.

'I'm sorry,' she said meekly, as he took her free hand and squeezed it. She gave him a weak squeeze back.

He felt a terrible panic rising inside him. Had she lost the baby? The man turned towards him. Grace could see from his badge that he was a registrar.

'You are this lady's husband?'

'Fiancé.' He was so choked he could barely get the word out. 'Roy Grace.'

'Ah, yes, of course.' The registrar glanced down at her engagement ring. 'Well, Mr Grace, Cleo is all right, but she's lost a lot of blood.'

'What's happened?' he asked.

Cleo's voice was weak as she explained, 'I'd just got to work – I was about to start preparing a body for post-mortem and I suddenly started bleeding, really heavily, as if something had exploded inside me. I thought I was losing the baby. Then I felt terrible pain, like cramps in my stomach – and the next thing I remember I was lying on the floor with Darren standing over me. He put me in his car and drove me here.'

31

Darren was her assistant in the mortuary.

Grace stared at Cleo, relief mingled with uncertainty. 'And the baby?' His eyes shot to the registrar.

'Cleo's just had an ultrasound scan,' he replied. 'She has a condition that's called placenta praevia. Her placenta is abnormally low down.'

'What – what does that mean – in terms of our baby?' Grace asked, filled with dread.

'There are complications, but your baby is fine at the moment,' the registrar said, pleasantly enough but with foreboding in his voice. Then he turned towards the door and nodded a greeting.

Grace saw a solidly built, bespectacled man enter. He had dark hair shorn to stubble, a balding pate, and was dressed in an open-necked blue shirt, grey suit trousers and black brogues. He had the air of a benign bank manager.

'Mr Holbein, this is Cleo's fiancé.'

'How do you do?' He shook Grace's hand. 'I'm Des Holbein, the consultant gynaecologist.'

'Thank you for coming in.'

'Not at all, that's what I'm here for. But I'm very glad you've arrived. We're going to have to make some decisions.'

Roy felt a sudden stab of anxiety. But the consultant's business-like attitude at least gave him some confidence. He waited for him to continue.

The consultant sat down on the bed. Then he looked up at Roy.

'Cleo came in for a routine ultrasound scan five weeks ago, at twenty-one weeks. At that time the placenta was very low but the baby was normal-sized.'

He turned to Cleo. 'Today's scan shows your baby has hardly grown at all. This is unusual and cause for concern, to be honest with you. It signifies that the placenta is not working well. It's doing its job just about enough to keep the baby alive, but not enough to enable it to grow. And I'm afraid there's a further complication that I don't like the look of. It's a very rare condition known as placenta percreta – the placenta is growing much further into the wall of the uterus than it should.'

From feeling a fraction upbeat seconds ago, Roy's heart plunged again. 'What does that mean?'

Des Holbein smiled at him – like a bank manager approving a loan, but with tough strings attached. 'Well, one option would be to deliver the baby now.'

'Now?' Grace said, astounded.

'Yes. But I would really not be happy to do this. Although 50 per cent of normal babies would live if delivered at this time – and probably a little more than that – the survival rate for one that has not grown since twenty-one weeks is much, much lower. In another month that would increase substantially – if we can get your baby's growth normalized, we'd be looking at above 90 per cent. If we could get to thirty-four weeks, that would rise to 98 per cent.'

He looked at each of them in turn, his face placid, giving nothing away.

Roy stared at the consultant, feeling sudden, irrational anger towards him. This was their child he was talking about. He was gaily reeling off percentages as if it was something you could put a spread bet on. Roy felt totally out of his depth. He had no idea about any of this. It wasn't in any of the books he had read; nor was it in *Emma's Diary* or any of the other booklets Cleo had been given by the NHS. All of those dealt with perfect pregnancies and perfect births.

'What's your advice?' Grace asked. 'What would you do if it was your child?'

'I would advise waiting and monitoring the placenta very closely. If Cleo suffers further blood loss, we will try to keep the baby inside by transfusing against that loss. If we deliver now and your baby does survive, the poor little thing is going to have to spend several months in an incubator, which is not ideal for the baby or the mother. Cleo seems otherwise healthy and strong. The ultimate decision is yours, but my advice is that we keep you here, Cleo, for a few days, and try to support your circulation and hope that the bleeding settles.'

'If it does, will I be able to go back to work?'

'Yes, but not immediately and no heavy lifting. And – this is very important – you will need to take a rest at some point during the day. We'll have to keep a careful eye on you for the rest of the pregnancy.'

'Could this happen again?' Grace asked.

'To be truthful, in 50 per cent of cases, no. But that means in 50 per cent of cases, yes. I run a *three strikes and you're out* rule here. If there's a second bleed, I will insist on further reductions to your fiancée's workload, and depending on how the percreta condition develops, I may require Cleo to be hospitalized for the rest of her term. It's not only the baby that is at risk in this situation.' He turned to Cleo. 'You are too.'

'To what extent?' Grace asked.

'Placenta percreta can be life-threatening to the mother,' the consultant said. He turned back to Cleo again. 'If there is a third bleed, there is no doubt about it. You'll have to spend the rest of your pregnancy in hospital.'

'What about damage to our baby?' Grace questioned.

The consultant shook his head. 'Not at this stage. What's happened is that a part of the placenta is not working so well. The placenta is an organ, just like a kidney or a lung. The baby can lose some placenta without a problem. But if it loses too much it won't grow well. And then, in extreme cases, yes, he or she can die.'

Grace squeezed Cleo's hand again and kissed her on the forehead, terrible thoughts churning inside him. He felt sick with fear. Bloody statistics. Percentages. Fifty per cent was crap odds. Cleo was so strong, so positive. They'd get through this. DC Nick Nicholl had been through something similar last year with his wife and the baby had ended up strong and healthy.

'It's going to be fine, darling,' he said, but his mouth felt dry.

Cleo nodded and managed a thin, wintry smile.

Grace glanced at his watch, then turned to the doctors. 'Could we have a few minutes together? I have to get to a meeting.'

'Of course.'

The doctors left the room.

Roy nuzzled his face against Cleo's and laid his hand gently on her midriff. Fear spiralled through him and he had a terrible sense of inadequacy. He could do something about criminals, but it seemed at this moment that he couldn't do a damned thing for the woman he loved or their unborn baby. Things were totally out of his hands.

'I love you,' he said. 'I love you so much.'

He felt her hand stroking his cheek. 'I love you, too,' she replied. 'You're soaking wet. Is it still raining?'

'Yes.'

'Did you see the car? The Alfa?'

'I had a brief look. I'm not sure if it's practical.' He stopped himself short of saying *with a baby*.

He held her hand and kissed the engagement ring on her finger. It gave him a strange feeling every time he saw it, a feeling of utter joy, yet always tinged with foreboding. There was still one big obstacle in the way of their actually getting married: the minefield of formalities that had to be gone through before his wife, Sandy, missing for ten years now, could be declared legally dead.

He was being scrupulously careful to tick every box in the process. On the instructions of the registrar, he had recently had notices placed in the local Sussex newspapers and the national press, requesting Sandy, or anyone who might have seen her in the past ten years, to contact him. So far, no one had.

A fellow officer and friend, and his wife, were both sure they had seen Sandy in Munich, while on holiday there the previous summer, but despite alerting his German police contacts and travelling over there himself, nothing more had come of it, and he was increasingly certain that his friend and his wife were mistaken. Nevertheless, he had declared this to the registrar, who had requested that he also place notices in the appropriate German newspapers, which he had now done.

He'd had to swear an affidavit listing all the people he had made enquiries with, including the last person who had seen Sandy alive. That had been a colleague at the medical centre where she worked part-time, who had seen her leaving the office at 1 p.m. on the day she vanished. He'd had to include information about all police enquiries and which of her work colleagues and friends he had contacted. He'd also had to swear that he had searched the house after she had gone and had found nothing missing, other than her handbag and her car.

Her little Golf had been found twenty-four hours later in a bay at the short-term car park at Gatwick Airport. There were two transactions on her credit card on the morning of her disappearance, one for £7.50 at Boots and the other for £16.42 for petrol from the local branch of Tesco. She had taken no clothes and no other belongings of any kind.

He was finding the process of filling in these forms therapeutic in a way. Finally he was starting to feel some kind of closure. And with luck the process would be complete in time for them to get married before their child was born.

He sighed, his heart heavy, and squeezed her hand again.

Please be OK, my darling Cleo. I couldn't bear it if anything happened to you, I really couldn't.

12

In his eight years' experience with the Road Policing Unit, PC Dan Pattenden had learned that if you were the first car to arrive at a crash scene, you would find chaos. Even more so if it was raining. And to make matters worse, as he hurtled along Portland Road on blues and twos, because of budget cuts, he was single-crewed.

The information he was receiving on his screen and over the radio was chaotic, too. The first indication that the accident was serious was the number of people who had phoned to report it – eight calls logged by the Control Room so far.

A lorry versus a bicycle; a car also involved, he had been informed.

A lorry versus a bicycle was never going to be good news.

He began slowing down as he approached, and, sure enough, what he observed through the rain-spattered windscreen was a scene of total confusion. An articulated refrigerated lorry facing away from him and an ambulance just beyond it. He saw, lying in the road, a buckled bicycle. Broken reflector glass. A baseball cap. A trainer. People all over the place, most frozen with shock but others snapping away with their mobile phone cameras. A small crowd was gathered around the rear offside of the lorry. On the other side of the road a black Audi convertible, with a buckled bonnet, was up against a café wall.

He halted the brightly marked BMW estate car at an angle across the road, the first step to sealing off the scene, and radioed for backup, hoping to hell that it would arrive quickly – he needed about twenty different pairs of hands all at once. Then, tugging on his cap and his fluorescent jacket he grabbed an Accident Report pad and jumped out of the car. Then he tried to make a quick assessment of the scene, remembering all the elements that had been drummed into him from his initial training, his refresher courses and his own considerable experience.

A rain-drenched young man in a tracksuit ran over to him. 'Officer, there was a van, a white van, that went through a red light, hit him and drove off.'

'Did you get the van's licence number?'

He shook his head. 'No – sorry – it all happened so fast.'

'What can you tell me about the van?'

'It was a Ford, I think. One of those Transit things. I don't think it had any writing on it.'

Pattenden made a note, then looked back at the young man. Witnesses often disappeared quickly, especially in rain like this. 'I'll need your name and phone number, please,' he said, writing the information in his pad. 'Could you jump in the car and wait?'

The young man nodded.

At least he might stay around if he was warm and dry, Pattenden reasoned. He passed the information to the Control Room, then sprinted over to the lorry, clocking a severed leg lying in the road but ignoring it for the moment, and knelt beside the paramedics. He looked briefly at the mangled, unconscious cyclist and the coiled intestines on the road, and the blood, but was too wrapped up in all he had to deal with to be affected by it at this moment.

'What can you tell me?' he said, although he barely needed to ask the question.

The male paramedic, whom he recognized, shook his head. 'Not looking good. We're losing him.'

That was the only information the police constable required at this moment. All road fatalities were viewed as potential homicides, rather than accidents, until proved otherwise. As the only officer present, his first duty was to secure the area around the collision as a crime scene. His next was to try to ensure that no vehicles were moved and to stop witnesses from leaving. To his relief, he could now hear the distant wail of sirens as, hopefully, more vehicles approached.

He ran back to his car, calling out at everyone he passed, 'Please, if you witnessed the incident come over to my car and give me your names and phone numbers.'

He opened the tailgate and dragged out a folding POLICE ROAD CLOSED sign, which he erected a short distance behind his car. At the same time he shouted into his radio that there was a potential hit and run and he needed the fire brigade, the Collision Investigation Unit, the inspector and backup PCSOs and uniformed officers.

Then he grabbed a roll of blue and white POLICE LINE DO NOT CROSS tape, tied one end around a lamp post and ran across the road, securing the other end around a parking sign on the pavement. As he was finishing he saw two more officers from his unit running towards him. He instructed them to tape off the road on the far side of the lorry and grab names and phone numbers from anyone else who might be witnesses.

Then, inside the taped cordon, he pulled off his reflective jacket and threw it over the severed leg, wanting both to spare people the horror of it and to stop one particular ghoul in a raincoat taking any more photographs of it.

'Get the other side of the tape!' he shouted at him. 'If you're a witness, go to my car. If not, move along please!'

More emergency vehicles were arriving. He saw a second ambulance and a paramedic car which would be bringing a specialist trauma doctor. But his main focus now was on identifying the drivers of the lorry and the Audi from the mass of rubberneckers and potential witnesses.

He saw a smartly dressed woman with rain-bedraggled hair standing near the open driver's door of the Audi. She was staring, transfixed, at the lorry.

Hurrying over to her, he asked, panting, 'Are you the driver of this car?'

She nodded, eyes vacant, still staring over his shoulder.

'Are you injured? Do you need medical assistance?'

'He just came out of nowhere, came out of that side street, straight at me. I had to swerve, otherwise I'd have hit him.'

'Who?' Surreptitiously he leaned forward, close enough to smell her breath. There was a faint reek of stale alcohol.

'The cyclist,' she said numbly.

'Were there any other vehicles involved?'

'A white van was right behind me, tailgating me.'

He had a quick look at the Audi. Although the bonnet was

crumpled and the airbags had deployed, the interior of the car looked intact.

'OK, madam, would you mind getting back into your car for a few minutes?'

He gently took her shoulders and turned her round, away from the lorry. He knew that if drivers of vehicles involved in an accident stared at a serious casualty for too long, they would become traumatized. This woman was already partway there. He steered her over to the Audi and waited as she climbed in, then with some difficulty pushed the door, which seemed to have a bent hinge, closed.

As he did so, he saw a PCSO running over towards him. 'Any more of you around?' Pattenden asked him.

'Yes, sir.' The man pointed at two more Police Community Support Officers approaching, a short distance away along the pavement.

'OK, good. I want you to stay here and make sure this lady does not leave her vehicle.'

Then he ran towards the two PCSOs, delegating each of them to scene-guard at either end of the crash site and to log anyone crossing the police line.

At this point, to his relief, he saw the reassuring sight of his inspector, James Biggs, accompanied by his duty sergeant, Paul Wood, coming, grim-faced, through the rain towards him, both men holding a reel of police tape and a police traffic cone under each arm.

At least now the buck no longer stopped with him.

13

Carly sat numbly in her car, grateful for the rain which coated the windscreen and the side windows like frosted glass, at least making her invisible and giving her some privacy. She was aware of the dark figure of the PCSO standing like a sentry outside. Her chest was pounding. The radio was on, tuned as it always was to the local news and chat station, BBC Radio Sussex. She could hear the lively voice of Neil Pringle, but wasn't taking in anything he said.

The image of what was going on underneath the lorry behind her was going round and round inside her head. Suddenly Pringle's voice was interrupted by a traffic announcement that Portland Road in Hove was closed due to a serious accident.

Her accident.

The car clock said 9.21.

Shit. She dialled her office and spoke to her cheery secretary, Suzanne. Halfway through telling her that she did not know when she would be in and asking her to phone the chiropodist, she broke down in tears.

She hung up, debating whether to phone her mother next or her best friend, Sarah Ellis. Sarah, who worked at a law firm in Crawley, had been her rock after Kes's death five years ago in an avalanche while skiing in Canada. She dialled her number, then listened to the phone ringing, hoping desperately she was free.

To her relief, Sarah answered on the fifth ring. But before Carly could get any words out, she started sobbing again.

Then she heard a tap on her window. A moment later, her car door opened and the police officer she had seen earlier, the one who had told her to wait in her car, peered in. He was a sturdy-looking man in his mid-thirties, with a serious face beneath his white cap, and was holding a small device that resembled some kind of meter.

'Would you mind stepping out of the car please, madam?'

'I'll call you back, Sarah,' she spluttered, then climbed out into the rain, her eyes blurry with tears.

The officer asked her again if she was the driver of the car, and then for her name and address. Then, holding a small instrument in a black and yellow weatherproof case, he addressed her in a stiffer, more formal tone. 'Because you have been involved in a road traffic collision, I require you to provide a specimen of breath. I must tell you that failure or refusal to do so is an offence for which you can be arrested. Do you understand?'

She nodded and sniffed.

'Have you drunk any alcohol in the past twenty minutes?'

How many people had an alcoholic drink before 9 a.m., she wondered? But then she felt a sudden panic closing in around her. Christ, how much had she drunk last night? Not that much, surely. It must be out of her system by now. She shook her head.

'Have you smoked in the last five minutes?'

'No,' she said. 'But I bloody need a fag now.' She was shaking and her throat felt tight.

Ignoring her comment, the officer asked her age.

'Forty-one.'

He tapped it into the machine, then made a further couple of entries before holding the machine out to her. A tube wrapped in cellophane protruded.

'If you could pull the sterile wrapper off for me.'

She obliged, exposing the narrow white plastic tube inside it.

'Thank you. I'd like you to take a deep breath, seal your lips around the tube and blow hard and continuously until I tell you to stop.'

Carly took a deep breath, then exhaled. She kept waiting for him to tell her to stop, but he stayed silent. Just as her lungs started to feel spent, she heard a beep, and he nodded his head. 'Thank you.'

He showed her the dial of the machine. On it were the words *sample taken*. Then he stepped back, studying the machine for some moments.

She watched his face anxiously, shaking even more now with nerves. Suddenly, his expression hardened and he said, 'I'm sorry to tell you that you have failed the breath test.' He held the machine up so she could read the dial again. The one word on it: *fail*.

She felt her legs giving way. Aware that a man was watching her from inside the café, she steadied herself against the side of her car. This wasn't possible. She could not have failed. She just couldn't have.

'Madam, this device is indicating that you may be over the prescribed limit and I'm arresting you for providing a positive breath sample. You do not have to say anything, but it may harm your defence if you do not mention when questioned something which you may later rely on in court. Anything you say may be given in evidence.'

She shook her head. 'It's not possible, she said. 'I didn't – I haven't – I was out last night, but—'

A few minutes ago Carly could not have imagined her day getting any worse. Now she was walking through the rain, being steered by the guiding arm of a police officer towards a marked car just beyond a line of police tape. She saw two ambulances, two fire engines and a whole host of other police vehicles. A tarpaulin had been erected around the rear section of the lorry and her imagination went into hyperdrive, guessing what was happening on the far side of it.

There was a terrible, almost preternatural stillness. She was vaguely aware of the steady patter of the rain, that was all. She walked past a fluorescent yellow jacket lying on the road. It had the word POLICE stencilled on the back and she wondered why it had been discarded.

A tall, thin man with two cameras slung around his neck snapped her picture as she ducked under the tape. 'I'm from the *Argus* newspaper. Can I have your name please?' he asked her.

She said nothing, the words 'I'm arresting you' spinning around inside her head. She climbed lamely into the rear of the BMW estate and fumbled for the seat belt. The officer slammed the door on her.

The slam felt as final as a chapter of her life ending.

14

'Dust. OK? See that? Can't you see that?'

The young woman stared blankly at where her boss was pointing. Her English wasn't too good and she had a problem understanding her, because the woman spoke so quickly that all her words seem to get joined together into one continuous, nasally undulating whine.

Did this idiot maid have defective vision or something? Fernanda Revere strutted angrily across the kitchen in her cerise Versace jogging suit and Jimmy Choo trainers, her wrist bangles clinking. A slightly built woman of forty-five, her looks surgically enhanced in a number of places and her wrinkles kept at bay with regular Botox, she exuded constant nervous energy.

Her husband, Lou, hunched on a barstool in the kitchen's island unit, was eating his breakfast bagel and doing his best to ignore her. Today's *Wall Street Journal* was on the Kindle lying beside his plate and President Obama was on the television above him.

Fernanda stopped in front of twin marble sinks that were wide enough to dunk a small elephant in. The vast bay window had a fine view across the rain-lashed manicured lawn, the shrubbery at the end and the dunes beyond, down to the sandy Long Island Sound beachfront and the Atlantic Ocean. On the floor was a megaphone which her husband used, on the rare occasions when he actually asserted himself, to shout threats at hikers who tramped over the dunes, which were a nature reserve.

But she wasn't looking out of the window at this moment.

She ran her index finger along one of the shelves above the sinks and held it up inches in front of her maid's eyes.

'See that, Mannie? You know what that is? It's called *dust.*'

The young woman stared uncomfortably at the dark grey smudge on her boss's elegant manicured finger. She could also see the almost impossibly long varnished nail. And the diamond-encrusted Cartier watch on her wrist. She could smell her Jo Malone perfume.

Fernanda Revere tossed her short, peroxide-blonde hair angrily, then she wiped the dust off the finger on the bridge of her maid's nose. The young woman flinched.

'You'd better understand something, Mannie. I don't allow dust in my house, got that? You want to stay here working for me or you want to go on the next plane back to the Philippines?'

'Hon!' said her husband. 'Give it a break. The poor kid's learning.'

Lou Revere looked back up at Obama on the television. The President was involved in a new diplomatic initiative in Palestine. Lou could do with Obama's diplomacy in this house, he decided.

Fernanda rounded on her husband. 'I don't listen to you when you wear those clothes. You look too dumb to say anything intelligent in them.'

'These are my golf clothes, OK? The same as I always wear.'

The ones that made him look ridiculous, she thought.

He grabbed the remote, tempted to turn the sound up and drown her voice out.

'Jesus, what's wrong with them?'

'What's wrong with them? You look like you're wearing a circus clown's pants and a pimp's shirt. You look so – so . . .' She flapped her hands, searching for the right word. 'Stupid!'

Then she turned to the maid. 'Don't you agree? Doesn't my husband look stupid?'

Mannie said nothing.

'I mean, why do you all have to dress like circus clowns to play golf?'

'It's partly so we can see each other easily on the course,' he said defensively.

'Why don't you just wear flashing lights on your heads, instead?' She looked up at the clock on the wall, then immediately checked her watch: 9.20. Time for her yoga class. 'See you later.' She gave him a quick, loveless wave of her hand, as if she were brushing away a fly.

They used to embrace and kiss, even if they were only going to be apart for half an hour. Lou couldn't remember when that had stopped – and in truth he didn't care any more.

'Seeing Dr Gottlieb today, hon?' he asked.

'He's just so stupid, too. Yes, I'm seeing him. But I think I'm going to change. I need a different shrink. Paulina, in my yoga class, is seeing someone who's a lot better. Gottlieb's useless.'

'Ask him for stronger medication.'

'You want him to turn me into a zombie or something?'

Lou said nothing.

15

Carly sat in the back of the police car, trails of rain sliding down the window beside her, tears sliding down her cheeks. They were heading up a hill on the A27. She stared out at the familiar grassy landscape of the Brighton outskirts, which were blurred by the film of water on the glass. She felt detached, as if out of her body and watching herself.

Scared and confused, she kept seeing that cyclist underneath the lorry. Then the white van in her rear-view mirror that had disappeared, like a ghost.

Had she imagined the van? Had she struck the cyclist? The past hour was as fogged in her mind as the view through the glass. She clenched and unclenched her hands, listening to the intermittent crackle and bursts of words that came through the radio. The car smelled of damp anoraks.

'Do you – do you think he's going to be all right?' she asked.

PC Pattenden replied to something on the radio, either not hearing or ignoring her. 'Hotel Tango Three Zero Four en route to Hollingbury with suspect,' he said, indicating left and taking the slip road.

Suspect.

She shivered, a knot tightening in her stomach. 'Do you think the cyclist is going to be OK?' she asked again, more loudly this time.

Pattenden glanced at her in the mirror. His white cap was on the front passenger seat beside him. 'I don't know,' he said, shuffling the wheel through his hands as he negotiated a mini-roundabout.

'He came out of nowhere, just straight at me. But I didn't hit him, I'm sure.'

They were heading downhill now. His eyes were on her, briefly, again. There was kindness in them behind the hardness.

'I should warn you that everything that's said in this car is recorded automatically.'

47

'Thank you,' she said.

'Let's hope he'll be OK,' Pattenden said. 'What about you? Are you OK?'

She was silent for a moment, then she shook her head.

He braked as they passed a vaguely art deco building that always reminded Carly of the superstructure of a tired old cruise ship. Several police cars were parked out the front. Ironically, she knew a lot about this building. There were photographs of it on the wall of the firm of quantity surveyors, BLB, for whom she had done legal work at the start of her career, when she'd been a trainee solicitor. The firm had managed the conversion of the premises from an American Express credit card manufacturing plant to its current use as the HQ CID for Sussex Police.

At the end of the building PC Pattenden slowed and turned sharp left up a driveway, then halted in front of a green reinforced-steel gate. There was a high spiked green fence to their right and behind it was a tall, drab brick structure. They had stopped beside a blue sign with white lettering announcing BRIGHTON CUSTODY CENTRE. The officer reached out of the window and swiped a plastic card. Moments later the gate began sliding open.

They drove up a steep ramp towards a row of what looked like factory loading bays at the rear of the brick building, then turned left into one of them, and into semi-darkness, out of the rain. Pattenden climbed out and opened the rear door, holding Carly's arm firmly as she stepped from the car. It felt more like he wanted to stop her running away than to support her.

There was a green door ahead, with a small viewing window. He swiped his card on a panel, the door slid open and he ushered her forward into a bare, narrow room about fifteen feet long and eight wide. The door closed behind them. At the far end of the room was another identical door. The walls were painted a stark, institutional cream and the floor was made of some speckled brown substance. There was no furniture in here at all, just a hard, bare bench with a green surface.

'Take a seat,' he said.

She sat down, resting her chin against her knuckles, feeling badly in need of a cigarette. No chance. Then her phone rang.

She fumbled with the clasp of her handbag and pulled the phone out. But before she could answer the officer shook his head.

'You'll have to switch that off, I'm afraid.' He pointed at a sign on the wall which read: NO MOBILE PHONES TO BE USED IN THE CUSTODY AREA.

She stared at him for a moment, trying to remember what the law was about making calls when you were arrested. But she'd only done a tiny bit of criminal law in her studies – it wasn't her area – and she didn't have the will at this moment to argue. If she complied, just did everything she was told, then maybe this nightmare would end quickly and she could go to the office. As for her particularly demanding client, she'd have to see him another day, but she absolutely had to be in the office for 2 p.m. for a conference with the barrister and another client, a woman who was due in court tomorrow morning for a hearing about financial matters in her divorce. Missing that meeting was not an option.

She switched off the phone and was about to put it back in her bag when he held out his hand, looking embarrassed.

'I'm sorry, but I'm going to have to take that phone off you for forensic analysis.'

'My phone?' she asked, angry and bewildered.

'I'm sorry,' he repeated, taking it from her.

Then she stared at the bare wall in front of her. At another laminated plastic notice stuck to it: ALL DETAINED PERSONS WILL BE THOROUGHLY SEARCHED BY THE CUSTODY OFFICER. IF YOU HAVE ANY PROHIBITED ITEMS ON YOUR PERSON OR IN YOUR PROPERTY TELL THE CUSTODY AND ARRESTING OFFICER NOW.

Then she read another: YOU HAVE BEEN ARRESTED. YOU WILL HAVE YOUR FINGERPRINTS, PHOTOGRAPH, DNA TAKEN RIGHT AWAY.

She tried to think exactly how much she had drunk last night. Two glasses of Sauvignon Blanc in the pub – or was it three? Then a Cosmopolitan at the restaurant. Then more wine over dinner.

Shit.

The door beyond her slid open. The officer gestured for her to go through, then followed, staying close to her. His prisoner.

She walked into a large, brightly lit room dominated by a raised semicircular central station made from a shiny, speckled grey composite and divided into sections. Behind each section sat men and women dressed in white shirts with black epaulettes and black ties. Around the edge of the room were green metal doors and internal windows looking on to what were probably interview rooms. It felt like another world in here.

In front of one section she saw a tall, balding, slovenly man in a shell suit and trainers, with a uniformed police officer wearing blue rubber gloves at his side, searching his pockets. In front of another, there was a gloomy youth in baggy clothes, hands cuffed behind his back, with an officer on either side of him.

Her own officer steered her across to the console and up to the counter, which was almost head-high. Behind it sat an impassive-looking man in his forties. He wore a white shirt with three stripes on each epaulette and a black tie. His demeanour was pleasant but he had the air of a man who had never, in his entire life, allowed the wool to be pulled over his eyes.

On a blue video monitor screen, set into the face of the counter, at eye level, Carly read:

DON'T LET PAST OFFENCES COME BACK TO HAUNT YOU.

A POLICE OFFICER WILL SPEAK TO YOU ABOUT ADMITTING OTHER CRIMES YOU HAVE COMMITTED.

She listened numbly as PC Pattenden outlined the circumstances of her arrest. Then the shirt-sleeved man spoke directly to her, his voice earnest, almost as if he was doing her a favour.

'I am Custody Sergeant Cornford. You have heard what has been said. I'm authorizing your detention for the purpose of securing and preserving evidence and to obtain evidence by questioning. Is that clear to you?'

Carly nodded.

He passed across the counter to her a folded yellow A4 sheet that was headed SUSSEX POLICE NOTICE OF RIGHTS AND ENTITLE-MENTS.

'You may find this helpful, Mrs Chase. You have the right to have someone informed of your arrest and to see a solicitor. Would you like us to provide you with a duty solicitor?'

'I'm a solicitor,' she said. 'I'd like you to contact one of my colleagues, Ken Acott at Acott Arlington.'

Carly got some small satisfaction from seeing the frown that crossed his face. Ken Acott was widely regarded as the top criminal solicitor in the city.

'May I have his number?'

Carly gave him the office number, hoping Ken was not in court today.

'I will make that call,' the Custody Sergeant said. 'But I am required to inform you that although you have a right to see a solicitor, the drink-driving process may not be delayed. I am authorizing you to be searched.' He then produced two green plastic trays and spoke into his intercom.

PC Pattenden handed Carly's phone to the sergeant and stepped aside as a young uniformed woman police officer walked across, snapping on a pair of blue gloves. She studied Carly for a moment, expressionless, before beginning to pat her down, starting with her head and rummaging in each of her coat pockets. Then she asked her to remove her boots and socks, knelt down and searched between each of her toes.

Carly said nothing, feeling utterly humiliated. The woman then scanned her with a metal detector, put that instrument down and started emptying out her handbag. She placed Carly's purse, her car keys, a packet of Kleenex, her lipstick and compact, chewing gum and then, to her embarrassment, as she saw PC Pattenden eyeing everything, a Tampax into one of the trays.

When the woman had finished, Carly signed a receipt, then PC Pattenden led her into a small side room, where she was finger-printed by a cheery male officer, also in blue gloves. Finally he took a swab of her mouth for DNA.

Next, holding a yellow form, PC Pattenden escorted her out, past the console, up a step and into a narrow room that felt like a laboratory. There was a row of white kitchen units to her left, followed by a sink and a fridge, and a grey and blue machine at the far end, with a video monitor on the top. To her right was a wooden desk and two blue chairs. The walls were plastered in notices.

She read: NO MORE THAN ONE DETAINEE IN THIS ROOM AT A TIME, THANK YOU.

Then: YOU'LL COME BACK.

Next to that was a sign in red with white letters: WANT TO GO THROUGH THIS AGAIN?

PC Pattenden pointed at a wall-mounted camera. 'OK, what I must tell you now is that everything seen and heard in this room is recorded. Do you understand?'

'Yes.'

The officer then told her about the breath-test machine. He explained that he required her to give two breath specimens and that the lower of the readings would be taken. If the reading was above 40 but below 51 she would have the further option of providing a blood or urine sample.

She blew into the tube, desperately hoping that she was now below the limit and this nightmare – or at least this part of it – would be over.

'I can't believe it. I didn't drink that much – really, I didn't.'

'Now blow again for the second test,' he said calmly.

Some moments later he showed her the printout of the first test. To her horror it was 55. Then he showed her the second reading.

It was also 55.

16

Roy Grace's phone rang in the hospital room. Releasing his grip on Cleo's hand he tugged it out of his pocket and answered it.

It was Glenn Branson, sounding in work mode. 'Yo, chief. How is she?'

'OK, thanks. She'll be fine.'

Cleo looked up at him and he stroked her forehead with his free hand. Then she suddenly winced.

He covered the mouthpiece, alarmed. 'You OK?'

She nodded and smiled thinly. 'Bump just kicked.'

Glenn Branson said, 'We've had a call from Inspector James Biggs, Traffic. A fatal at Portland Road. Sound like a hit and run. They're requesting assistance from Major Crime Branch as it looks like death by dangerous driving or possibly manslaughter.'

As the duty Senior Investigating Officer for the week, Roy Grace was in charge of any Major Crime inquiries that came in. This would be a good opportunity for Glenn, whom he considered his protégé, to show his abilities, he decided.

'Are you free?'

'Yes.'

'OK, organize a Crime Scene Manager for them, then go down yourself and help the rats. See if they've got everything they need.'

Rats were known to eat their own young and traffic officers had long been known as the *Black Rats*. This dated back to the time when all police cars were black and was because of their reputation for booking other police officers and even members of their own family. Some of them today wore a black rat badge with pride.

'I'm on my way.'

As Grace put his phone back in his pocket, Cleo took his hand.

'I'm OK, darling. Go back to work,' she said. 'Really, I'm fine.'

He turned and looked at her dubiously, then kissed her on the forehead. 'I love you.'

'I love you too,' she said.

'I don't want to leave you here.'

'You have to get out there and catch bad guys. I want them all locked up before Bump is born!'

He smiled. She looked so frail, so vulnerable, lying in this bed. With their child inside her. Cleo's life and the life of their unborn child hanging on a thread more slender than he wanted to think about. Cleo was such a strong and positive person. It was one of the thousands of qualities about her that he had fallen in love with. It seemed impossible that things could go wrong. That their child could be threatening her life. She would get through this. She would be fine. Somehow. Whatever it took.

It was Cleo who had given him his life back after the years of hell following Sandy's disappearance. Surely she could not be taken away from him?

He stared at her face, her pale, soft complexion, her blue eyes, her exquisite snub nose, her long, graceful neck, her pursed-lip grin of defiance, and he knew, he absolutely *knew*, it was all going to be OK.

'We'll be fine, Bump and me!' she said, squeezing his hand, as if reading his mind. 'Just a few teething problems. Go back to your office and make the world a safer place for Bump and me!'

*

He stayed for another hour, waiting to get a chance to speak privately to Mr Holbein, the consultant gynaecologist, but the man was not able to add much to what he had already said. It was going to be a case of taking things one day at a time from now on.

After saying goodbye to Cleo and promising to return later in the day, he drove out of the hospital and down to Eastern Road. He should have turned left and headed around the outskirts of the city back to his office. But instead he turned right, towards Portland Road and the accident.

Like many colleagues in the Major Crime Branch, murders fascinated him. He'd long become immune to the most grisly of crime scenes, but road fatalities were different. They almost always disturbed him – a tad too close to home. But what he needed right now was the solace of his mate, Glenn Branson. Not that the DS, who was going through a marriage break-up from hell, was exactly a comfort zone much of the time at the moment, but he had at least been in a cheerier mood this morning than Grace had seen him in for a while.

What's more, Grace had a plan to lift him from his gloom. He wanted Glenn to try for promotion to Inspector this year. He had the ability and he possessed that most essential quality for all good coppers: a high degree of emotional intelligence. If he could just lift his friend out of his screwed-up mental state over his marriage, he was convinced he could get him there.

The mid-morning Brighton traffic was light and the rain had eased to a thin drizzle. Portland Road, with its shops and cafés, surrounded by large residential areas, was normally busy at most times of the day and night, but as Grace turned the silver Ford Focus into it, it was as quiet as a ghost town. A short distance ahead he saw a Road Policing Unit BMW estate parked sideways in the middle of the road, with crime scene tape beyond it, a uniformed PCSO scene guard with his log and a gaggle of rubberneckers, some snapping away with cameras and phones.

Beyond the tape was a hive of quiet, businesslike activity. He saw a large articulated lorry, its rear section screened off by a green tarpaulin. A black Audi convertible on the opposite side of the road against a café wall. A fire engine and the dark green coroner's van, beside which he noticed the slim, youthful figure of Darren Wallace, Cleo's Assistant Anatomical Pathology Technician, as the deputy chief mortician was known, and his colleague, Walter Hordern, a dapper, courteous man in his mid-forties. Both were smartly dressed in anoraks over their white shirts, black ties, black trousers and black shoes.

Further along was another tape across the road, a scene guard and another RPU vehicle parked sideways, with more rubberneckers just beyond. Alongside it were a VOSA – a Vehicle and Operator Services Agency – inspection van and a Collision Investigation Unit van.

He saw several police officers he recognized, including the uniformed Road Policing Unit Inspector, James Biggs, and a SOCO photographer, James Gartrell, working away methodically. Some of them were combing the road and one senior Road Collision Investigation Unit officer he knew well, Colin O'Neill, was walking the area and taking notes, while talking to Glenn Branson, to Tracy Stocker, the Major Crime Branch Crime Scene Manager, and to the Coroner's Officer, Philip Keay. Unlike at most crime scenes, none of those present was wearing protective suits and overshoes. RTC sites were generally considered already too contaminated.

A buckled bicycle lay on the road, with a numbered yellow crime scene marker beside it. There was another marker next to some debris that looked like a broken bicycle lamp. A short distance behind the lorry he saw a fluorescent jacket covering something, with another marker beside that. More markers were dotted around.

Before he had a chance to hail Branson, suddenly, materializing out of the ether, as he seemed to do at every crime scene Grace attended these days, was Kevin Spinella, the young crime reporter from the local paper, the *Argus*. In his mid-twenties, with bright eyes and a thin face, he was chewing gum with small, sharp teeth that always reminded Grace of a rat. His short hair was matted to his head by the rain and he was wearing a dark mackintosh with the collar turned up, a loud tie with a massive knot and tasselled loafers.

'Good morning, Detective Superintendent!' he said. 'A bit nasty, isn't it?'

'The weather?' Grace said.

Spinella grinned, making a curious movement with his jaw, as if a piece of gum had got stuck in the wrong place.

'Na! You know what I'm talking about. Sounds like it could be a murder from what I hear – is that what you think?'

Grace was guarded, but tried to avoid being openly rude to the man. The police needed the local media on their side as they could be immensely useful. But equally, he knew, they could at times bite you hard and painfully.

'You tell me. I've only just arrived, so you probably know more than I do.'

'Witnesses I've spoken to are talking about a white van that went through a red light and hit the cyclist, then accelerated off at high speed.'

'You should be a detective,' Grace said, seeing Glenn Branson making a beeline towards him.

'Think I'll stick to reporting. Anything you'd like to tell me?'

Yes. Fuck off, Grace thought. Instead, he replied pleasantly, 'Anything we find out, you'll be the first to know.' He nearly added, You always are anyway, even if we don't tell you.

It was an ongoing cause of irritation to Roy Grace that Spinella had a mole inside Sussex Police that enabled him always to get to the scene of any crime way ahead of the rest of the press pack. For the past year he had been quietly digging away to discover that person's identity, but so far he had made no progress. One day, though, he promised himself, he would hang that creep out to dry.

He turned away, signed his name on the log and ducked under the tape to greet Glenn Branson. Then they both walked off towards the lorry, safely out of earshot of the reporter.

'What have you got?' Grace asked.

'Young male under the lorry. They've found a student ID card. His name's Anthony Revere, he's at Brighton Uni. Someone's gone there to get his full details and next of kin. From what the Collision Investigation Unit's been able to piece together so far, seems like he came out of a side road – St Heliers Avenue – turned right, east, on the wrong side of Portland Road, causing that Audi travelling west to swerve on to the pavement. He was then hit by a white van that had gone through the red light, a Transit or similar, that was behind the Audi, also travelling west. The van flipped him across the road, under the wheels of the artic, which was travelling east. Then the van did a runner.'

Grace thought for a moment. 'Anyone ID the driver?'

Branson shook his head. 'There are a lot of witnesses. I've got a team covering the area for any CCTV footage. I've put an alert out to the RPU to stop any white van within two hours' driving distance of here. But that's kind of needle in a haystack territory.'

Grace nodded. 'No registration?'

'Not yet – but with luck we'll get something from a CCTV.'

'What about the drivers of the Audi and the lorry?'

'Woman Audi driver's in custody – failed a breath test. Lorry driver's in shock. Colin O'Neill from the Collision Investigation Unit's had a look at his tachometer – he's way out of hours.'

'Well, that's all looking great, then,' Grace said sarcastically. 'A drunk driver in one vehicle, an exhausted one in another and a third who's scarpered.'

'We do have one piece of evidence so far,' Branson said. 'They've found part of a damaged wing mirror that looks like it's from the van. It has a serial number on it.'

Grace nodded. 'Good.' Then he pointed along the road. 'What's under the fluorescent jacket?'

'The cyclist's right leg.'

Grace swallowed. 'Glad I asked.'

17

Specially trained Family Liaison Officers were used whenever possible but, depending on circumstances and availability, any member of the police force could find themselves delivering a death message. It was the least popular duty, and officers of the Road Policing Unit tended, reluctantly, to get the lion's share.

PC Tony Omotoso was a muscular, stocky black officer with ten years' experience in the unit, who'd once had his own brush with death on a police motorcycle. Despite all the horrors he had seen, and experienced personally, he remained cheerful and positive, and was always courteous, even to the worst offenders he encountered.

His first task had been to make next-of-kin enquiries from the information that he'd found in the victim's rucksack, which had been lying underneath the lorry. The most useful item in it had been the deceased's student card from Brighton University.

A visit to the registrar's office at the university had revealed that Tony Revere was a US citizen, twenty-one years old and cohabiting with another student, Susan Caplan, who was English, from Brighton. No one had seen her on campus today and she wasn't due to attend any lectures until tomorrow, so it was likely that she was at home. The university had the contact details of Revere's family in New York, but Omotoso and the registrar made the decision that Susan Caplan should be informed first. Hopefully she would have more details about him and would be able to formally identify his body.

As much for moral support as anything else, Omotoso drove back down to the incident scene and collected his regular shift partner, PC Ian Upperton. A tall, lean officer with fair hair cropped to a fuzz, Upperton had a young family. Bad accidents were a part of his everyday routine, but those involving youngsters, such as this, were the ones he took home with him, like most officers.

He greeted PC Omotoso's request to join him with a resigned

shrug. In the Road Policing Unit you learned to get on with the job, however grim. And once a week, on average, it would be really grim. Last Sunday afternoon, he had found himself sweeping up the body parts of a motorcyclist. Three days later he was now heading off to deliver a death message.

If you allowed it to get to you, you were sunk, so he tried as hard as he could never to let it. But sometimes, like now, he just couldn't help it. Particularly as he himself had recently bought a bicycle.

They were both silent as Tony Omotoso drove the marked police car slowly down Westbourne Villas, a wide street that ran south from New Church Road to the seafront. Both of them peered out at the numbers on the large detached and semi-detached Victorian properties. Every few seconds the wipers made a sudden *clunk-clunk* against the light drizzle, then fell silent. Ahead of them, beyond the end of the street, the restless waters of the English Channel were a dark, ominous grey.

Like their hearts.

'Coming up on the right,' Upperton said.

They parked the car outside a semi-detached house that looked surprisingly smart for student accommodation, then walked along the black and white tiled path to the front door, tugging on their caps. Both of them looked at the Entryphone panel with its list of names. Number 8 read: *Caplan/Revere*.

PC Omotoso pressed the button.

Both of them were secretly hoping there would be no answer.

There wasn't.

He pressed the buzzer again. Give it a few more tries, then they could leave and with any luck it might become someone else's problem.

But to his dismay there was a crackle of static, followed by a sleepy-sounding voice.

'Hello?'

'Susan Caplan?' he asked.

'Yes. Who is it?'

'Sussex Police. May we come in, please?'

There was a silence lasting a couple of seconds but felt much longer. Then, 'Police, did you say?'

Omotoso and Upperton shot each other a glance. They were both experienced enough to know that a knock on the door from the police was something that was rarely welcomed.

'Yes. We'd like to speak to you, please,' Omotoso said pleasantly but firmly.

'Uh – yuh. Come up to the second floor, door at the top. Are you calling about my handbag?'

'Your handbag?' he said, thrown by the question.

Moments later there was a rasping buzz, followed by a sharp click. Omotoso pushed the door open and they went into a hallway which smelled of last night's cooking – something involving boiled vegetables – and a faint hint of old wood and old carpet. Two bicycles leaned against the wall. There was a crude rack of pigeon-hole mail boxes and several advertising leaflets for local takeaways were lying on the floor. The exterior might look smart, but the common parts inside looked tired.

They walked up the manky, threadbare stair carpet and, as they reached the top of the second flight, a door with flaking paintwork directly in front of them opened. A pretty girl, about twenty, Omotoso estimated, parcelled in a large white bath towel and barefoot, greeted them with a sleepy smile. Her shoulder-length dark hair was in need of some attention.

'Don't tell me you've found it!' she said. 'That would be amazing!'

Both men courteously removed their caps. As they entered the narrow hallway of the flat, there was a smell of brewing coffee and a tinge of masculine cologne in the air.

Tony Omotoso said, 'Found what?'

'My handbag?' She squinted at them quizzically.

'Handbag?'

'Yes. The one some shit stole at Escape Two while we were dancing on Saturday night.'

It was a nice flat, he clocked, walking into the open-plan living area, but untidy and sparsely furnished, in typical student fashion. It had polished bare oak flooring, a big flat-screen television, expensive-looking hi-fi and minimalistic but tatty dark brown leather furniture. A laptop on a desk near the window overlooking the street was switched on, showing a Facebook homepage. Strewn haphazardly around the floor were a pair of trainers, a screwed-up cardigan, female panties, a single white sock, piles of paperwork, a half-empty coffee mug, several DVDs, an iPod with earphones plugged in and the remains of a Chinese takeaway.

It had been Ian Upperton who'd had to break the news last time they had done this, so they had agreed between them that today it was Omotoso's turn. Every officer had their own way of doing it and Omotoso favoured the gentle but direct approach.

'No, Susan, we haven't come about your handbag – I don't know about that, I'm afraid. We're from the Road Policing Unit,' he said, registering her sudden look of confusion. 'According to the records from Brighton University, you are living with Tony Revere. Is that correct?'

She nodded, eyeing each of them with sudden suspicion.

'I'm afraid that Tony has been involved in a road traffic accident on his bicycle.'

She stared at him, suddenly fixated.

'I'm sorry to say, Susan, that following the injuries he received he didn't survive.'

He fell silent deliberately. It had long been his policy to let the recipient of the message come out with the words themselves. That way, he found, it sank in better and more immediately.

'You mean Tony's dead?' she said.

'I'm very sorry, yes.'

She started reeling. PC Upperton caught her arm and guided her down, on to the large brown sofa opposite a glass coffee table. She sat there in silence for some moments, while the two officers stood awkwardly. There was never an easy way. Each time the reaction was different. Susan Caplan's was to fall silent and then start to shake, little tremors rippling through her body.

They remained standing. She was shaking her head from side to side now. 'Oh shit!' she said suddenly. 'Oh shit.' Then she seemed to collapse in on herself, burying her face in her hands. 'Oh shit, please tell me it's not true.'

The two officers glanced at each other. Tony Omotoso said, 'Do you have someone who could come round and be with you today? A girlfriend? Any member of your family you'd like us to call?'

She closed her eyes tight. 'What happened?'

'He was in a collision with a lorry, but we don't have all the details.'

There was a long silence. She hugged herself and began sobbing.

'Susan, do you have a neighbour who could come round?' Omotoso asked.

'No. I – I don't – I – we – I – oh shit, shit, shit.'

'Would you like a drink?' Ian Upperton asked. 'Can we make you a cup of tea or coffee?'

'I don't want a sodding drink, I want my Tony,' she sobbed. 'Please tell me what happened?'

Omotoso's radio crackled. He turned the volume right down. There was another long silence before eventually he said, 'We're going to need to make sure it is Tony Revere. Would you be willing to identify the body later today? Just in case there's been a mistake?'

'His mother's a control freak,' she blurted. 'She's the one you're going to have to speak to.'

'I'll speak to anyone you'd like me to, Susan. Do you have her number?'

'She's in New York – in the Hamptons. She hates my guts.'

'Why's that?'

'She'll be on the first plane over, I can tell you that.'

'Would you prefer her to identify Tony?'

She fell silent again, sobbing. Then she said, 'You'd better get her to do that. She'd never believe me anyway.'

18

Tooth was small. It was an issue he'd had to deal with since childhood. He used to be picked on by other kids because of his size. But not many of them had ever picked on him twice.

He was one of the tiniest babies Brooklyn obstetrician Harvey Shannon had ever delivered, although he wasn't premature. His mother, who was so off her face with junk she hadn't figured out she was pregnant for six months, had gone to full term. Dr Shannon wasn't even sure that she realized she had actually given birth, and staff at the hospital told him she kept looking at the infant in bewilderment, as if trying to figure out where it had come from.

But the obstetrician was worried about a bigger problem. The boy had a central nervous system that seemed to be wired all wrong. He appeared to have no pain receptors. You could stick a needle in the tiny mite's arm and get no reaction, while all normal babies would bawl their lungs out. There were any number of possible causes, but the most likely, he figured, was the mother's substance abuse.

Tooth's mother died from a rogue batch of heroin when he was three, and he spent most of his childhood being shunted around America from one foster home to the next. He never stayed long because no one liked him. He scared people.

At the age of eleven, when other kids began taunting him about his size, he learned to defend himself by studying martial arts and soon responded by hurting anyone who angered him, badly. So badly he never stayed in any school for more than a few months, because other kids were too frightened of him and the teachers requested he be moved.

At his final school he learned how to make a buck out of his abnormality. Using his martial arts skills of self-control, he could hold his breath for up to five minutes, beating anyone who tried to challenge him. His other trick was to let kids punch him in the stomach as hard as they liked, for a dollar a go. For five bucks they could stick a ballpoint pen into his arm or leg. Letting them do this was the closest he ever came to any of his fellow pupils. He'd never had an actual friend in his life. At the age of forty-one he still didn't. Just his dog, Yossarian.

But Tooth and his dog weren't so much friends as *associates*. Same as the people he worked for. The dog was an ugly thing. It had different-colour eyes, one bright red, the other grey, and looked like the progeny of a Dalmatian that had been screwed by a pug. He'd named it after a character in one of the few books he'd read all the way through, *Catch-22*. The book started with a character called Yossarian irrationally falling in love, at first sight, with his chaplain. This dog had fallen irrationally in love with him at first sight, too. It had just started following him, in a street in Beverly Hills four years ago, when he was casing a house for a hit.

It was one of those wide, quiet, swanky streets with bleached-looking elm trunks, big detached houses and gleaming metal in the driveway. All the houses had lawns that looked like they'd been trimmed with nail scissors, the sprinklers *thwack-thwacking* away, looked after by armies of Hispanic gardeners.

The dog was wrong for the street. It was mangy and one eye was infected. Tooth didn't know a thing about dogs, but this one didn't look much like any recognizable breed and it didn't look designer enough to have come from this area. Maybe it had jumped out of a Hispanic's truck. Maybe someone had thrown it out of a car here in the hope of some rich person taking pity on it.

Instead it had found him.

Tooth gave it food, but no sympathy.

He didn't do sympathy.

'What – what happens now?' Carly asked the police officer.

'I'd like you to sign your name here,' Dan Pattenden said, handing her a long thin strip of white paper, which was headed SUBJECT TEST. Halfway down it had her name, date of birth and the words SUBJECT SIGNATURE. Below was a box containing the words *Specimen 1: – 10.42 a.m. – 55* and *Specimen 2: 10.45 a.m. – 55.*

With her hand shaking so much she could barely hold the pen he gave her, she signed her name.

'I'm going to take you to a cell where you'll wait for your solicitor to arrive,' he said, signing the same form along the bottom. 'You will be interviewed with your solicitor.'

'I have a really important meeting with a client,' she said. 'I have to get to the office.'

He gave her a sympathetic smile. 'I'm afraid that everyone involved in the incident has something important to do today, but it's not up to me.' He pointed to the door and gently, holding her right arm, escorted her towards it. Then he stopped and answered his radio phone as it crackled into life.

'Dan Pattenden,' he said. There was a brief silence. 'I see. Thank you, guv. I'm up at Custody now with my prisoner.'

Prisoner. The word made her shudder.

'Yes, sir, thank you.' He clipped the phone back in its holder on his chest and turned to her. His expression was blank, unreadable. 'I'm sorry, but I'm now going to repeat the caution I gave you earlier at the collision scene. Mrs Chase, I'm rearresting you now on suspicion of causing death by driving while under the influence of alcohol. You do not have to say anything, but it may harm your defence if you do not mention when questioned something which you may later rely on in court. Anything you say may be given in evidence.'

She felt her throat constricting, as if a ligature was being tightened. Her mouth was suddenly parched.

'The cyclist has died?' Her words came out almost as a whisper.

'Yes, I'm afraid so.'

'It wasn't me,' she said. 'I didn't hit him. I crashed because I was – because I avoided him. I swerved to avoid him because he was on the wrong side of the road. I would have hit him if I hadn't.'

'You'd best save all that for your interview.'

As he propelled her across the custody reception floor, past the large, round central station, she turned to him in sudden panic and said, 'My car – I need to get the RAC to collect it – I need to get it repaired – I—'

'We'll take care of it. I'm afraid it's going to have to be impounded.'

They began walking down a narrow corridor. They stopped at a green door with a small glass panel. He opened it and, to her horror, ushered her into a cell.

'You're not putting me in here?'

His phone crackled into life again and he answered it. As he did so, she stared at the cell in bewilderment. A small, narrow room with an open toilet and a hand basin set into the wall. At the far end was a hard bench, with a blue cushion behind it propped up against the wall. There was a sanitized reek of disinfectant.

PC Pattenden ended the call and turned back to her. 'This is where you will have to wait until your solicitor gets here.'

'But – but what about my car? When will it go to be repaired?'

'That will depend on what the Senior Investigating Officer decides, but it could be months before your car gets released.'

'Months?'

'Yes, I'm sorry. It will be the same for all the vehicles today.'

'What – what about my stuff in it?'

'You'll be able to collect personal belongings from the car pound it's taken to. You'll be notified where that is. I have to get back now, so I'm leaving you. OK?'

It was not OK. It was so totally not OK. But she was too shocked to argue. Instead she just nodded lamely.

Then he shut the door.

Carly stared up at a CCTV camera staring down at her. Then she turned towards the bench and looked at the frosted, panelled window set high above it. She sat down, not bothering with the cushion, trying to think straight.

But all she could focus on was the accident, replaying over and over in her mind. The white van behind her. The image of the cyclist underneath the lorry.

Dead.

There was a knock on the door and it opened. She saw a short, plump woman in a white shirt with black lapels and the word *Reliance Security* embroidered across her chest. The woman had a trolley laden with tired-looking paperback books.

'Something from the library?' she asked.

Carly shook her head. Her thoughts suddenly flashed to Tyler. He was staying late after school, having a cornet lesson.

Moments later the door shut again.

She suddenly felt badly in need of a pee, but there was no way she was going to squat here with a camera watching her. Then she felt a sudden surge of rage.

Sodding Preston Dave! If he hadn't been such a tosser she wouldn't have drunk so much. She hardly ever got smashed. Sure, she liked a glass of wine or two in the evening. But she never normally drank the way she had last night.

If only she had said no to him.

If only she had dropped Tyler at school just a few minutes earlier.

So many damned *if onlys*.

Dead.

The cyclist was dead.

One instant he had been riding straight at her. He'd come out of nowhere. Now he was dead.

But she had not hit him, she was sure of that.

He was on the wrong fucking side of the road, for God's sake! And now she was being blamed.

Suddenly her door opened. She saw a tall, thin man in a white shirt with black epaulettes. Standing next to him was the suave figure of one of the senior partners at her firm, Ken Acott.

Several of her colleagues said that the criminal lawyer reminded them of a younger Dustin Hoffman and at this moment he certainly looked like a movie star hero. With his short dark hair, sharp grey pinstripe suit and small black attaché case, he exuded an air of authority and confidence as he strode forward into the cell, the buckles of his Gucci loafers sparkling.

Acott had a well-deserved reputation as one of the best in the business. If anyone could sort out this mess she was in, he could.

Then the look of reassurance on his face cracked her up and, losing all her composure, she stumbled forward, towards him, her eyes welling with tears.

20

Shortly before 5 p.m., Roy Grace sat in his first-floor office in the Major Crime Branch of Sussex CID, sipping his mug of tea. It was almost stone cold, because he had been concentrating on searching on the Internet for anything he could find about Cleo's condition.

He didn't mind the tea, he was used to cold food and tepid drinks. Ever since he had joined the police force in his late teens, over twenty years ago, he had learned that getting anything to eat or drink at all was a luxury. If you were the kind of person who insisted on freshly ground coffee beans and healthy home cooking, you were in the wrong profession.

His mountain of paperwork seemed to grow of its own accord, as if it was some fast-breeding organism, and it seemed today that emails were pouring in faster than he could read them. But he was finding it hard to focus on anything other than Cleo. Since leaving the hospital this morning, he had made repeated calls to check. The ward sister was probably starting to think he was some kind of obsessive compulsive, but he didn't care.

He looked down at a thick file that was open on his desk. In his current role as Head of Major Crime, in addition to being an active Senior Investigating Officer, Grace was familiar with all the current cases in the entire Major Crime Branch. For some police officers, the work ended with the arrest of the suspect, but for him, that was merely the first stage. Securing convictions was in many ways far harder and more time-consuming than catching the villains in the first place.

The world he inhabited was filled with an endless succession of nasty people, but few came nastier than the overweight creep whose custody face-on and side profile photographs currently lay in front of him. Carl Venner, a former US Army officer, now residing in the remand wing at Sussex's Category-B prison, Lewes, had made himself a lucrative business out of snuff movies – films of real people being tortured and killed – which he sold on a subscription basis, via the Internet, to wealthy, extremely warped people. Glenn Branson had been shot during the arrest of this creep, which made it even more personal than usual. The trial was looming.

Taking a momentary break, Roy Grace leaned back in his chair and stared out of his window towards the south. The CID headquarters, Sussex House, was in an industrial estate on the outskirts of the city of Brighton and Hove. Directly below him he could see a skeletal tree, planted in the earth and surrounded by an oval-shaped brick wall, and the cracked concrete paving of the building's narrow car park. Beyond was a busy road with a steel barrier, on the far side of which, thinly masked by a row of trees, was the grey slab of an ASDA supermarket, which served as the unofficial canteen for this place. And beyond that, on a clear day, he could see the distant rooftops of Brighton and sometimes the blue of the English Channel. But today there was just a grey haze.

He watched a green ASDA articulated lorry pull out on to the road and begin to crawl up the hill, then he turned back to his screen, tapped the keyboard and brought up the serials, as he did every half-hour or so. This was the log of all reported incidents with their constant updates. Scanning through, he saw nothing new, other than the Portland Road accident, to interest him. Just the usual daily stuff. Road traffic collisions, a noisy-neighbour incident, a missing dog, assaults, burglaries, a van break-in, a stolen car, signings for bail, a broken shop window, a domestic, two bike thefts, suspicious youths spotted by a car, some chocolates stolen from a Tesco garage, a G5 (sudden death) of an elderly lady that was not suspicious – at this stage, anyway.

With the exception of a major rape case, on which Grace had been the Senior Investigating Officer, the first two months of the year had been relatively quiet. But since the start of spring, the whole city seemed to be kicking off. Three of the average twenty murders that Sussex could expect annually had taken place during the past six weeks. In addition there had been an armed robbery on a jewellery shop, resulting in an officer who had given chase being shot in the leg, and four days ago there had been a brutal stranger rape of a nurse walking along Brighton's seafront.

As a consequence, most of the four Major Incident Suites around the county had been in full use, including both the Major Incident Rooms here. Rather than relocate from Sussex House to the Major Crime Suite in Eastbourne, some thirty minutes' drive away, which had available space, Roy Grace had borrowed Jack Skerritt's office, next door to his, for the first briefing of *Operation Violin* – the name the computer had given to the hit-and-run fatality involving the cyclist in Portland Road this morning. The head of HQ CID was away on a course and had a much larger conference table than the small round one in Grace's office.

He planned to keep the inquiry team small and tight. From his study of the evidence so far, and the initial eyewitness reports, it seemed a straightforward case. The van driver could have had any number of reasons for doing what he did – possibly he had stolen the vehicle, or had no insurance, or was worried about being breathalysed, or was carrying something illegal. Grace did not think it would be a hard job to find him. His favoured Deputy Senior Investigating Officer, Lizzie Mantle, was away on leave, so he was using the opportunity to make Glenn his Deputy SIO for this case. It would be a good test of the Detective Sergeant's abilities, he thought – and it would help to distract him from his current marital problems. Further, it would give him an opportunity to really shine before his all-important boards for promotion to inspector, which would be coming up later this year, by showing his ability to manage real-life inquiries.

There was a knock on the door and DC Nick Nicholl entered. He was beanpole tall, wearing a grey suit that looked as if it had been made for someone even taller, and bleary-eyed, courtesy of his young baby. 'You said 5 p.m. for the briefing, guv?'

Grace nodded. He was holding the meeting earlier than his favoured 6.30 for evening briefings, because he was anxious to get back to the hospital and be with Cleo.

'Next door in Detective Chief Superintendent Skerritt's office.'

He followed the DC in there.

'I hear Cleo's in hospital. Is she OK?' Nick Nicholl asked.

'Thanks – yes, so far so good. I seem to remember your wife had problems during her pregnancy, Nick. Is that right?'

'Yeah, internal bleeding twice. First at about twenty-four weeks.'

'Sounds similar. But she was all right?'

'No, not at first.'

'It's a worrying time.'

'Yep, you could say that! You need to see she gets a lot of rest, that's vitally important.'

'Thanks, I will.'

Grace, who managed the police rugby team, was proud of having converted Nick Nicholl from football to rugby, and the young DC was a great wing three-quarter. Except that since the birth of his son some months ago, his focus tended to be elsewhere and he was often zapped of energy.

Nicholl sat down at the long meeting table and was followed a few moments later by Bella Moy. The Detective Sergeant was in her mid-thirties, cheery-faced beneath a tangle of hennaed brown hair and a little carelessly dressed; she carried a box of Maltesers in one hand and a bottle of water in the other. She was stuck in her life beyond work, caring for her elderly mother. Give her a makeover, Grace always thought, and she would be one attractive lady.

Next came DC Emma-Jane Boutwood. A slim girl with an alert face and long fair hair scooped up into a ponytail, the DC had made a miraculous recovery after being nearly killed by a stolen van the previous year.

She was followed by the shambling figure of DS Norman Potting. Because of the pension system in operation for the police, most officers took retirement after thirty years' service. The system worked against them if they stayed on longer. But Potting wasn't motivated by money. He liked being a copper and seemed determined to remain one as long as he possibly could. Thanks to the endless disasters of his private life, Sussex CID was the only family he had – although, with his old-school, politically incorrect attitudes, a lot of people, including the Chief Constable, Grace suspected, would have liked to see the back of him.

However, much though he irritated people at times, Grace couldn't help respecting the man. Norman Potting was a true copper in the golden sense of the word. A Rottweiler in a world increasingly full of politically correct pussycats. Pot-bellied, with a comb-over like a threadbare carpet, dressed in what looked like his father's demob suit from the Second World War, and smelling of pipe tobacco and mothballs, Potting sat down and exhaled loudly, making a sound like a squashed cushion. Bella Moy, who loathed the man, looked at him warily, wondering what he was about to say.

He did not disappoint her. In his gruff rural burr, Potting complained, 'What is it with this city and football? How come Manchester's got Man United, London's got the Gunners, Newcastle's got the Toon Army. What have we got in Brighton? The biggest bloody poofter colony in England!'

Bella Moy rounded on him. 'Have you ever kicked a football in your life?'

'Actually, yes, I have, Bella,' he said. 'You might not believe it, but I used to play for Portsmouth's second team when I was a lad. Centre half, I was. I was planning to be a professional footballer, until I got my kneecap shattered in a game.'

'I didn't know that,' Grace said.

Norman Potting shrugged, then blushed. 'I'm a Winston Churchill fan, chief. Always have been. Know what he said?'

Grace shook his head.

'Success is the ability to go from one failure to another, with no loss of enthusiasm.' He shrugged.

Roy Grace looked at him sympathetically. The Detective Sergeant had three failed marriages behind him and his fourth, to a Thai girl he had found on the Internet, seemed like it was heading in the same direction.

'If anyone would know, you would,' Bella Moy retorted.

Roy Grace looked down at the briefing notes typed out by his assistant as he waited for Glenn Branson, who had just come in, to sit down. Glenn was followed by the cheery uniformed figure of the Road Policing Unit Inspector, James Biggs, who had requested the involvement of the Major Crime Branch in this inquiry.

'OK,' Grace said, placing his agenda and policy book in front of him. 'This is the first briefing of *Operation Violin*, the inquiry into the death of Brighton University student Tony Revere.' He paused to introduce Biggs, a pleasant, no-nonsense-looking man with close-cropped fair hair, to his team. 'James, would you like to start by outlining what happened earlier today?'

The Inspector summarized the morning's tragic events, placing particular focus on the eyewitness reports of the white van which had disappeared from the scene, having gone through a red light and struck the cyclist. So far, he reported, there were two possible sightings of the van from CCTV cameras in the area, but neither was of sufficient quality, even with image enhancement, to provide legible registration numbers.

The first sighting was of a Ford Transit van, matching the description, heading fast in a westerly direction from the scene, less than thirty seconds after the collision. The second, one minute later, showed a van, missing its driver's wing mirror, making a right turn half a mile on. This was significant, Biggs told them, because of pieces of a wing mirror recovered from the scene. Its identity was now being traced from a serial number on the casing. That was all he had to go on so far.

'There's a Home Office post-mortem due to start in about an hour's time,' Grace said, 'which Glenn Branson, temporarily deputizing for me, will attend, along with Tracy Stocker and the Coroner's Officer.' He looked at Glenn, who grimaced.

Then Glenn Branson raised his hand. Grace nodded at him.

'Boss, I've just spoken to the Family Liaison Officer from Traffic who's been assigned to this,' he said. 'He's just had a phone call from an officer in the New York Police Department. The deceased, Tony Revere, was a US citizen, doing a business studies degree at Brighton University. Now, I don't know if this is going to have any significance, but the deceased's mother's maiden name is Giordino.'

All eyes were on him.

'Does that name mean anything to anyone?' Glenn asked, looking at each of the faces.

They all shook their heads.

'Sal Giordino?' he then asked.

There was still no recognition.

'Anyone see *The Godfather*?' Branson went on.

This time they all nodded.

'Marlon Brando, right? The Boss of Bosses? The Godfather, right? *The Man*. The Capo of Capos?'

'Yes,' Grace said.

'Well, that's who her dad is. Sal Giordino is the current New York Godfather.'

21

Standard protocol on receipt of notification of the death of a US citizen overseas was for the NYPD's Interpol office to inform the local police force where the next of kin resided and they would then deliver the death message. In the case of Tony Revere, this would have been Suffolk County Police, which covered the Hamptons.

But anything involving a high-profile family such as the Giordinos was treated differently. There were computer markers on all known Mob family members, even distant cousins, with contact details for the particular police departments and officers that might currently be interested.

Detective Investigator Pat Lanigan, of the Special Investigations Unit of the Office of the District Attorney, was seated at his Brooklyn desk when the call from a detective in the Interpol office came through. Lanigan was online, searching through the affordable end of the Tiffany catalogue, trying to decide on a thirtieth anniversary present for his wife, Francene. But within seconds he picked up his pen and was focusing 100 per cent on the call.

A tall man of Irish descent, with a pockmarked face, a greying brush-cut and a Brooklyn accent, Lanigan had started life in the US Navy, then worked as a stevedore on the Manhattan wharves before joining the NYPD. He had the rugged looks of a movie tough guy and a powerful physique that meant few people were tempted to pick a fight with him.

At fifty-four, he'd had some thirty years' experience of dealing with the *Wise Guys* – the term the NYPD used for the Mafiosi. He knew personally many of the rank and file in all the Mob families, partly helped by his having been born and raised in Brooklyn, where the majority of them – the Gambinos, Genoveses, the Colombos, Lucheses, Bonnanos and Giordinos – lived.

Back in the 1970s, soon after he'd first joined the NYPD, Lanigan had been assigned to the team hunting down the killers of mobster

Joe Gallo, several years on from his death. The mobster had been shot in a retaliation killing during a meal in Umberto's Clam House in Little Italy. But he'd found it hard to feel too much sympathy for the man. *Crazy Joey*, as he had been known, kept a full-grown lion in his basement. He used to starve it for three days, then introduce his debtors to the snarling creature, asking them if they would like to pay up what they owed him or play with his pet.

From that point on, Lanigan had spent most of his career to date on busting the Mafia.

He listened to the information that the Interpol officer relayed. He didn't like the hit-and-run part. Retaliation was a big part of Mob culture. Each of the families had its enemies, the old, historic rivals, as well as new ones created almost daily. He decided that the best way to see if that line of thought had any relevance would be to take a ride to East Hampton and check out the family himself. He liked to visit Wise Guys in their lairs. You got to see a different side of them than you did in a police interview room. And delivering the shock message just might make one of them blurt out a giveaway.

Thirty minutes later, having washed down the chicken pasta salad his wife had made him with a Diet Coke followed by a shot of coffee, he tightened his necktie, pulled on his sports coat and scooped up his regular work buddy, Dennis Bootle. Then they headed out to the parking lot and climbed into an unmarked, sludge-brown Ford Crown Victoria.

Pat Lanigan was an Obama man who spent much of his free time doing charity work for wounded veterans. Dennis Bootle was a diehard Republican who spent most of his free time as an activist for the pro-gun lobby and out hunting. Although two years older than his colleague, Bootle had hair a youthful straw-blond colour, styled in a boyish quiff. Unlike Lanigan, who despite all his dealings with the Mafia had deliberately never once fired his handgun in all his years in service, Bootle had shot three people, on three different occasions, killing two of them. They were chalk and cheese. They argued constantly. Yet they were close.

As Lanigan started the engine and accelerated forward, a twelve-inch square of cardboard printed with the words ON BROOKLYN D.A.

BUSINESS slid off the top of the dash and fell on to Bootle's lap. Bootle stuck it on the rear seat, face down, saying nothing. He was a taciturn man and had moods in which he remained silent, sometimes for hours. But he never missed a thing.

As they headed off, Bootle suddenly said, 'What's this sound like to you?'

Lanigan shrugged. 'Dunno. You?'

Bootle shrugged. 'Sounds to me like a hit. Got *hit* written all over it.'

*

The early-afternoon traffic on Long Island was light and it stayed that way during the next ninety minutes as they approached the Hamptons. In high season, this stretch of road would be slow, the traffic fender to fender. Relaxed, Lanigan steered the car along the lush shrub- and grass-lined freeway with one hand, keeping a wary eye on the exit signs, distrustful of the occasional instructions of the satnav he had stuck to the windshield.

Bootle had a new girlfriend who was rich, he told Pat, and had a big spread in Florida. He was planning to retire and move down there with her. The news made Pat sad, because he would miss his buddy. He did not want to think about retirement just yet – he loved his job too much.

The satnav was showing a right turn ahead, as the trees and shrub gave way to the outskirts of East Hampton, with its large houses, set well back from the road, and then a parade of white-painted, expensive-looking shops. They turned right in front of a Mobil Oil garage and headed along a leafy lane with a double yellow line down the middle.

'You know what you can guarantee about the Hamptons?' Bootle said suddenly, in his clipped Bostonian accent, breaking twenty minutes of silence.

'Uh? What's that?' Lanigan always sounded like he was rolling a couple of marbles around in his mouth.

Bootle nodded at a vast colonial-style mansion with a colonnaded portico. 'You ain't going to find any retired NYPD guys living in this area!'

'This isn't ordinary Wise Guy terrain either,' Pat Lanigan retorted.

'This kid's mother, she's married to Lou Revere, right?'

'Uh huh.'

'He's the Mob's banker. You know that? Last election, rumour has it he gave the Republicans ten million.'

'All the more reason to bust him.'

'Go fuck yourself.'

Pat Lanigan grinned.

The double yellow line ended and the lane narrowed to single-track. On both sides there were trim hedges.

'Are we right?'

'Yeah.'

The satnav told them they had arrived.

Directly in front of them were closed, tall, grey-painted gates. A sign below the speaker panel said ARMED RESPONSE.

Pat stopped the car, lowered his window and reached out to press a button on the panel by the gates. The cyclops eye of a CCTV camera peered suspiciously down at them.

A voice speaking broken English crackled out: 'Yes, hello, please?'

'Police,' Pat said, pulling his shield out and holding it up for the camera to see.

Moments later the gates swung slowly open and they drove through.

Ahead of them, beyond an expanse of lawn and plants straight from a tropical rainforest, rose the grey superstructure of an imposing modern mansion, with a circular building to the left that reminded Pat of the conning tower of a nuclear submarine.

'This a bit like your new lady's pad?' Pat asked.

'Nah. Hers is much bigger than this – this would be like her pool house.'

Pat grinned as he drove along woodchip, towards a garage large enough to accommodate an aircraft carrier, and pulled up alongside a gold Porsche Cayenne. They climbed out and took in the surroundings for a moment. Then, a short distance away, the front door opened and a uniformed Filipina maid stared out nervously.

They strode over.

'We're looking for Mr and Mrs Revere,' Pat Lanigan said, holding up his shield.

Dennis Bootle flashed his, too.

The maid looked even more nervous now and Pat instantly felt sorry for her. Someone wasn't treating her right. You could always tell that with people.

She mouthed something too quiet for him to hear, then ushered them through into a vast hallway with a grey flagstone floor and a grand circular staircase sweeping up in front of them. The walls were hung with ornately framed mirrors and abstract modern art.

Following her nervy hand signals, they walked after her through into a palatial, high-ceilinged drawing room, with a minstrel's gallery above them. It was like being on the set of a movie about Tudor England, Pat Lanigan thought. There were exposed oak beams and tapestries hanging on the walls, alongside ancestral portraits – none of which he recognized. Bought at auctions rather than inherited, he surmised.

The furniture was all antiques: sofas, chairs, a chaise longue. A large picture window looked out over a lawn, bushes and Long Island Sound beyond. The flagstone floor in here was strewn with rugs and there was a faintly sweet, musky smell that reminded him of museums.

It was a house to die for, and a room to die for, and he was certain of just one thing at this moment. A lot of people had.

Seated in the room was an attractive but hard-looking woman in her mid-forties, with short blonde hair and a made-to-measure nose. She was dressed in a pink tracksuit and bling trainers, holding a pack of Marlboro Lights in one hand and a lighter in the other. As they entered she shook a cigarette out, pushed it between her lips, then clicked the lighter, as if challenging them to stop her.

'Yes?' she said, drawing on the cigarette and exhaling the smoke towards the ceiling.

Lanigan held up his shield. 'Detective Investigator Lanigan and Detective Investigator Bootle. Are you Mrs Fernanda Revere?'

She shook her head, as if she was tossing imaginary long tresses of hair from her face. 'Why do you need to know?'

'Is your husband here?' Lanigan asked patiently.

'He's playing golf.'

The two police officers stared around the room. Both were looking for photographs. There were plenty, over the fireplace, on tables, on shelves. But all of them, so far as Pat Lanigan could ascertain in a quick sweep, were of Lou and Fernanda Revere and their children. Disappointingly, there were no pictures of any of their friends – or *associates*.

'Will your husband be home soon?'

'I don't know,' she said. 'Two hours, maybe three.'

The officers exchanged a glance. Then Lanigan said, 'OK, I'm sorry to have to break this to you, Mrs Revere. You have a son, Tony, is that right?'

She was about to take another drag on her cigarette, but stopped, anxiety lining her face.

'Yes?'

'We've been informed by the police in Brighton, Sussex, in England, that your son died this morning, following a road traffic accident.'

Both men sat down, uninvited, in chairs opposite her.

She stared at them in silence. 'What?'

Pat Lanigan repeated what he had said.

She sat, staring at them like an unexploded bomb. 'You're shitting, right?'

'I'm afraid not,' Pat said. 'I'm very sorry. Do you have someone who could come round until your husband gets home? A neighbour? Friend?'

'You're shitting. Yeah? Tell me you're shitting.'

The cigarette was burning down. She tapped some ash off into a large crystal ashtray.

'I'm very sorry, Mrs Revere. I wish I was.'

Her pupils were dilating. 'You're shitting, aren't you?' she said after a long silence.

Pat saw her hands trembling. Saw her stab the cigarette into the ashtray as if she was knifing someone. Then she grabbed the ashtray and hurled it at the wall. It struck just below a painting, exploding into shards of glass.

'No!' she said, her breathing suddenly getting faster and faster. 'Nooooooooooooooo.'

She picked up the table the ashtray had been on and smashed it down on the floor, breaking the legs.

'Noooooooo!' she screamed. 'Nooooooooo! It's not true. Tell me it's not true. Tell me!'

The two officers sat there in silence, watching as she jumped up and grabbed a painting off the wall. She then jerked it down hard over her knees, ripping through the face and body of a Madonna and child.

'Not my Tony. My son. Noooooooooooooo! Not him!'

She picked up a sculpture of a tall, thin man holding dumbbells. Neither officer had any idea who the sculptor was, or of its value. She smashed its head against the floor.

'Get out!' she screamed. 'Get out, get out, get out!'

22

Tyler sat hunched over the pine kitchen table in his grey school trousers, with his white shirt unbuttoned at the neck and his red and grey uniform tie at half-mast. On the wall-mounted television he was watching one of his favourite episodes of *Top Gear*, the one in which the team wrecked a caravan. The sound was up loud.

His straight brown hair fell across his forehead, partially shading his eyes, and with his oval wire-framed glasses several people said he looked like a young Harry Potter. Tyler had no problem with that, it gave him some kudos, but he reminded Carly much more of her late husband, Kes. Tyler was like a miniature version and, as the microwave pinged, she fought back tears. God, how she could have done with Kes now. He'd have known what to do, how best to deal with this mess, how to make her feel a little less terrible than she did at this moment. She removed the plate.

'Elbows off!' she said.

Otis, their black Labrador-something cross, followed her across the tiled floor, ever hopeful. She set the plate down in front of her son, grabbed the remote and muted the sound.

'Meatballs and pasta?' Tyler said, screwing up his face.

'One of your favourites, isn't it?' She put down a bowl of salad beside him.

'I had this for lunch today at school.'

'Lucky you.'

'They make it better than you.'

'Thanks a lot.'

'You told me always to be truthful.'

'I thought I also told you to be tactful.'

He shrugged. 'Whatever.' Then he prodded a meatball suspiciously. 'So, how'm I going to get to school tomorrow?'

'You could walk.'

'Oh great, thanks a lot.' Then he perked up. 'Hey, I could bike!'

The idea sent a chill through her. 'No way. You are so not biking to school. OK? I'll sort out a taxi.'

Otis stared up at Tyler expectantly.

'Otis!' she warned. 'No begging!'

Then she sat down next to her son. 'Look, I've had a shit day, OK?'

'Not as shit as that cyclist, right?'

'What's that meant to mean?'

Tyler suddenly stood up and ran towards the door, yelling, 'I bet he didn't have a drunk for a mother.' He slammed the door behind him.

Carly stared at the door. She half rose from the chair, then sat back down. Moments later she heard the furious pounding of drums upstairs. Otis barked at her, two *woof-woofs* in quick succession. Waiting for a titbit.

'Sorry, Otis, not feeling great, OK? I'll take you for a walk later.'

The smell of the meatballs was making her feel sick. Even sicker than she already felt. She got up, walked over to the door and opened it, ready to shout up the stairs at Tyler, but then thought better of it. She sat back down at the table and lit a cigarette, blankly lip-reading the *Top Gear* characters as she smoked. She felt utterly numb.

The phone rang. Sarah Ellis. Married to a solicitor, Justin, Sarah was not just her closest friend, she was the most sensible person Carly knew. And at this moment, on the day her world had turned into a nightmare – the worst since the day she'd been told that her husband was dead – she badly needed *sensible*.

'How are you, Gorgeous?'

'Not feeling very gorgeous,' Carly replied grimly.

'You were on television – we just saw you on the local news. The accident. The police are looking for a white van. Did they tell you?'

'They didn't tell me much.'

'We're on our way over with a bottle of champagne to cheer you up,' Sarah said. 'We'll be with you as soon as we can.'

'Thanks, I could do with the company – but the last thing I need is a bloody drink.'

23

Cleo was asleep in the hospital bed. The sleeve of her blue hospital gown had slipped up over her elbow and Grace, who had been sitting beside her for the past hour, stared at her face, then at the downy fair hairs of her slender arm, thinking how lovely she looked when she was asleep. Then his eyes fell on the grey plastic tag around her wrist and another coil of fear rose inside him.

Wires taped to her abdomen were feeding a constant flow of information into a computer at the end of the bed, but he did not know what the stuff on the screen meant. All he could hope was that everything was OK. In the weak, stark light and flickering glow of the television she looked so pale and vulnerable, he thought.

He was scared. Sick with fear for her.

He listened to her steady breathing. Then the mournful sound of a siren cut the air as an ambulance approached somewhere below. Cleo was so strong and healthy. She looked after herself, ate the right stuff, worked out and kept fit. Sure, before she had become pregnant she liked a drink in the evening, but the moment she knew she was expecting, she had reduced it right down to just the occasional glass, and during the past few weeks she'd dutifully cut even that out completely.

One of the things he so loved about her was her positive attitude, the way she always saw the good side of people, looked for the best aspects of any situation. He believed she would be a wonderful mother. The possibility that they might lose their baby struck him harder each time he thought about it.

Even worse was the unthinkable idea that, as the consultant had warned, Cleo might die.

On his lap lay a document listing all the files needed for the prosecution case against the snuff-movie creep Carl Venner. For the past hour he'd been trying to concentrate on it – he had to read through it tonight, to check nothing had been omitted, before a meeting with Emily Curtis, a financial investigator, in the morning, to finalize the confiscation documentation – but his mind was all over the place. He reminded himself that he must ask Emily about her dog, Bobby. Besotted with him, she was always talking about Bobby and showing Grace pictures of him.

It was 9.10 p.m. A new crime show was on television, with the volume turned right down. Like most police officers, Grace rarely watched cop shows because the inaccuracies he invariably found drove him to distraction, and he'd given up on the first episode of this one last week, after just fifteen minutes, when the central character, supposedly an experienced detective, trampled all over a murder scene in his ordinary clothes.

His mind returned to the fatal accident this morning. He'd heard summaries of the first accounts from eyewitnesses. The cyclist was on the wrong side of the road, but that was not unusual – idiots did often ride on the wrong side. If it was a planned hit, then the cyclist had given the van the perfect opportunity. But how would the van have known that he was going to be on the wrong side of the road? That theory didn't fit together at all and he wasn't happy with it, even though the van had gone through a red light.

But the New York crime family connection bothered him, for reasons he could not define. He just had a really bad feeling about that.

Plenty of people said that the Italian Mafia, as portrayed in movies like *The Godfather*, was today a busted flush. But Grace knew otherwise. Six years ago he had done a short course at the FBI training centre at Quantico, in Virginia, and become friendly with one particular Brooklyn-based detective whose field of expertise was the Mafia.

Yes, it was a different organization from in its heyday. During Prohibition, the crime families of the US Mafia grew from strength to strength. By the mid-1930s, with command structures modelled on Roman legions, their influence touched almost everyone in America in some way. Many major unions were under their control. They were involved with the garment industry, the construction industry, all rolling stock, the New York docks, cigarettes, gambling, nightclubs, prostitution, extortion through protection rackets of thousands of businesses and premises, and loan-sharking.

Today the traditional established crime families were less visible, but no less wealthy, despite some competition from the growing so-called Russian Mafia. A major portion of their income now came from narcotics, once a taboo area for them, fake designer goods and pirated films, while large inroads had been made into online piracy.

Before leaving the office this evening he had Googled *Sal Giordino* and what he found did not make comfortable reading. Although Sal Giordino was languishing in jail, his extensive crew were highly active. They seemed to be above the law and as ruthless as any crime families before them in eliminating their rivals.

Could their tentacles have reached Brighton?

Drugs were a major factor in this city. For nine years running, Brighton had held the unwelcome title of Injecting Drug Death Capital of the UK. It was big business supplying the local addicts, but recreational drugs like cocaine were an even bigger business. The current police initiative in this sphere, *Operation Reduction*, had been extremely effective in busting several major rings, but no matter how many people were arrested, there were always new players waiting in the wings to step into their shoes. The Force Intelligence Bureau had not to date established links to any US crime families, but could that be about to change?

Suddenly his phone rang.

He stepped out of the room as he answered, not wanting to risk waking Cleo. The consultant had told him she needed all the rest she could get at this moment.

It was Norman Potting, still diligently at work in the Incident Room. Grace knew the sad reason, which was that Potting had such a terrible home life, he preferred to stay late at his desk, in an environment where at least he was wanted.

'Boss, I've just had a phone call from Interpol in New York. The parents of the deceased young cyclist, Tony Revere, are on their way over in a private jet. They are due into Gatwick at 6 a.m. Thought you should know. They've booked a room at the Metropole in Brighton. Road Policing have arranged a Family Liaison Officer to take them to the mortuary a bit later in the morning, but I thought you might want to send someone from Major Crime as well.'

'Smart thinking, Norman,' Grace said, and thanked him.

After he had hung up, he thought hard. He would have liked to meet and assess the parents himself. But he did not want to alert them to any possible police suspicions at this stage and they might just think it odd that an officer of his rank turned up. It wasn't worth the risk, he decided. If there was anything to be gained from meeting the parents, it would be best achieved by keeping things low key. So it would be better to send a more junior policeman – that way it would simply appear to be respect.

He dialled a number and moments later Glenn Branson answered. In the background, Grace could hear a theme tune he recognized from an old Clint Eastwood movie, *The Good, the Bad and the Ugly*. Branson's passion was old movies.

He could picture his friend lounging on the sofa in his – Grace's – house, where he had been lodging for months now since his wife had thrown him out. But not for much longer, as Grace had recently put the place on the market.

'Yo, old-timer!' Branson said, sounding as if he had been drinking.

He'd never been much of a drinker before the collapse of his marriage, but these days Branson was drinking enough to make Grace worry about him.

'How was the post-mortem?'

'It hasn't revealed anything unexpected so far. There was white paint on the boy's anorak on the right shoulder, consistent with abrasions on his skin – probably where the Transit van struck him. Death from multiple internal injuries. Blood and other fluid samples have been sent off for drug testing.'

'All the witness statements say he was on the wrong side of road.'

'He was American. Early morning. Might have been tired and confused. Or just a typical mad cyclist. There's no CCTV of the actual impact.'

Changing the subject, Grace asked, 'Did you remember to feed Marlon?' He had to remind Branson daily to feed his goldfish.

'Yeah, took him to Jamie Oliver's. He had three courses, including dessert.'

Grace grinned.

Then Branson said, 'He looks sad, you know. He needs a mate.'

So do you, badly, Grace thought, before explaining, 'I've tried, but he always bloody eats every mate.'

'Sounds like Ari.'

Ignoring Branson's barb about his wife, he said, 'Hope you weren't planning a lie-in tomorrow?'

'Why's that?'

'I need you back on parade at the mortuary.'

24

At 7.15 a.m., just twelve hours after he had left the place, Glenn Branson parked the unmarked silver Hyundai Getz in the deserted visitors' parking area at the rear of the Brighton and Hove City Mortuary. He switched off the engine, then dug his fingers hard into his temples, trying to relieve the searing pain across the front of his head. His mouth was dry and his throat felt parched, despite having drunk a couple of pints of water, and the two paracetamols he'd taken an hour ago, when he'd woken up, had not yet kicked in. He wasn't feeling confident that they were going to kick in at all.

His hangovers were getting worse. Probably, he reasoned, because his drinking was getting heavier. This time he had a bottle of a special-offer red wine he'd bought in ASDA to thank. He'd only intended to have one glass with his microwaved chicken casserole, in front of the telly, last night, but somehow he'd drained it.

Drowning his anger.

Trying to numb that terrible hurt inside his heart. The constant yearning for his kids, the sharp twist in his guts each time he thought about the new man who was living with his wife, playing with his kids, bathing them, God damn it. Some smarmy personal trainer he was extremely close to killing. And on top of that, all her lies in the divorce papers. They lay beside him, inside the white envelope on the passenger seat.

He had a meeting with his solicitor scheduled for this afternoon to deal with the divorce papers, and to take further advice about the financial repercussions and his contact with the children.

Everything seemed so unfair. While the police busted a gut and risked their lives to prevent crime and to lock up villains, all the moral codes had been thrown out of the window. Your wife didn't have to be faithful. She could go off and shag whoever she wanted, throw you out of the house and move her lover in.

He climbed out despondently into the light drizzle and popped open his umbrella. His clothes weren't helping his mood. He was attired in a navy raincoat over his dark suit, an unusually sombre tie and the plainest pair of black shoes he possessed, polished, like all his footwear, to a mirror shine. One of the few sartorial tips that he had ever been given by Roy Grace, that he actually took notice of, was how to dress respectfully on occasions like this.

With the fresh air reviving him a little, he stared uncomfortably at the closed door of the receiving bay. This place gave him the heebie-jeebies each time he came here, and it was even worse with a hangover.

The building looked greyer, darker. From the front it resembled a long suburban bungalow, with pebbledash walls and opaque windows. At the rear it looked more like a warehouse, with drive-through doors at each end, for the delivery and collection of corpses away from public view. It was situated off the busy Lewes Road gyratory system in the centre of Brighton, shielded from a row of houses next door by a high wall, and had the leafy silence of Woodvale Cemetery rising up the steep hill behind it.

He waited as he heard a car approaching. Moments later Bella Moy drove around the corner in her purple Nissan Micra and parked beside him. She was here at Roy Grace's suggestion because, in addition to being a detective with the Major Crime Branch, she was also a trained and experienced Family Liaison Officer.

Politely, Glenn opened her door and held the umbrella over her as she climbed out.

She thanked him, then gave him a wan smile. 'You OK?'

He grimaced and nodded. 'Thanks, yep. Bearing up.'

He was conscious of her blue eyes looking searchingly at his and wondered if she was noticing they were bloodshot. He was out of shape, that was for sure. It had been a couple of months since he had been to the gym and for the first time in his life his six-pack had been replaced by the slight hint of a belly. Wondering if she could smell alcohol on his breath, he dug his hands into his pocket and pulled out a packet of peppermint gum. He offered it to her, but she shook her head politely. Then he popped a piece in his mouth and began to chew.

He felt sad for his colleague. Bella was a fine detective but a total fashion disaster. She had a nice face, but it was framed by shapeless hair, and she was dressed as messily as usual today, in a bulky red puffa over an old-fashioned bottle-green two-piece and clumsy black ankle boots. Everything about her lacked style, from her dull Swatch with its worn webbing strap down to her choice of wheels – a real old person's car, in his view.

It was as if, at the age of thirty-five, she had resigned herself to a life divided between work and caring for her elderly mother, and didn't give a damn how she looked. If he had the courage to give her a makeover, the way he had modernized Roy Grace, he could transform her into a beautiful woman, he often thought. But how could he say that to her? And besides, in today's politically correct world, you had to walk on eggshells all the time. She might fly back at him and accuse him of being sexist.

Both of them turned at the sound of another car. A blue Ford Mondeo swung into view, pulling up next to them. Branson recognized the driver, PC Dan Pattenden from the Road Policing Unit. Beside him, hunched forward, sat an arrogant-looking man in his early fifties, with slicked-back silver hair and a suspicious expression. As he turned his head, he reminded Branson of a badger. A woman sat behind him.

The badger climbed out and yawned, then peered around, blinking, with a weary, defeated expression. He was wearing an expensive-looking fawn Crombie coat with a velvet collar, a loud orange and brown tie and brown loafers with gold buckles, and he sported an ornate emerald ring on his wedding finger. His skin had the jaundiced pallor of fake tan and a sleepless night.

He'd just lost his son and, regardless of who he might be in the US crime world, Glenn could not help feeling sorry for him at this moment.

The rear door of the car flew open as if it had been kicked. Branson breathed in a sudden snatch of perfume as the woman emerged, swinging her legs out and then launching herself upright. She was a little taller than her husband, with an attractive but hard face that looked tight with grief. Her short blonde hair was fashionably styled and immaculate, and her camel coat, dark brown handbag and matching crocodile boots had a quietly expensive aura.

'Mr and Mrs Revere?' Branson said, stepping forward with his hand outstretched.

The woman looked at him like he was air, like she didn't speak to black people, and tossed her head disdainfully away from him.

The man smiled meekly and gave him an even meeker nod. 'Lou Revere,' he said. 'This is my wife, Fernanda.' He shook Glenn's hand with a much firmer grip than Glenn had expected.

'I'm Detective Sergeant Branson and this is Detective Sergeant Moy. We're here to take care of you and help you in any way we can, along with PC Pattenden. We are very sorry about your son. How was your journey?'

'Fucking awful, if you have to know,' the woman said, still not looking at him. 'They had no ice on the plane. You want to believe that? No ice. And just a bunch of stale sandwiches. Do we have to stand out here in the fucking rain?'

'Not at all. Let's get inside,' Glenn said, and indicated the way forward.

'Honey,' the man said. 'Honey—' He looked apologetically at the two detectives. 'It was a last-minute thing. An associate had just flown in, luckily, and had the plane on the tarmac at La Guardia. So it picked us up from our local airport. Otherwise we wouldn't have been here until much later – if not tomorrow.'

'We paid twenty-five thousand dollars and they didn't have any fucking ice,' she repeated.

Glenn Branson was finding it hard to believe that anyone whose son had just died was going to be worried by something so trivial as lack of ice, but he responded diplomatically. 'Doesn't sound good,' he said, stepping forward and leading the way around to the front of the building. Then he stopped in front of the small blue door, with its frosted glass panel, beneath the gaze of the CCTV camera up above, and rang the bell.

It was opened by Cleo Morey's assistant, Darren Wallace. He was a cheery-looking man in his early twenties, with black hair gelled in spikes, already gowned up in blue scrubs, his trousers tucked inside white gum boots. He greeted them with a pleasant smile and ushered them inside.

The smell hit Glenn Branson immediately, the way it always did, almost making him retch. The sickly sweet reek of Trigene disinfectant could mask, but could never get rid of, the smell of death that permeated the whole place. The smell you always took away with you on your clothes.

They went through into a small office and were introduced to Philip Keay, the Coroner's Officer. A tall, lean man, wearing a sombre dark suit, he had swarthy good looks beneath dark, buzz-cut hair and thick eyebrows, and his manner was courteous and efficient.

The Assistant Anatomical Pathology Technician then led the way along the tiled corridor, past the glass window of the isolation room. He hurried them past the open door of the post-mortem room, where three naked corpses were laid out, and into a small conference room. It had an octagonal table with eight black chairs around it and two blank whiteboards on the wall. A round clock in a stainless-steel frame was fixed to the wall. It read: 7.28.

'Can I offer you any tea or coffee?' Darren Wallace asked, indicating for them to sit down.

Both Americans shook their heads and remained standing.

'I didn't know this was a goddamn Starbucks,' Fernanda Revere said. 'I've flown here to see my son, not to drink fucking coffee.'

'Hon,' her husband said, raising a warning hand.

'Stop saying *Hon*, will you?' she retorted. 'You're like a fucking parrot.'

Darren Wallace exchanged a glance with the police officers, then the Coroner's Officer addressed the Americans, speaking quietly but firmly.

'Thank you for making the journey here. I appreciate it can't be easy for you.'

'Oh really?' Fernanda Revere snapped. 'You do, do you?'

Philip Keay was diplomatically silent for some moments, sitting erect. Then, ignoring the question, he addressed the Reveres again, switching between them as he spoke.

'I'm afraid your son suffered very bad abrasions in the accident. He has been laid on his best side, which might be the way you would like to remember him. I would recommend that you look through the glass of the viewing window.'

'I haven't flown all this way to look at my son through a window,' Fernanda Revere said icily. 'I want to see him, OK? I want to hold him, hug him. He's all cold in there. He needs his mom.'

There was another awkward exchange of glances, then Darren Wallace said, 'Yes, of course. If you'd like to follow me. But please be prepared.'

They all walked through a spartan waiting room, with off-white seats around the walls and a hot-drinks dispenser. The three police officers remained in there, as Darren Wallace led the Reveres and Philip Keay through the far door and into the narrow area that served as a non-denominational chapel and viewing room.

The walls were wood-panelled to shoulder height and painted cream above. There were fake window recesses, in one of which was a display of artificial flowers in a vase, and in place of an altar was an abstract design of gold stars against a black background, set between heavy clouds. Blue boxes of tissues for the convenience of grieving visitors had been placed on shelving on both sides of the room.

In the centre, and dominating the viewing room, was a table on which lay the shape of a human body beneath a cream, silky cover.

Fernanda Revere began making deep, gulping sobs. Her husband put an arm around her.

Darren Wallace delicately pulled back the cover, exposing the young man's head, which was turned to one side. His bereavement training had taught him how to deal with almost any situation at this sensitive moment, but even so he could never predict how anyone was going to react at the sight of a dead loved one. He'd been present many times before when mothers had screamed, but never in his career had he heard anything quite like the howl this woman suddenly let rip.

It was as if she had torn open the very bowels of hell itself. —

25

It was over an hour before Fernanda Revere came back out of the viewing room, barely able to walk, supported by her drained-looking husband.

Darren Wallace guided each of them to a chair at the table in the waiting room. Fernanda sat down, pulled a pack of cigarettes out of her handbag and lit one.

Politely Darren Wallace said, 'I'm very sorry, but smoking is not permitted in here. You can go outside.'

She took a deep drag, stared at him, as if he had not said a word, and blew the smoke out, then took another drag.

Branson diplomatically passed his empty coffee cup to her. 'You can use that as an ashtray,' he said, giving a tacit nod to Wallace and then to his colleagues.

Her husband spoke quietly but assertively, with a slight Brooklyn accent, as if suddenly taking command of the situation, looking at each of the police officers in turn.

'My wife and I would like to know exactly what happened. How our son died. Know what I'm saying? We've only heard second-hand. What are you able to tell us?'

Branson and Bella Moy turned to Dan Pattenden.

'I'm afraid we don't have a full picture yet, Mr and Mrs Revere,' the Road Policing Officer said. 'Three vehicles were involved in the accident. From witness reports so far, your son appears to have come out of a side road on to a main road, Portland Road, on the wrong side, directly into the path of an Audi car. The female driver appears to have taken avoiding action, colliding with the wall of a café. She subsequently failed a breathalyser test and was arrested on suspicion of drink driving.'

'Fucking terrific,' Fernanda Revere said, taking another deep drag.

'At this stage we're unclear as to the extent of her involvement in the actual collision,' Pattenden said. He peered down at his notepad on the table. 'A white Ford Transit van behind her appears to have travelled through a red stop light and struck your son, the impact sending him and his bicycle across the road, into the path of an articulated lorry coming in the opposite direction. It was the collision with this vehicle that probably caused the fatal injuries.'

There was a long silence.

'Articulated lorry?' asked Lou Revere. 'What kind of a vehicle is that?'

'I guess it's what you would call a truck in America,' Glenn Branson said helpfully. 'Or maybe a tractor-trailer.'

'Kind of like a Mack truck?' the husband asked.

'A big truck, exactly.'

Dan Pattenden added, 'We have established that the lorry driver was out of hours.'

'Meaning?' Lou Revere asked.

'We have strict laws in the UK governing the number of hours a lorry driver is permitted to drive before he has to take a rest. All journeys are governed by a tachometer fitted to the vehicle. From our examination of the one in the lorry involved in your son's fatal accident, it appears the driver was over his permitted limit.'

Fernanda Revere dropped her cigarette butt into the coffee cup, then pulled another cigarette from her handbag and said, 'This is great. Like, this is so fucking great.' She lit the cigarette contemptuously, before lowering her face, a solitary tear trickling down her cheek.

'So, this white van?' her husband queried. 'What's this guy's story? The driver?'

Pattenden flipped through a few pages of his pad. 'He drove on without stopping and we don't have a description of him at this moment. There is a full alert for the vehicle. But we have no description of the driver to go on. We are hoping that CCTV footage may provide us with something.'

'Let me get this straight,' Fernanda Revere said. 'You have a drunk driver, a truck driver who was over his permitted hours and a van driver who drove away from the scene, like a hit-and-run. I have that right?'

Pattenden looked at her warily. 'Yes. Hopefully more information will emerge as we progress our enquiries.'

'You *hope* that, do you?' she pressed. Her voice was pure vitriol. She pointed through the closed door. 'That's my son in there.' She looked at her husband. '*Our* son. How do you think we feel?'

Pattenden looked at her. 'I can't begin to imagine how you feel, Mrs Revere. All that I, my Road Policing Unit and the Collision Investigation Unit can do is try to establish the facts of the incident as best we can. I'm deeply sorry for you both and for all of your relatives. I'm here to answer any questions you may have and to give you assurances that we will do all we can to establish the facts pertinent to your son's death.' He passed her his card. 'These are my contact details. Please feel free to call me, any time, twenty-four-seven, and I'll give you whatever information I can.'

She left the card lying on the table. 'Tell me something. Have you ever lost a child?'

He stared back at her for some moments. 'No. But I'm a parent, too. I can't imagine what it would be like. I can't imagine what you are going through and it would be presumptuous to even try.'

'Yeah,' she said icily. 'You're right. Don't even try to go there.'

26

Tooth and his associate, Yossarian, sat out on the deck area of the Shark Bite Sports Bar, overlooking the creek at the south end of Turtle Cove Marina, on Providenciales Island. Thirty miles long and five wide, Provo, as it was known to the locals, sat in the Caribbean, south of the Bahamas. It was the main tourist island in the Turks and Caicos archipelago, although it was still mostly undeveloped and that suited Tooth. The day it got too developed, he planned to move on.

The evening air was thirty-six degrees and the humidity was high. Tooth, dressed in denims cut off at the knees, a T-shirt printed with a picture of Jimmy Page and flip-flops, was perspiring. Every few minutes he slapped at the mosquitoes that landed on his bare skin. He was smoking a Lucky Strike and drinking a Maker's Mark bourbon on the rocks. The dog sat beside him, glaring at the world, and occasionally drank from a bowl of water on the wood-planked floor.

It was Happy Hour in the bar and the air-conditioned interior was full of expat Brits, Americans and Canadians who mostly knew each other and regularly got drunk together in this bar. Tooth never talked to any of them. He didn't like talking to anyone. It was his birthday today, and he was content to spend it with his associate.

His birthday present to himself was to have his head shaved and then fuck the black girl called Tia, whom he visited most weeks in Cameos nightclub on Airport Road. She didn't care that it was his birthday and nor did Yossarian. That was fine by him. Tooth didn't do *caring*.

There was a roar of laughter from inside the bar. A couple of weeks ago there had been gunshots. Two Haitians had come in waving semi-automatics, yelling at everyone to hit the deck and hand over their wallets. A drunk, pot-bellied expat English lawyer, dressed in a blazer, white flannels and an old school tie, pulled out a Glock .45 and shot both of them dead. Then he had shouted at the bartender for another pink gin.

It was that kind of a place.

Which was why Tooth chose to live here. No one asked questions and no one gave a damn. They left Tooth and his associate alone and he left them alone. He lived in a ground-floor apartment in a complex on the far side of the creek, with a small garden where his associate could crap to its heart's content. He had a cleaning lady who would feed the dog on the occasions, two or three times a year, when he was away on business.

The Turks and Caicos Islands were a British protectorate that the British did not need and could not afford. But because they sat strategically between Haiti, Jamaica and Florida, they were a favoured stopover for drug runners and illegal Haitian immigrants bound for the USA. The UK made a pretence of policing them and had put in a puppet governor, but mostly they left things to the corrupt local police force. The US Coast Guard had a major presence here, but they were only interested in what happened offshore.

Nobody was interested in Tooth's business.

He drank two more bourbons and smoked four more cigarettes, then headed home along the dark, deserted road with his associate. This might be the last night of his life, or it might not. He'd find that out soon enough. He truly didn't care and it wasn't the drink talking. It was the hard piece of metal in the locked closet at his home that would decide.

Tooth had quit school at fifteen and drifted around for a while. He fetched up in New York City, first doing shift work as a ware-house man, then as a fitter in a Grumman fighter aircraft factory on Long Island. When George Bush Senior invaded Iraq, Tooth enlisted in the US Army. There he discovered that his natural calm gave him one particular talent. He was a very accurate long-range rifle shot.

After two tours in that particular theatre, his commanding lieu-tenant recommended he apply for the Sniper School. That was the place where Tooth discovered his metier. A range of medals testify-ing to that hung on one wall of his apartment. Every now and then he would look at them in a detached way, as if he was in a museum looking at the life of some long-dead stranger.

One of the items was a framed certificate for bravery he'd received for pulling a wounded colleague out of the line of fire. Part of the wording read, *A Great American Patriot*.

That drunk English lawyer, in the Shark Bite Sports Bar, who had shot dead the two Haitians, had once insisted on buying him a drink a few years ago. The lawyer had sat there, knocking back a gin, nodding his head, then had asked him if he was a patriot.

Tooth had told him no, he wasn't a patriot, and had moved on.

The lawyer had called out after him, 'Good man. Patriotism is the last refuge of a scoundrel!'

Tooth remembered those words now, as he took one last look at those medals and those framed words, on the night of his forty-second birthday. Then, as he did each year on his birthday, he went out on to his balcony with his associate, and a glass of Maker's Mark.

He sat smoking another cigarette, drinking another whiskey, mentally calculating his finances. He had enough to last him for another five years, at his current cash burn, he figured. He could do with another good contract. He'd accumulated about $2.5 million in his Swiss bank account, which gave him a comfort zone, but hey, he didn't know how much longer he had to live. He had to feed his boat with fuel, his thirty-five-foot motor yacht, *Long Shot*, with its twin Mercedes engines that took him out hunting for his food most days.

His days out on *Long Shot* were his life.

And he never knew how they were numbered.

Each year, his birthday ritual was to play Russian roulette. He would thumb the bullet into one of the six barrels, spin it, listening to the metallic *click-click-click*, then point the gun at his temple and squeeze the trigger, just once. If the hammer clicked on an empty chamber, that was meant to be.

He went back inside, unlocked the cabinet and removed the gun. The same single .38 bullet had been in the chamber for the past ten years. He broke the gun open and tipped it out into the palm of his hand.

Ten years ago he had dum-dummed it himself. Two deep vertical slits in the nose. It meant the bullet would rip open on impact, punching a hole the size of a tennis ball in whatever it hit. He would have no possible chance of survival.

Tooth carefully slid the bullet back into the barrel. Then he spun it, listening to the steady *click-click-click*. Maybe it would end up in the firing chamber, maybe not.

Then he pressed the barrel of the revolver to the side of his head. To the exact part of his temple he knew would have maximum destructive effect.

He pulled the trigger.

27

Grace changed the venue of the morning briefing from Jack Skerritt's office to the conference room, to accommodate the extra people now attending. These included Tracy Stocker, the Crime Scene Manager, James Gartrell, the SOCO photographer, Paul Wood, the sergeant from the Collision Investigation Unit who had attended at the scene yesterday, and his own Crime Scene Manager as well.

Grace had brought in two additions to his own inquiry team. The first was a young PC, Alec Davies, twenty-two, who had previously impressed him when in uniform and whom he had fast-tracked into CID by requesting him for his team now. A quiet, shy-looking man, Davies was to be in charge of the outside inquiry team of PCSOs, who were trawling every business premise within a mile of the accident in the hope of finding more CCTV footage.

The second member was David Howes, a tall, suave DC in his mid-forties. Dressed in a pinstriped grey suit and checked shirt, with neatly brushed ginger hair, he could have passed muster as a stockbroker or a corporate executive. One of his particular skills in the CID was as a trained negotiator. He was also a former Prison Liaison Officer.

This room could hold twenty-five people seated on the hard, red chairs around the open-centred rectangular table and another thirty, if necessary, standing. One of its uses was for press conferences, and it was for these that there stood, at the far end opposite the video screen, a concave, two-tone blue board, six feet high and ten feet wide, boldly carrying the Sussex Police website address and the *Crimestoppers* legend and phone number. All press and media statements were given by officers against this backdrop. Vertical venetian blinds screened off the dismal view of the custody block towering above them.

On the wall beside the video screen was a whiteboard on which

James Biggs had drawn a diagram of the position of the vehicles involved, immediately following the impact with the cyclist.

The white Transit van which had subsequently disappeared was labelled **VEHICLE 1**. The bicycle was labelled **VEHICLE 2**, the lorry **VEHICLE 3** and the Audi car **VEHICLE 4**.

Reading from his prepared notes, Roy Grace said, 'The time is 8.30 a.m., Thursday 22 April. This is the second briefing of *Operation Violin*, the investigation into the death of Brighton University student Anthony Vincent Revere, conducted on day two, following his collision in Portland Road, Hove, with an unidentified van, then a lorry belonging to Aberdeen Ocean Fisheries. Absent from this meeting are DS Branson, PC Pattenden and DS Moy, who are currently attending the viewing of his body with his parents, who have flown over from the United States.'

He turned to Sergeant Wood. 'Paul, I think it would be helpful to start with you.'

Wood stood up. 'We've fed all the information from the initial witness statements, skid marks and debris pattern into the CAD program we are currently using for accident simulation. We have created two perspectives of the accident. The first being from the point of view of the Audi car.'

He picked up a digital remote and pressed it. On the video screen appeared a grey road, approximating the width of Portland Road, but with the pavement and all beyond on either side blanked out in a paler grey. The screen showed the white van tailgating the Audi, the cyclist emerging from a side street ahead and the articulated lorry some way ahead, on the other side of the road, approaching in the distance.

He pressed a button and the animation came to life. On the far side of the road, the lorry began to approach. Suddenly the cyclist began to move, swinging out of the side street, on the wrong side, heading straight for the Audi. At the last minute, the cyclist swerved to the left, towards the centre of the road, and the Audi swerved left on to the pavement. An instant later, the van clipped the cyclist, sending him hurtling across the far side of the road and straight underneath the lorry, between its front wheels and rear wheels. The cyclist spun around the rear wheel arch as the lorry braked to a halt, his right leg then flying out from underneath it.

When the animation stopped, there was a long silence.

Grace finally broke it, turning to the RPU Inspector. 'James, from this simulation it doesn't look as if the Audi driver, Mrs Carly Chase, had any contact with Revere.'

'I would agree with that based on what we have heard so far. But I'm not yet convinced we've heard the full story. It might be that she was unlucky to be breathalysed on a morning-after offence. But it's too early to rule out her culpability at this stage.'

Grace turned to the Major Crime Branch Crime Scene Manager. 'Tracy, do you have anything for us?'

Tracy Stocker, a senior SOCO, a little over five feet tall, was a diminutive power house and one of the most respected Crime Scene Managers in the force. She had a strong, good-looking face framed with straight brown hair and was dressed today in civvies, a navy trouser suit with a grey blouse. A standard police ID card hung from a lanyard around her neck, printed with the words SERVING SUSSEX in blue and white.

'Yes, chief, we have something that may be significant. We have sent the serial number on the part of the wing mirror that was recovered at the scene to Ford. They will be able to tell us if it's from a Ford Transit and the year of manufacture.'

'It's going to be thousands of vans, right?' Nick Nicholl said.

'Yes,' she conceded. But then she added, 'Most of them should have two wing mirrors. Maybe a CCTV camera will give us a shot of a van with one missing. The mirror itself has been shattered, but I've requested fingerprint analysis of the casing. Most people adjust their wing mirrors, so there's a good chance we'll get something off that. It may take a while, though, because the plastic was wet from the rain and it's not good material to get prints off at the best of times.'

'Thanks. Good work, Tracy.'

Grace then turned to Alec Davies. 'Any luck so far from CCTV?'

The young PC shook his head. 'No, sir. We've looked at all the images taken and the angles and distance don't give us enough detail.'

As Davies spoke, Grace's mind began to wander, distracted by his thoughts of Cleo, as he had been every few minutes. He'd spoken to her earlier and she'd sounded a lot better this morning. Hopefully by tomorrow she would be ready to come home.

After a while he realized that Davies was still speaking. He stared blankly at the young PC, then had to say, 'I'm sorry, could you repeat that?'

Once Davies had obliged, Grace gathered his thoughts together and said, 'OK, Alec, I think you should widen the net. If the van is travelling at thirty miles per hour, that's one mile every two minutes. Expand your trawl to a ten-mile radius. Let me know how many people you need to cover that and I'll authorize you.'

Norman Potting raised his hand and Grace signalled to him to speak.

'Boss, in view of the information that came to light yesterday, about the relationship of the deceased to the New York Mafia, should we be concerned that there is more to this than just a traffic accident? I know we have the hit-and-run van to investigate, but could this possibly be a hit in a different sense of the word?'

'It's a good point to raise, Norman,' Grace replied. 'I'm starting to think, from what I've seen so far, that this is unlikely to be some kind of gangland killing. But we need a line of enquiry to ensure that it's not Mafia-related. We need to do some intelligence gathering.' He looked at the crime analyst he had brought into his team, Ellen Zoratti, a bright twenty-eight-year-old. 'Ellen is already in contact with police in New York to try to establish if Tony Revere's family, or his mother's family, are in any kind of dispute with other members of their own family – or other crime families.'

At that moment, Grace's phone rang. Excusing himself, he pressed the answer button. It was his boss, ACC Rigg, saying he needed to see him right away. He did not sound in a happy mood.

Grace told him he would be there in half an hour.

28

Malling House, the headquarters of Sussex Police, was a fifteen-minute drive from Grace's office. It was on the outskirts of Lewes, the county town of East Sussex, and much of the administration and key management needed for the 5,000 officers and employees of the force was handled from this complex of modern and old buildings.

As he pulled the silver Ford Focus up at the security barrier, Roy Grace felt the kind of butterflies in his stomach he used to get when summoned to the headmaster's study at school. He couldn't help it. It was the same each time he came here, even though the new ACC, Peter Rigg, to whom he now reported, was a far more benign character than his predecessor, the acidic and unpredictable Alison Vosper.

He nodded at the security guard, then drove in. He made a sharp right turn, passing the Road Policing Unit's base and driving school, and pulled into a bay in the car park. He tried to call Glenn Branson for an update, but his phone went straight to voicemail. He left a message, then tried Bella Moy's, again without success. Finally, he strode across the complex, head bowed against the steady drizzle.

Peter Rigg's office was on the ground floor at the front of the main building, a handsome Queen Anne mansion. It had a view through a large sash window out on to a gravel driveway and a circular lawn beyond. Like all the rooms, it contained handsome woodwork and a fine stuccoed ceiling, which had been carefully restored after a fire nearly destroyed the building some years back. So far, since the ACC had taken over at the start of this year, Grace knew he had made a good impression. He rather liked the man, but at the same time he always felt he was walking on eggshells in his presence.

Rigg was a dapper, distinguished-looking man in his mid-forties, with a healthy complexion, fair hair neatly and conservatively cut, and a sharp, public school voice. Although several inches shorter than Grace, he had fine posture, giving him a military bearing which made him seem taller than his actual height. He was dressed in a plain navy suit, a gingham shirt and a striped tie. Several motor-racing pictures adorned his walls.

He was on the phone when Grace entered, but waved him cheerily to sit at one of the two leather-covered chairs in front of the huge rosewood desk, then put a hand over the receiver and asked Grace if he would like anything to drink.

'I'd love a coffee – strong with some milk, please, sir.'

Rigg repeated the order down the phone, to either his MSA or his Staff Officer, Grace presumed. Then he hung up and smiled at Grace. The man's manner was pleasant but no-nonsense. Like most of the force's ACCs, he struck Grace clearly as potential Chief Constable material one day. A position he himself never aspired to, because he knew he would not have sufficient self-control to play the required politics. He liked being a hands-on detective; that's what he was best at doing and it was the job he loved.

In many ways he would have preferred to remain a Detective Inspector, as he had been a couple of years ago, involved on the front line in every investigation. Accepting the promotion to his current role as Detective Superintendent, and more recently taking on the responsibility for Major Crime, burdened him with more bureaucracy and politics than he was comfortable with. But at least when he wanted to he still had the option to roll his sleeves up and get involved in cases. No one would stop him. The only deterrent was the ever-growing paper mountain in his office.

'I hear that your girlfriend's in hospital, Roy,' Rigg said.

Grace was surprised that he knew.

'Yes, sir. She has pregnancy complications.'

His eyes fell on two framed photographs on the desk. One showed a confident-looking teenage boy with tousled fair hair, dressed in a rugby shirt, smiling as if he didn't have a care in the world, and the other a girl of about twelve, in a pinafore, with long fair curls and a cheeky grin on her face. He felt a twinge of envy. Maybe, with luck, he'd have photos like that on his desk one day, too.

'Sorry to hear that,' Rigg said. 'If you need any time out, let me know. How many weeks is she?'

'Twenty-six.'

He frowned. 'Well, let's hope all's OK.'

'Thank you, sir. She's coming home tomorrow, so it looks like she's out of immediate danger.'

As the MSA came in with Grace's coffee, the ACC looked down at a sheet of printed paper on his blotter, on which were some handwritten notes. '*Operation Violin*,' he said pensively. Then he looked up with a grin. 'Good to know our computer's got a sense of humour!'

Now it was Grace's turn to frown. 'A sense of humour?'

'Don't you remember that film *Some Like It Hot*? Didn't the mobsters carry their machine guns in violin cases?'

'Ah, yes, right! Of course. I hadn't made the connection.'

Grace grinned. Then he felt a sudden, uncomfortable twinge. It had been Sandy's favourite film of all time. They used to watch it together every Christmas, when it was repeated on television. She could repeat some of the lines perfectly. Particularly the very last line. She'd cock her head, look at him and say, "Well, nobody's perfect!"'

Then the smile slipped from the Assistant Chief Constable's face. 'Roy, I'm concerned about the Mafia connection with this case.'

Grace nodded. 'The parents are over here now, to identify the body.'

'I'm aware of that. What I don't like is that we are not in terrain we're familiar with. I think this has the potential to go pear-shaped.'

'In what sense, sir?'

Immediately, Grace knew he shouldn't have said that, but it was too late to retract it.

Rigg's face darkened. 'We're in the middle of a bloody recession. Businesses in this city are hurting. Tourist trade is down. Brighton's had an unwarranted reputation as the crime capital of the UK for seven decades and we are trying to do something about it, to reassure people this city is as safe as anywhere on the planet to visit. The last thing we need is the bloody American Mafia headlining in the press here.'

'We have a good relationship with the *Argus* so I'm sure we can keep that aspect under control.'

'You are, are you?'

Rigg was starting to look angry. It was the first time Grace had seen this side of him.

'I think if we handle them carefully and give them plenty of information in advance of the national press, yes, we can, sir.'

'So what about this reward?'

The word hit Grace like a sledgehammer. 'Reward?' he asked, surprised.

'Reward. Yes.'

'I'm sorry. I don't know what you mean, sir.'

Rigg waved a hand, summoning Grace round to his side of the desk. He leaned forward and tapped on his keyboard, then pointed at his computer screen.

Grace saw the banner **THE ARGUS** in black letters underlined in red. Beneath were the words: **Latest Headlines. Updated 9.25 a.m.**

MAFIA BOSS'S DAUGHTER OFFERS
$100,000 REWARD FOR SON'S KILLER

His heart sinking, he read on:

> Fernanda Revere, daughter of New York Mafia Capo Sal Giordino, currently serving 11 consecutive life sentences for murder, this morning told *Argus* reporter Kevin Spinella outside the gates of Brighton and Hove City Mortuary, she is offering $100,000 for information leading to the identity of the van driver responsible for the death of her son, Tony Revere. Revere, 21, a student at Brighton University, was killed yesterday after his bicycle was in a multiple-vehicle collision involving an Audi car, a van and a lorry in Portland Road, Hove.
>
> Police are appealing for witnesses. Inspector James Biggs of Hove Road Policing Unit said, 'We are anxious to trace the driver of a white Ford Transit van involved in the collision, which drove off at speed immediately after. It was a callous act.'

'You know what I particularly don't like in this piece, Roy?'

Grace had a pretty good idea. 'The wording of the reward, sir?'

Rigg nodded. '*Identity*,' he said. 'I don't like that word. It worries me. The customary wording is *for information leading to the arrest and conviction.* I'm not happy about this *leading to the identity* wording here. It's vigilante territory.'

'It could just be that the woman was tired – and it wasn't actually what she meant to say.'

Even before he had finished, Grace knew this sounded lame.

Rigg looked back at him reproachfully. 'Last time we spoke, you told me you had this reporter, Spinella, in your pocket.'

At that moment, Grace could happily have killed Spinella with his bare hands. In fact a quick death would be too good for the man.

'Not exactly, sir. I told you that I had forged a good working relationship with him, but I was concerned that he had a mole somewhere inside Sussex Police. I think this proves it.'

'It proves something very different to me, Roy.'

Grace looked at him, feeling very uncomfortable suddenly.

Rigg went on, 'It tells me that my predecessor, Alison Vosper, was right when she said I should keep a careful eye on you.'

29

Grace drove out of the police headquarters and threaded his way around the outskirts of Brighton towards the hospital, seething with anger and feeling totally humiliated.

All the goodwill he'd built up with ACC Rigg on his previous case, the hunt for a serial rapist, was now down the khazi. He had hoped the spectre of Alison Vosper had gone away for good, but now he realized to his dismay that she had left a poisonous legacy after all.

He dialled Kevin Spinella's mobile phone number on his hands-free. The reporter answered almost immediately.

'You've just blown all the goodwill you ever had with me and with HQ CID,' Grace said furiously.

'Detective Superintendent Grace, why – whatever's the matter?' He sounded a tad less cocky than usual.

'You bloody well know what the issue is. Your front-page splash.'

'Oh – ah – right – yeah, that.' Grace could hear a clacking sound, as if the man was chewing gum.

'I can't believe you've been so damned irresponsible.'

'We published it at Mrs Revere's request.'

'Without bothering to speak to anyone on the inquiry team?'

There was a silence for some moments, then, sounding meeker by the moment, Spinella said, 'I didn't think it was necessary.'

'And you didn't think about the consequences? When the police put up a reward it is in the region of five thousand pounds. What do you think you are going to achieve with this? Do you want the streets of Brighton filled with vigilantes driving around in pick-up trucks with gun racks on their roofs? It may be the way Mrs Revere does things in her country, but it's not how we do it here, and you're experienced enough to know that.'

'Sorry if I've upset you, Detective Superintendent.'

'You know what? You don't sound at all sorry. But you will be. This'll come back to bite you, I can promise you that.'

Grace hung up, then returned a missed call from Glenn Branson.

'Yo, old-timer!' the Detective Sergeant said, before Grace had a chance to get a word out. 'Listen, I just realized something. *Operation Violin* – that's well clever! Kind of suitable for something involving the New York Mafia!'

'*Some Like It Hot*?' Grace said.

Branson sounded crestfallen. 'Oh, you're there already.'

'Yep, sorry to ruin your morning.' Grace decided not to spoil his rare moment of one-upmanship on films with his friend by revealing his source. Then rapidly changing the subject, he asked, 'What's happening?'

'We got doorstepped outside the mortuary by that shit Spinella. I imagine there'll be something in the *Argus* tonight.'

'There's already something in the online edition,' Grace said.

Then he told him the gist of the piece, his dressing-down from ACC Rigg and his conversation just now with the reporter.

'I'm afraid I couldn't do anything, boss. He was right outside the mortuary, knew exactly who they were and took them aside.'

'Who tipped him off?'

'Must have been dozens of people who knew the parents were coming over. Not just in CID – could have been someone in the hotel. I'll say one thing about Spinella, he's a grafter.'

Grace did not reply for a moment. Sure, it could easily have been someone at the hotel. A porter getting the occasional bung for tipping off the paper. Perhaps that's all it was. But there was just too much consistency about Spinella always being in the right place at the right time.

It had to be an insider.

'Where are the parents now?'

'They're with Bella Moy and the Coroner's Officer. They're not happy that the body's not being released to them right away – that it's up to the Coroner. The defence may want a second post-mortem.'

'What kind of people are they?' Grace asked.

'The father's creepy but he's pretty sensible. Very shaken. The mother's poison. But, hey, she identified her dead son, right? That's not a good place to judge anyone, so who can tell? But she wears the trousers, for sure, and I'd say she's the bitch queen from hell. I wouldn't want to tangle with either of them.'

Grace was heading west on the A27. Coming up on his right was the campus of Sussex University. He took the left slip, heading to Falmer, passing part of Brighton University on his right, where the dead boy had attended, and the imposing structure of the American Express Community Stadium where the local football team, the Albion, would soon be moving to, a building he was beginning to really like as it took shape, even though he wasn't a football fan.

'The wording Spinella used about the reward. Do you see anything sinister behind that – about paying money for the van driver's identity rather than his arrest and conviction?'

His question was greeted with silence and Grace realized the connection had dropped. He leaned forward and redialled on the hands-free.

When Glenn answered, Grace told him the ACC's concerns.

'What does he mean by *the potential to go pear-shaped*?' Branson queried.

'I don't know,' Grace answered truthfully. 'I think a lot of people get nervous at any mention of the word *Mafia*. The Chief Constable's under pressure to get rid of Brighton's historic image of a crime-ridden resort, so they want to keep the Mafia connection as low key as possible, I'm guessing.'

'I thought the New York Mafia had been pretty much decimated.'

'They're not as powerful as they used to be, but they're still players. We need to find that white van fast and get the driver under arrest. That'll take the heat off everything.'

'You mean get him into protective custody, boss?'

'You've seen too many Mafia movies,' Grace said. 'You're letting your imagination run away with you.'

'One hundred grand,' Glenn Branson replied, putting on an accent mimicking *The Godfather*, sounding as if he had a mouth full of rocks. 'That's gonna be an offer someone can't refuse.'

'Put a sock in it.'

But, Grace thought privately, Branson could well be right.

30

Lou Revere didn't like it when his wife drank heavily, and these past few years, since their three kids had gotten older and left home, Fernanda hit the bottle hard most evenings. It had become the norm for her to be tottering unsteadily around the house by around 8 p.m.

The drunker she was, the more bad-tempered she became, and she would start blaming Lou for almost anything that came into her head that she was not happy about. One moment it was the height at which a television was fixed to the wall, because it hurt her neck to watch. The next might be because she didn't like the way he'd left his golf clothes on the bedroom floor. But the most consistent of her tirades was blaming him for their younger son, Tony, on whom she doted, going to live with that piece of trash in England.

'If you were a *man*,' she would shout at him, 'you'd have put your foot down and made Tony complete his education in America. My father would have never let his son go!'

Lou would shrug his shoulders and say, 'It's different for today's generation. You have to let kids do what they want to do. Tony's a smart boy. He's his own man and he needs his independence. I miss him, too, but it's good to see him do that.'

'Good to see him getting away from our family?' she'd reply. 'You mean, like, *my* family, right?'

He did mean that, but he would never dare say it. Privately, though, he hoped the boy would carve out a life for himself away from the clutches of the Giordinos. Some days he wished he had the courage himself. But it was too late. This was the life he had chosen. It was fine and he should count his blessings. He was rich beyond his wildest dreams. OK, being rich wasn't everything, and the money he handled came in dirty and sometimes bloody. But that was how the world worked.

Despite his wife's behaviour, Lou loved her. He was proud of her looks, proud of the lavish gatherings she hosted, and she could still be wild in bed – on the nights when she didn't fall into a stupor first.

It was true also, of course, that her connections had not exactly done his career any harm.

Lou Revere had started out as an accountant, with a Harvard business degree behind him. Although related to a rival New York crime family, during his early years he'd had no intention of entering the criminal world. That changed the night he met Fernanda at a charity ball. He was lean and handsome then, and she'd particularly liked him because he made her laugh, and something about him reminded her of the deep inner strength of her father.

Sal Giordino had been impressed with Lou's quietly strategic mind and for some time he had wanted to forge links with Lou Revere's own crime family. Wanting the best for his daughter, Sal saw the way to do that was to help the man she intended to marry. And then maybe, in turn, the guy could be of use to him.

Within five years, Lou Revere had become the principal financial adviser to the Giordino crime family, taking charge of laundering the hundreds of millions of dollars' income from their drugs, prostitution and fake designer goods businesses. Over the next twenty years he spread the money through smart investments into legitimate businesses, the most successful of all being their waste disposal empire, which stretched across the United States and up into Canada, and their pornographic film distribution. He also extended the family's property holdings, much of it overseas in emerging countries including China, Romania, Poland and Thailand.

During this period, Lou Revere had cunningly covered his own and his immediate family's backs. When Sal Giordino was initially indicted for tax evasion, Lou was untouched. A close associate of Giordino, faced with the loss of all his money, did a deal with the prosecutors and spent three months giving evidence against the Capo. As a result, what started out as a historic tax investigation ended up with Giordino on trial for multiple counts of conspiracy to murder. He would be dying in jail, and if that bothered the old monster, he was damned well not admitting it. When a newspaper reporter asked him how he felt about never getting out alive, he growled back at the man, 'Gotta die somewhere.'

Fernanda was drunk now. The crew of the Gulfstream jet, chastened by her abuse on the flight over to England, had stocked up with Grey Goose vodka, ice and cranberry juice for the flight back home, as well as an assortment of food which she had not touched. By the end of the seven-hour flight she had finished one bottle and started to make inroads into a second. She was still clutching a glass as the plane touched down at Republic Airport in East Farmingdale at 2.15 p.m. local time.

Lou helped her down the short gangway on to the tarmac. She was barely aware of much of what was happening as they re-entered America through the relaxed immigration control, and fifteen minutes later she was rummaging in the drinks cabinet in the back of the limousine that drove them the short distance home to East Hampton.

'Don't you think you've had enough, hon?' Lou asked her, putting out a restraining hand.

'My father would know what to do,' she slurred in reply. 'You don't know anything, do you?' Clumsily, she thumbed through the *Favourites* address list on her iPhone, squinting at the names and numbers, which were all slightly out of focus. Then she tapped her brother's name.

She was just sober enough to check that the glass partition to the driver's compartment was closed and the intercom was off, as she lifted the phone to her ear, waiting for it to ring.

'Who you calling?' Lou asked.

'Ricky.'

'You already told him the news, right?'

'I'm not calling to give him any news. I need him to do something.' Then she said, 'Shit, got his stupid voicemail. Ricky, it's me. Call me. I need to speak to you urgently,' she said into the phone, then ended the call.

Lou looked at her. 'What's that about?'

Her brother was a sleazebag. Lazy, smug and nasty. He'd inherited his father's ruthless violence, but none of the old man's cunning. Lou tolerated him because he had no choice, but he had never liked him.

'I'll tell you what it's about,' she slurred. 'It's about a drunk

118

woman driver, a goddamn van driver who didn't stop and a truck driver who should not have been on the road. That's what it's about.'

'What do you want Ricky to do?'

'He'll know someone.'

'Someone?'

She turned and glared at him, her eyes glazed, as hard as drill bits.

'My son's dead. I want that drunken bitch, that van driver and that truck driver who killed him, OK? I want them to suffer.'

31

Reading from his prepared notes to the team assembled in the conference room of Sussex House, Roy Grace said, 'The time is 8.30 a.m., Saturday 24 April. This is the sixth briefing of *Operation Violin*, the investigation into the death of Tony Revere, conducted at the start of day four.'

It was of little consequence that it was the weekend. For the first few weeks of any major crime inquiry, the team worked around the clock, though with the current financial cutbacks overtime was controlled much more tightly.

At the previous evening's briefing, PC Alec Davies played CCTV footage he had retrieved from a betting shop a short distance along the road from the scene of the accident. The video was grainy, but it showed that although it had been a near miss, there was no impact between the cyclist and the Audi car. Inspector James Biggs, from the Road Policing Unit, had confirmed that after a second interview with the woman driver, Mrs Carly Chase, and forensic examination of her vehicle, they were satisfied that no contact between the cycle and the Audi had occurred. Moreover they were not intending to charge her with any further offence other than driving while unfit through alcohol.

Carly Chase's mistake, Grace knew, was thinking, like most people, that the alcohol in her blood from the previous night would have all but gone by the following morning. It was something that used to bother him about Cleo. There were times before her pregnancy when she would drink quite heavily after work. He sometimes reckoned he would drink heavily if he did that job, too. He had hoped that she would be coming home yesterday, but at the last minute the consultant decided to keep her in for one more day. Grace was going to pick her up this afternoon.

A major focus of this morning's meeting was on damage limitation concerning the massive reward the dead boy's parents had offered. It had made big headlines in many of the nation's papers, prompting any number of conspiracy theories. These ranged from Tony Revere being murdered by a Brighton crime family in a drugs turf war to this being a revenge killing by a rival crime family or Tony being an undercover agent for the CIA.

Glenn Branson and Bella Moy took the team once more through the reactions of the dead boy's parents. It was agreed that there was no indication from them that their son's death might have been a targeted hit, or that he had any enemies. The only issue with the parents, DS Branson added, had been their anger that they could not take their son's body home with them and that it might be necessary to subject it to a second Home Office post-mortem. Philip Keay, the Coroner's Officer, had explained to them that it could be in their interests. If the van driver was found and brought to trial, his defence counsel would not necessarily be content with the results of the first post-mortem.

In reply, Tony Revere's father had told him, in plain English, that the cause of his son's death did not require *fucking Sherlock Holmes.*

Tracy Stocker, the Crime Scene Manager, raised her hand and Grace indicated for her to go ahead.

'Chief, Philip Keay and I explained to the parents that regardless of whether there needed to be a second PM, the Coroner would not release the body until after the results of the toxicology reports. We could be looking at two weeks minimum for those, maybe more. Tony Revere was on the wrong side of the road and that suggests to me that he might have had drugs or alcohol in his system, possibly from the night before.'

'Are we having a full tox scan, Roy?' asked David Howes.

The Chief Constable, Tom Martinson, was under the cosh from the government to lop £52 million from the annual police budget. CID had been asked to send only what was essential to the labs, as every forensic submission was a big expense. A full toxicology scan, including eye fluids, cost over £2,000.

Ordinarily, Grace would have tried to save this money. The cyclist was clearly in the wrong. The woman in the Audi had been driving while over the limit, but she had not, from what he'd seen, been a contributory factor in the accident. The van driver, however, had gone through a red light and when found would be facing serious charges. The lorry driver, regardless of being over his legal hours, could have done nothing to avoid the collision. The toxicology report was not going to add anything to the facts as they stood, other than to explain the possibility of why the cyclist was on the wrong side. But it could feature in any defence case by the van driver.

Besides, this was not a normal situation. The deceased's parents were demonstrating anger, a natural reaction by any parent, but these people were in a position to do something about their anger. He was pretty sure they would go straight to their lawyers back in New York. Tom Martinson was a belts-and-braces man. If a slew of claims were made by the parents against the woman driver of the Audi, against the missing van driver and against the lorry driver, the insurers would come to the police as their first port of call, wanting to see what they had done to establish the possible culpability of the cyclist. And they would be asking a lot of awkward questions if thorough toxicology tests had not been done.

'Yes, we are, David,' Grace replied. 'I'm afraid it's necessary.' He outlined his reasons to the team, then changed the subject. 'I'm pleased to report a possible breakthrough this morning,' he went on. 'A fingerprint taken from the damaged wing mirror found at the scene, and presumed to have snapped off the door of the Ford Transit van on impact with the cyclist, has been identified. This was from a further fragment discovered during the continued search of the scene yesterday.'

All eyes were on the Detective Superintendent. A sudden and complete silence had fallen in the room. Only to be broken by the *Indiana Jones* ring tone of Norman Potting's mobile phone. He silenced it, murmuring an apology to Grace. Then PC Davies's phone rang, with a stuttering chirrup. He checked the caller display, then quickly silenced that too.

'The print is from Ewan Preece, a thirty-one-year-old convicted drug dealer serving his last three weeks of a six-year sentence in Ford Prison,' Grace said. 'He's on a day-release rehabilitation programme, working on a construction site in Arundel. On Wednesday

21 April, the day of the collision, he failed to return for evening lock-in. I've had a vehicle check run on him at Swansea and the only thing registered in his name is a 1984 Vauxhall Astra which was impounded and destroyed some months ago for no tax or insurance.'

'I know that name,' Norman Potting said. 'Ewan Preece. Little bastard. Nicked him years ago for stealing cars. Used to be one of the Moulsecoomb troublemakers when he was younger.'

'Know anything about him now, Norman?' Grace asked. 'Where he might be? Why would anyone go over the wall with just three weeks left?'

'I know the people to ask, chief.'

Grace made an action note. 'OK, good. If you can follow that up. I spoke to a senior officer at Ford just before this meeting, Lisa Setterington. She told me Preece has been as good as gold in Ford. He's applied himself, learning the plastering trade. She says she knows him well and feels it's out of character for him to have done this.'

'Out of character for a villain like Preece?' Potting snorted. 'I remember him when he was fifteen. I was doing community policing then. He had a formal warning for being mixed up with a bunch of kids who'd been nicked for joyriding. I felt sorry for him and got him lined up for a job at the timber people, Wenban-Smith, but he never turned up for his interview. I stopped him one night a few weeks later, him and two others, and asked why he'd not gone. He gave me a story about his family getting evicted from their council house.' Potting nodded his head. 'It's not easy to be evicted from a council house if you've got young kids – his parents were scumbags. He never had a chance. But I thought maybe he was a decent kid and I felt sorry for him. I bet him a tenner that he'd be in jail by his sixteenth birthday. He took the bet.'

Bella Moy was staring at him incredulously. 'Your own money?'

Potting nodded. 'I knew it was a safe bet. He was banged up six months later for vehicle theft. Doesn't surprise me how he's ended up.' He nodded again, wistfully.

'So did he pay you?' David Howes asked.

'Ha-ha!' Potting replied.

Nick Nicholl suddenly interjected, 'Boss, might it be a good idea to get the word spread around Ford about the reward. It's likely someone in there will know what Preece was up to. All prisoners know each other's business.'

'Good point,' Grace said. 'You should go over there, Norman. See if any of the prisoners will talk to you.'

'I'll do that, chief. I know where to start looking in Brighton as well. A bloke like Ewan Preece isn't capable of hiding for long.'

'Especially,' Grace said, 'when there's a hundred-thousand-dollar price tag on finding him.'

32

Tooth was up at dawn, as he was every morning, before the heat of the sun became too intense. He was running his regular ten-mile circuit up in the arid hills close to his home, dressed in his singlet, shorts and trainers, with his associate loping along at his side.

When he arrived back home, ninety minutes later, he worked out with his weights in the gym in the small, air-conditioned spare room, while Yossarian waited patiently for his breakfast. Then he went through his martial arts routine. Sometimes, when he had been behind enemy lines, using a gun wasn't practical. Tooth was fine with his bare hands. He preferred them to using knives. You could hurt people a lot more with your bare hands, if you knew where to squeeze. You could pop their eardrums, their eyeballs or their testicles. You really could give them a lot of pain before you killed them. And you didn't leave a trail of blood.

He practised his movements in the gym. In particular he worked his hand muscles, slamming the punchbag with his hand weights attached, then worked on his squeezes. He might be small, but he could crush a brick into dust with either his right or his left hand.

When he had finished in the gym, he showered, poured some biscuits into his associate's bowl, opened a tin of dog food and scooped that in, then set it down out on the balcony. A few minutes later he joined Yossarian and had his own breakfast. He drank energy powder mixed with water, staring out at the flat surface of Turtle Bay Cove and the boats moored alongside the pontoon below the Shark Bite Sports Bar, reading today's *New York Times* on his Kindle.

It was a fine day, as it was most days here, and the shipping forecast was good. In a while he and Yossarian would head out to sea on *Long Shot*, switch on the side-scan sonar and start hunting fish. Whatever he caught, he would share with his associate. They were in this shitty life together and they took care of each other.

One time, a few months ago, a local scumbag had gone into his apartment when he'd been out shopping. It wouldn't have been hard, because he left the patio doors open on to the ground-floor terrace and garden in case Yossarian, who liked to lie asleep in the shade indoors, needed to go out to relieve himself. The only way Tooth knew that anyone had been in was from the four severed fingers leaking blood on to the floor tiles, close to the dining table. His associate had done his job.

Before they went fishing, Tooth had a job to do. A ritual, every morning after his birthday. Life was simple: you should take care of the things that took care of you. He took care of his associate and he took care of his Colt revolver.

He removed it from the locked cabinet now, laid it on newspaper and began to dismantle it. He liked the feel of the cold metal. Liked to see the barrel, the trigger, the frame, hammer, sights and trigger guard all laid out in front of him. He liked the knowledge that this inanimate, beautifully engineered machine made the decision for him about when he lived and when he died. It was a good feeling to abdicate all responsibility.

He tipped the can of gun oil on to a piece of rag and wiped along the barrel. He liked the smell of the oil the way some folk, he imagined, liked the smell of a fine wine. He'd seen wine experts on television talk about hints of cedar, cigar, pepper and cinnamon, or about gooseberries, and citrus. This oil had a metallic tang to it, a hint of linseed, copper and rotting apples. It was every bit as fine to him as the finest wine.

He'd spent so much time alone, in enemy territory, with his rifle and his handgun. The smell of the weapons, and of the oil that kept them running smoothly, was more potent to him than the smell of the most beautiful woman on earth. It was the one smell in all the world he could trust.

Suddenly his phone rang.

He looked down at the black Nokia on the table beside him. The number was displayed. A New York State number, but not one he recognized. He killed the call, then waited for some moments, composing his thoughts.

Only one person knew how to contact him. That man had the

number of his current pay-as-you-go phone. Tooth had five such phones in his safe. He would only ever take one call on a phone, then he would destroy it. It was a precaution that had served him well. The man, who was an underboss with a New York crime family, understood Tooth and, in turn, Tooth trusted him.

He removed the SIM card from the phone, then held it in the flame of his cigarette lighter until it had melted beyond recovery. Then he removed another phone from the safe, ensured that it was set to withhold the caller's number and dialled.

'Yep?' said the male voice the other end, answering almost immediately.

'You just called.'

'I'm told you can help me.'

'You know my terms?'

'They're fine. How soon could we meet? Tonight?'

Tooth did a quick calculation of flight times. He knew the flights out of here to Miami and the times of the connecting flights to most capitals that concerned him. And he could always be ready in one hour.

'The guy who gave you this number, he'll give you another number. Call me on that at 6 p.m. and give me the address.' Then Tooth hung up.

He phoned the cleaning lady who took care of Yossarian when he was away. Then he added a few items to his go-bag and ordered a taxi. While he waited for it to arrive he chatted to his associate and gave him an extra big biscuit in the shape of a bone.

Yossarian took it and slunk miserably away to the dark recess within the apartment, where he had his basket. He knew that when he got a big biscuit, his pack leader was going away. That meant no walks. It was like some kind of a punishment, except he didn't know what he had done wrong. He dropped the biscuit in the basket, but didn't start to eat it. He knew he would have plenty of time for that.

A few minutes later he heard a sound he recognized. Departing footsteps. Then a slam.

33

Shortly after 2.30 p.m., Roy Grace left his team at Sussex House, saying he would be back for the 6.30 p.m. briefing, then he drove the few miles down to his house. He wanted to collect his post, check the condition the place was in, as the estate agent had someone coming to view it tomorrow, and make sure that his goldfish, Marlon, had plenty of food in his hopper. He didn't trust Glenn, in his current distracted state over his marriage breakdown, to remember to keep it topped up.

It was a sunny afternoon and the air had warmed up with the first promises of approaching summer. As he made his way down Church Road, passing all the familiar landmarks, he felt a sudden twinge of sadness. A decade ago he used to feel a flutter of excitement each time he drove along the wide residential street, as in a few moments he would be home. Home to the woman he used to adore so much. Sandy.

He waited at the top of the street for an elderly man in a motorized wheelchair to pass in front of him, then drove down towards the seafront. The houses were similar on both sides of the road, three-bedroom mock-Tudor semis, with integral garages, small front gardens and larger plots at the back. Little changed here over the years, just the models of the neighbours' cars and the 'for sale' boards, like the Rand & Co. one outside his house now.

As he slowed and pulled on to the driveway, it felt like a ghost house. He'd made an attempt to remove all the reminders of Sandy during the past few months, even boxing up her clothes and taking them to charity shops, but he could still feel her presence strongly. He halted the Ford in front of the garage door, knowing that on the other side of it was Sandy's ancient black VW Golf, caked in dust, the battery long dead. He wasn't sure why he hadn't sold it, not that it was worth much now. It had been found twenty-four hours after she had disappeared in the short-term car park at Gatwick Airport's

South Terminal. Perhaps he kept it because part of him still wondered if it contained as yet undiscovered forensic clues. Or perhaps just for sentimental reasons.

Whoever had written those words, that the past was another country, was right, he thought. Despite so little having changed around here, this house and this street felt increasingly alien to him each time he came here.

Climbing out of the car, he saw one of the Saturday afternoon constants of this street – a neighbour directly opposite, Noreen Grinstead. A hawk-eyed jumpy woman in her mid-seventies, whose husband had died a couple of years ago from Alzheimer's, she was out there, in her Marigold rubber gloves, polishing her elderly Nissan car as if her very life depended on it. She glanced round, checking him out, and gave him a forlorn wave.

He almost had to pluck up the courage to enter the house these days, the memories becoming increasingly painful. It had been a wreck when they bought it, as an executor sale, and with her great taste and her passion for Zen minimalism Sandy had transformed it into a cool, modern living space. Now, with the house and its Zen garden totally neglected, it was slowly reverting to its former state.

Perhaps some other young couple, full of happiness and dreams, would buy it and make it into their special place. But with the property market in its current long slump, few properties were shifting. The boss of the estate agency, Graham Rand, had suggested he drop the asking price, which he had done. Now it was spring, the market might lift and with luck the house would finally be sold. Then, along with the impending certification of Sandy's death, he would finally be able to move on. He hoped.

To his surprise, his post was in a tidy pile on the hall table, and to his even greater surprise, the hallway looked as if it had been cleaned. So did the living room, which Glenn had turned into a tip these past few months. Grace sprinted upstairs and checked out Glenn's bedroom. That looked immaculate too, the bed beautifully tidy. The place was looking like a show home. Had Glenn done this?

Yet, in a strange way, it made the house seem even more alien. It was as if the ghost of Sandy had returned. She had always kept it almost obsessively tidy.

Marlon's hopper was full and, as far as you could tell with a goldfish, his pet seemed genuinely pleased to see him. It whizzed around the bowl for several laps, before stopping and placing its face close against the glass, opening and shutting its mouth with a mournful expression.

It never ceased to amaze Grace that the creature was still alive. He'd won the fish by target shooting at a fairground, eleven years ago, and he could still remember Sandy's shriek of joy. When he'd later Googled *fairground goldfish,* and posted a request for advice, he'd been told that providing a companion was very important. But Marlon had eaten all the subsequent companions he had bought.

He glanced out of the window and got another shock. The lawn was mown. What, he wondered, was going inside his friend's head? Had the 'for sale' board freaked Glenn out – and did he think by tidying the place up, Grace might relent and take it off the market?

He glanced at his watch. It was coming up to three o'clock and he'd been told he could collect Cleo from the hospital any time after four, when the consultant had done his rounds. He made a cup of tea and sifted through his post, binning the obvious junk mail. The rest was mainly bills, plus a tax disc renewal reminder for his written-off Alfa Romeo. Then he came to one addressed to Mrs Sandy Grace. It was an invitation to a private view at a Brighton art gallery. Modern art had been one of her passions. He binned that, thinking she must be on a very old computer list that was long overdue an update.

*

Twenty minutes later, as he headed off along the seafront towards Kemp Town, he was still puzzling about what had made Glenn Branson tidy the place up so much. Guilt? Then he thought back to the bollocking he'd had from Peter Rigg, which was still hurting him a lot. He could not believe that bitch Alison Vosper had warned the ACC he needed to keep a careful eye on him.

Why? His track record in the past twelve months had been good. Every case he had been on had ended with a result. OK, there had been the deaths of two suspects in a car, and two of his team, Emma-Jane Boutwood and Glenn Branson, had been injured. Perhaps he could have been more careful – but would he have got the results? And even if the ACC did not have total confidence in him, he knew he had the backing of Detective Chief Superintendent Jack Skerritt, the head of HQ CID.

And, shit, he'd already produced one impressive result for the ACC, solving a serial rape case that went back twelve years, hadn't he?

He turned his mind to the current case. Ewan Preece, the driver of the hit-and-run van. First point was they could not be certain he was the driver, even though his fingerprints had been on the mirror. But the fact that he had not returned to Ford Prison that night was a good indicator of guilt. And applying the simple principle of Occam's Razor, which he always interpreted as *the simplest and most obvious is usually the right answer*, he was fairly confident Preece would turn out to be the driver.

He was equally confident the man would be caught quickly. His face was known to half the police in Brighton, both the uniform and CID divisions, and Grace had seen his mugshot on posters of wanted people on police station walls many times. If the police didn't spot him first, someone would grass him up for that reward money, for sure.

With a bit of luck, they'd pot him within a few days – and find out why he did a runner. Probably, Grace speculated, because he should have been working on a construction site near the prison at nine on Wednesday morning and not driving a van in Brighton, twenty-five miles away. Almost certainly with something illegal inside it.

If they could get an explanation out of Preece, he should be able to wrap up the inquiry by the end of next week. And hopefully win some brownie points with Peter Rigg. It all looked pretty straightforward.

Fortunately for Roy Grace's mood at this moment, he didn't know how brutally different things were going to turn out to be.

34

There was a long jam on the approach to the roundabout opposite the Palace Pier – wrongly, in Roy Grace's traditionalist view, renamed *Brighton Pier*. As he sat, slowly crawling forward in the traffic, he watched a couple pushing their stroller along the promenade. He found himself looking at them with intense curiosity. That was something, he realized, that had definitely changed inside him. He'd never, ever, been remotely interested in babies. Yet in recent weeks, wherever in the city he had been, he had suddenly found himself staring at babies in buggies.

A few days ago, buying a sandwich in the ASDA superstore opposite his office, he began making inane comments to the mother and father of a tiny infant in a stroller, as if the three of them were members of a very exclusive club.

Now, as the engine idled, and an old Kinks song played on BBC Radio Sussex, he found himself looking around for more buggies. A few evenings ago, the night before Cleo had gone into hospital, they'd spent a long time studying them on the Internet and had made a shortlist of ones they thought might be suitable.

Cleo was keen on ones he could go jogging with. She thought it would help him to bond with the baby, as his work would preclude them from spending much time together otherwise. One pregnancy book they had been reading together warned of this, that while the mother would be at home, developing her relationship with the baby, the father would be at work, becoming increasingly remote.

Across the road he could see a man about his own age jogging along with a baby in a Mountain Buggy Swift. Then he saw a female jogger with one they favoured, an iCandy Apple Jogger. Moments later he saw another they liked, because of the name, a Graco Cleo. And over on the far side of the promenade he saw a single woman pushing the one that they liked most of all – which was unfortunately one of the most expensive – a Bugaboo Gecko.

Money was no object, luckily. Cleo had told him that her parents wanted to buy it for them. Ordinarily Grace would have insisted on paying for everything himself. That was the way he had been brought up. But he had done the sums and the cost of having a baby was terrifying. And seemingly endless. Starting with having to turn the spare room at Cleo's house into the baby's room. They had been advised that it should be painted well in advance, so there was no danger to their baby from paint fumes. Then there were the digital baby monitors Cleo wanted, so they could hear the baby's breathing. The Moses basket for the baby to sleep in during its first few months. Decorations for the room. Clothes – which they could not buy yet as they did not know whether it was a boy or a girl.

It was strange not being able to put a sex to the baby. Just an *it*. Neither he nor Cleo wanted to know. But Cleo had told him on several occasions she believed it would be a boy, because the bump was high up, and because, another old wives' tale, she had been craving savoury rather than sweet things.

He did not mind. All he cared was that the baby was healthy and, more importantly to him, that Cleo was fine. He had read that fathers sometimes, when things went badly wrong, had to make a decision between saving the life of the baby and of the mother. In his mind there was absolutely no question at all. He would save Cleo every time.

A Ziko Herbie stroller went by on the promenade. Followed by a Phil & Teds Dash, a Mountain Buggy and a Mothercare Mychoice. It was sad, he thought, that he had acquired this encyclopedic knowledge of buggies in such a short space of time. Then his phone rang.

It was Norman Potting. 'Boss,' he said. 'I've got good news and – ah – not good news. But I'm running out of battery on my BlackBerry.'

'Tell me?'

All he got in reply was silence.

35

Someone had left the *Münchner Merkur* further along on the wooden trestle table where she sat, alone, beside the Seehaus lake in the Englischer Garten. The *Merkur* was one of Munich's two local papers. On the front page was a photograph of a large silver coach that had rolled on to its side, straddling and buckling an autobahn crash barrier. Emergency service crews in orange suits were standing around it and there was a bleeding victim partially visible on a stretcher.

The headline, which she translated into English in her head as she read, said, SEVEN DIE IN AUTOBAHN COACH CRASH.

Although now fluent in German, she still *thought* in English and, she realized some mornings, still dreamed in English. She wondered if one day that would change. She had German blood. Her grandmother on her mother's side had come from a small town near here and she felt increasingly strongly, with every day that passed, that Bavaria was her true spiritual home. She loved this city.

And this park was her favourite place in it. She came here every Saturday morning that she could. Today the April sunshine was unseasonably hot and she was grateful for the breeze blowing off the lake. Although dressed lightly in a T-shirt, Lycra jogging shorts and trainers, she was perspiring heavily after a ten-kilometre run. Gratefully, she gulped down half the bottle of the cold mineral water she had just bought in one draught.

Then she sat still, breathing in the sweet scents of grass and lake water and wood varnish and pure clean air. Suddenly she caught a waft of cigarette smoke from someone nearby. Instantly, as it did almost every time, that smell brought a twinge of sadness – memories of the man she had once loved so much.

She took another swig of the bottle and reached over to pick up the paper, as no one seemed to be coming back to claim it. Only eleven o'clock and the Englischer Garten was busy already. Dozens of people sat at the beer garden tables, some obviously tourists but many of them locals, enjoying the start to the weekend. Most had a *Maß* of beer in front of them, but some like herself were drinking water or Cokes. Several people were out on the lake in rowing boats and pedalos, and she watched for a moment as a mother duck, following by a string of tiny brown ducklings, rounded the wooded island.

Then suddenly a very determined-looking Nordic walker in her sixties, wearing bright red Lycra, teeth clenched, ski poles clacking on the ground, was heading straight towards her.

Leave me alone, don't invade my space, she thought, planting her elbows on the table and giving the woman a defiant glare.

It worked. The woman clacked off and settled at a table some distance away.

There were times, such as now, when she craved solitude, and there were precious few moments when she was able to find it. That was one of the things she most treasured about her Saturday morning runs. There was always so much to think about and not enough time to focus on it. Her new masters gave her new thoughts to work on every week. This week they had told her, *Before you can seek new horizons, first you have to have the courage to lose sight of the shore.*

Surely she had done that ten years ago?

Then another waft of cigarette smoke set off another sudden pang. She was going through a bad day, a bad week. Doubting everything. Feeling alone and bleak and questioning herself. She was thirty-seven, single, with two failed relationships behind her and what ahead?

Nothing at this moment.

That good old German philosopher Nietzsche said that if you looked long enough into the void, the void would begin to look back into you.

She understood what he meant. To distract herself, she began to read the newspaper report of the coach disaster. All the passengers were members of a Christian fellowship group in Cologne. Seven dead, twenty-three seriously injured. She wondered what they thought of God now. Then she felt bad for letting her mind go there and turned the page.

There was a picture of a cyclist fleeing the police and another road accident, this time a VW Passat that had rolled over. Then on the next page was the story of a factory closure, which did not interest her. Nor did a photograph of a school football team. She turned the page again. Then froze.

She stared at the printed words, unable to believe her eyes, translating each of them into English inside her head.

She read them, then reread them.

Then she just stared at them again, as if she had been turned into a pillar of salt.

It was an advertisement. Not big, just one column wide and six centimetres deep. The wording read:

> SANDRA (SANDY) CHRISTINA GRACE
>
> Wife of Roy Jack Grace of Hove, City of Brighton and Hove, East Sussex, England.
>
> Missing, presumed dead, for ten years. Last seen in Hove, East Sussex. She is five feet, seven inches tall (1.70 metres), slim build and had shoulder-length fair hair when last seen.
>
> Unless anyone can provide evidence that she is still alive to Messrs Edwards and Edwards LLP at the address beneath, a declaration will be sought that she is legally dead.

She continued staring, reading it, rereading it, then rereading it again.

And again.

36

'Do you know what I'm really looking forward to?' Cleo asked. 'What I'm absolutely craving?'

'Wild sex?' Roy Grace said hopefully, giving her a sideways grin.

They were in the car, heading home from hospital, and she looked a thousand times better. The colour had returned to her face and she looked radiant. And more beautiful than ever. The rest in hospital had clearly done her good.

She ran a finger suggestively a long way up his thigh. 'Right now?'

He halted the car at traffic lights on Edward Street, almost in view of John Street Police Station – known colloquially as *Brighton nick.*

'Probably not the best place.'

'Wild sex would be good,' she conceded, continuing to stroke the inside of his thigh provocatively. 'But at a risk of denting your ego, there is something I desire even more than your body right now, Detective Superintendent Grace.'

'And what might that be?'

'Something I can't have. A big slice of Brie with a glass of red wine!'

'Terrific! I'm in competition with cheese for your affections?'

'No competition. The cheese wins hands down.'

'Maybe I should take you back to the hospital.'

She leaned across and kissed him on the cheek. Then, as the lights turned green, she pressed her fingers even further into his thigh and said, 'Don't take it badly.'

As he drove forward, he pouted in a mock-sulk and said, 'I'm going to arrest every sodding piece of Brie in this city.'

'Great. Put them in the cooler for after Bump is born and I'll devour them. But I will devour you first, I promise!'

As he turned south into Grand Parade and moved over into the right-hand lane, with the Royal Pavilion ahead of him to the right, Grace was aware of a sudden feeling of euphoria. After all his fears for Cleo and their baby these past few days, everything suddenly seemed good again. Cleo was fine, back to her normal cheery, breezy self. Their baby was fine. The bollocking from ACC Rigg suddenly seemed very small and insignificant in comparison. The two-bit petty crook van driver, Ewan Preece, would be found within days, if not hours, and that would put Rigg back in his box. The only thing that really mattered to him at this moment was sitting beside him.

'I love you so much,' he said.

'You do?'

'Yep.'

'You sure about that? Even with my big tummy and the fact that I prefer cheese to you?'

'I like your big tummy – more to love.'

She suddenly took his left hand and held it to her abdomen. He could feel something moving, something tiny but strong, and he felt a lump of joy in his throat.

'Is that Bump?'

'Kicking away! He's telling us he's happy to be going home!'

'Awwww!'

Cleo released his hand, then pushed her hair back from her forehead. Grace stopped in the right-turn lane, in front of the Pavilion.

'So have you missed me?' she said.

'Every second.'

'Liar.'

'I have.' The lights turned green and he drove across the junction and doubled back around the Old Steine. 'I've kept busy googling buggies and baby names.'

'I've been thinking a lot about names,' she said.

'And?'

'If it's a girl, which I don't think it is, I like Amelie, Tilly or Freya best so far.'

'And if it's a boy?'

'I'd like Jack, after your father.'

'You would?'

She nodded.

Suddenly his phone rang. Raising an apologetic finger, he hit the hands-free button to answer.

It was Norman Potting. 'Sorry about that, chief, my battery is still down. But I thought you should know—'

Then there was silence.

'Know what?' Grace asked.

But he was talking into thin air.

He dialled the Incident Room number to ask if Potting had left any message. But Nick Nicholl, who answered, said no one had heard from him. Grace told him he would be back for the evening briefing, then hung up.

Cleo looked at him provocatively. 'So, this wild sex, then? It'll have to be a quickie?'

'Hard cheese,' he replied.

'It's the soft ones that have listeria.' She kissed him again. 'Hard sounds good.'

37

She did not feel like running any more. She felt in need of alcohol. When the waitress came round, she ordered a *Maß* of beer. One whole litre of the stuff. Then she stared back again at the words in the *Münchner Merkur*.

She could feel blind fury welling inside her. Somehow she had to contain it. It was one of the things she had been learning, anger management. She was much better at it, but she needed to focus hard to do it. Had to spiral back inside her mind to the place she was before she was angry. To the *Münchner Merkur*, lying on the table.

She closed the paper and pushed it away, calming a little. But struggling. A fury inside her was threatening to erupt and she must not let it, she knew. She could not let her anger win. It had already ruled too much of her life and had not ruled it well or wisely.

Extinguish it, she thought. *Extinguish it like the flame of a match in the wind. Just let it blow out. Watch it go.*

Calmer now, she opened the paper again and turned back to the page. She looked at the details at the bottom. There was a mailing address, an email address and a phone number.

Her next reaction was *Why?*

Then, calming a little further, she thought, *Does it matter?*

She'd kept some tabs on him, especially in recent years, now that the local Sussex newspaper, the *Argus*, was available online. As an increasingly prominent police officer it was easy; he was frequently being quoted in the news doing his stuff. Doing what he loved, being a copper. A crap husband, but a great copper. As a wife you'd always be second to that. Some accepted it. Some wives were coppers themselves, so they understood. But it had not been the life she had wanted. Or so she had thought.

But now here, alone, with each passing day she was less certain of the decision she had made. And this announcement was really unsettling her more than she could ever have imagined.

Dead?

Me?

How very convenient for you, Detective Superintendent Roy Grace, now in charge of Major Crime for Sussex. Oh yes, I've been following you. I'm only a few footsteps behind you. The ghost that haunts you. Good for you, with your passion for your career. Your dad only made it to Sergeant. You've already gone higher than your wildest dreams – at least the ones you told me about. How much higher will you go? How high do you want to go? All the way to the very top? The place you told me you didn't actually want to reach?

Are you happy?

Do you remember how we used to discuss happiness? Do you remember that night we got drunk at the bar in Browns and you told me that it was possible to have happy moments in life, but that only an idiot could be happy all of the time?

You were right.

She opened the paper and reread the announcement. Anger was boiling inside her again. A silent rage. A fire she had to put out. It was one of the first things they had taught her about herself. About that anger, which was such a big problem. They gave her a mantra to say to herself. To repeat, over and over.

She remembered the words now. Spoke them silently.

Life is not about waiting for the storms to pass. It is about learning to dance in the rain.

As she repeated them, again and again, slowly she began to calm down once more.

38

Tony Case, the Senior Support Officer at HQ CID, phoned Roy Grace early in the afternoon, to tell him one of the current inquiries at Sussex House had ended in a result sooner than expected and was now winding down, which meant MIR-1 – Major Incident Room One – had become free. Case, with whom Grace got on well, knew that was the place the Detective Superintendent favoured for conducting his inquiries.

As he made his way towards MIR-1 for the 6.30 p.m. briefing, his phone rang. He stopped in the corridor, in front of a diagram on the wall – a white sheet pinned to a red board which was headed CRIME SCENE ASSESSMENT.

It was Kevin Spinella on the line.

'Detective Superintendent, do you have a second for me?'

'Not even a nanosecond, I'm afraid. Nor a picosecond. I don't even have a femtosecond.'

'Ha-ha, very witty. One millionth of one billionth of a second. You can't even spare that?'

'You actually know what that is?' Grace was a little astonished.

'Well, I know that a nanosecond is one billionth of a second and a picosecond is one trillionth of a second. So, yeah, actually, I do know what a femtosecond is.'

Grace could hear him chewing gum, as ever, over the phone. It sounded like a horse trotting through mud.

'Didn't know you were a physicist.'

'Yeah, well, life's full of surprises, isn't it? So, do you have time to talk about *Operation Violin*?'

'I'm just going into a meeting.'

'Your 6.30 p.m. briefing?'

Grace held his temper with difficulty. Was there anything this little shit did not know?

'Yes. You probably know the agenda better than me.'

Ignoring the barb, Spinella said, 'Ewan Preece, your prime suspect . . .'

Grace said nothing for a while. His brain was whirring. How did Spinella know that? How?

But he realized there were dozens of potential sources that could have leaked this name to him, starting with Ford Prison. There was nothing to be gained from going there at this moment.

'We don't have a prime suspect at this stage,' he told the reporter, thinking hard. About how he could make Spinella useful to the investigation. Stalling for time, he said, 'We are interested in interviewing Ewan Preece to eliminate him from our enquiries.'

'And have him back under lock and key at Ford? You must be wondering why someone with only three weeks of his sentence to run would go over the wall, right?'

Grace again thought carefully before replying. It was a question he had been considering in some depth himself. He had tried to put himself in Preece's position. Difficult, because the mindset of a recidivist was unique to his – or her – circumstances. But only an idiot would escape three weeks before the end of a sentence unless there was a pressing reason. Jealousy could be one; a commercial opportunity another.

Perhaps being in the wrong place, at the wrong time was a third? Driving a van in Brighton, when you were meant to be labouring on a construction site in Arundel?

'I'm sure that hundred-thousand-dollar reward is going to help find you the van driver,' Spinella said. 'Presume you've had some calls to the Incident Room?'

There had actually been remarkably few, which had surprised Grace. Normally rewards brought every nutter and chancer out of the woodwork. But this call was an opportunity for more publicity – and especially to put pressure on anyone out there who might know Preece's whereabouts.

'Yes,' he lied. 'We are delighted with the response of the general public and we are urgently following several leads which we believe have come to us directly as result of this massive reward.'

'I can quote you on that?'

'You can.'

Grace ended the call and entered MIR-1. As ever, with a major crime inquiry, some wag had put a humorous picture on the back of the door, making fun of the inquiry name. It was a particularly good one today – a cartoon of a man in a fedora and turned up mackintosh, clutching a violin case and smoking a huge stogie.

The two Major Incident Rooms at Sussex House, MIR-1 and MIR-2, were the nerve centres for major crime inquiries. Despite opaque windows too high to see out of, MIR-1 had an airy feel, good light, good energy. It was his favourite room in the entire head-quarters building. While in other parts of Sussex House he missed the messy buzz of police station incident rooms that he had grown up with, this room felt like a powerhouse.

It was an L-shaped space, divided up by three large workstations, each comprising a long curved desk with room for up to eight people to sit, and several large whiteboards. One, headed OPERATION VIOLIN, had the diagram of the vehicles involved in the accident, which Inspector Biggs from the Road Policing Unit had produced earlier. Another had the start of a family tree of Tony Revere, including the name and immediate family of his girlfriend. On a third was a list of names and contact numbers of principal witnesses.

There was an air of intense concentration, punctuated by the constant warbling of phones, which the members of his expanding team answered haphazardly.

He saw Norman Potting on the phone, making notes as he spoke. He still had not spoken to him since the two attempted calls in his car. He sat down at an empty workstation and placed his notes in front of him.

'Right!' he said, as Potting ended his call, raising his voice to get everyone's attention. 'The time is 6.30 p.m., Saturday 24 April. This is the seventh briefing of *Operation Violin*, the investigation into the death of Tony Revere.' He looked at the Crime Scene Manager. 'Tracy, I understand you have a development?'

There was a sudden blast of house music. Embarrassed, PC Alec Davies quickly silenced his phone.

'Yes, chief,' Stocker replied. 'We've had a positive ID of the van type back from Ford, from their analysis of the serial number on the wing mirror. They've confirmed it was fitted to the '06 model. So, considering the time and location where the mirror-casing fragment was found, I think we can say with reasonable certainty it belonged to our suspect Ford Transit.' She pointed up at the whiteboard. 'Vehicle 1 on the diagram.'

'Do we know how many of these vans were made in that year?' Emma-Jane Boutwood asked.

'Yes,' Stocker answered. 'Fifty-seven thousand, four hundred and thirty-four Ford Transit vans sold in the UK in 2006. Ninety-three per cent of them were white, which means fifty-three thousand, four hundred and thirteen vans fit our description.' She smiled wryly.

Sergeant Paul Wood of the Collision Investigation Unit said, 'One line that would be worth pursuing would be to contact all repair shops and see if anyone's brought a Transit in for wing mirror repair. They get damaged frequently.'

Grace made a note, nodding. 'Yes, I've thought of that. But he'd have to be pretty stupid to take the van in for repairs so quickly. More likely he'd tuck it away in a lock-up.'

'Ewan Preece doesn't sound like the sharpest tool in the shed,' Glenn Branson chipped in. 'I don't think we should rule it out, boss.'

'I'll put it down as an action for the outside inquiry team. Perhaps we can put a couple of PCSOs on it.' Then he turned to Potting. 'Norman, do you have your update from Ford Prison?'

Potting pursed his lips, taking his time before answering. 'I do, chief,' he said finally, in his rich rural burr.

In another era, Grace could have envisaged him as a bloody-minded desk sergeant plod in some remote country town. Potting spoke slowly and methodically, partly from memory and partly referring to his notebook. Every few moments he would squint to decipher his handwriting.

'I interviewed Senior Prison Officer Lisa Setterington, the one you spoke to, chief,' Potting said.

Grace nodded.

'She confirmed that Preece appeared to be a model prisoner, determined to go straight.'

Potting was interrupted by a couple of snorts from officers who'd had previous dealings with the man.

'So if he was a model prisoner,' asked Bella Moy sarcastically, 'how come he was driving a van twenty-five miles away from where he was supposed to be on Wednesday morning?'

'Exactly,' Potting said.

'Model prisoners don't go over the wall either,' she added tartly.

'They don't, Bella, no,' he agreed condescendingly, as if talking to a child.

Grace eyed both of them warily, wondering if they were about to have another of their regular spats.

'Now the good news is,' Potting went on, 'that word of this reward has spread around the prison, as you might imagine. Several inmates who've had contact with Preece have come forward to the Governor, offering suggestions where he might be, and I've got a list of six addresses and contact names for immediate follow-up.'

'Good stuff, Norman,' Grace said.

Potting allowed himself a brief, smug smile and took a swig from his mug of tea before continuing, 'But there's some bad news too. Ewan Preece had a friend in Ford Prison, another inmate – they go back years.' He checked his notes. 'Warren Tulley – had about the same amount of form as Preece. They were thick together inside. The officer had arranged for Tulley to talk to me. Someone went to fetch him to bring him over to the office – and found him dead in his cell. He'd hanged himself.'

There was a momentary silence while the team absorbed this. Grace's first reaction was that this news had not yet reached Spinella.

DC David Howes asked, 'What do we know about his circumstances?'

'He had two months to serve,' Potting said. 'Married with three young kids – all fine with the marriage apparently. Lisa Setterington knew him too. She assured me he was looking forward to getting out and spending time with his kids.'

'Not someone with any obvious reason to top himself?' Howes, who was a former Prison Liaison Officer, probed.

'Doesn't sound like it, no,' Potting replied.

'I'm just speculating, but what it sounds like to me,' Howes went on, 'is that possibly Warren Tulley knew where to find Preece.' He shrugged.

'Which might be why he died?' Grace said. 'Not suicide at all?'

'They're launching a full investigation, working closely with the West Area Major Crime Branch Team,' Potting said. 'Seems a bit coincidental to them.'

'How hard would it be to hang yourself in Ford?' Glenn Branson asked.

'Easier than in a lot of prisons. They've all got private rooms, like motel rooms,' Potting said. 'Being an open prison, they've got much more freedom and are left alone much more than in a higher-category place. If you wanted to hang yourself, you could do so easily.'

'And equally easily hang someone else?' Howes asked.

There was a long, uncomfortable silence.

'One hundred thousand dollars is a lot of folding to someone inside,' Glenn said.

'It's a lot of folding to anyone,' Nick Nicholl replied.

'More than enough to kill for,' Howes said grimly.

PC Alec Davies put up a hand. He spoke quite shyly. 'Sir, I might be stating the obvious, but if Warren Tulley did know where Preece was, then if someone did kill him, he possibly did it for one reason. Because he knows where Preece is too.'

39

Fernanda Revere sat restlessly on the edge of the green sofa. She gripped a glass in one hand and held a cigarette in the other, tapping the end impatiently, every few seconds, into a crystal ashtray. Then, with a sudden snort, she put down her cigarette, snatched up her cellphone and glared at it.

Outside a storm raged. Wind and rain were hurtling in from Long Island Sound, through the dunes and the wild grasses and the shrubbery. She heard the rain lashing against the windows and could feel the icy blast through them.

This huge living room, with its minstrel's gallery, ornate furniture and walls hung with tapestries, felt like a mausoleum tonight. A fire crackled in the grate but she could get no warmth from it. There was a ball game on television, the New York Giants playing some other team, which her brother shouted at intermittently. Fernanda didn't give a shit for football. A stupid men's game.

'Why don't those stupid people in England call me back?' she demanded, staring at her phone again, willing it to ring.

'It's the middle of the night there, hon,' her husband replied, checking his watch. 'They're five hours ahead. It's one in the morning.'

'So?' She took another angry drag on her cigarette and puffed the smoke straight back out. 'So this *associate*, where is he? He's going to show up? You sure? You sure about this, Ricky?'

She stared suspiciously at her brother, who was sitting opposite her, cradling a whiskey and sucking on a cigar that looked to her the size of a large dildo.

Lou, in a checked alpaca V-neck over a polo shirt, chinos and boat shoes, looked at Ricky, his face hard suddenly, and said, 'He's going to show, right? He's reliable? You know this guy?'

'He's reliable. One of the best there is. He's in the car – be here any moment.'

Ricky picked up the brown envelope he had prepared, checked its contents once more, then put it down again, satisfied, and turned his focus back to the game.

At forty, Ricky Giordino had the Italian looks of his father, but not the old man's strong face. His face was weak, a tad pudgy, like a baby's, and pockmarked. It shone with an almost permanent shiny patina of grease, from a congenital problem with his sweat glands. His black hair was styled with a quiff and his mouth was slightly misshapen, as if he'd had an operation for a harelip as a child. He was dressed in a thick black cardigan with metal buttons, baggy blue jeans which concealed the handgun permanently strapped to his calf and black Chelsea boots. So far, to their mother's dismay, he had remained single. He had a constant succession of brainless bimbos in tow, but tonight he had come alone, as his particular way of showing respect.

'You done business with this guy before?' Fernanda asked.

'He's recommended.' Ricky gave a self-satisfied smile. 'By an associate of mine. And there's a bonus. He knows this city, Brighton. He did a job there one time. He'll do what you want done.'

'He'd better. I want them to suffer. You told him that, didn't you?'

'He knows.' Ricky puffed on his cigar. 'You spoke to Mamma? How was she?'

'How do you think she was?' Fernanda drained the rest of her Sea Breeze and got up, unsteadily, to walk towards the drinks cabinet.

Ricky turned his attention back to the game. Within moments, he leapt out of his armchair, shaking a hand at the screen and showering cigar ash around him.

'The fuck!' he shouted. 'These guys, the fuck they doing?'

As he sat back down a series of sharp chimes came from the hall.

Ricky was on his feet again. 'He's here.'

'Mannie'll get it,' Lou said.

*

Tooth sat in the back of the Lincoln Town Car, dressed casually but smartly in a sports coat, open-neck shirt, chinos and brown leather loafers, the kind of clothes in which he could go anywhere without raising an eyebrow. His brown holdall lay on the seat beside him.

The driver had wanted to put it in the trunk when he had collected him from Kennedy Airport, but Tooth never let it out of his sight. He never checked it in, it came inside the plane with him on every flight. The bag contained his clean underwear, a spare shirt, pants, shoes, his laptop, four cellphones, three spare passports and an assortment of forged documents all concealed inside three hollowed-out paperback books.

Tooth never travelled with weapons, other than a quantity of the incapacitating agent 3-quinuclidinyl benzilate – BZ – disguised as two deodorant sticks, in his washbag. It wasn't worth the risk. Besides he had his best weapons on the end of his arms. His hands.

In the beam of the headlights he watched the high grey electric gates opening and the rain pelting down. Then they drove on through, until ahead he could see the superstructure of a showy modern mansion.

The driver had said nothing during the journey, which suited Tooth fine. He didn't do conversation with strangers. Now the man spoke for almost the first time since he had checked Tooth's name at the arrivals lobby at the airport.

'We're here.'

Tooth did not reply. He could see that.

The driver opened the rear door and Tooth stepped out into the rain with his bag. As they reached the porch, the front door of the house was opened by a nervous-looking Filipina maid in uniform. Almost immediately, she was joined by a mean-faced, pot-bellied man in a fancy black cardigan, jeans and black boots, holding a big cigar.

Tooth's first reaction was that the cigar was a good sign, meaning he could smoke in here. He stepped inside, into a huge hall with a grey flagstone floor.

A wide circular staircase swept up ahead of him. There were gilded mirrors and huge, bizarre abstract paintings which made no sense to him. Tooth didn't do art.

The man held out a fleshy hand covered in glinting rings, saying, 'Mr Tooth? Ricky Giordino. Y'had a good journey?'

Tooth shook the man's clammy hand briefly, then released it as fast as he could, as if it was a decomposing rodent. He didn't like to shake hands. Hands carried germs.

'The journey was fine.'

'Can I fix you a drink? Whiskey? Vodka? Glass of wine? We got just about everything.'

'I don't drink when I'm working.'

Ricky grinned. 'You haven't started yet.'

'I said I don't drink when I'm working.'

The smile slid from Ricky's face, leaving behind an awkward leer. 'OK. Maybe some water?'

'I had water in the car.'

'Great. Terrific.' Ricky checked his cigar, then sucked on it several times, to keep it burning. 'Maybe you want something to eat?'

'I ate on the plane.'

'Not great, that shit they give you on planes, is it?'

'It was fine.'

After five military tours, some of them solo, fending for himself behind enemy lines, eating beetles and rodents and berries sometimes for days on end, anything that came on a plate or in a bowl was fine by Tooth. He wasn't ever going to be a gourmet. He didn't do fine food.

'We're good, then. All set. Do you want to put your bag down?'

'No.'

'OK. Come with me.'

Tooth, still holding his bag, followed him along a corridor furnished with a fancy antique table, on which sat ornate Chinese vases, and past a living room that reminded him of an English baronial hall in a movie he'd seen long ago. A bitch in navy velour was sitting on a sofa, smoking a cigarette, with an ashtray full of butts beside her, and a loser was sitting opposite her, watching a bunch of dumb fuckwits playing American football.

This is what I risked my life for, gave my all for, so assholes like these could sit in their swell homes, with their fancy phones, watching dickheads playing games on big television screens?

Ricky ducked into the room and reappeared almost immediately carrying a brown envelope. He ushered Tooth back along the corridor to the hall, then led him down the stairs and into the basement. At the bottom was an abstract painting, as tall as Tooth, covered in what looked like photographs with weird faces. His eyes flickered with mild interest.

'That's pretty special,' the man said. 'A Santlofer. One of the up-and-coming great modern American artists. You wanted to buy that now, you'd pay thirty grand. Ten years time, you'll pay a million. The Reveres are great patrons. That's one of the things my sister and my brother-in-law do, they spot rising talents. You gotta support the arts. Y'know? Patrons?'

The painting looked to Tooth like one of those distorting mirrors you saw in fairgrounds. He followed the man through into a huge poolroom, the table itself almost lost against the patterned carpet. There was a bar in one corner, complete with leather stools and a stocked-up wine fridge with a glass door.

The man sucked on his cigar again, until his face was momentarily shrouded in a billowing cloud of dense grey smoke.

'My sister's pretty upset. She lost her youngest son. She doted on the kid. You gotta understand that.'

Tooth said nothing.

'You shoot pool?' the man said.

Tooth shrugged.

'Bowl?'

The man indicated him to follow and walked through into the room beyond. And now Tooth was impressed.

He was staring at a full-size, underground ten-pin bowling alley. It had just one lane, with polished wooden flooring. It was immaculate. Balls were lined up in the chute. All down the wall, beside the lane, was wallpaper that gave the illusion of rows of stacked bookshelves.

'You play this?'

As his reply, Tooth selected a ball and placed his fingers and thumb in the slots. Then he squinted down the length of the lane and could see that all the pins, white and shiny, were in place.

'Go ahead,' the man said. 'Enjoy!'

Tooth wasn't wearing the right shoes, so he made the run-up carefully and sent the ball rolling. In the silence of the basement it rumbled, like distant thunder. It clouted the front pin exactly where he had aimed it, slightly off centre, and it had the desired effect. All ten pins went straight down.

'Great shot! Gotta say, that's not at all bad!'

The man drew again on his cigar, puffing out his cheeks, blowing out the heavy smoke. He hit the reset button and watched the mechanical grab scoop up the pins and start to replace them.

Tooth dug his hand into his pocket, pulled out a pack of Lucky Strikes and lit one. After he had taken the first drag, the man suddenly snatched it out of his hand and crushed it out in an onyx ashtray on a ledge beside him.

'I just lit that,' Tooth said.

'I don't want that fucking cheap thing polluting my Havana. You want a cigar, ask me. OK?'

'I don't smoke cigars.'

'No cigarettes in here!' He glared challengingly at Tooth.

'She was smoking a cigarette upstairs.'

'You're down here with me. You do business my way or you don't do it. I'm not sure I like your attitude, Mr Tooth.'

Tooth considered, very carefully, killing this man. It would be easy, only a few seconds. But the money was attractive. Jobs hadn't exactly been flooding in just recently. Even without seeing this house, he knew about the wealth of this family. This was a good gig. Better not to blow it.

He picked up another ball, rolled it and hit another strike, all ten pins down.

'You're good, aren't you?' the man said, a little grudgingly.

Tooth did not respond.

'You've been to a place in England called Brighton? Like in Brighton Beach here in New York, right?'

'I don't remember.'

'You did a job for my cousin. You took out an Estonian ship captain in the local port who was doing side deals on cargoes of drugs.'

'I don't remember,' he said, again being deliberately vague.

'Six years ago. My cousin said you were good. They never found the body.' Ricky nodded approvingly.

Tooth shrugged.

'So, here's the deal. In this envelope are the names and all we have on them. My sister's prepared to pay one million dollars, half now, half on completion. She wants each of them to suffer, real bad. That's your specialty, right?'

'What kind of suffering?'

'Rumour has it you copied the Iceman's stunt with the rat. That right?'

'I don't copy anyone.'

The Iceman had been paid to make a victim he'd been hired to hit suffer. The client had wanted proof. So he wrapped the man, naked, in duct tape, with just his eyes, lips and genitals exposed. Then he left him in an underground cavern filled with a bunch of rats that had been starved for a week, and a video recorder. Afterwards his client had been able to watch the rats eating him, starting with the exposed areas.

'Good. She'd appreciate you being creative. We have a deal?'

'One hundred per cent cash upfront only,' Tooth said. 'I don't negotiate.'

'You know who you're fucking dealing with?'

Tooth, who was a good six inches shorter, stared him hard in the eye. 'Yes. Do you?' He shook another cigarette out of the pack and stuck it in his mouth. 'Do you have a light?'

Ricky Giordino stared at him. 'You got balls, I tell you that.' He hit the reset button again. 'How can I be sure you'll deliver? That you'll get all three hits?'

Tooth selected another ball from the chute. He lined himself up, ran, then crouched and sent the ball rolling. Yet again all ten pins scattered. He dug his hand in his pocket and pulled out a plastic lighter. Then he held it up provocatively, willing the man to try to stop him.

But Ricky Giordino surprised him by pulling out a gold Dunhill, clicking it open and holding up the flame to his cigarette.

'I think you and I – we're pretty close to understanding each other.'

Tooth accepted the light but did not reply. He didn't do understanding.

40

Self-confident, successful, tender and empa-
thetic man, 46, likes rock & classical music,
Belgian chocolate, bushcraft, integrity and
loyalty. WLTM intelligent and warm female
40–50 to share so many things.

Bushcraft?

Carly was curled up on the sofa with a glass of red Rioja in one hand and *Top Gear* about to start on the television. The Sunday supplements were spread all around her. It was her first drink since the accident and she needed it, as she was feeling very depressed.

The page of the *Sunday Times* she most looked forward to each week, the Encounters dating column, was open in front of her. Searching, as ever, not for Mr Right, but for someone to at least go out with and have fun with.

Bushcraft? What the hell did that mean? She'd learned from long experience that much of the wording in these ads had a subtext. How did this bloke get his rocks off? By walking around naked outside? Going back to nature? Shooting animals with a bow and arrow? The rest of him sounded fine. But bushcraft? No thanks.

Maybe if he had written *fossils* instead or *archaeology*, subjects that would appeal to Tyler, she might have given him a whirl. But she had visions of a bearded weirdo clambering out of an elderly Land Rover in a Davy Crockett hat and grass underpants. Nothing would surprise her any more.

It had been a long time since she'd slept with anyone. Over a year now and that last one had been a disaster. And the one before that. All the dates had been bloody disasters, with Preston Dave just the latest in the long line of them.

He'd sent her three more texts this weekend, each of which she'd deleted.

God, five years on and at times she still missed Kes so much.

Often clients told her they felt confident with her because she was so tough. But the truth was, she knew today more than ever, that she wasn't tough at all. That was an act she put on for them. A mask. The *Carly Chase at Work* mask. If she had really been tough, she'd be able to leave her clients behind at the end of each day. But she couldn't, not with a lot of them.

Kes used to tell her sometimes that she cared about her clients too much, to the point where it was getting her down. But she couldn't help that. Good marriages, like theirs had been, gave you a wonderful inner strength and sense of fulfilment in life. Bad marriages, as she encountered every day, in the tears and trembling voices and shakily signed statements of her clients, were a prison.

The *Argus* had been running stories on the accident every day, except today, when, being a Sunday, fortunately it wasn't printed. The front-page headline on Thursday had been the $100,000 reward put up by the dead boy's family for information leading to the van driver's identity. Her photograph had been on the second page: **Brighton Solicitor Arrested At Death Crash**.

She'd been in the paper again on Friday, yesterday too. It had made the national press also, with a big splash in the tabloids, as well as being in the *Sunday Times* today. It was big news that Tony Revere was the grandson of the New York Mafia capo Sal Giordino. She'd even had reporters phoning her at the office, but on the advice of Acott, her colleague and also her solicitor, she had not spoken with them. Although she had badly wanted to – to point out that she had not caused the accident, or even collided with the cyclist.

It seemed that everything that could possibly go wrong, in the house and in her life, was all going wrong at once. A dark gloom swirled inside her. That Monday morning feeling arriving an unwelcome twelve hours early, as it had done for as far back in her life as she could remember, way into early childhood.

Sunday evenings had been worse for her since Kes had died. It had been around this time, five years ago, that two police officers had turned up at her front door. They'd been contacted, via Interpol, by an RCMP officer from Whistler in Canada, asked to inform her that her husband was missing, presumed dead, in an avalanche while heli-skiing. It had been a further four days of anxious waiting, hoping against hope for some miracle, before they had recovered his body.

She often thought of selling the house and moving to a different part of the city. But she wanted to give Tyler some continuity and stability, and several of her friends, and her mother, whom she adored, had advised her in the months immediately following Kes's death not to make any hasty decisions. So she was still here, five years on.

The house wasn't particularly attractive from the outside. It was 1960s red brick, with a double garage beneath it, a clumsy extension, plus ugly secondary double-glazing put in by the previous owners which Carly and Kes had been planning to change. But they had both particularly loved the huge living room, with its patio doors opening on to the large, pretty sloping garden. There were two small ponds, a rockery and a summer house at the top which Kes and Tyler had made into a male domain. Tyler liked to play his drums there, while Kes liked to sit and do his thinking and smoke his cigars.

Kes and Tyler had been close, not just father and son, but proper mates. They went to football together to support the Albion every home match during the season. In the summer they went fishing, or to the cricket, or more often than not to Tyler's favourite place in Brighton, the Booth Museum of Natural History. They were so close that at times she'd found herself almost feeling jealous, thinking that she was being left out of some of their secrets.

After Kes's death, Tyler had moved his drum kit indoors, up to his room, and she had never seen him go to the summer house again. He'd been withdrawn for a long time. She had made a big effort, even taking him to football and to cricket herself, and on a fishing trip on a boat out of Brighton Marina – and she had been violently seasick for her troubles. They'd developed a certain closeness, but there was still a distance between them, a gap she could never quite close. As if the ghost of his father would always be the — elephant in the room.

She stared at a spreading brown stain on the wallpaper opposite her. Damp coming in. The house was falling apart around her. She was going to have to get to grips with it, either give it a massive makeover or finally move. But where? And besides, she still liked the place. She liked the feel of Kes's presence. Particularly in this living room.

They'd made it cosy, with two big sofas in front of the television and a modern electric fire with dancing flames. On the mantelpiece above it were invitations to parties and weddings and other social events they'd been planning to go to in the months after Kes got back from his annual boys' skiing trip. She still had not had the heart to remove them. It was like living in a time warp, she knew. One day she would move on. But not yet. She still wasn't ready.

And after the traumas of the past few days, she was less ready than ever.

She looked up at Kes's photograph on the mantelpiece amid the invitations. Standing next to her on the grass outside All Saints' Church, Patcham, on their wedding day, in a black morning coat, striped trousers, holding his top hat in his hand.

Tall and handsome, with slightly unruly jet-black hair, he had a certain air of arrogant insouciance about him. That was if you didn't know him. Behind that façade, which he regularly used with devastating effect in courtroom appearances, was a kind and surprisingly insecure man.

She drank some more wine and batted away a particularly dense and smelly fart from Otis, who was asleep at her feet. Then she increased the volume on the remote. Normally Tyler would come running into the room and curl up on the sofa beside her. This was his favourite programme, and one of the few times they sat and watched anything together. On this particularly gloomy, rain-lashed night, she felt more in need of his company than ever.

'Tyler!' she shouted. '*Top Gear*'s starting!'

Her voice woke up Otis, who jumped to his feet, then suddenly pricked up his ears and ran out of the room, growling.

Jeremy Clarkson, in a louder jacket and even baggier jeans than usual, was talking about a new Ferrari. She grabbed the remote again and froze the image, so that Tyler wouldn't miss anything.

He'd had been in a strange mood these past few days, since her accident. She was not sure why, but it was upsetting her. It was almost as if he was blaming her for what had happened. But as she replayed those moments again, for the thousandth time since Wednesday morning, she still came to the same conclusion: that she was not to blame. Even if she had not been distracted by her phone, and had braked half a second earlier, the cyclist would still have swerved out and then been hit by the van.

Wouldn't he?

Suddenly she heard the clack of the dog flap in the kitchen door, then the sound of Otis barking furiously out in the garden. What at, she wondered? Occasionally they had urban foxes, and she often worried that he might attack one and find he had met his match. She jumped up, but as she entered the kitchen, the dog came running back in, panting.

'Tyler!' she called out again, but still there was no answer from him.

She went upstairs, hoping he wasn't watching the programme on his own in his room. But to her surprise, he was sitting on his chair in front of his desk, going through the contents of his father's memory box.

Tyler had an unusual ambition for a twelve-year-old. He wanted to be a museum curator. Or more specifically the curator of a natural history museum. His ambition showed in his little bedroom, which was itself like a museum, reflecting his changing tastes as he had grown older. Even the colour scheme, which he had chosen himself, of powder-blue walls and pastel-green wood panelling, and the gaily coloured pennants criss-crossing the ceiling, gave the room an ecological feel.

His bookshelves were covered in plastic vegetation and models of reptiles, and crammed with volumes of *Tintin* and *Star Wars* stories, natural history reference books, palaeontology books, and one, so typical of him, called *Really Really Big Questions*.

The walls were covered with carefully selected and mounted photographs, wild life and fossil prints and some cartoon sketches of his own, all divided into sections. One of her favourites of his drawings was headed: *Tyler's Dream*. It depicted himself looking like a mad professor, with a crude skeleton of a prehistoric monster to his left, labelled *Tylersaurus*, and rows of squiggly little objects to his right, labelled *Fossils*. At the bottom of the cartoon he had written,

I want to be a fossil expert at the Natural History Museum . . . Have the biggest fossil collection in the world . . . Discover a dinosaur.

There was also a *Tintin* section, on part of one wall, neatly plastered in cartoons. And his music section, where his drum kit was set up. A guitar hung from the wall, along with a solitary bongo, and his cornet lay on a shelf, with a book beside it entitled *A New Tune a Day.*

'Tyler, *Top Gear*'s on!' she said.

He didn't stir. He was sitting in silence, in his grey cagoule with NEW YORK JETS on the back, with the old shoebox that he had filled with items that reminded him of his dad in the months following Kes's death in front of him. She wasn't sure where he had got the idea of the memory box from, some American TV series he had been watching, she thought, but she had liked it and still did.

He'd moved his computer keyboard and mouse pad aside, and was laying the contents out on the small amount of space not already occupied by his lava lamp, telescope, microscope and slide projector. She saw him take out his father's spotted silk handkerchief, his blue glasses case, fishing permit, a Brighton & Hove Albion season ticket, a box of trout flies and a small cartoon he had drawn, depicting his dad as a winged angel, flying past a signpost directing him up to heaven.

She eased her way carefully around the drum kit and placed her hands on his shoulders.

'What's up?' she said tenderly.

Ignoring her, he removed his father's fishing knife. At that moment there was a dark snarl from Otis. A second later she heard the bang of the dog flap, then Otis was out in the garden again, barking furiously. Puzzled, she walked across to the window and peered down.

It wasn't fully dark and there was some lighting from her windows and those of her neighbours. She looked up the steep lawn, past the ponds, towards the summer house, and saw Otis running around, barking furiously. At what? She could see nothing. But at the same time it unsettled her. This wasn't his normal behaviour. Had there been an intruder? Otis stopped barking and rushed around the lawn again, nose to the ground, as if he had picked up a scent. A fox, she thought. Probably just a fox. She turned back to Tyler and saw to her surprise that he was crying.

She walked the few steps back over to him, knelt and hugged him.

'What is it, darling? Tell me?'

He stared at her, eyes streaming behind his glasses. 'I'm scared,' he said.

'What are you scared of?'

'I'm scared after your crash. You might have another crash, mightn't you?' Then he looked at her solemnly. 'I don't want to have to make another memory box, Mummy. I don't want to have to make one about you.'

Carly put her arms around him and gave him a hug. 'Mummy's not going anywhere, OK? You're stuck with me.' She kissed his cheek.

Out in the garden, Otis suddenly began barking even more ferociously.

Carly got up and moved to the window. She peered out again, feeling a deepening sense of unease.

41

The plane landed hard, hitting the runway like the pilot hadn't realized it was there. All the stuff in the galley rattled and clanked, and one of the locker doors flew open, then slammed back shut. Flying didn't bother Tooth. Since his military days, he considered it a bonus to be landing any place where people weren't shooting at you. He sat impassively, braced against the deceleration, thinking hard.

He'd slept fine, bolt upright in this same position for most of the six-and-a-half-hour flight from Newark. He had gotten used to sleeping this way when he was on sniper missions in the military. He could remain in the same place, in the same position, for days when he needed to, relieving himself into bottles and bags, and he could sleep anywhere, wherever he was and whenever he needed to.

He could have charged the client for a business or first-class seat if he'd wanted, but he preferred the anonymity of coach. Flight crew paid you attention when you travelled up front and he didn't want the possibility of any of them remembering him later. A small precaution. But Tooth always took every small precaution going. For the same reason, he'd flown out of Newark rather than Kennedy Airport. It was a lower-profile place; in his experience it had less heavy security.

Trails of rain slid down the porthole. It was 7.05 a.m. UK time on his watch. The watch had a built-in digital video recorder with the pinhole camera lens concealed in the face. It had its uses for clients who wanted to see his handiwork. Like his current client.

A female voice was making an announcement about passengers in transit which did not concern him. He looked out across the grey sky and concrete, the green grass, the parked planes and signposts and runway lights and slab-like buildings of Gatwick Airport. One civilian airport looked pretty much like another, in his view. Sometimes the colour of the grass differed.

The bespectacled American in the seat next to him was clutching his passport and landing card, which he had filled out.

162

'Bumpy landing,' he said, 'huh?'

Tooth ignored him. The man had tried to strike up a conversation the moment he'd first sat down last night and Tooth had ignored him then, too.

*

Fifteen minutes later a turbaned immigration officer opened the UK passport up, glanced at the photograph of James John Robertson, brushed it across the scanner and handed it back to the man without a word. Just another British citizen returning home.

Tooth walked through, then followed the signs to the baggage reclaim and exit. No one gave a second glance to the thin, diminutive, shaven-headed man who was dressed in a dark brown sports coat over a grey polo shirt, black jeans and black Cuban-heeled boots. He strode towards the green Customs channel, holding his small bag in one hand and a thick beige anorak folded over his arm.

The Customs hall was empty. He clocked the two-way mirror above the stainless-steel examining benches as he walked through, passing the second-chance duty-free shop and out into the Arrivals Hall, into a sea of eager faces and a wall of placards bearing names. He scanned the faces, out of habit, but saw nothing familiar, no one looking particularly at him, nothing to be concerned about.

He made his way to the Avis car rental desk. The woman checked his reservation.

'You requested a small saloon, automatic, in a dark colour, Mr Robertson?'

'Yes.' He could do a good English accent.

'Would you be interested in an upgrade?'

'If I wanted a better model I'd have ordered one,' he said flatly.

She produced a form for him to sign, wrote down the details of his UK licence, then handed it back to him, along with an envelope with a registration number written on it in large black letters.

'You're all set. Keys are in here. Will you be returning it full?'

Tooth shrugged. If his plans for the days ahead worked out the way he intended, and they usually did, the company would not be seeing the car again. He didn't do rental returns.

42

If there were no developments, the initial energy of any new major crime inquiry could fade fast. Roy Grace had always seen one of his essential duties as the SIO as being to keep his team focused and energized. You *had* to make them feel they were making progress.

And in truth, if you didn't get a quick, early resolution, many major crime inquiries became painstakingly long and drawn out. Too slow-moving for the brass in Malling House, who were always mindful of the press, their obligations to the community and the ever present shadow of crime statistics, as well as far too slow for the families of the victims. Days could quickly become weeks, and weeks would drag into months. And occasionally months could turn into years.

One of his heroes, Arthur Conan Doyle, was once asked why, having trained as a doctor, he had turned to writing detective stories. His reply had been, 'The basis of all good medical diagnosis is the precise and intelligent recognition and appreciation of minor differences. Is this not precisely what is required of a good detective?'

He thought hard now about those words, as he sat with his team in the Monday morning briefing. Day six of the inquiry. 8.30 a.m. A wet, grey morning outside. A sense of frustration inside. It took Norman Potting to say what they were all feeling.

'He's vermin, this Ewan Preece. And he's thick. We're not dealing with someone smart. This is a cretin who lives off the slime at the bottom of the gene pool. My bogies are smarter than he is.'

Bella Moy screwed up her face in disgust. 'Thank you, Norman. So what's your point, exactly?'

'Just what I've said, Bella. That he's not smart enough to hide – not for any length of time. Someone'll shop him, if he isn't spotted by a police officer before then. A reward of a hundred thousand dollars – the bugger doesn't have a prayer.'

'So you're saying we should just wait, not bother with this line of enquiry?' Bella dug into him harder.

Potting pointed at a whiteboard, at the centre of which Ewan Preece's name was written in large red letters and circled, with his prison mugshot pasted beside it. It showed a thin-faced young man. He had short, spiky hair, a scowling mouth that reminded Grace of a braying donkey and a single gold hooped earring. Various lines connected the circle around him to different names: members of his family, friends, known associates, contacts.

'One of that lot, they'll know where Preece is. He's around, here in the city, mark my words.'

Grace nodded. Someone like Preece wouldn't have any contacts outside his small world of petty criminals within Brighton and Hove. This was likely to be the limit of his horizons. Which made it even more irritating that the little toerag had managed to remain at large for five days already without a sighting.

On the typed notes from his MSA he had headings for four of the different lines of enquiry so far.

1. Ewan Preece – family, friends, known associates and contacts
2. Search for the van – local witnesses and CCTV
3. Ford Transit wing mirror
4. Ford Prison – (link to 1.)

He looked up at the whiteboard, at the family tree of Preece's relatives and social network that they were putting together. He stared at the weasely, scarred face of Preece, so thin he looked almost emaciated. He'd had dealings with him before when he'd done a two-year spell on Response, before he'd joined the CID. Preece was like many in this city, a kid of a single parent from a rough estate, who'd never had guidance from his rubbish mother. Grace remembered going round to see her after Preece, then aged fourteen, had been arrested for joyriding. He could still recall her opening the door with a fag in her mouth, saying, 'What do you expect me to do? I'm on me way to play bingo.'

He turned to PC Davies, who was looking tired. 'Anything to report, Alec?'

'Yes, chief.' He yawned. 'Sorry, been up all night going through

CCTV footage. There were several sightings of what might be our van within the timeline.'

'Did any of the cameras get the index?'

He shook his head. 'No, but several are fairly positive sightings because you can see the wing mirror's missing. In the first of these at the junction of Carlton Terrace and Old Shoreham Road it was heading west. It was still heading west, according to the camera at Benfield Way and Old Shoreham Road. The same at the one sited on Trafalgar Road and on Applesham Way. Then the last sighting was the van heading south towards Southwick.'

'Do any show the driver?' Glenn Branson asked.

Davies nodded. 'Yes, but not clearly enough to identify him. I've given the footage to Chris Heaver in the Imaging Unit to see if he can enhance it for us.'

'Good,' Grace said.

'I think he may have gone to ground somewhere in central Southwick,' Alec Davies said. He stood up and walked uncertainly over to another whiteboard, on which was pinned a large-scale street map of the city. 'My reasoning is this. The vehicle was last sighted here.' He pointed. 'This CCTV camera is outside an off-licence, close to Southwick Green. So far there are no further sightings. I've had officers checking all around that area and there are a number of cameras that would almost certainly have picked up the van if it had gone down to the harbour, or doubled back and along the Old Shoreham Road, or if it had headed on to the A27.' He looked directly at Grace. 'It could be an indication it's still within this area, sir.' Then he circled with his finger around Southwick and Portslade, taking in the northern perimeter of Shoreham Harbour.

'Good work,' Grace said. 'I agree. Map the area out with boundaries and get the Outside Inquiry Team, and local officers who know the area, to do a street-by-street search. Get them to knock on the door of every house that's got an enclosed garage and ask permission to look inside. And see if there are any lock-ups in the area, or anywhere else that a van could be kept concealed. At the same time, get your team to talk to people in the area. Maybe there are witnesses who saw the van driving fast or erratically around that time.'

'Yes, sir.'

'And now I think you need to get some rest.'

Davies grinned. 'I'm tanked on caffeine, sir. I'm fine.'

Grace looked at him hard for a moment, before saying, 'Good lad, but don't exhaust yourself.' He looked down at the next item on his list, then addressed Sergeant Paul Wood from the Collision Investigation Unit. 'Have we got any more information from the van's wing mirror?'

'I wasn't happy, because we hadn't recovered all the parts from the scene, chief,' Wood replied. 'I had the Specialist Search Unit take a look down all the gutters and they found a bit I was missing. Unless there's anything else we haven't found, and I don't think there is, there's a clean break on the arm, which means it's probable the actual mountings for the mirror unit on the van are still intact. Replacing it would be a simple task of buying – or stealing – a replacement wing mirror unit. It could be fitted by anyone in a few minutes with basic tools.'

Grace made a note, thinking that most, if not all, spare parts depots would have been closed yesterday, on a Sunday, then looked up at Norman Potting, who he could always rely on to be thorough. Nick Nicholl was a grafter, too.

'Norman and Nick, I'm tasking you to cover all places where you could obtain a new or second-hand wing mirror for this vehicle. Ford dealers, parts depots, accessories shops like Halfords, breakers' yards – and check to see if there have been any reports of wing mirror thefts off similar vans in the Brighton and Hove area. If you need extra manpower let me know. I want every possibility covered by this evening's briefing, if possible.'

Nicholl nodded like an eager puppy. Potting made a note, his face screwed up in concentration.

'What about eBay? That could be a likely port of call to replace something like this.'

'Good point, Norman. Give that to Ray Packham in the High-Tech Crime Unit. He'll know the most effective way to search it.'

Then he returned to his list. 'OK, the last agenda item is Ford Prison. Glenn and Bella, I want you to go there and see what you can get out of any of the inmates who knew Preece or Warren Tulley.

I spoke to Lisa Setterington, the officer there who was in charge of Preece, and she's lining them up for you. And she's been working with our Prison Liaison Officer. I think your strategy should be to focus on Preece as someone who's gone missing, rather than as a suspect in the hit-and-run, and don't even refer to Tulley. Setterington's an experienced officer. She'll deliver all Preece's associates inside Ford to you. If any of them open up, emphasize the reward ticket. And put the frighteners on them – tell them Preece is going to be shopped by someone, so it might as well be them.'

'Do we have a post-mortem report on Tulley yet, chief?' asked Nick Nicholl.

'I'm waiting for it,' Grace replied. Then he looked back at his notes. 'Preece is a good suspect. All of you speak to any informants you know. Put the word out on the street that we're looking for him – and about the reward. Not everyone reads the papers or listens to the news.'

DC Boutwood raised a hand. 'Chief, I've spoken with an under-cover member of *Operation Reduction* who's running a number of informants. He's asked around for me, but none of Preece's regular contacts have heard from him in the past week.'

I don't think I'd talk to my regular contacts with a $100K price tag on my head either, Grace thought, but what he actually said was, 'He's obviously keeping his head down, E-J. But he'll surface somewhere.'

Had he possessed a crystal ball, he might have used a different turn of phrase.

43

When the meeting ended Grace asked Glenn Branson to come and see him in his office in ten minutes' time. Then, as he walked alone along the corridor, he rang Cleo. Despite the consultant's instructions for her to rest, she had insisted on going back to work today, although she had promised Roy she would not do any heavy lifting.

She sounded fine but was too busy to speak for more than a moment. Lots of people died at weekends, falling off ladders doing DIY, born-again bikers going out for fast rides, men pegging out during their solitary bonk of the week and the lonely who found the weekends too much to bear. Her enthusiasm for her grim work never ceased to amaze him. But by the same token, she frequently said the same of him.

He made himself a coffee in the space the size of a small closet, with a kettle, worktop, sink and fridge, that was Sussex House's apology for a canteen and carried it through to his office. He had barely sat down when Glenn entered.

'Yo, old-timer. What's popping?'

Grace grinned at his use of that word. He'd recently circulated to Sussex CID a DVD he'd been sent by a senior detective in Los Angeles, whom he had met last year at the International Homicide Investigators Association annual symposium. It was on the large number of Hispanic gangs prevalent on the streets of LA and in the prisons, giving guidance on how to recognize and interpret their slang, the symbols on their clothing and in their tattoos, and their hand signals, all of which were copied by the less organized but equally nasty UK street gangs.

'Popping?'

'Uh-huh.'

'What's *popping* is that I want you to take this evening's briefing.' Grace grinned, clocking Branson's even sharper than usual suit

– grey with purple chalk stripes. 'That's if you haven't got an appointment with your tailor.'

'Yep, well, I need to make you one, get you some new summer gear.'

'Thanks, you did that last year and cost me two grand.'

'You've got a beautiful young fiancée. You don't want to take her out dressed like an old git.'

'Actually, that's why I need you to take over from me this evening. I'm taking her out tonight. Got tickets for a concert at the O_2 in London.'

Branson's eyes widened. 'Cool. What concert?'

'The Eagles.'

Branson gave him a *sad bastard* stare and shook his head. 'Get real! The Eagles? That's old git's music! She's an Eagles fan?'

Grace tapped his chest. 'No, I am.'

'I know that, old-timer. Seen them in your house. Can't believe how many of their albums you have.'

' "Lyin' Eyes" and "Take It Easy" are two of the best singles of all time.'

Branson shook his head. 'You've probably got Vera Lynn on your iPod, as well.'

Grace blushed. 'Actually I still haven't got an iPod.'

'That figures.' Branson sat down, put his elbows on Grace's desk and stared him hard in the eyes. 'She's just come out of hospital and you're going to inflict the Eagles on her? I can't believe it!'

'I bought the tickets ages ago, for a fortune. Anyhow, it's a quid pro quo.'

'Oh yeah?'

'In exchange, I've promised to take Cleo to a musical.' He gave Glenn a helpless look. 'I don't like musicals. Give and take, right?'

Branson's eyes widened. 'Don't tell me. *The Sound of Music*?'

Grace grinned. 'Don't even go there.'

44

Tooth drove from the Avis section of the car park, made a circuit of the airport and drove in through the entrance marked Long Term Car Park. Instead of following the directions to Today's Parking Area, he headed off, steadily driving up and down the lanes of cars already parked there, looking for other Toyota Yaris models that were of the same year and colour as his own.

Within twenty minutes he had identified five. Three of them were parked in deserted areas, out of sight of any CCTV cameras. Working quickly, he removed each of their front and rear licence plates and put them in the boot of his car. Then, paying the minimum fee, he drove back out of the car park and headed towards the Premier Inn, one of the hotels close to the airport perimeter.

There he requested a second-floor room, one with a view of the hotel parking area and the main entrance. He favoured second-floor rooms. No one outside could see in and should he need to leave in a hurry, via the window, that was a survivable jump, for him. He also told the woman receptionist he was expecting delivery of a FedEx package.

He locked the door, placed his bag on the bed, opened it and took out the brown envelope Ricky Giordino had given him. Then he moved the wooden desk in front of the window, climbed on to it and taped over the smoke detector on the ceiling, before sitting in the purple chair and staring out and down. The hotel had taken trouble over the parking area. Well-trimmed bushes, low ornamental hedges, round wooden tables, a covered smoking shelter. Seventy-two cars, including his small dark grey Toyota, were parked in neat rows. He remembered the make, colour and position of them all. That was something he had learned from his days in the military. You remembered what you could see. When some detail, however small, changed, that was the time to be concerned.

Beyond the far end of the lot was a tall red crane and beyond that the dark hulk of a building rising in the distance with the words GATWICK NORTH TERMINAL near the roofline in large white letters.

He made himself an instant coffee and then studied once more the contents of the envelope.

Three photographs. Three names.

Stuart Ferguson. A stocky man of forty-five with a shaven head and a triple chin, wearing a green polo shirt with the words ABERDEEN OCEAN FISHERIES in yellow. Carly Chase, forty-one, a passably attractive woman, in a chic black jacket over a white blouse. Ewan Preece, thirty-one, spiky-haired scumbag, in a dark cagoule over a grey T-shirt.

He had addresses for the first two, but only a phone number for Preece.

He took out one of his cellphones and inserted the UK pay-as-you-go SIM card he had purchased at Gatwick Airport a short while ago, then dialled the mobile phone number.

It answered on the sixth ring. An edgy-sounding man said, 'Yeah?'

'Ricky said to call you.'

'Oh yeah, right. Hang on.' Tooth heard a scraping sound, then the voice again, quieter, furtive. 'Yeah, with you now. Difficult to talk, you see.'

Tooth didn't see. 'You have an address for me.'

'That's right, yeah. Ricky knows the deal, right?'

He didn't like the way the man sounded. He hung up.

Then he glared up at the smoke detector, feeling in need of a cigarette. Moments later his cellphone rang. The display showed no number. He hit the answer button but said nothing.

After a moment the man he had just spoken to said, 'Is that you?'

'You want to give me the address or you want to go fuck yourself?' Tooth replied.

The man gave him the address. Tooth wrote it down on the hotel notepad, then hung up without thanking him. He removed the SIM card, burned it with his cigarette lighter until it started melting and flushed it down the toilet.

Then he unfolded the street map of the City of Brighton and

Hove he had bought at the WH Smith bookstall and searched for the address. It took him a while to locate it. Then he pulled out another phone he had with him, his Google Android, which was registered in the name of his associate, Yossarian, and entered the address into its satnav.

The device showed him the route and calculated the time. By car it was forty-one minutes from the Premier Inn to this address.

Then on his laptop Tooth opened up Google Earth and entered Carly Chase's address. Some moments later he was zooming in on an aerial view of her house. It looked like there was plenty of secluded garden around it. That was good.

He showered, changed into his fresh underwear and made himself some more coffee. Then, returning to Google Earth, he refreshed his memory of another part of the city, an area he had got to know well the last time he was here, the port to the west of Brighton, Shoreham Harbour. Seven miles of waterfront, it was a labyrinth with a large number of places where no one went. And twenty-four-hour access. He knew it as well as he had known some enemy terrain.

Shortly after 11 a.m., the room phone rang. It was the front desk, telling Tooth that a courier was waiting with a package for him. He went down and collected it, took it up to his room and removed the contents, placing them in his bag. Then he burned the receipt and delivery note, and everything on the packaging that revealed its origins.

He packed everything else back into his bag, too, then picked it up and took it with him. He had already prepaid the room charge for a week, but he didn't yet know when he would return, if he returned at all.

45

Carly did not start the week in a good frame of mind. Her only small and bleak consolation was that, with luck, this week would be marginally less shitty than the previous one. But with the client settling into the chair in front of her now, Monday was not starting on a promising note.

Ken Acott had informed her that the court hearing was set for Wednesday of the following week. He was going to try to get her Audi released from the police pound as soon as possible, but the car was badly damaged and there was no likelihood of it being repaired within the next ten days. She was going to lose her licence for sure, hopefully getting only the minimum of one year's ban.

Clair May, another mother with a son at St Christopher's with whom she was very friendly, had taken Tyler to school this morning and would bring him home this evening. She had told Carly that she was happy to do this for as long as was needed, and Carly was grateful at least for that. It had never occurred to her quite how lost she would be without a car, but today she was determined not to let it get her down. Kes used to tell her to view every negative as a positive. She was damned well going to try.

First thing this morning she had looked into contract taxi prices, Googled bus timetables and had also checked out buying a bike. It was a fair hike to the nearest bus stop from her home and the bus schedule was not that great. A bike would be the best option – at least on days when it wasn't pissing down with rain. But with the memory of the accident scene still vivid in her mind, she could not contemplate cycling with any enthusiasm at this moment.

Her client's file was open in front of her. Mrs Christine Lavinia Goodenough. Aged fifty-two. Whatever figure the woman might once have had was now a shapeless mass and her greying hair appeared to have been styled in a poodle parlour. She laid her fleshy hands on her handbag, which she had placed possessively on her lap, as if she did not trust Carly, and had a look of total affront on her face.

It was rarely the big things that destroyed a marriage, Carly thought. It wasn't so much the husband – or the wife – having an affair. Marriage could often survive problems like that. It was often more the small things, with the tipping point being something really petty. Such as the one the woman in front of her now revealed.

'I've been thinking since last week. Quite apart from his snoring, which he flatly refuses to acknowledge, it's the way he *pees* at night,' she said, grimacing as she said the word. 'He does it deliberately to irritate me.'

Carly widened her eyes. Neither her office nor her desk was grand or swanky in any way. The desk was barely big enough to contain her blotter, the in and out trays, and some pictures of herself and Tyler. The room itself, which had a fine view over the Pavilion – and a less fine constant traffic roar – was so spartan that, despite having been here six years, it looked like she had only just moved in, apart from the stack of overflowing box files on the floor.

'How do you mean, *deliberately*?' she asked.

'He pees straight into the water, making a terrible splashing sound. At precisely two o'clock every morning. Then he does it again at four. If he were considerate, he'd pee against the porcelain, around the sides, wouldn't he?'

Carly thought back to Kes. She couldn't remember him peeing during the night, ever, except perhaps when he had been totally smashed.

'Would he?' she replied. 'Do you really think so?'

Although Carly made her money for the firm in dealing with matrimonial work, she always tried to dissuade her clients from litigation through the court. She got much more satisfaction from helping them negotiate resolutions to their problems.

'Perhaps he's just tired and not able to concentrate on where he is aiming?'

'Tired? He does it deliberately. That's why God gave men willies, isn't it? So they can aim direct where they're pissing.'

Well, God really thought of everything, didn't he?

Though she was tempted to say it, instead Carly advised, 'I think you might find that hard to get across in your hearing.'

'That's coz judges are all blokes with little willies, aren't they?'

Carly stared at the woman, trying to maintain her professional integrity – and neutrality. But she was rapidly coming to the conclusion that if she was this cow's husband, she would long ago have tried to murder her.

Not the right attitude, she knew. But sod it.

46

Tooth wasn't happy as he turned into the residential street and drove over a speed bump. It was wide and exposed, with little tree cover. It was a street you could see a long way down, on both sides, without obstruction. A hard street to hide in. A little parade of shops and mixture of semi-detached houses and bungalows. Some had integral garages, others had had this area converted into an extra front room. Cars were parked along the kerb on both sides, but there were plenty of free spaces. There was a school some way down and that wasn't good news. These days people kept an eye on single men in cars parked near schools.

He saw the house he had come to find, number 209, almost immediately. It was directly opposite the shops and had an attached garage. It was the house where he had been informed that his first target, Ewan Preece, was holed up.

He drove past, continuing along the street for some distance, then meandered along various side roads, before returning to his target street five minutes later. There was an empty space a short distance from the house, between a dilapidated camper van and an original cream Volkswagen Beetle with rusted wings. He reversed into the space.

This was a good position, giving him an almost unobstructed view of the house. It seemed to be in poor repair. The exterior paintwork had once been white but now looked grey. The window-sills were rotten. There were black trash bags in the front garden, along with a rusted washing machine that looked like it had been there for years. People ought to have more self-respect, he thought. You shouldn't leave trash in your front yard. He might mention that to Preece. They'd have plenty of time to chat.

Or rather, Preece would have plenty of time to listen.

He opened his window a little and yawned, then switched the engine off. Although he had slept on the plane, he felt tired now and could use another coffee. He lit a Lucky Strike and sat smoking it, staring at the house, thinking. Working out a series of plans, each contingent on what happened in the coming hours.

He pulled out the photograph of Ewan Preece and studied it yet again. Preece looked an asshole. He'd recognize him if he left – or returned to – the house. Assuming the information was correct and he was still there, in number 209.

There was important stuff he did not know. Starting with who else might be in the house with Preece. Not that it would be a problem. He'd deal with it. The kind of person who would shield a man like Ewan Preece was going to be similar low-life vermin. Never a problem. A few spots of rain fell on the windshield. That was good. Rain would be helpful. Nice heavy rain would frost the glass and make him less visible in here, and keep people off the streets. Fewer witnesses.

Then, suddenly, he stiffened. Two uniformed male police officers came into view around the corner, at the far end of the street. He watched them strut up to the front door of a house and ring the bell. After some moments they rang again, then knocked on the door. One of them pulled out a notebook and wrote something down, before they moved on to the next house, nearer to him, and repeated the procedure.

This time the door opened and he saw an elderly woman. They had a brief conversation on the doorstep, she went back inside, then came out again with a raincoat on, shuffled around to the garage and lifted the up-and-over door.

It didn't take a rocket scientist to figure out what they might be looking for. But their presence here threw him totally. He watched as the two officers nodded, then turned away and walked down to the next house, moving closer still to him. He was thinking fast now.

Driving away was one option. But the police were so close, that might draw attention to him, and he didn't want them taking note of the car. He glanced over the road at the parade of shops. Better to stay here, remain calm. There didn't appear to be any parking restrictions. There was no law against sitting in your car, smoking a cigarette, was there?

He crushed the butt out into the car's ashtray and sat watching them. They got no answer at the next house, had a brief conversation on the pavement, then split, one of them crossing the road, heading up the pavement and entering the first shop in the parade.

His colleague was now knocking on the door of number 209.

Tooth felt in need of another cigarette. He shook one from the pack, put it in his mouth and lit it, watching the windows of the house as the policeman stood on the doorstep, his knock unanswered. Then he glimpsed an upstairs curtain twitch, just a fraction. Such a tiny movement, he wouldn't have noticed it if he hadn't been watching so closely.

It was enough to know there was someone in there. Someone who wasn't going to open the door to a cop. Good.

The officer knocked again, then pressed what Tooth assumed was a bell. After some moments he pushed it again. Then he turned away, but instead of walking to the front door of the next house in the row, he came over to the car.

Tooth remained calm. He took another drag of his cigarette, dropping the photograph of Ewan Preece on the floor between his feet.

The policeman was now bending, tapping on his passenger side window.

Tooth switched on the ignition and powered the window down.

The policeman was in his mid-twenties. He had sharp, observant eyes and a serious, earnest expression.

'Good morning, sir.'

'Morning,' he replied, in his English accent.

'We're looking for a white Ford Transit van that was seen driving erratically in this area last Wednesday. Does that ring any bells?'

Tooth shook his head, keeping his voice quiet. 'No, none.'

'Thank you. Just as a formality, can I check what you are doing here?'

Tooth was ready for the question. 'Waiting for my girlfriend. She's having her hair done.' He pointed at the salon, which was called Jane's.

'Likely to be a long wait, if she's like my missus.'

The officer stared at him for a second, then stood up and walked towards the next house. Tooth powered the window back up, watching him in the mirror. The cop stopped suddenly and turned back to look at his car again. Then he walked up to the front door of the house.

Tooth continued to watch him, and his colleague, working their way along every house, all the way down the street, until they were safely out of sight. Then, in case they returned, he drove off. Besides, there wasn't any point in hanging out in this street in daylight. He would return after dark. In the meantime, he had plenty of work to do.

47

Taking his seat at the workstation in MIR-1, with a coffee in his hand, Roy Grace felt tired and a little despondent. Ewan Preece had gone to ground and there was no telling how long he might remain in hiding. Tomorrow would be a whole week since the collision, without a single reported sighting of the man, despite the reward.

On the plus side was the fact that Preece was not bright, and sooner or later he would make a mistake and be spotted, for sure – if he wasn't shopped first by someone. But in the meantime there was a lot of pressure on him from ACC Rigg, who in turn was under pressure from the Chief Constable, Tom Martinson, to get a fast result.

Sure, it would all die down as time passed, especially when a bigger news story came along, but for the moment *Operation Violin* was making a lot of people uncomfortable. In particular the new Chief Executive of Brighton and Hove City Council, John Barradell, who was doing his best to rid the city of its unwelcome sobriquet Crime Capital of the UK. It was he in turn who was putting the most pressure on the police chiefs.

'The time is 8.30 a.m., Tuesday 27 April,' Grace said at the start of the morning briefing. He looked down at his printed notes. 'We have new information from Ford Prison on the death of Warren Tulley, Ewan Preece's mate.'

He looked at Glenn Branson, then at the rest of his team, which was growing by the day. They had now spilled over into both the other workstations in this large office. The latest addition was DS Duncan Crocker, whom he had brought in as the Intelligence Manager. Crocker, who was forty-seven, had receding wavy hair turning grey at the edges and a constantly jovial demeanour that implied, no matter how grim the work, there would always be a decent drink waiting for him at the end of the day. This belied the man's efficiency. Crocker was a thorough professional, a sharp and astute detective, and a stickler for detail.

Glenn Branson said, 'I have the post-mortem report on Tulley, boss. He was hanging from a steel beam in his cell from a rope made out of strips of bedding sheet. The officer who found him cut him down above the knot and proceeded to perform CPR on him, but he was pronounced dead at the scene twenty minutes later by a paramedic. To summarize the report –' he held it up to indicate that it was several pages long – 'there are a number of factors to indicate this was not suicide. The ACCT – Assessment, Care in Custody, and Teamwork – report on this prisoner indicates no suicidal tendencies, and, like Ewan Preece, he was due to be released in three weeks' time.'

Norman Potting's mobile phone rang, the *James Bond* theme blaring out. Grunting, he silenced it.

'Have you just changed that from *Indiana Jones*?' Bella Moy said.

'It sort of came with the phone,' he replied evasively.

'That's just so cheesy,' she said.

Branson looked down at his notes. 'There was evidence of a struggle in Tulley's cell and several bruises have been found on his body. The pathologist says that it appears he was asphyxiated by strangling first and then hung. He also found human flesh under some of his fingernails, which has been sent off for DNA analysis. These are all indicative of a struggle.'

'If he was strangled by another prisoner at Ford, that DNA analysis will give us him,' Duncan Crocker said.

'With luck,' Branson said. 'It is being fast-tracked and we should have a result back later today or tomorrow.' He glanced down at his notes again, then looked at Roy Grace as if for reassurance. Grace smiled at him, proud of his protégé. Branson went on. 'According to Officer Setterington, who has spoken with several of the prisoners whom Preece and Tulley hung out with, Tulley was shooting his mouth off about the reward money. They all saw it on television and in the *Argus*. He was boasting he knew where Preece was and was weighing up his loyalty to his friend against the temptation of a hundred thousand dollars.'

'Did he genuinely know?' asked Bella Moy.

Branson raised a finger, then tapped his keypad. 'Every prisoner in a UK jail gets given a PIN code for the prison phone, right? And they have to nominate the numbers they will call – they can have a maximum of ten.'

'I thought they all had mobile phones,' Potting said with a sly grin.

Branson grinned back. It was a standard joke. Mobile phones were strictly forbidden in all prisons – and as a result they were an even more valuable currency than drugs.

'Yeah, well, luckily for us, this fellow didn't. Listen to this recording on the prison phone of a call made by Warren Tulley to Ewan Preece's number.'

He tapped the keypad again, there was a loud crackle, then they heard a brief, hushed conversation, two scuzzy, low-life voices.

'Ewan, where the fuck are you? You didn't come back. What's going on?'

'Yeah, well, had a bit of a problem, you see.'

'What kind of fucking problem? You owe me. It's my money in this deal.'

'Yeah, yeah, yeah, keep yer hair on. I just had a bit of an accident. You on the prison phone?'

'Yeah.'

'Why don't you use a private?'

'Coz I ain't got one, all right?'

'Fuck. Fuck you. I'm lying low for a bit. All right? Don't worry about it. I'll see you right. Now fuck off.'

There was a clank and the call ended.

Branson looked at Roy Grace. 'That was recorded at 6.25 p.m. last Thursday, the day following the accident. I've also checked the timing. Prisoners working on paid resettlement, which is what Preece was doing, are free to leave the prison from 6.30 a.m. and don't have to be back until 10 p.m. That would have given him ample time to be driving in Portland Road around 9 a.m.'

'*Lying low*,' Grace said pensively. 'You need someone you can trust to lie low.' He stood up and went over to the whiteboard where Ewan Preece's family tree was sketched out. Then he turned to Potting. 'Norman, you know a fair bit about him. Any ideas who he was close to?'

'I'll speak to some of the neighbourhood teams, boss.'

'My guess is, since the van seems to have disappeared in Southwick, that he'll be there, with either a girlfriend or a relative.' Grace looked at the names on the whiteboard.

As was typical with the child of a single, low-income parent, Preece had a plethora of half-brothers and sisters as well as step-brothers and sisters, with many of the names well known to the police.

'Chief,' Duncan Crocker said, standing up. 'I've already been doing work on this.' He went over to the whiteboard. 'Preece has three sisters. One, Mandy, emigrated to Perth, Australia, with her husband four years ago. The second, Amy, lives in Saltdean. I don't know where the youngest, Evie, lives, but she and Preece were pretty thick as kids. They got nicked, when Preece was fourteen and she was ten, for breaking into a launderette. She was in his car later when he was done for joyriding. She'd be a good person to look for.'

'And a real bonus if she just happens to be living in Southwick,' Grace replied.

'I know someone who'll be able to tell us,' Crocker said. 'Her probation officer.'

'What's she on probation for?' Branson asked.

'Handling and receiving,' Crocker said. 'For her brother!'

'Phone the probation officer now,' Grace instructed.

Crocker went over to the far side of the room to make the call, while they carried on with the briefing. Two minutes later he returned with a big smile on his face.

'Chief, Evie Preece lives in Southwick!'

Suddenly, from feeling despondent, Grace felt a surge of adrenalin. He thumped the worktop with glee. *Yayyy!*

'Good work, Duncan,' he said. 'You have the actual address?'

'Of course! Two hundred and nine Manor Hall Road.'

The rest of this briefing now seemed redundant.

Grace turned to Nick Nicholl. 'We need a search warrant, PDQ, for two hundred and nine Manor Hall Road, Southwick.'

The DC nodded.

Grace turned back to Branson. 'OK, let's get the Local Support Team mobilized and go pay him a visit.' He looked at his watch.

'With a bit of luck, if the warrant comes through and we get there fast enough, we'll be in time to bring him breakfast in bed!'

'Don't give him indigestion, chief,' Norman Potting said.

'I won't, Norman,' Grace replied. 'I'll tell them to be really gentle with him. Ask him how he likes his eggs and if we should cut the crusts off his toast. Ewan Preece is the kind of man who brings out the best in me. He brings out my inner Good Samaritan.'

48

An hour and a half later, Grace and Branson cruised slowly past 209 Manor Hall Road, Southwick. Branson was behind the wheel and Grace studied the house. Curtains were drawn, a good sign that the occupants were not up yet, or at least were inside. Garage door closed. With luck the van would be parked in there.

Grace radioed to the other vehicles in his team, while Branson stopped at their designated meeting point, one block to the south, and turned the car around. The only further intelligence that had come through on Evie Preece was that she was estranged from her common-law husband and apparently lived alone in the house. She was twenty-seven years old and had police markers going back years, for assault, street drinking, possession of stolen goods and handling drugs. She was currently under an ASBO banning her from entering the centre of Brighton for six months. All three of her children, by three different fathers, had been taken into care on the orders of the Social Services. She and her brother were two peas in a pod, Grace thought. They'd no doubt be getting plenty of lip from her when they went in.

'So, old-timer, tell me, how was the concert last night? What did Cleo think of your sad old git band?'

'She thought the Eagles were great, actually!'

Branson looked at him quizzically. 'Oh yeah?'

'Yeah!'

'You sure she wasn't just humouring you?'

'She said she'd like to see them again. And she bought a CD afterwards.'

Branson tapped his head. 'You know, love does make people go a bit crazy.'

'Very funny!'

'You probably had an old person's nap in the middle of it. The band probably did too.'

'You're so full of shit. You are talking about one of the greatest bands of all time.'

'And you going to London on Friday night to see *Jersey Boys*?' Glenn said.

'Are you going to trash them, too?'

'Frankie Valli and the Four Seasons – they're all right.'

'You actually like their music?'

'Some of it. I don't think *all* white music's rubbish.'

Grace grinned and was about to say something to Glenn, but then he saw in the mirror the dog handler's marked van pulling up behind them. After another few moments the unmarked white minibus, containing eight members of the Local Support Team, halted alongside them, momentarily blocking the road. Two other marked police cars reported they were now in position at the far end of the street.

Jason Hazzard, the Local Neighbourhood Team Inspector, looked in at them and Grace gave him the thumbs up, mouthing, 'Rock 'n' roll.'

Hazzard pulled his visor down and the three vehicles moved forward, accelerating sharply with a sense of urgency now, then braking to a halt outside the house. Everyone bundled out on to the pavement. Thanks to Google Earth they'd had a clear preview of the geography of the place.

Two sets of dog handlers ran up the side to cover the back garden. The members of the Local Support Team, in their blue suits, protective hard plastic knee pads, military-style helmets with visors lowered and heavy-duty black gloves, ran up to the front door. One of them carried a metal cylinder, the size of a large fire extinguisher – the battering ram, known colloquially as the *Big Yellow Door Key*. Two others, bringing up the rear, carried the back-up hydraulic ram and its power supply, in case the front door was reinforced. Two more stood outside the garage to prevent anyone escaping that way.

The first members of the team to reach the door pounded on it with their fists, at the same time yelling, 'POLICE! OPEN UP! POLICE! OPEN UP!' It was a deliberate intimidation tactic.

One officer swung the battering ram and the door splintered open.

All six of them charged in, shouting at the tops of their voices, 'POLICE! POLICE!'

Grace and Branson followed them into a tiny hallway that stank of stale cigarette smoke. Grace's adrenalin was pumping. Like most officers, he'd always loved the thrill of raids, and the fear that went with it. You never knew what you were going to find. Or what missiles or weapons might be used against you. His eyes darted everywhere, warily, ever conscious of the possibility that someone might appear with a weapon, and that both himself and Glenn were less well protected than the members of this team, wearing only stab vests beneath their jackets.

The LST members, all experienced and well trained in this kind of operation, had split up in here. Some were bursting into different downstairs rooms and others at the same time were charging up the stairs, yelling menacingly, 'POLICE! STAY WHERE YOU ARE! DON'T MOVE!'

The two detectives stayed in the narrow, bare hallway and heard doors banging open above them. Heavy footsteps. Then a female member of the team, whom Grace knew and rated as a particularly bright and plucky officer, Vicky Jones, called out to him in a concerned voice, 'Sir, you'd better come in here!'

Followed by Glenn Branson, he walked through the open doorway to his right, into a small and disgustingly cluttered sitting room that reeked of ingrained cigarette smoke and urine. He noticed a wooden-framed settee, bottles of wine and beer littering a manky carpet, along with unwashed clothes, and a massive plasma TV screen on the wall.

Face down, occupying whatever floor space wasn't littered with detritus, was a writhing, moaning woman in a fluffy pink dressing gown, bound hand and foot with grey duct tape, and gagged.

'No one upstairs!' shouted Jason Hazzard.

'Garage is empty!' another voice called out.

Grace ran upstairs very quickly, glanced into the two bedrooms and the bathroom, then went back down and knelt beside the woman, as Vicky Jones and another member of the team worked away the tape over her mouth, then the rest of the bindings.

The woman, in her mid-twenties, had a shock of short, fair hair and a hard face with a flinty complexion. She spoke the moment her mouth was freed.

'Fuckers!' she said. 'What took you so fucking long? What's the fucking time?'

'Five past ten,' Vicky Jones said. 'What's your name?'

'Evie Preece.'

'Are you injured, Evie?' She turned to another officer and said, 'Call an ambulance.'

'I don't need no fucking ambulance. I need a bleedin' drink and a fag.'

Grace looked at her. He had no idea at this stage how long she had been there, but she looked remarkably composed for someone who had been tied and gagged. He wondered if it was a set-up. This was not a woman you could trust with any story.

'Where's your brother?' Roy Grace asked her.

'Which bruvver?'

'Ewan.'

'In prison. Where you pigs put him.'

'So he hasn't been staying here?' he pressed.

'I didn't have no one staying.'

'Someone's been sleeping in your spare bed,' Grace said.

'Must have been the Man in the Moon.'

'Was that who tied you up? The Man in the Moon is into bondage, is he?'

'I want a solicitor.'

'You're not under arrest, Evie. You only get a solicitor if you are charged with something.'

'So charge me.'

'I will do in a minute,' Grace said. 'I'll charge you with obstructing a police officer. Now tell me who slept in your spare room?'

She said nothing.

'The same person who tied you up?'

'No.'

Good, he thought. That was a big step forward.

'We're concerned about your brother,' he said.

'That's bleedin' touching, that is. You been nicking him since he was a kid, but you're suddenly concerned about him? That's rich!'

49

At the evening briefing, Grace brought his team up to speed on the raid. Evie Preece was unable to give any information about her assailant, but the fact that she consented, albeit reluctantly, to a medical examination was an indication to Grace that the attack on her had been real and not a put-up job by herself and her brother, as he had first suspected. The house was such a tip it was hard to gauge whether it had been rifled through, which could have given robbery as a possible motive for the attack.

The police doctor's opinion was that the severe bruising to her neck was indicative of a sharp blow. She added that the side of the neck, just above the collarbone, was the place where someone experienced in martial arts would strike, if they wanted to render their victim instantly unconscious.

This was consistent with Evie's story that around eleven the previous night she had gone out into the garden to let her cat out, and the next thing she had found herself lying, trussed up, on her living-room floor. She was continuing to refute the allegation that her brother had been in the house and she denied vehemently that any vehicle had been in her garage recently, despite evidence to the contrary. The first piece of which was a pool of engine oil on the surface of the garage floor, which looked recent. The second and even more significant was the discovery of male clothing in the spare bedroom. A pair of trainers and jeans that were consistent with Ewan Preece's size, and a T-shirt, also his size, found in her washing machine.

Grace had ordered her to be arrested on suspicion of harbouring a fugitive and obstructing the police, and assigned a trained inter-view adviser, Bella Moy, to come up with an interview strategy for her while she was being held in police custody.

In addition, he had put a highly experienced POLSA – Police Search Advisor – and a search team under him into the property to see if they could find anything else in the house or garden. So far, in addition to the oil and the clothes, they had come up with what they believed to be signs of a forced entry through kitchen patio doors at the rear of the house. It was very subtly done, with an instrument such as a screwdriver handled by someone with a good knowledge of locks.

To Grace's mind that ruled out the kind of low-life Ewan Preece and his sister dealt with, who might have been after money or drugs. Their scumbag associates would have broken a window or jemmied a lock. Whoever had come in here was skilled. Not just in breaking and entering, but in assault and in bindings. They had found no fingerprints so far, nothing that might yield DNA and no other clues. It was still early days, but it wasn't looking good.

50

Dressed in a heavy fleece jacket, thick jeans, a lined cap and rubber boots, David Harris began his workday at 7.00 a.m. sharp, as he had every day for the past forty-one years, by checking the rows of smokehouses, where the fish had been curing overnight. He was in a cheery frame of mind: business was booming despite the recession and he genuinely loved his work.

He especially loved the sweet scents of the burning wood and the rich, oily tang of the fish. It was a fine, sunny morning, but there was still a crisp chill in the air. The kind of mornings he liked best. He looked at the dew sparkling on the grassy slopes of the South Downs, which towered up behind the smokery, a view which still, after a lifetime of working here, he never tired of looking at.

He might have been less cheery had he known he was being watched and had been since the moment he arrived here this morning.

Springs Smoked Salmon was a household name throughout Europe and the family were proud of the quality. Harris was second-generation, running the company that had been started by his parents. The location, tucked away in a valley in the South Downs, close to Brighton, was an improbable one for a fish company, and the place had an unprepossessing air – the ramshackle collection of single-storey buildings could have belonged to a tumbledown farm rather than containing a business that had become an international legend.

He walked up an incline, past a fork-lift truck and a line of parked delivery vans, between the identical cold-storage sheds. Inside them the rows of headless Scottish salmon and trout, his company's speciality, were being smoked, hung on hooks suspended from overhead racks that stretched back the full hundred-foot length of the shed, or lay packed in white Styrofoam boxes, ready for dispatch to gourmet stores, restaurants and catering companies around the globe. Also stacked on pallets were other fish and seafood products they supplied to their customers, in particular langoustines and scampi, most of which came from Scotland as well as scallops, lobsters and crabs.

He unlocked the padlock on the first door and pulled it open, checking that the temperature was fine. Then he checked each of the next three sheds as well, before moving on to the smokery ovens. These were nearly fifty years old, but still going strong. Huge, grimy, brick and steel walk-in boxes, each with a wood-fired kiln in the base, and the ceiling covered with racks and hooks, on which hung rows of pink and golden-brown fillets of smoking fish.

When he had finished his inspections, and had topped up the burners with oak logs, he entered the shop. This was a long, narrow building with a counter running the entire length of one side, while on the other side shelving was piled with every conceivable canned seafood delicacy, as well as jams, pâtés and preserves. His staff who ran the retail side, all wearing dark blue overalls and white hats, were busy putting out the displays of freshly smoked fish and making up the orders that had come in overnight by phone and email.

Jane, the manageress, flagged up a problem. One of the over-night orders was from a hamper company who were infuriatingly slow payers. They had run up an alarmingly high bill and no payment had been received for nearly three months.

'I think we should tell them we need payment before we dis-patch any more, Mr Harris,' she said.

He nodded. For the next ten minutes they continued to work on the orders, then he sat down and began, on the computer, to check his stock. At that moment the phone rang. As he was the nearest to it, he answered.

An American voice the other end asked, 'How quickly could you supply two thousand, five hundred langoustines?'

'What size and how quickly do you need them, sir?'

After a moment, the American said, 'The biggest available. Before the end of next week. We've been let down by a supplier.'

Harris asked him to hold for a moment, then checked on the computer. 'We are low on stock at the moment, but we do have a delivery coming down overnight from our supplier in Scotland on Tuesday, arriving here early Wednesday morning. If you want that quantity I could get it added to the consignment.'

'When would you need me to confirm?'

'Really as soon as possible, sir. Would you like me to give you the price?'

'That won't be an issue. The consignment would definitely be here? You could guarantee Wednesday morning?'

'We have a delivery from Scotland every Wednesday, sir.'

'Good. I'll come back to you.'

*

In his rental car parked a short distance along the road from the smokery, Tooth ended the call on his cellphone. Then he turned the car round and drove back down the narrow road, passing the sign that said SPRINGS SMOKED SALMON – SHOP OPEN.

He wondered for a moment whether to pull into the customer car park and have a recce inside the shop. Perhaps buy something. But he'd already seen all he wanted and decided there wasn't any point in showing his face. That was just an unnecessary risk.

Besides, he didn't do smoked fish.

51

The week proceeded without any significant progress being made by Roy Grace's team. This was despite the DNA from the flesh found under Preece's fingernails producing a suspect within Ford Prison – a giant of a man called Lee Rogan. Rogan was serving out the final months of a sentence for armed robbery and grievous bodily harm, prior to being released on licence.

Rogan had been arrested on suspicion of murdering Warren Tulley but was claiming in his defence that they'd had a fight over money earlier the same evening Tulley had died. So far the internal investigation had not unearthed any calls made by Rogan using his PIN code, or any mobile phone concealed in his cell. If he had been intending to claim the reward, they had no evidence of it as yet. But with the number of illegal mobile phones that were inside Ford, it was more than possible he had borrowed – or rented – one off another prisoner. Which would be almost impossible to establish. The West Area Major Crime Branch Team were keeping Grace informed of progress.

Thanks to her sharp Legal Aid solicitor, a man called Leighton Lloyd, with whom Grace had had many run-ins previously, Evie Preece had gone *no comment* and had been released on police bail after eighteen hours. Grace had put surveillance on her house, in case her brother returned. It was unlikely, he knew, but at the same time, Preece was stupid enough to do that.

He'd had a conversation with a helpful law enforcement officer in New York, Detective Investigator Pat Lanigan, of the Special Investigations Unit of the Office of the District Attorney, who had given him detailed background on the dead boy's parents, but Lanigan had no specific intelligence on the current situation, other than to tell him of Fernanda Revere's fury when he had broken the news of her son's death to her – which had been confirmed by her actions when she was over in the UK.

Grace always knew it was a bad sign when the reporter from the

Argus stopped phoning him and he had not heard from Spinella for several days now. He decided to call a press conference for the following day, Friday, his hope being to spark some memories in the public, followed by a reconstruction at the collision scene. Apart from other considerations, he needed to show the Revere family that everything possible was being done to find the driver so callously involved in their son's fatal accident.

*

At 11 a.m. the conference room at Sussex House was crammed. The Mafia connection and the $100,000 reward had generated massive media attention – far more even than Roy Grace had anticipated. He appealed to members of the public who might have been in the vicinity of Portland Road on the morning of Wednesday 21 April to cast their minds back and see if they remembered a white Ford Transit van and to attend the reconstruction, which would be held the following day.

Then he appealed specifically to the residents of Southwick, and Manor Hall Road in particular, asking if anyone remembered the van or seeing Ewan Preece – at this point he showed a series of police and prison photographs of the man. Although it stuck in his craw to continue to deal with Spinella, the little shit was now at least being cooperative.

Heading back along the corridors towards his office immediately after the press conference, Grace checked his diary on his Black-Berry. There was an exhibits meeting scheduled for 2 p.m., which he needed to attend.

Glenn Branson caught up with him, saying, 'You know, for an old-timer, you do pretty good at these conferences.'

'Yep, well, that's something you're going to have to learn. We need the press. Love them or loathe them. How do you feel about taking one on your own?'

Branson looked at him. 'Why are you asking?'

'I was thinking I might let you handle the next one.'

'Shit.'

'That's what I say every time, before I start. Another thing, I need you to take this evening's briefing. You OK with that?'

'Yeah, fine. I don't have a life, remember?'

'What's the latest?'

'According to Ari's lawyer, I was bullying and aggressive and made unreasonable sexual demands on her.'

'You did?'

'Yeah, apparently I asked her to sit on me. Goes against her religious principles of the missionary position only.'

'Religious principles?' Grace said.

'In some states in the US it's still illegal to do it any other way than the missionary position. She's now going religious fundamentalist on me. I'm a deviant in God's eyes apparently.'

'Doesn't that make Him a voyeur?'

At that moment Grace's mobile phone rang. Nodding apologetically at Glenn, he answered it.

It was Crime Scene Manager, Tracy Stocker.

'Roy,' she said. 'I'm at Shoreham Harbour. You'd better come down here. I think we might have found Preece.'

52

Grace let Glenn Branson drive. Ever since gaining his green Response and Pursuit driving ticket, Branson was keen to show his friend his prowess. And every time he allowed Branson to take the wheel, Roy Grace quickly regretted it.

They headed down the sweeping dip in the A27, passing the slip road off to the A23 and up the far side, the speedometer needle the wrong side of the 120mph mark, with Glenn, in Grace's view, having a totally misplaced confidence in the blue flashing lights and wailing siren. It didn't take a normal, sane police officer many days of response driving to realize that most members of the public on the road were deaf, blind or stupid, and frequently a combination of all three.

Grace pressed his feet hard against the floor, willing his friend to slow down as they raced past a line of cars, any one of which could have pulled out and sent them hurtling into the central barrier and certain oblivion. It was more by sheer good luck than anything he would want to attribute to driving skill that they finally ended up on the approach road to Shoreham Port, passing Hove Lagoon – a short distance from Grace's home – on their left, with their lives, if not his nerves, still intact.

'What do you think of my driving, old-timer? Getting better, yeah? Think I've nailed that four-wheel-drift thing now!'

Grace was not sure where his vocal cords were. It felt like he had left them several miles back.

'I think you need to be more aware about what other road users might do,' he replied diplomatically. 'You need to work on that.'

They drove straight over a mini-roundabout, narrowly missing a Nissan Micra being driven by a man in a pork-pie hat, and entered an industrial area. There was a tall, brick-walled warehouse to their right, double yellow lines and a blue corrugated metal warehouse to their left. They passed a gap between two buildings, through which

Grace caught a glimpse of the choppy water of Aldrington Basin, the extreme eastern end of the Shoreham Port canal. They passed a van marked D & H Electrical Installations and saw ahead of them a sign above a building advertising pet foods. Then, immediately in front of them was a marked police car, its lights flashing in stationary mode.

As they approached, they saw several parked vehicles, including the Crime Scene Manager's, and a second marked car, turned sideways, between two buildings. It was blocking the entrance to an open gate in the middle of a chain-link fence. Beyond was the quay. A line of crime scene tape ran between the walls of the two buildings and a PCSO scene guard stood in front of it.

They climbed out of the car into the blustery, damp wind, walked up to her and gave their names.

'Need you both to suit up, please, sirs,' she said to Grace, then nodded respectfully at Branson. 'CSM's request.'

The moment a Crime Scene Manager arrived at a potential crime scene, the site became his or her responsibility. One of the key elements was the number of people allowed access, and what they could wear, to minimize their chances of contaminating the scene with such minute items as clothing fibres that could lead to false trails.

They returned to the car and wormed their way into hooded blue paper oversuits. Although he had put one on hundreds of times, Grace found it never became any easier. Your shoes got jammed in them halfway down. Then they seemed to get stuck as you tugged them up over your hips.

When they were finally ready they ducked under the tape and walked down to the quay, passing a grimy sign which read ALL DRIVERS MUST REPORT TO RECEPTION. Grace looked around for CCTV cameras but couldn't see any, to his disappointment. Directly ahead of them was the rear of the large yellow mobile operations truck of the Specialist Search Unit, the prow of a moored fishing boat, a rusty fork-lift truck, a skip piled with rubbish and, on the far side, across the water, the warehouses and piles of lumber of one of the port's major timber depots.

He had always loved this part of the city. He took a deep breath, savouring the tangy smells of salt, oil, tar and rope that reminded him of his childhood, coming down here with his dad to fish off the end of the harbour mole. As a child, he had found Shoreham Harbour a mysterious, exciting place: the tankers and cargo ships along the quay with their international flags, the massive gantries, the trucks, the bollards, the warehouses and the huge power station.

As they rounded the corner, he saw a hive of activity. There were several police officers, all in protective oversuits, and he immediately picked out the short, sturdy figure of the Crime Scene Manager, Tracy Stocker, the tall figure of the SOCO photographer, James Gartrell, and the lean figure of the Coroner's Officer, Philip Keay.

Members of the Specialist Search Unit stood around, dressed in dark blue fleeces, waterproof trousers, rubber boots and black baseball caps with the wording POLICE above the peaks. One of them was standing beside a coil of cable, coloured red, yellow and blue, that ran from a box of apparatus and down over the edge of the quay into the water. Grace realized there was a diver below.

Sitting centre stage on the quay was a dull white, beat-up-looking Ford Transit van, its roof and sides streaked with mud. A steady stream of water poured from its doorsills. Grace could see that the driver's-side wing mirror was missing. Four steel hawsers ran vertically from its wheel arches high above to the pulley on the arm of a mobile crane parked beside it.

But Grace barely gave the crane a second glance. All his focus was on the man clearly visible in the driver's seat, hunched motionless over the steering wheel.

Tracy Stocker walked up to greet Grace and Branson. She was accompanied by a burly, rugged-looking man in his fifties with a weather-beaten face, wind-blown salt and pepper hair and bare arms sporting nautical tattoos. He wore a fluorescent yellow jacket over a white, short-sleeved shirt, dark workman's trousers and heavy-duty rubber boots and seemed impervious to the biting wind.

'Hi, Roy and Glenn,' she said cheerily. 'This is Keith Wadey, the Assistant Chief Engineer of Shoreham Port. Keith, this is Detective Superintendent Grace, the Senior Investigating Officer, and Detective Sergeant Glenn Branson, the Deputy SIO.'

They shook hands. Grace took an instant liking to Wadey, who exuded a friendly air of confidence and experience.

He turned back to Tracy. 'Have you run a check on the van's index?'

'Yes, chief. False plates. The serial number's been filed off the chassis and engine block, so it's almost certainly nicked, but that's about all we know.'

Grace thanked her, then spoke to Wadey. 'What do we have?' he asked, looking at the figure in the van again.

'Well, sir,' Wadey said, addressing Grace but including Branson. 'We carry out regular side-scan sonar sweeps of the canal, checking for silt levels and for any obstructions. Yesterday afternoon at around 4.30 p.m. we identified what looked like a vehicle about a hundred and twenty feet off the edge of this quay, in twenty-five feet of water. It was upside down, wheels in the air. That tends to happen with motor vehicles that go into deep water – the engine in the front pulls them down and they flip over as they sink.'

Grace nodded.

'There's zero visibility down there. The current caused by the opening and closing of the lock gates churns up the deep layer of mud. I found the vehicle with the aid of a shot line and jackstay, sunk into four feet of mud. I then contacted the police dive team – the Specialist Search Unit – our standard procedure, and we assisted them recovering the vehicle from the water this morning, approximately one hour ago. I'm afraid we found a poor sod in there. Dunno if he's a suicide – we get quite a few of them – because he doesn't seem to have made any effort to get out.'

Grace glanced at their surroundings. A large, rusting warehouse that looked derelict, although the presence of the skip indicated some work was going on.

'What is this place?' he asked.

'It now belongs to Dudman, the aggregates company. They bought it a couple of months ago. It had been empty for several years – a bankruptcy.'

'Anyone working here? Any security guards?'

'No security guards or cameras, sir. There were some workmen here last week, but they've been diverted to do some maintenance on another of the company's buildings.'

This was a secluded spot, Grace thought. Carefully chosen? It wasn't the kind of place you find by accident.

'Is it locked at night?'

'Padlocked with a chain, yes,' Wadey said. 'But it was open when we got here. Either someone unlocked it or picked the lock.'

Grace walked across to the driver's side of the van.

'How long has he been in the water?'

'My guess would be a maximum of three or four days,' the engineer replied. 'You can see the bloating, which starts to happen within twenty-four hours, but he's intact – the fish and crustaceans like to wait for a week or so, until the flesh has started to break down, before they set to work.'

'Thanks.'

Grace peered in through the driver's window, which was down, as was the passenger's, he noted. To help the vehicle sink more quickly, he wondered? The rear doors were open, too. The immediate question in his mind was whether this was an accident, suicide or murder. His experience had taught him never to jump to conclusions.

Even though the body was bloated from gases, the face was still thin, streaked with mud, eyes wide open, staring ahead with a look of shock. In the flesh, he looked even paler than in the photographs, and the gelled hair of the picture was now lifelessly matted to the scalp. But his identity was still clear. Just to double-check, Roy Grace pulled the photograph of Ewan Preece from his pocket and held it up.

And now he was certain. From the knife scar below his right eye, the thin gold chain around his neck and the leather wrist bracelet. Even so, it would take a fingerprint or DNA sample to confirm it beyond doubt. Grace was not inclined to trust a next-of-kin identification by any member of Preece's crooked family. He looked at the dead man's hands.

Preece was gripping the steering wheel as if with grim determination. As if he had thought that somehow, if he kept hold of it, he could steer himself out of trouble.

And that did not make sense.

'Dead man's grip,' said a female voice beside him.

He turned to see the sergeant in charge of the Specialist Search Unit, Lorna Dennison-Wilkins.

'Lorna!' he said. 'How are you?'

She grinned. 'Understaffed, underappreciated and busy as heck. How about you?'

'Couldn't have put it better myself!' He nodded at the dead man and, at the same time, heard a curious metallic scuttling sound from inside the van. 'Dead man's grip?'

'Rigor mortis,' she said. 'It's the suddenness of immersion that brings it on very fast. If someone drowns and they're holding on to something at that moment, it's really hard to prise their fingers off it.'

He stared at Preece's fingers. They were wrapped tightly around the large steering wheel.

'We haven't tried to remove them,' she said. 'In case we damage any forensic evidence.'

As in his past dealing with this woman and her team, Roy Grace was impressed by her understanding of the importance of not contaminating a potential crime scene. But why was Preece holding on to the steering wheel? Had he frozen in stark terror? Grace knew that if he'd just driven off a harbour quay into water, he'd be doing everything he could to get out – not trying to steer.

Had he been knocked unconscious by the impact? That was one possibility. There was no apparent mark on his head, and he was wearing a seat belt, but that was something the pathologist would be able to determine at the post-mortem. What other reason did he have for clinging to the wheel? Trying deliberately to drown? But Ewan Preece seemed an unlikely suicide candidate. From the intel-ligence he had read about him, and his own prior experience with the man, Preece didn't give a shit about anything in life. He was hardly going to be driven into a state of suicidal grief over the death of a cyclist. And in a short time he would have been out of prison.

Grace snapped on a pair of disposible gloves which he kept in his oversuit pocket, then leaned in through the window and attempted to prise the dead man's right index finger away from the wheel. But it would not move. A tiny crab the size of a fingernail scuttled across the top of the dashboard.

Once more from somewhere in the back of the van he heard the metallic scuttling sound. He tried again to prise the finger off the wheel, conscious of not wanting to risk tearing the flesh and lose the potential for a print, but it would not move.

'Bloody hell!' Keith Wadey said suddenly.

The port engineer ducked in through the rear doors. Moments later he stood up again, holding a large black lobster. It was a good two feet long, with claws the size of a man's hand, and was wriggling furiously.

'This is a nice specimen!' Wadey called out at a group of the SSU, showing them his find.

Immediately he had the attention of everyone on the quay.

'Anyone fancy treating their loved one to lobster thermidor tonight?'

There were no takers. Only looks of disgust and a few exclamations.

He tossed the creature back out into the canal and it disappeared beneath the choppy surface.

53

After a phone discussion with Roy Grace and the Crime Scene Manager, the Home Office pathologist agreed with them that she should definitely see the body in situ, prior to its being taken to the mortuary. But she was finishing a job at a lab in London at the moment, which meant a long wait for the team on the cold harbour front.

The good news was that of the two regular Home Office pathologists for this area, they had been allocated Nadiuska De Sancha, the one whom Grace and everyone else preferred to work with. As an added bonus to the fact that the statuesque, red-haired Spaniard was both good and swift at her job, and extremely helpful with it, she also happened to be very easy on the eye.

In her late forties, Nadiuska De Sancha could easily pass for a decade younger. If people wanted to be bitchy, they might comment that perhaps her plastic-surgeon husband's skills had something to do with her continuing to look so youthful. But because of her warm and open nature, few people were bitchy about her. Far more were envious of her appearance, and half of the males in the Major Crime Branch lusted after her – as well as lusting after Cleo Morey.

A body found in the sea, on its own, would have been taken to the mortuary, where the post-mortem would be carried out the following day by one of the team of local pathologists. But when there were any grounds to give the Coroner suspicion, a full forensic post-mortem would need to be carried out by a trained specialist, of which there were thirty in the UK. A standard post-mortem usually took less than an hour. A Home Office one, depending on the condition of the body and the circumstances, and very much on who was performing it, could take from three to six hours, and sometimes even longer.

As the Senior Investigating Officer, Roy Grace had a duty to attend. And that meant, he realized with dismay, that he did not have a snowball's chance in hell of making it to *Jersey Boys* in London tonight with Cleo. He'd booked a hotel up there, and tomorrow, the start of the May Day holiday weekend, they had tickets to the Army and Navy rugby match at Twickenham – at the invitation of Nobby Hall and his wife, Helen. Nobby was an old friend who had been running the Maritime Police in Cyprus.

At least Cleo would understand – unlike Sandy, he thought, with a sudden twinge of sadness. Although Sandy was fading further from his mind by the week, whenever he did think of her it was like a dark cloud engulfing him and leaving him disoriented. Sandy used to go off at the deep end, regardless of the fact he had carefully explained to her that a murder inquiry meant dropping everything, and the reasons why.

She would tell him she disliked it that she came second to his work. No matter how much he tried to refute this, she was adamant about it, to the point of fixation.

Who would you pick? she had once asked him. *If you had to choose between me and your work, Grace?*

She always called him 'Grace'.

You, he had replied.

Liar! She had grinned.

It's the truth!

I watched your eyes. That movement trick you taught me – if they move one way you are lying, the other you are telling the truth. Yours moved to the right, Grace, that's the side you look to when you are lying!

A gull cried overhead. He glanced at his watch. Almost 12.30 p.m.

A dredger slipped past them in mid-channel, heading towards the lock and then on to the open sea. Nadiuska estimated she would be here by about 2 p.m. She would take a good hour on site at the very minimum, studying and noting the exact position of the body, photographing everything, checking Preece's body for bruises and abrasions that might or might not be consistent with contact with the interior of the van, and searching for clothing fibres, hairs and anything else that might be lost as a result of the body being moved. Although, after several days' immersion in water, Grace doubted there could be much in the way of fibres or hairs on the body, he was constantly surprised at the details good forensic pathologists could find that had eluded hawk-eyed detectives and trained police search officers.

He stared in through the open driver's window. Preece's lean, sharply delineated features from his photographs were unaltered, but his skin now had a ghostly, almost translucent sheen. At least no visible nibbles had been taken from him by any scavengers. Preece was wearing a white, mud-spattered T-shirt and black jeans, and was barefoot. Odd to be driving barefoot, Grace thought, and cast his mind back to the pair of trainers that had been found in the spare bedroom of his sister's house. Had Preece left in too much of a hurry to put them on?

An undignified end to a short, sad and squandered life, he thought. At least Preece had been saved from the crustaceans. Or perhaps, with this particular specimen of human trash, it was the other way around.

54

Grace phoned the Incident Room to tell them to call off the search for Ewan Preece and the Ford Transit and instead to concentrate on the immediate neighbours of Preece's sister, to see if anyone had seen or heard anything during the night of Monday 26 April or early morning of Tuesday the 27th. He also wondered whether the dead man's sister might be sufficiently shocked into telling the truth about what had happened that night – if she genuinely knew.

An hour later, Grace completed a careful inspection of the surrounding area. He was looking in particular for any CCTV cameras that might have the approaches to this quay in view, but without success. Freezing cold, he gratefully accepted the offer of coffee inside the Specialist Search Unit truck, where there was a snug seating area around a table.

He clambered up the steps, followed by Branson, both of them rubbing some warmth back into their hands. A PCSO had been dispatched to a nearby supermarket to get some sandwiches. They were joined moments later by the tall figure of Philip Keay, the Coroner's Officer, and Tracy Stocker, who announced that Nadiuska De Sancha had phoned to say she was only a few minutes away. Two members of the SSU, one a burly man nicknamed Juice by his colleagues and the other, slightly built with fair hair, who was nicknamed WAFI, which stood for Water Assisted Fucking Idiot, moved over to make room.

Grace tried to call Cleo, but both her mobile phone and the mortuary phone went to voicemail. He felt a prick of anxiety. What if she was alone in the place and had collapsed? Most of the time, when no post-mortems were being carried out, there were only three people – Cleo, Darren and Walter – in the building. If Darren and Walter went out to recover a body, she could have been left on her own. If anything happened to her, she could lie undiscovered for a couple of hours.

He had often worried in the past about her being in that place on her own, but now he felt it even more acutely. He rang her house, but there was no answer there either. He was seriously considering driving to the mortuary to make sure she was OK, when suddenly, to his surprise, he heard her voice.

'Oi! Call this working?' she called out cheekily, standing at the door of the truck.

Grace stood up. Not many people make blue paper oversuits look like a designer garment, he thought, but Cleo did. With the trousers tucked into her boots, her hair clipped up and the bump in her stomach, she looked like someone who had just arrived in a spaceship from a planet where everyone was much more beautiful than here on earth. A new world that he still could not totally believe he was now a part of. His heart flipped with joy, the same way it did each time he saw her.

Juice and WAFI both wolf-whistled at her.

With some colour back in her face now, Cleo looked more radiant than ever, he thought, going down the steps to greet her with a light peck on the cheek.

'What are you doing here?' he asked, wanting to hug her, but not in front of a bunch of cynical colleagues who would rib him at the slightest opportunity.

'Well, I figured the musical was off, so I thought I'd take a trip to the seaside instead. Gather you've got a particularly interesting species of underwater creature.'

He grinned. 'You are under strict doctor's orders not to do any lifting, OK?'

She jerked her head, pointing. 'It's OK. I'll use that fork-lift truck!' Then she smiled. 'Don't worry, Darren's here with me. Walter's off sick today.'

A voice came through Grace's radio. It was the scene guard at the entrance. 'Sir, there's someone here to see you – says you're expecting him. Kevin Spinella?'

Grace was expecting him, the way he would expect to see blowflies around a decomposing cadaver. He walked around the corner and up to the barrier. Spinella stood there, short and thin, collar of his beige mackintosh turned up in the clichéd fashion of a movie gumshoe, chewing a piece of gum with his ratty teeth, his gelled spiky hair untouched by the wind.

'Good morning, Detective Superintendent!' he said.

Grace tapped his watch. 'It's afternoon, actually.' He gave the reporter a reproachful glance. 'Unlike you to be behind the times.'

'Ha-ha,' Spinella said.

Grace stared at him quizzically but said nothing.

'Hear you've got a body in a van,' the reporter said.

'Surprised it took you so long,' Grace replied. 'I've been here for hours.'

Spinella looked nonplussed. 'Yeah, right. So, what can you tell me about it?'

'Probably not as much as you can tell me,' he retorted.

'Don't suppose it could be Ewan Preece, could it?'

An educated guess, Grace wondered? Or had one of the team here phoned Spinella?

'There is a body in a van, but the body has not been identified at this stage,' Grace replied.

'Could it be the van you are looking for?'

He saw Nadiuska De Sancha, gowned up in an oversuit and white boots, walking towards them, carrying her large black bag.

'Too early to tell.'

Spinella made a note on his pad.

'It's ten days since the accident. Do you feel you are making progress with your enquiries regarding the van and its driver, Detective Superintendent?'

'We are very pleased with the level of response from the public,' Grace lied. 'But we would like to appeal to anyone in the Southwick area who saw a white van between the hours of 6 p.m. Monday 26 April and 8 a.m. Tuesday 27 April to contact us on our Incident Room number, or to call *Crimestoppers* anonymously. Do you want the numbers?'

'I've got them,' Spinella said.

'That's all I have for now,' Grace said, nodding a silent greeting at the pathologist and signalling he would be with her in a moment. 'Perhaps you'll be kind enough to let me know when you've identified the body and confirmed what the van is?'

'Very funny.'

Nadiuska signed the scene guard's log, then ducked under the tape which Grace lifted for her.

'Home Office pathologist?' Spinella said. 'Looks to me like you could have a murder inquiry going on.'

Grace turned and eyeballed him. 'Makes a change, does it, being the last to know?'

He turned, with great satisfaction, and escorted Nadiuska De Sancha towards the quay and across to the right, out of the reporter's line of sight. Then, knowing that she liked to work alone, in her own time, he left the pathologist and went to join Cleo and the rest of the team inside the warmth of the SSU truck.

*

Half an hour later Nadiuska De Sancha came up the steps and said, 'Roy, I need to show you something.'

Worming himself into his anorak, Grace followed her outside and around to the white van. The pathologist stopped by the driver's door, which was open.

'I think we can safely rule out accidental death, Roy, and I'm fairly confident we can rule out suicide, too,' she said.

He looked at her quizzically.

She pointed up at a small cylindrical object Grace had not taken in before, clipped to the driver's-side sun visor. 'See that? It's a digital underwater camera – and transmitter. And it's switched on, although the battery's dead.'

Grace frowned and at the same time felt annoyed that he had not spotted it. How the hell had he missed it? About an inch in diameter and three inches long, with a dark blue metal casing and a fish-eye lens. What was it there for? Had Preece been filming himself?

Then, interrupting his thoughts, she pointed at the man's hands and gave him a bemused look.

'Dead man's grip is caused by rigor mortis, right?'

Grace nodded.

She reached in with a blue, latex-gloved hand and raised one of Preece's fleshy, alabaster-white fingers. The skin of the tip remained adhered to the steering wheel. It looked like a blister with tendrils attached.

'I'll need to do some lab tests to confirm it, but there's some kind of adhesive that's been applied here. Looks to me, as an educated guess, that the poor man's hands have been superglued to the steering wheel.'

55

Tooth sat at the desk in his room at the Premier Inn, in front of his laptop, sipping a mug of coffee and editing the video of Ewan Preece's last few minutes. The smoke detector in the ceiling was still taped up and a pack of cigarettes and a plastic lighter lay beside the saucer that he was using as an ashtray.

He had used three cameras: the one on his wrist, the one he had fitted to the interior of the van and one he had balanced on the edge of the skip. The film, still in rough-cut stage, which he would refine, began with an establishing exterior shot of the van at night, at the edge of the quay. There was a bollard to its right. A time and date print at the top right of the frame showed it was 2 a.m., Tuesday 27 April. Preece could be seen at the wheel, apparently unconscious, with duct tape over his mouth.

Then it cut to the interior. There was a wide-angle shot of Preece, buckled into his seat, in a grubby white T-shirt. He was opening his eyes as if awaking from sleep, seemingly confused and disoriented. Then he peered down at his hands, which were on the steering wheel, clearly puzzled as to why he could not move them.

He began to struggle, trying to free his hands. His eyes bulged in fear as he started to realize something was wrong. A hand appeared in frame and ripped the duct tape from his mouth. Preece yelped in pain, then turned his head towards the door, speaking to a person out of shot. His voice was insolent but tinged with fear.

'Who are you? What are you doing? What the fuck are you doing?'

The driver's door slammed shut.

The camera angle changed to an exterior shot. It showed the whole driver's side of the van and a short distance behind it. A figure, wearing a hoodie, his face invisible, drove a fork-lift truck into view, steered it right up to the rear of the van, rammed it a few inches forward and began to push it steadily towards the edge of the quay.

Then the van suddenly lurched downwards, as the front wheels went over and the bottom of the chassis grounded on the stonework, with a metallic grating sound.

The film cut back to the interior of the van. Ewan Preece was bug-eyed now and screaming, 'No, no! What do you want? Tell me what you want? Please tell me! Fucker, tell me!' Then he visibly lurched forward, held by the seat belt, and his mouth opened in a long, silent scream, as if, in his terror, he could not get any more words out.

The film cut back to the exterior again. The fork-lift truck gave a final shove and the rear of the van disappeared over the edge of the quay and momentarily out of sight. There was a hollow splash.

Now there was a new exterior angle. It was the van floating, rocking in the waves, a short distance away from the quay. It was looking distinctly nose-heavy, and sinking slowly but steadily, bubbles erupting around it

The viewpoint returned to the camera inside the van. Preece's face was a mask of terror. He was fighting to free his hands – frantically pumping his body backwards and forwards as much as he could against the seat belt, jigging his arms and shoulders, his mouth contorted, yammering in terror. 'Please . . . Please . . . Please . . . Help me! Help me! Someone help me!'

There was now a long exterior shot, with the van conveniently rotated broadside on to the quay. Preece could be seen gyrating like a contortionist through the open window as the nose sank lower, the whole van now starting to tip forward, water pouring over the sills of the open windows.

The viewpoint returned to the interior again. There was a loud, muffled roaring sound. Dark water with white, foaming bubbles was flooding in. The level was rising rapidly, increasingly covering more of Preece's thrashing chest. He was rocking himself backwards and forwards, sharp, violent jerks of desperation, trying to free himself, whimpering now, a steady low 'No . . . No . . . No . . . No . . .'

The water now covered his neck to just below his chin, then the bottom of his earring, and it was rising rapidly. In seconds it was over his chin. Some went into his mouth and he spat it out. Then his mouth was submerged. In desperation he threw his head back, his chin breaking free from the water. He was crying pitifully now: 'Help me, please. Someone help me.'

The water rose relentlessly, swallowing up his exposed neck until it reached his chin again. He thrashed his head from side to side.

Tooth took a sip of his coffee, then lit a fresh cigarette, watching dispassionately. He listened to the man breathing, taking deep gulps of air, as if frantically trying to stock up with the stuff.

Then the water reached the ceiling of the van. Preece's head was twitching, his eyes still wide open. The image became very blurred. A stream of bubbles jetted from his mouth. The twitching slowed, then stopped, and his head moved more gently now, rocking with the current.

The last shot in the sequence was another exterior one. It showed the rear section of the van now, the doors open, slipping beneath the surface of the choppy, inky water. There were some bubbles, then the waves closed over it, like curtains.

56

The post-mortem room at the Brighton and Hove City Mortuary had recently been doubled in size. The work had been necessary both to increase the number of bodies that could be prepared for post-mortem at the same time and to replace the existing fridges with a new, wider generation able to cope with the growing trend for obesity in society.

Roy Grace had always found the previous room claustrophobic, especially when it was occupied by the considerable numbers required for a Home Office post-mortem. Now at least there was more space for them. Although this place, with its tiled walls and stark, cold lighting, still gave him the creeps just as much as ever.

When he had been at the police training college, learning to be a detective, an instructor had read out the FBI moral code on murder investigation, written by its first director, J. Edgar Hoover:

> No greater honor will ever be bestowed on an officer or a more
> profound duty imposed on him than when he is entrusted with
> the investigation of the death of a human being.

Grace always remembered those words, and the burden on him as the Senior Investigating Officer, on every case. Yet at the same time as feeling that weight of responsibility, he would feel other emotions in this room, too. Always a tinge of sadness for the loss of a life – even the life of a scumbag like Ewan Preece. Who knew what kind of a person Preece might have been under different circumstances, if life had dealt him a less hopeless hand?

In spite of his sense of responsibility, Grace also at times felt like an intruder in this room. To be a corpse, opened up and splayed out here was the ultimate loss of privacy. Yet neither the dead nor their loved ones had any say in the matter. If you died under suspicious circumstances, the Coroner would require a post-mortem.

At this moment, Ewan Preece was a surreal sight, lying on his back, in his jeans and T-shirt, on the stainless-steel PM table, his hands still gripping the black steering wheel, which Nadiuska De Sancha had requested be detached from the vehicle and brought with him to the mortuary. He looked, in death, as if he was driving some spectral vehicle.

At a PM table on the other side of the archway, the bloody internal organs of another corpse were laid out for a student, who was receiving instructions from one of Brighton's consultant path-ologists, and Grace's stomach was heaving, as ever, from the stench of disinfectant, blood and decaying human innards. He glanced over, clocked the brains, liver, heart and kidneys sitting there, and the electronic weighing scales on a shelf just beyond. Beside them, on another table, lay the corpse from which they had been removed – an elderly woman the colour of alabaster, her mouth gaping, her midriff wide open, the yellow fatty tissue of the insides of her breasts facing upwards, her sternum laid across her pubis as if in some attempt by the pathologist to protect her modesty.

He shuddered and took a few steps closer to Preece, his green gown rustling as he walked. Nadiuska was plucking delicately at the skin of one of the fingers with tweezers. James Gartrell, the SOCO photographer, was steadily working his way around the body. Glenn Branson was in a corner, surreptitiously talking on his phone. To his wife, Ari? Grace wondered. Or his solicitor? The Coroner's Officer, Philip Keay, was standing in a green gown, blue mask hanging from its tapes just below his chin, dictating into a machine with a worried frown.

Cleo and her assistant, Darren, stood by, ready to assist the pathologist, but at the moment they had nothing to do but watch. Occasionally she would look in Grace's direction and give him a surreptitious smile.

The Detective Superintendent was thinking hard. Preece's hands glued to the wheel confirmed, beyond any doubt in his mind, that the man had been murdered. And the presence of that camera in the vehicle was bothering him a lot. Put there by the killer? Some sadistic bounty-hunter associate of Preece who had known where he had been hiding?

Or was there an even darker aspect to this? The Mafia connection was weighing heavily on his mind. Could this have been a sadistic revenge hit?

The body had not yet been formally identified. That would be done later by his mother or sister. Nadiuska said she would be able to dissolve the glue with acetone, leaving Grace's team able to get fingerprints which would further confirm his identity, and as backup they would be able to get a DNA sample. But from the tattoos on his body and the scar on his face, Ford Prison had already confirmed his identity beyond much doubt.

With Kevin Spinella from the *Argus* and the rest of the press having been kept well away from the crime scene, only the immediate team at the quay, and those here in the mortuary, knew that the man's hands had been glued to the steering wheel. Grace intended to keep this information quiet for the moment. If it made the press during the next few hours, he would know where to look for the leak.

He stepped out of the PM room and made a call to MIR-1, instructing Norman Potting to organize a group within the inquiry team to find out all they could about the camera, in particular where such a device was available for sale, in Brighton or beyond, and any recent purchases that had been made.

Next he made a phone call to Detective Investigator Pat Lanigan, who was their liaison officer with the Revere family in America, to ask him whether in his experience the dead boy's parents were the kind of people who might be sufficiently aggrieved to go for a revenge killing.

Lanigan informed him that they had the money, the power and the connections – and that with people like this a whole different set of rules applied. He said that he would see what intelligence he could come up with. Sometimes, when a contract was put out, they would get to hear of it. He promised to come back to Grace as soon as he found out anything.

Grace hung up with a heavy heart. Suddenly he found himself hoping that whoever had killed Preece was just a local chancer. The notion of a Mafia-backed killing in the heart of Brighton was not something that would sit well with anyone – not the council, not the tourist board, not his boss, ACC Rigg, and not with himself, either.

He sat on a sofa in the small front office of the mortuary, poured himself a stewed coffee from the jug that was sitting on the hotplate and felt a sudden grim determination. Lanigan had said *a whole different set of rules applied.*

Well, not in his beloved city, they didn't.

57

'The time is 8.30 a.m. Saturday 1 May,' Roy Grace announced to his team in MIR-1. 'This is the eighteenth briefing of *Operation Violin*. The first thing I have to report is the positive identification of Ewan Preece.'

'Shame to have lost such an upstanding member of Brighton society, chief,' said Norman Potting. 'And such a tacky way to die.'

There was a titter of laughter. Grace gave him a reproachful look.

'Thank you, Norman. Let's hold the humour. We have some serious issues on our hands.'

Bella Moy rattled her Malteser box, extracted a chocolate and popped it into her mouth, biting into it with a crunch. Grace looked back down at his notes.

'It will be some days before we get the toxicology reports, but I have significant findings from the PM. The first is that there was bruising to the side of Preece's neck very similar to the bruising that was found on his sister, Evie, who is claiming to have remembered nothing after going outside on Monday night to let her cat out. According to Nadiuska De Sancha, this is consistent with a martial arts blow with the side of a hand to cause instant loss of consciousness. This could be the way Preece was overpowered by his assailant.'

Grace looked down again. 'The seawater present in Preece's lungs indicates that he was alive at the time the van went into the water and he died from drowning. The fact that his hands were glued to the steering wheel makes this extremely unlikely to have been suicide. Does anyone have a different view?'

'If he was unconscious, sir,' said Nick Nicholl, 'how did the van actually get into the water? It would have been difficult for someone to physically push it, because when the front wheels went over the edge of the quay, surely the bottom of the chassis would have grounded on it. Wouldn't it have needed to be driven at some speed?'

'That's a good point,' Grace said. 'Dudman, who own that particular section of the wharf, say that their fork-lift truck had been moved. It could have been used to push the van in.'

'Wouldn't that have required someone with an ignition key?' asked Bella Moy.

'I'm told that particular kind of fork-lift has a universal ignition key,' Grace replied. 'One key operates all of those vehicles in the UK. And anyone with a basic knowledge could have started it with a screwdriver.'

'Has the kind of glue been established?' asked DS Duncan Crocker.

'It has been sent for lab analysis. We don't have that information yet.'

'There was no tube of glue found in the vehicle?' Crocker asked.

'No,' Grace replied. 'The Specialist Search Unit did an extensive dive search around the area where the van was recovered, but so far they have found nothing. There is almost zero visibility down there, which is not helpful. They are continuing searching today and doing a fingertip search of the quay areas. But my sense is that they are not going to find anything helpful.'

'Why do you think that, chief?' Glenn Branson asked.

'Because this smells to me like the work of a professional. It has all the hallmarks,' Grace said. Then he looked around at his team. 'I did not like the mention of the hundred-thousand-dollar reward from the get-go. It wasn't put up, as is usual, for information leading to the arrest and conviction, but just for the driver's identity. I think we could be looking at an underworld hit here.'

'Does that change anything in this inquiry, sir?' Emma-Jane Boutwood asked.

'In the 1930s this city got the sobriquet Murder Capital of Europe,' Grace retorted. 'I don't intend to let anyone think they can come here, kill someone for a bounty and get away with it. And that's what we could be dealing with right now.'

'If it's a professional Mafia hit,' Nick Nicholl said, 'whoever did this could already be back in America. Or wherever he came from.'

'Evie Preece does not have an internal door into her garage,' Grace replied. 'If our man knocked Preece out, he would have had to carry him out of the house and into the garage – on a street in a densely populated neighbourhood. When he got to Shoreham Harbour, he would have had to leave him in the van while he opened the gates. Then he would have had to glue his hands to the wheel, start the fork-lift truck and use it to push the van into the water. OK, I'm speculating. But Evie Preece had a whole bunch of neighbours. Also, there are houses all around Shoreham Harbour. It's possible Preece's killer got lucky and no one saw a thing. But I want to ramp up those house-to-house enquiries in her street and around the harbour. Someone might have been out walking their dog or whatever. Someone must have seen *something*, and we have to find them.'

He looked down at his notes again, then turned to DC Howes. 'David, do you have anything to report from Ford?'

'Not so far, boss,' he replied. 'It's the usual prison situation, with everyone closing ranks. No one saw anything. They're still working on it – going through all the recorded phone conversations around the time in question, but that could take several days.'

Grace then turned to DC Boutwood and DC Nicholl, to whom he had delegated the line of enquiry regarding the camera found in the van.

'Do you have anything to report?'

E-J shook her head. 'Not so far, sir. The camera is a Canon model widely on sale here, at a price of around a grand, and overseas. There are seventeen retail outlets in Brighton that stock it, as well as numerous online stores, including Amazon. In the US there are thousands of retail outlets, Radio Shack, a national chain, being among the major discounters.'

'Great. So we're looking for a needle in a haystack, is that what you're saying?'

'That's about it, sir.'

'OK,' Grace replied, staring her back, hard, in the eye. 'That's one of the things we do best. Finding needles in haystacks.'

'We'll try our hardest, sir!'

He made another note, then sat in silent thought for some

moments. He could not put a finger on it, but he had a bad feeling. *Copper's nose*, they used to call it. Gut feelings. Instinct.

Whatever.

The little shit Kevin Spinella was pushing him to hold another press conference. But he wasn't ready for that yet and he would stall for time. All the reporter knew at this stage – unless he had something from his inside source – was that a dead body in a van had been recovered from Shoreham Harbour. The fact that the story merited only a handful of lines in today's paper, both in its print and online editions, indicated to him that, so far at least, the reporter was in the dark.

And that was good.

Except, Grace thought, he was in the dark too. And that was not a good place to be at all.

58

Tooth was also in the dark. And that was exactly where he wanted to be. Dressed all in black, with a black baseball cap pulled low over his face, he knew he would be almost invisible outside.

Tuesday night: 11.23 p.m. It was dry and the motorway was dark and busy. Just tail lights, headlights and occasional flashing indicators. He concentrated as he drove, thinking, working out his next steps, covering alternatives, best- and worst-case scenarios.

At long last the lorry he had been following from Aberdeen was pulling into a service station. The driver had been going steadily for nearly five hours since he had stopped for a break on the A74M, just south of Lockerbie, and Tooth needed to urinate. The need had been getting so pressing he had been close to using the expandable flask he kept in the car for such purposes. The same kind he used to take with him behind enemy lines so he didn't leave any traces for them to track him.

He followed the tail lights of the truck along the slip road and up a slight incline. They passed signs with symbols for fuel, food, accommodation and another one for the goods vehicles' parking area.

Conveniently, as if obeying Tooth's silent wishes, the driver headed the articulated refrigeration lorry along past rows of parked lorries, then pulled into a bay several spaces beyond the last one, in a particularly dark area of the car park.

Tooth switched off his lights. He had already, some miles earlier, disabled the Toyota's interior light. He halted the car, jumped out and ran, crouching low, invisible. There were no signs of activity around him. He couldn't see CCTV cameras in this area. The lorry nearest to his target had its blinds pulled. The driver was either asleep or watching television or having sex with a motorway hooker. Despite his desperate need to pee, he held off, waiting and watching.

*

Inside the cab of his sixteen-wheel, twenty-four-ton Renault fridge-box artic, Stuart Ferguson reached down for the parking brake, then remembered it was in a different position from the one in the Volvo he normally drove. That vehicle was currently in a Sussex Police vehicle pound, where, apparently, it would remain until the inquest on the young man the vehicle had run over and killed – a fortnight ago tomorrow – was complete.

He switched off the engine and killed the lights, and the voice of Stevie Wonder on the CD player fell silent with them.

He was still badly shaken and had been having nightmares. Several times during these past two weeks, sweet Jessie had woken him gently, telling him he was crying and shouting out. He kept seeing that poor laddie tumbling across the road towards him, coming straight at him, still gripping the handlebars of his bike. Then the severed leg, in his rear-view mirror, some yards behind the vehicle when he had stopped.

On top of that, he had been worrying this could be the end of his trucking career. Because he was over his allotted hours, he'd had the threat of a Death by Dangerous Driving charge hanging over him, and it had been a relief to hear the police were only going to prosecute him for the relatively minor and straightforward hours offence. Despite the accident, he loved this job, and besides, with his ex-wife, Maddie, pretty much cleaning him out, he needed to earn a substantial wage just to pay her maintenance and to make sure the kids had everything they needed.

At least it felt OK being back behind the wheel again. In fact it felt much better than he had thought it would. He'd missed his regular journey to Sussex last Tuesday because the company did not have a spare vehicle available and his boss had given him the week off. In fact, all things considered, the company was being very supportive to him, despite his pending prosecution. Driving out of hours was not something they could ever sanction officially, but everyone knew it went on. Hell, they were in a recession, everyone needed business.

If there had been one silver lining to the cloud of horrors, Jessie, four months pregnant with their child, had been so incredibly caring. He'd seen yet another lovely side to her. More than ever he longed to get his cargo of frozen fish and seafood offloaded and head back home to her. If there were no hitches, he could be climbing into bed with her, slipping his arms around her warm, naked body, in the early hours of Thursday morning. He so much looked forward to that and was tempted to call her one more time this evening. But it was now half-past eleven. Too late.

He looked forward also, at this moment, to a strong coffee and a sugar hit. A doughnut or a custard Danish would go down a treat, and a chocolate bar as well, to sustain him for the last leg to Sussex. When he was a few miles north of Brighton, he would pull into a lay-by and have a few hours' kip.

He climbed down on to the footplate, and closed and locked the door. Then, as his right foot touched the tarmac, he felt a blow on his neck and his head filled with dazzling white streaks, followed by a shower of electric sparks. Like a psychedelic light show, he thought, in the fraction of a second before he blacked out.

*

Tooth knelt, holding the limp body of the short, sturdy man in his arms, and looked around him. He heard the hum of traffic on the motorway a short way away. The rattle of a diesel engine firing up. Strains of music, very faint, from a parked lorry somewhere nearby.

He dragged the man the short distance to his car, the lorry driver's heavy-duty Totectors scraping noisily along the tarmac, but Tooth was confident no one was around to hear them. He hauled him on to the rear seat, closed the doors, then drove a short way across the car park and pulled up in an area of total darkness, away from all the vehicles.

Next he tugged the man's polo shirt out of his trousers. With his thumbs he felt up the man's spine before carefully counting down again from the top to C4. Then, using a movement he had been taught in the military for disabling or killing the enemy silently, with bare hands, he swung him out of the car, lifted him up, then dropped him down hard, backwards, across his knees, hearing the snap. This location on the spine he had chosen would not kill the lorry driver. It would just stop him from running away.

He manoeuvred him back into the car and set to work, binding the man's mouth and arms with duct tape. Then he jammed him down into the gap between the front and rear seats and covered him with a rug he had bought for the purpose, just in case he got stopped later by the police for any reason, then locked up.

He had one more job to do, which involved a screwdriver. It took him only fifteen minutes. Afterwards, he sauntered across to the service station cafeteria, pulling the baseball cap even lower over his face and turning the collar of his jacket up as he spotted the CCTV camera. He walked past, facing away, as he entered the building.

Tooth finally used the restroom, then bought himself a large black coffee and a custard Danish. He chose a table in a quiet section, ate his pastry and sipped some scalding coffee. Then he carried the cup outside, leaned against a wall, lit a cigarette and drank some more. The cigarette tasted particularly good. He felt good. His plan was coming together, the way his plans always came together.

He didn't do abortive missions.

59

Stuart Ferguson woke feeling confused. For an instant he thought he was home with his ex-wife, Maddie. But the room felt unfamiliar. Jessie? Was he with Jessie? Swirling darkness all around him, like a void. His head was throbbing. He heard a noise, a hum, a faint whine like tyres on tarmac. His head was jigging, vibrating, rocking slightly, as if it was floating in space.

Was he asleep in his cab?

He tried to think clearly. He had pulled into the service station to get something to eat and to have a rest. Had he gone to sleep in his bunk? He tried to reach out for the light switch, but nothing seemed to be happening – it was as if he had forgotten how to move his arm. He tried again. Still nothing. Was he lying on it? But he could not feel any of his limbs at all, he realized.

His head became hot, suddenly, with panic. Beads of sweat trickled down his face. He listened to the hum. The whine. He tried to speak, then realized he could not move his mouth.

He was face down. Was he trussed up? Why couldn't he feel anything? Had he had an accident? Was he being taken to hospital?

Sweat was in his eyes now. He blinked, the salt stinging them. His left cheek itched. What had happened? Shit. He concentrated on listening for a moment. He was definitely in a moving vehicle. He was conscious of lights. Headlights. But he could see nothing of where he was. Just dark fibres. There was a smell of dusty carpet in his nostrils.

Something was very wrong. Panic and fear swirled through his head. He wanted Jessie. Wanted to be in her arms. Wanted to hear her voice. He grunted, tried to turn his head. He could hear a clicking sound now. Steady, every few seconds, *click-click-click*. The vehicle was decelerating. His fear accelerated.

He thought about Jessie. Sweet Jessie. He so desperately wanted to be with her. He cried out to her, but no sound came through his taped mouth.

60

David Harris, dressed as usual in his heavy fleece, thick jeans, cap and rubber boots, looked up at the sky as he made his morning inspection of the smokery. The solid cloud cover of earlier this morning seemed to be breaking up, with shards of glassy blue sky appearing in the gaps. The air felt a little bit warmer today, too. Spring was late but perhaps it was finally starting.

He glanced at his watch: 7.45. The delivery driver from Aberdeen Ocean Fisheries was usually here at 7.30 a.m. every Wednesday, on the nail. A cheery little Scot called Stuart Ferguson. The man was always quick and businesslike. He would unload, help Harris and his staff into the sheds with the cargo, getting the items checked and ticked on his docket, then have it signed and be on his way. He always seemed in a hurry to get off.

Last week was one of the few times in all the years Harris could remember when there'd been no delivery from Aberdeen. The previous week the lorry had been involved in that bad accident that had been all over the news. Some big New York crime family's son had been killed. Ferguson had been named as the lorry driver – and Harris had worked out that the accident must have happened only a short while after the driver had made his delivery here.

He wondered if it would be Ferguson again today or whether they would have put a different driver on. He hoped it would be Ferguson, because it would be interesting to find out from him what had actually happened. But perhaps the man had lost his job over this. Or was suspended. He looked at his watch again and listened for a moment, to see if he could hear the sound of an approaching lorry. But all he could hear was the faint, insistent bleating of sheep up on the Downs above him. Must be a new driver, he thought, either with a different schedule or perhaps lost – not hard on the narrow, winding roads to this place.

He walked up the incline between two low buildings, passing a

229

row of his parked delivery vans, then, to his surprise, he noticed the padlock on the first of the smokehouse doors, which one of his staff always locked last thing at night, was hanging loose and open. He felt a sudden twist of unease inside him. Each of the brick and steel smokehouses contained many thousands of pounds' worth of fish, and so far, in the company's history, they'd never been burgled. Which was why he'd never thought it necessary to invest in expensive security systems such as alarms or CCTV. Perhaps he might have to now, he thought.

Hurrying over, he pulled the door open and stepped inside. The strong, familar fug that he loved, of smoke and fish, enveloped him. Inside the dim interior, everything looked fine, the fish – all wild Scottish salmon in this kiln – hung in dense, packed rows on hooks from the ceiling. He was about to leave, when he decided to do a quick check, and cranked the handle that moved the fish along the ceiling rail, so they could be rotated for inspection purposes. At the halfway point, he suddenly saw four large fish had fallen from their hooks and lay on the draining tray beneath.

How the hell could they have fallen, he wondered?

Had there been a problem with this kiln during the night? One of the pieces of high-tech they had invested in was a temperature alarm system. If the temperature in one of the kilns dropped too low, or the temperature in one of the cold-storage sheds rose too high his engineer, Tom White, would get a call on his mobile phone and have to come straight over. Had Tom needed to do some work on this kiln? But even if he had, Tom was a careful man; he wouldn't leave four expensive salmon lying in the draining tray.

He called the engineer's mobile – the man would probably be in his workshop at the far end of the smokery at this time of day. White answered immediately, but it wasn't the reply David Harris had hoped for. There hadn't been any problems overnight. No call-out.

As he hung up, he wondered if there been an attempted burglary. Hurriedly, he hooked the salmon back up, then checked each of the next four kilns, but everything was fine. Then he walked along to the cold-store sheds and stared, in growing bewilderment and unease, at the sight of the padlock on the first shed door, also hanging loose and open.

Shit!

He strode over and yanked the heavy, sealed sliding door open, fully expecting to find the entire contents of the shed missing. Instead he stared, in momentary disbelief, as the blast of refrigerated air greeted him. Everything looked normal, fine, undisturbed. Rows of smoked salmon hung from hooks from ceiling rails on the motorized pulley system. Six rows, with not enough space to walk between them, forming an almost solid wall. He slid the door shut again, relieved.

It wasn't until much later in the day, when his staff began to package the fish for dispatch to customers, that they would discover what he had missed in this shed.

61

'The time is 8.30 a.m. Wednesday 5 May,' Roy Grace read from his notes to his team in MIR-1. 'This is the twenty-sixth briefing of *Operation Violin*.' *And we're not making any sodding progress*, he felt like adding, but he refrained. There were flat spots like this in almost every inquiry.

He was in a bad and worried mood. His biggest worry was Cleo. She had almost fainted stepping out of the shower this morning. She insisted it was purely because the water had been too hot, but he had wanted to take her straight to hospital. She'd refused, saying that she felt fine, right as rain; they were short-handed at the mortuary and she needed to be there.

He was worried about this case, too. This was a full-on murder inquiry, yet he sensed a spark was missing. Although he had most of his trusted regulars in his team, there didn't seem to be the air of commitment and focus that he was used to feeling. He knew the reason. It was the wrong reason, but it was human nature. It was because the murder victim was Ewan Preece.

Despite the horrific nature of his death, no one from Sussex Police was going to be shedding a tear at Preece's funeral – although he would send a couple of undercover officers along, to keep an eye on who turned up, or lurked nearby.

But regardless of however undesirable a character Preece was, he had been murdered. And Grace's job was not to be judgemental, but to find the killer and lock him up. To do that, he needed to get his team better motivated.

'Before we go through your individual reports,' he said, 'I want to recap on our lines of enquiry.' He stood up and pointed to the whiteboard, on which there were three numbered headings, each written in caps in red. 'In the first, we look into the possibility that there is no link between Preece's killing and the death of cyclist Tony Revere, clear? Preece was a man who made enemies naturally.

We could be looking at a drugs turf war or something like a double-crossing. He could have just screwed the wrong person.'

Duncan Crocker put up his hand. 'The camera's the thing that bothers me with that line of enquiry, chief. Why wouldn't they just kill him? Why chuck away an expensive camera like that?'

'There are plenty of sadists out there,' Grace replied. 'But I agree with your point about the camera. We'll come back to that. OK, right, the second line of enquiry is that Preece was killed by someone who was after the reward money.'

'Doesn't the same apply with the camera, boss?' asked Bella Moy. 'If they're after the reward, why chuck away a camera of that value?'

'It would be a good idea to remind ourselves of the wording of the reward, Bella,' Grace replied. 'It's not the usual, *for information leading to the arrest and conviction.*' He looked down at his notes for a moment and searched through a few pages. Then he read, 'This reward is for information leading to *the identity* of the van driver responsible for the death of her son.' He looked up. 'That's a big difference.'

'Do you think something might have gone wrong, Roy?' Nick Nicholl asked. 'Perhaps the killer was planning to get Preece to fess up into the camera and it didn't happen.'

'Maybe it did happen,' Glenn Branson said. 'The camera transmits – we don't know what was said or transmitted to whom.'

'He probably didn't say too much underwater,' Norman Potting butted in, and chortled.

Several of the others stifled grins.

'I can't speculate on whether anything went wrong, Nick,' Grace replied to DC Nicholl. Then he pointed at the whiteboard again. 'Our third line of enquiry is whether, bearing in mind Revere's family's connection with organized crime, this was a professional revenge killing – a hit. So far, from initial enquiries I've made to connections I have in the US, there is no intelligence of any contract of any kind that's been put out regarding this, but we need to look at the US more closely.' He turned to Crocker. 'Duncan, I'm tasking you with getting further and better information on the Revere family and their connections.'

'Yes, boss,' the DS said, and made a note.

'I have a 3.30 p.m. meeting with the ACC. I need to take him something to show that we're not all sodding asleep here.'

At that moment his phone rang. Raising a hand apologetically, Roy Grace answered it. Kevin Spinella was on the other end and what the reporter from the *Argus* told him suddenly made his bad mood a whole lot worse.

62

This Wednesday was not promising to be one of the best days of Carly's life. She was due to meet her solicitor and colleague, Ken Acott, outside Brighton Magistrates' Court at 9.15 a.m., and have a coffee with him before her scheduled court appearance.

Quite unnecessarily in her view, Ken had warned her not to drive, as she was certain to lose her licence and the ban would be effective instantly. As her smashed Audi was still currently in the police pound, driving had not been an option in any event and she had come by taxi.

She was wearing a simple navy two-piece, a white blouse and a conservative Cornelia James silk square, with plain navy court shoes. Ken had advised her to look neat and respectable, not to power-dress and not to be dripping with bling.

As if she ever was!

Then, as she stepped out of the taxi, her right heel broke, shearing almost clean off.

No, no, no! Don't do this to me!

There was no sign of Acott. A couple of teenagers and an angry-looking, scrawny middle-aged woman were standing nearby. One youth, in a tracksuit and baseball cap, had a pathetic, stooping posture, while the other, in a hoodie, was more assertive-looking. All three of them were smoking and not talking. The woman was the mother of one or both of them, she presumed. The boys looked rough and hard, as if they were already seasoned offenders.

Carly felt the warmth of the sun, but the promise of a fine day did little to relieve the dark chill inside her. She was nervous as hell. Acott had already warned her that a lot depended on which trio of magistrates she came in front of this morning. In the best-case scenario she would get a one-year driving ban – the minimum possible for drink-driving in the UK – and a hefty fine. But if she got a bad call, it could be a lot worse. The magistrates might decide that even if the police were not going to prosecute her for death by careless or dangerous driving, they would come up with a punishment to fit the circumstances and throw the book at her. That could mean a three-year ban, or even longer, and a fine running into thousands.

Fortunately, money had not been a problem for her so far, since Kes's death, but provincial law firms did not pay highly and next year Tyler would move on to his public school, where the fees would be treble what she was currently paying at St Christopher's. She was going to be stretched. So the prospect of a three-year driving ban and all the costs of taxis involved, and a huge fine as well, quite apart from the fact that her conviction was bound to be splashed over the local news, was not leaving her in the best frame of mind.

And now her sodding heel had broken. How great an impression was that going to make, hobbling into court?

She leaned against a wall, catching a tantalizing whiff of cigarette smoke, and tugged her shoe off. A gull circled overhead, cawing, as if it was laughing at her.

'Fuck off, gull,' she said sullenly.

The heel was hanging by a strip of leather. Two tiny, bent nails protruded from the top of it. She looked at her watch: 9.07. She wondered if she had enough time to hobble to a heel bar and get it fixed, but where was the nearest one? She'd noticed one quite recently, not far from here. But where?

Her iPhone pinged with an incoming text. She took it out of her handbag and checked the display. It was Ken Acott, saying he'd be there in two minutes.

Then she flicked across the phone's apps screen to Friend Mapper, to check that her friend Clair May had safely delivered Tyler to school. His mood was upsetting her. She'd always been close to him – and Kes's death had created a special bond between them – but now he'd put a wall around himself and was even resenting putting Friend Mapper on each day.

'Don't you want to be able to see where I am?' she had asked him yesterday.

'Why?' He'd shrugged.

For the past two years they had used this GPS app daily. A

small blue dot marked her precise position on a street map and a purple one – his choice of colour – marked his. Each time either of them logged on they could see where the other was. It was like a game to Tyler and he'd always enjoyed following her, sending her the occasional text when she was away from the office, saying: **I can c u** ☺

To her relief the purple dot was where it should be, near the corner of New Church Road and Westbourne Gardens, where St Christopher's School was located. She put the phone back in her bag.

At that moment Ken Acott came around the corner, looking sharp in a dark grey suit and a green tie, swinging his massive attaché case. He was smiling.

'Sorry I'm late, Carly. Had to deal with an urgent custody hearing, but I've got some good news!'

From the expression in his face it looked as if he was going to tell her that the case had been dropped.

'I've just had a quick conversation with the clerk of the court. We've got Juliet Smith in the chair. She's very experienced and very fair.'

'Great,' Carly said, greeting the news with the same level of enthusiasm someone under a death sentence might have shown on being told that the execution chamber had recently been redecorated.

63

Tooth was tired but he had to keep going, keep up the pace. Speed was vital. Cut the police some slack and they could catch up with you very fast. He needed to keep two jumps ahead of them. Equally, it was when you were tired that you risked making a mistake.

He was running on adrenalin and catnaps, the way he used to in the military, when he was behind enemy lines. Five minutes' shut-eye and he was good to go again. That had been part of his sniper school training. He could function for days like that. Weeks if he had to. But those catnaps were vital. Deprive a cat of sleep and it would die in two weeks. Deprive a human and he would become psychotic.

He would sleep later, when the job was complete, then he could do so for as long as he wanted, until that day the Russian roulette finally came good. Not that he had ever slept for more than four hours at a stretch in his life. He wasn't comfortable sleeping – didn't like the idea that stuff could happen around you while you weren't aware of it.

He peered out at the neighbourhood as he drove. It didn't take a rocket scientist to figure that people had to be well off to live around here. Detached houses, nice lawns, smart cars. Money bought you isolation. Better air to breathe. Privacy. These houses had big gardens. Gardens were urban jungles. He was good at urban jungles.

There was a big park on his left as he drove around the wide, curved road. Tennis courts. An enclosed playground with kids in it and their mothers watching. Tooth scowled. He didn't like children. He saw a woman picking up her dog's shit in a plastic bag. Saw a game going on between soccer posts. This was the kind of safe neighbourhood that five centuries of winning wars against invaders bought you. Here you didn't have to worry any more about marauding soldiers killing the menfolk and raping the women and children

– unlike some places in the world that he had seen, where that went on.

The comfort zone of civilization.

The comfort zone Carly Chase inhabited, or so she thought.

He turned into her street. Hove Park Avenue. He'd already paid a visit here earlier on his way back from Springs Smoked Salmon.

This was going to be easy. His client would like it, a lot. He was certain.

64

Grace was still seething at the thought of his conversation with Kevin Spinella as he entered Peter Rigg's office punctually at 3.30 p.m. The ACC, looking dapper in a chalk-striped blue suit and brightly coloured polka-dot tie, offered him tea as he sat down, which he accepted gratefully. He hoped some biscuits might come along with it, as he'd had no lunch. He'd been working through the day, trying to gather some positive scraps of information to give his boss about *Operation Violin*, but he had precious little. In his hand he held a brown envelope containing the latest exhibits list, which he had taken away from the exhibits meeting an hour earlier.

'So how are we doing, Roy?' Rigg asked chirpily.

Grace brought him up to speed on his team's three current lines of enquiry, as well as their growing involvement in the investigation into the murder of Warren Tulley at Ford Prison. Then he handed him a copy of the exhibits list and ran through the key points of that with him.

'I don't like the camera, Roy,' the ACC said. 'It doesn't chime.'

'With what, sir?'

Rigg's MSA brought in a china cup and saucer on a tray, with a separate bowl of sugar and, to Grace's delight, a plate of assorted biscuits. A bonus he never had in the days of the previous ACC. Rigg gestured for him to help himself and he gulped down a round one with jam in the centre, then eyed a chocolate bourbon. To his dismay his boss leaned across the table and grabbed that one himself.

Speaking as he munched it, Rigg said, 'We've seen plenty of instances of low-life filming their violent acts on mobile phone cameras, *happy slapping*, all that. But this is too sophisticated. Why would someone go to that trouble – and, more significantly, that expense?'

'Those are my thoughts too, sir.'

'So what are your conclusions?'

'I'm keeping an open mind. But I think it has to have been done by someone after that reward. Which brings me on to something I want to raise. We have a real problem with the crime reporter from the *Argus*, Kevin Spinella.'

'Oh?'

Rigg reached forward and grabbed another biscuit Grace had been eyeing, a custard cream.

'I had a call from him earlier. Despite all our efforts at keeping from the press, at this time, that Ewan Preece's hands were glued to the steering wheel of the van, Spinella has found out.'

Grace filled him in on the history of leaks to the reporter during the past year.

'Do you have any view on who it might be?'

'No, I don't at this stage.'

'So is the *Argus* going to print with the superglue story?'

'No. I've managed to persuade him to hold it.'

'Good man.'

Grace's phone rang. Apologizing, he answered.

It was Tracy Stocker, the Crime Scene Manager, and what she had to say was not good news.

Grace asked her a few brief questions, then ended the call and looked back at his boss, who was studying the exhibits list intently. He eyed once more a chocolate digestive on the plate, but all of a sudden he'd lost his appetite. Rigg put down the list and looked back at him quizzically.

'I'm afraid we have another body, sir,' Grace said.

He left the office, then hurried across the Police HQ complex to his car.

65

One of the many things Roy Grace loved about Brighton was the clear delineation to its north between the city limits and stunning open countryside. There was no urban sprawl, just a clean dividing line made by the sweep of the A27 dual carriageway between the city and the start of the Downs.

The part of that countryside he was driving towards now, the Devil's Dyke, was an area that never ceased to awe him, no matter how often he came here and no matter his purpose, even this afternoon, when he knew it was going to be grim.

The Devil's Dyke was the beauty spot where he used to bring Sandy in their courting days and they often hiked here at weekends after they were married. They would drive up to the car park at the top and walk across the fields, with their spectacular views across the rolling hills in one direction and towards the sea in another. They would take the path past the old, derelict and slightly creepy fort that he used to love coming to as a child with his parents. He and his sister would play games of cowboys and Indians, and cops and robbers in and around its crumbling walls – always being careful to avoid treading in one of the numerous cowpats that were its major hazard.

If it was too blustery on the top, he and Sandy used to walk down the steep banks into the valley below. Legend had it that the Devil had dug out a vast trench – in reality a beautiful, natural valley – to allow the sea to come inland and flood all the churches in Sussex. It was one of the least true of the myths about his city's dark heritage.

In those first few years after Sandy had vanished, he often came up here alone and either just sat in his car, staring through the windscreen, or got out and walked around. There was always the dim hope in his mind that she might just turn up here. It was one of the beliefs he had clung to that she might have lost her memory. A neurologist he had consulted told him that sometimes people with this condition regain fragments of their memory and might go to places familiar to them.

But sometimes in those lonely years he came here just to feel close to her, to feel her spirit in the wind.

He had never done any of these walks with Cleo. He didn't want the memories casting clouds over their relationship. Didn't want Cleo meeting his ghosts. They'd made other parts of the city and its environs their own special places.

He drove as fast as he dared along the high top road, on blue lights and wailing siren. Open land stretched away on both sides, shimmering beneath the almost cloudless afternoon sky. A mile or so to the south, the fields gave way to the houses of the residential area of Hangleton and, even further to the south, Shoreham and its harbour. Taking his eyes off the empty road ahead for a fleeting second, he caught a glimpse of the tall smokestack of the power station, a landmark for the city and for sailors.

As he swept the silver Ford Focus around a long right-hander, he saw a car some distance off about to pull out of the car park of the Waterhall Golf Club into his path and he jabbed the button on the panel in the centre of the dash to change the pitch of the siren to a stentorian *honk-whup-honk-whup* bellow. It did the trick and the car, to his relief, halted sharply.

Each time he headed towards a crime scene, Roy Grace went through a series of mental checks. Reminding himself of all the key elements in the detective's bible, the *Murder Investigation Manual*. A summary sheet, with its headings and flow-chart diagrams, was prominently pinned to the wall in the main corridor of the Major Crime Branch. Every detective who worked there would walk past it several times a week. No matter how many times you ran an investigation, you had to remind yourself to start with the basics. Never get complacent. One of the qualities of a good detective was to be methodical and painstakingly anal.

Grace felt the burden of responsibility just as strongly every time. He'd felt it last week on the quay, with Ewan Preece, and he was feeling it now. The first stage was always the crime scene assessment. Five big headings were ingrained in his mind: LOCATION. VICTIM. OFFENDER. SCENE FORENSICS. POST-MORTEM.

This first, crucial stage of an investigation, literally the hour immediately following the discovery of a murder victim, was known as the *golden hour*. It was the best chance of getting forensic evidence before the crime scene became contaminated by increasing numbers of people, albeit in protective clothing, and before weather, such as rain or strong wind, might change things.

He drove flat out through the picture-postcard village of Poynings, then the even prettier village of Fulking, taking the sharp right-hand bend past the Shepherd and Dog pub, where he had brought Sandy for a drink and a meal on one of their first dates. Then he accelerated along the road at the bottom of the Downs.

Springs Smoked Salmon was a Sussex institution with a world-wide reputation. He'd eaten in many restaurants which boasted their smoked fish as a hallmark of quality, and he'd always wondered about their choice of location, here in the middle of, effectively, nowhere. Maybe they had selected this place originally because there were no neighbours to offend with the fishy smells.

He passed a cluster of farm buildings and dwellings, then slowed as he went down a sharp dip. Rounding the next bend he saw the flashing lights of a halted police car. Several more vehicles, some marked police cars, the Crime Scene Investigator's estate car and a SOCO van were pulled tightly into the bushy side of the road.

He drew up behind the last car, switched off his engine, pressed the button on the dash-mounted panel marked STATIONARY LIGHTS and climbed out. As he wormed himself into his paper oversuit, he could smell wood smoke and the sharper, heavier tang of fish mixed with the fresh, grassy countryside smells.

There was a line of blue and white police tape across the entrance to the smokery and a young constable, acting as a scene guard, whom he did not recognize.

Grace showed his ID.

'Good afternoon, sir,' he said, a little nervously.

Grace pulled on a pair of gloves and ducked under the tape. The constable directed him to walk up a steep incline, between two rows of sheds. Grace only had to go a short distance before he saw a cluster of people similarly attired in oversuits. One of them was Tracy Stocker.

'We can't go on meeting like this, Roy!' she said chirpily.

He grinned. He liked Tracy a lot. She was brilliant at her work, a true professional, but – compared to some of her colleagues, or at least one in particular – she had managed to avoid becoming cynical. As an SIO you soon learned that an efficient Crime Scene Manager could make a big difference to the start of your investigation.

'So what do we have?'

'Not the prettiest picture I've ever seen.'

She turned and led the way. Grace nodded at a couple of detectives he knew. They would have been called here immediately by the response officers to assess the situation. He followed her across to the first of a row of grey, single-storey sheds, each of which had a thick asphalt roof and sliding white door. The door of the building was open.

He suddenly caught a whiff of vomit. Never a good sign. Then Tracy stepped aside, gesturing with her arm for him to enter. He felt a blast of icy air on his face and became aware of a very strong, almost overpowering, reek of smoked fish. Straight ahead he saw a solid wall of large, headless, dark pink fish, hanging in rows, suspended by sturdy hooks to a ceiling rack. There were four rows of them, with narrow aisles between them, hardly wide enough for a person to walk through.

Almost instantly his eyes were drawn to the front of the third row. He saw what at first looked like a huge, plump animal, its flesh all blackened, hanging among the fish. A pig, he thought, fleetingly.

Then, as his brain began to make sense of the image, he realized what it actually was.

66

She loved her view of the Isar, the pretty river that bisected Munich, running almost entirely through parkland. She liked to sit up here at the window, in her fourth-floor apartment above the busy main road of Widenmayerstrasse, and watch people walking their dogs, or jogging, or pushing infants in their strollers along the banks. But most of all she liked to look at the water.

It was for the same reason she liked to go to the Englischer Garten and sit near the lake. Being close to water was like a drug to her. She missed the sea so much. That was what she missed most of all about Brighton. She loved everything else about this city but some days she pined for the sea. And there were other days when she pined for something else, too – the solitude she used to have. Sure, she had resented it at times, that enforced solitude, when work would summon her husband and their plans would be cancelled at the drop of a hat, and she'd find herself alone for an entire weekend, and the following weekends too.

The Italian author Gian Vincenzo Gravina wrote that *a bore is a person who deprives you of solitude without providing you with company.*

This was how it was starting to feel now in her new life. He was so damned demanding. Her new life totally revolved around him. She checked her watch. He would be back soon. This was what it was like now. Every hour of her new life accounted for.

On the screen of her computer on her desk was the online edition of the Sussex newspaper the *Argus*. Since seeing the announcement in the local Munich paper that Roy Grace had placed, about having her declared legally dead, she now scanned the pages of the *Argus* daily.

If he wanted to have her declared dead, after all this time, there had to be a reason. And there was only one reason that she could think of.

She took a deep breath, then she reminded herself of the mantra to control her anger. *Life is not about waiting for the storms to pass. It is about learning to dance in the rain.*

She said it aloud. Then again. And again.

Finally she felt calm enough to turn to the Forthcoming Marriages section of the newspaper. She scanned the column. His name was not there.

She logged off with the same feeling of relief she had every day.

67

Over the years Roy Grace had seen a lot of horrific sights. Mostly, as he had grown more experienced, he was able to leave them behind, but every now and then, like most police officers, he would come across something that he took home with him. When that happened he would lie in bed, unable to sleep, unpacking it over and over again in his mind. Or wake up screaming from the nightmare it was giving him.

One of his worst experiences was as a young uniformed officer, when a five-year-old boy had been crushed under the wheels of a skip lorry. He'd been first on the scene. The boy's head had been distorted and, with his spiky blonde hair, the poor little mite reminded Grace absurdly and horrifically of Bart Simpson. He'd had a nightmare about the boy two or three times a month for several years. Even today he had difficulty watching Bart Simpson on television because of the memory the character triggered.

He was going to take this one in front of him home too, he knew. It was horrific, but he couldn't stop looking, couldn't stop thinking about the suffering during this man's last moments. He hoped they were quick, but he had a feeling they probably weren't.

The man was short and stocky, with a buzz cut and a triple chin, and tattoos on the backs of his hands. He was naked, with his clothes on the ground, as if he had taken them off to have a bath or a swim. His blue overalls, socks and a green polo shirt that was printed with the words ABERDEEN OCEAN FISHERIES sat, neatly folded, next to his heavy-duty boots. Patches of his skin were smoke-blackened and there were some tiny crystals of frost on his head and around his face and hands. He was hung from one of the heavy-duty hooks, the sharp point of which had been pushed up through the roof of his wide-open jaw and was protruding just below his left eye, like a foul-hooked fish.

It was the expression of shock on the man's face – his bulging, terrified eyes – that was the worst thing of all.

The icy air continued to pump out. It carried the strong smell of smoked fish, but also those of urine and excrement. The poor man had both wet and crapped himself. Hardly surprising, Grace thought, continuing to stare at him, thinking through the first pieces of information he had been given. One of the smokehouses had been broken into as well. Had the poor sod been put in there first, and then in here to be finished off by the cold?

The mix of smells was making him feel dangerously close to retching. He began, as a pathologist had once advised him, to breathe only through his mouth.

'You're not going to like what I have to tell you, Roy,' Tracy Stocker said breezily, seemingly totally unaffected.

'I'm not actually liking what I'm looking at that much either. Do we know who he is?'

'Yes, the boss here knows him. He's a lorry driver. Makes a regular weekly delivery here from Aberdeen. Has done for years.'

Grace continued to stare back at the body, fixated. 'Has he been certified?'

'Not yet. A paramedic's on the way.'

However dead a victim might appear, there was a legal require-ment that a paramedic attend and actually make the formal certifi-cation. In the old days it would have been a police surgeon. Not that Grace had any doubt about the man's condition at this moment. The only people who looked more dead than this, he thought cynically, were piles of ash in crematorium urns.

'Have we got a pathologist coming?'

She nodded. 'I'm not sure who.'

'Nadiuska, with any luck.' He looked back at the corpse. 'Hope you'll excuse me if I step out of the room when they remove the hook.'

'I think I'll be stepping out with you,' she said.

He smiled grimly.

'There's something that could be very significant, Roy,' she said.

'What's that?'

'According to Mr Harris, the guv'nor here, this is the driver involved in our fatal in Portland Road. Stuart Ferguson.'

Grace looked at her. Before the ramifications of this had fully sunk in, the Crime Scene Manager was speaking again.

'I think we ought to get a bit closer, Roy. There's something you need to see.'

She took a few steps forward and Grace followed. Then she turned and pointed to the interior wall, a foot above the top of the door.

'Does that look familiar?'

Grace stared at the cylindrical object with the shiny glass lens.

And now he knew for sure that his worst fears were confirmed.

It was another camera.

68

Carly greeted the woman who entered her office with a smile as she ushered her into a seat. The appointment was late, at 4.45, because her whole day was out of kilter. At least it was her last client, she thought with relief.

The woman's name was Angelina Goldsmith. A mother of three teenagers, she had recently discovered that her architect husband had been leading a double life for twenty years and had a second family in Chichester, thirty miles away. He hadn't actually married this woman, so he wasn't legally a bigamist, but he sure as hell was morally. The poor woman was understandably devastated.

And she deserved a solicitor who was able to focus a damned sight better than Carly was capable of doing at the moment, Carly thought.

Angelina Goldsmith was one of those trusting, decent people who was shocked to the core when her husband dumped her and went off with another woman. The woman had a gentle nature, she was a nice-looking brunette with a good figure, and had given up her career as a geologist for her family. Her confidence was shattered and she needed advice urgently.

Carly gave her sympathy and discussed her options. She gave her advice that she hoped would enable her to see a future for herself and her children.

After the client had left, Carly dictated some notes to her secretary, Suzanne. Then she checked her voicemail, listening to a string of messages from clients, the final one from her friend, Clair May, who had driven Tyler to school and back home again. Clair said that Tyler had been crying all the way home, but would not tell her why.

At least her mother was there to look after him, until she got home. He liked his gran, so hopefully he'd cheer up. But his behaviour was really troubling her. She'd try and have a long chat with him as soon as she got home. She rang for a taxi, then left the office.

*

In the taxi on the way home, Carly sat immersed in her thoughts. The driver, a neatly dressed man in a suit, seemed a chatty fellow and he kept trying to make conversation, but she did not respond. She wasn't in the mood for conversation.

Ken Acott had been right about the magistrate. She'd got a one-year ban and a £1,000 fine, which Ken Acott said afterwards was about as lenient as it could get. She'd also accepted the court's offer for her to go on a driver-education course which would reduce her ban to nine months.

She'd felt an idiot, hobbling up to the dock on her uneven shoes and out again. Then, just when she was looking forward to lunch with Sarah Ellis, to cheer her up, Sarah had phoned with the news that her elderly father, who lived alone, had had a fall, and a suspected broken wrist, and she was on her way to hospital with him.

So Carly had thought, sod it, and instead of going to find a shoe repair place, she stumbled along to a store in Duke's Lane for a spot of retail therapy. She was wearing the result now, a pair of reassuringly expensive and absurdly high-heeled Christian Louboutins in black patent leather with twin ankle straps and red soles. They were the only thing today that had made her feel good.

She looked out of the window. They were moving steadily in the heavy rush-hour traffic along the Old Shoreham Road. She texted Tyler to say she'd be home in ten minutes and signed it with a smile and a row of kisses.

'You're towards the Goldstone Crescent end, aren't you, with your number?'

'Yes. Well done.'

'Uh-huh.'

The driver's radio briefly burst into life, then was silent. After a few moments he said, 'Do you have a low-flush or high-flush toilet in your house?'

'A high-flush or low-flush toilet, did you say?'

'Uh-huh.'

'I've no idea,' she replied.

She got a text back from Tyler: **U haven't got Mapper on** ☹

She replied: **Sorry. Horrible day. Love you XXXX**

'High flush, you'd have a chain. Low flush, a handle.'

'We have handles. So low flush, I guess.'

'Why?'

The man's voice was chirpy and intrusive. If he didn't shut up about toilets he wasn't going to get a damned tip.

Mercifully he remained silent until they had halted outside her house. The meter showed £9. She gave him £10 and told him to keep the change. Then, as she stepped out on to the pavement, he called out, 'Nice shoes! Christian Louboutin? Size six? Uh-huh?'

'Good guess,' she said, smiling despite herself.

He didn't smile back. He just nodded and unscrewed the cap of a Thermos flask.

Creepy guy. She was minded to tell the taxi company that she didn't want that driver again. But maybe she was being mean; he was just trying to be friendly.

As she climbed up the steps to her front door, she did not look back. She entered the porch and fumbled in her bag for her key.

On the other side of the road, Tooth, in his dark grey rental Toyota that was in need of a wash, made a note on his electronic pad: **Boy 4.45 p.m. home. Mother 6 p.m. home.**

Then he yawned. It had been a very long day. He started the car and pulled out into the street. As he drove off, he saw a police car heading down slowly, in the opposite direction. He tugged his baseball cap lower over his face as they crossed, then he watched in his rear-view mirror. He saw its brake lights come on.

69

Carly could hear the clatter of dishes in the kitchen, which sounded like her mother clearing up Tyler's supper. There was a smell of cooked food. Lasagne. Sunlight was streaking in through the window. Summer was coming, Carly thought, entering the house with a heavy heart. Normally her spirits lifted this time of year, after the clocks had gone forward and the days were noticeably longer. She liked the early-morning light, and the dawn chorus, too. In those first terrible years after Kes died, the winters had been the worst. Somehow, coping with her grief had been a little easier in the summer.

But what the hell was *normally* any more?

Normally Tyler would come running out of the school gates to greet her. Normally he would come rushing to the front door to hug her if she had been out. But now she stood alone in the hallway, staring at the Victorian coat stand that still had Kes's panama hat slung on a hook, and the fedora he'd once bought on a whim, and his silver duck-handled umbrella in its rack. He'd liked cartoons and there was a big framed Edwardian one of people skating on the old Brighton rink in West Street hanging on the wall, next to a print of the long-gone Brighton chain pier.

The realization was hitting her that everything was going to be a hassle this summer with no driving licence. But, sod it, she thought. She was determined to think positively. She owed it to Tyler – and herself – not to let this get her down. After her father died, four years ago, her mother told her, in the usual philosophical way she had of coping with everything, that life was like a series of chapters in a book and now she was embarking on a new chapter in her life.

So that's what this was, she decided. The *Carly Has No Licence* chapter. She would just have to get to grips with bus and train timetables, like thousands of other people. And as one bonus, how *green* would that be? She was going to use her holidays to give Tyler exactly the same kind of summer he always had. Days on the beach.

Treat days to zoos and amusement parks like Thorpe Park and to the museums in London, particularly the Natural History Museum, which he loved best of all. Maybe she'd get to like travelling that way so much she wouldn't bother with a car again.

Maybe the skies would be filled with flying pigs.

As she walked into the kitchen, her mother, wearing an apron printed with the words TRUST ME, I'M A LAWYER over a black roll-neck and jeans, came up and gave her a hug and a kiss.

'You poor darling, what an ordeal.'

Her mother had been there for her throughout her life. In her mid-sixties, with short, auburn hair, she was a handsome, if slightly sad-looking woman. She had been a midwife, then a district nurse, and these days kept herself busy with a number of charities, including working part-time at the local Brighton hospice, the Martlets.

'At least the worst part's over,' Carly replied. Then she saw the *Argus* lying on the kitchen table. It looked well thumbed through. She hadn't bought a copy because she hadn't had the courage to open it. 'Am I in it?'

'Just a small mention. Page five.'

The main story on the front page was about a serial killer called Lee Coherney, who had once lived in Brighton. The police were digging up the gardens of two of his former residences. The story was on the news on the small flat-screen TV mounted on the wall above the kitchen table. A good-looking police officer was giving a statement about their progress. The caption at the bottom of the screen gave his name as Detective Chief Inspector Nick Sloan of Sussex CID.

She riffled through the pages until she found her tiny mention and felt momentarily grateful to this monster, Coherney, for burying her own story.

'How's Tyler?' she asked.

'He's fine. Upstairs, playing with that lovely little friend of his, Harrison, who just came over.'

'I'll go and say hi. Do you need to get off?'

'I'll stay and make you some supper. What do you feel like? There is some lasagne and salad left.'

'I feel like a sodding big glass of wine!'

'I'll join you!'

The doorbell rang.

Carly looked at her mother quizzically, then glanced at her watch. It was 6.15 p.m.

'Tyler said another friend might be joining them. They're playing some computer battle game tonight.'

Carly walked into the hall and across to the front door. She looked at the safety chain dangling loose, but it was early evening and she didn't feel the need to engage it. She opened the door and saw a tall, bald black man in his mid-thirties, dressed in a sharp suit and snazzy tie, accompanied by a staid-looking woman of a similar age. She had a tangle of hennaed brown hair that fell short of her shoulders and wore a grey trouser suit over a blouse with the top button done up, giving her a slightly prim air.

The man held up a small black wallet with a document inside it bearing the Sussex Police coat of arms and his photograph.

'Mrs Carly Chase?'

'Yes,' she answered, a tad hesitantly, thinking she really did not want to have to answer a whole load more questions about the accident tonight.

His manner was friendly but he seemed uneasy. 'Detective Sergeant Branson and this is Detective Sergeant Moy from Sussex CID. May we come in? We need to speak to you urgently.'

He threw a wary glance over his shoulder. His colleague was looking up and down the street.

Carly stepped back and ushered them in, unsettled by something she could not put a finger on. She saw her mother peering anxiously out of the kitchen door.

'We need to speak to you in private, please,' DS Branson said.

Carly led them into the living room, signalling to her mother that all was fine. She followed them in and pointed to one of the two sofas, then shut the door, casting an embarrassed glance at the spreading brown stain on the wallpaper, which now covered almost entirely one wall. Then she sat down on the sofa opposite them, staring at them defiantly, wondering what they were going to throw at her now.

'How can I help you?' she asked eventually.

'Mrs Chase, we have reason to believe your life may be in immediate danger,' Glenn Branson said.

Carly blinked hard. 'Pardon?'

Then she noticed for the first time that he had a large brown envelope in his hand. He was holding it in a strangely delicate way for such a big man, the way he might have held a fragile vase.

'It's concerning the road traffic collision two weeks ago today, which resulted in the death of a young student at Brighton University, Tony Revere,' he said.

'What do you mean exactly by *immediate danger*?'

'There were two other vehicles involved, Mrs Chase – a Ford Transit van and a Volvo refrigerated lorry.'

'They were the ones that actually struck the poor cyclist, yes.' She caught the eye of the female DS, who smiled at her in a sympathetic way that irritated her.

'Are you aware of who the cyclist was?' he asked.

'I've read the papers. Yes, I am. It's very sad – and very distressing to have been involved.'

'You're aware that his mother is the daughter of a man purported to be the head of the New York Mafia?'

'I've read that. And the reward she offered. I didn't even know they existed any more. I thought that the Mafia was something from the past, sort of out of *The Godfather*.'

The DS exchanged a glance with his colleague, who then spoke. 'Mrs Chase, I'm a Family Liaison Officer. I think as a solicitor you may be familiar with this term?'

'I don't do criminal law, but yes.'

'I'm here to help you through the next steps you choose. You know the Ford Transit van that was just mentioned?'

'The one that was right behind me?'

'Yes. You need to know that the driver of this van is dead. His body was found in the van on Friday, in Shoreham Harbour.'

'I read in the *Argus* that a body had been found in a van in the harbour.'

'Yes,' Bella Moy said. 'What you won't have read is that he was the driver we believe was involved in the collision. You also won't have read that he was murdered.'

Carly frowned. 'Murdered?'

'Yes. I can't give you details, but please trust us, he was. The reason we are here is that just a few hours ago the driver of the Volvo lorry involved in the death of Tony Revere was also found murdered.'

Carly felt a cold ripple of fear. The room seemed to be swaying and there was a sudden, terrible, intense silence. Then it seemed as if she wasn't really inside her body any more, that she had left it behind and was drifting in a black, freezing, muted void. She tried to speak but nothing came out. The two officers drifted in and out of focus. Then her forehead was burning. The floor seemed to be rising beneath her, then sinking away, as if she was on a ship. She put her right hand on the arm of the sofa, to hold on.

'I—' she began. 'I – I – I thought the reward that – that the mother – that the mother had put up – was for the identification of the van driver.'

'It was,' Bella Moy said.

'So – so why would they be murdered?' A vortex of fear was swirling inside her.

'We don't know, Mrs Chase,' Glenn Branson replied. 'This could just be an extraordinary coincidence. But the police have a duty of care. The inquiry team have made a threat assessment and we believe your life may be in danger.'

This could not be happening, Carly thought. This was a sick joke. There was going to be a punchline. There was some kind of subtle entrapment going on. Her lawyer's mind was kicking in. They'd come in order to scare her into some kind of confession about the accident.

Then Glenn Branson said, 'Mrs Chase, there is a range of things we can do to try to protect you. One of them would be to move you away from here to a safe place somewhere in the city. How would you feel about that?'

She stared at him, her fear deepening. 'What do you mean?'

Bella Moy said, 'It would be similar to a witness being taken into protective custody, Mrs Chase – can I call you Carly?'

Carly nodded bleakly, trying to absorb what she had just been told. 'Move me away?'

'Carly, we'd move you and your family under escort to another house, as a temporary measure. Then, if we feel the threat level is going to be ongoing, we could look at moving you to a different part of England, change your name and give you a completely new identity.'

Carly stared at them, bewildered, like a hunted animal. 'Change my name? A new identity? Move to somewhere else in Brighton? You mean right now?'

'Right now,' Glenn Branson said. 'We'll stay here with you while you pack and then arrange a police escort.'

Carly raised her hands in the air. 'Wait a second. This is insane. My life is in this city. I have a son at school here. My mother lives here. I can't just up sticks and move to another house. No way. Certainly not tonight. And as for moving to another part of England, that's crazy.' Her voice was trembling. 'Listen, I wasn't part of this accident. OK, I know, I've been convicted of driving over the limit – but I didn't hit the poor guy, for Christ's sake! I can't be blamed for his death, surely? The traffic police have already said so. It was said in court today, as well.'

'Carly,' Bella Moy said, 'we know that. The dead boy's parents have been given all the information about the accident. But as my colleague has said, Sussex Police have a legal duty of care to you.'

Carly wrung her hands, trying to think clearly. She couldn't. 'Let's clarify this,' she said. 'The driver behind me, in the white van, you say he is dead – that he's been murdered?'

Glenn Branson looked very solemn. 'There's not any question about it, Mrs Chase. Yes, he has been murdered.'

'And the lorry driver?'

'Not any question about his death either. We've carried out intelligence as best we can on the dead boy's family and, unfortunately, they are fully capable of revenge killings such as this. Dare I say it, these things are part of their culture. It's a different world they inhabit.'

'That's fucking great, isn't it?' Carly said, her fear turning to anger. She suddenly felt badly in need of a drink and a cigarette. 'Can I get either of you something to drink?'

Both officers shook their heads.

She sat still for a moment, thinking hard, but it was difficult to focus her mind. 'Are you saying there's a hit man, or whatever they're called, hired by this family?'

'It's a possibility, Carly,' Bella Moy said gently.

'Oh, right. So what are the other possibilities? Coincidence? It would be a big, bloody coincidence, right?'

'One hundred thousand dollars is a lot of money, Mrs Chase,' DS Branson said. 'It is indicative of the parents' anger.'

'So you're saying my son and I might need to move away from here? Get a new identity? That you'll protect us for the rest of our lives? How's that going to work?'

The two detectives looked at each other. Then DS Moy spoke. 'I don't think any police force has the resources to provide that level of protection, Mrs Chase, unfortunately. But we can help you change identity.'

'This is my home. This is our life here. Our friends are here. Tyler's already lost his dad. Now you want him to lose all his friends? You seriously want me to go into hiding, with my son, tonight? To consider quitting my job? And what if we do move house – and then county? If these people are for real, don't you think they're going to be able to find us? I'm going to spend the rest of my life in fear of a knock on the door, or a creak in the house, or the crack of a twig out in the garden?'

'We're not forcing you to move out, Carly,' Bella Moy said. 'We're just saying that would be the best option in our view.'

'If your decision is to stay we will give you protection,' Glenn Branson said. 'We'll provide CCTV and a Close Protection Unit, but it will be for a limited period of two weeks.'

'Two weeks?' Carly retorted. 'Why's that – because of your budget?'

Branson raised his hands expansively. 'These are really your best two options.' Then he picked up the envelope and removed a document from it. 'I need you to read and sign this, please.'

Carly looked down at it. Seeing it in print sent an even deeper chill swirling through her.

70

APPENDIX F – SUSSEX POLICE

'Osman' Warning

Notice of Threat to Personal Safety

Mrs Carly Chase
37 Hove Park Avenue
Hove
BN3 6LN
East Sussex

Dear Mrs Chase

I am in receipt of the following information, which suggests that your personal safety is now in danger.

I stress that I will not under any circumstances disclose to you the identity of the source of this information and whilst I cannot comment on the reliability or otherwise of the source or the content of this information, I have no reason to disbelieve the account as provided. I am not in receipt of any other information in relation to this matter nor do I have any direct involvement in this case.

I have reason to believe, following the deaths of Ewan Preece, the driver of the van which collided with cyclist Tony Revere, and Stuart Ferguson, driver of the lorry which also collided with Tony Revere, that your own life is in immediate and present danger from revenge killings ordered by person or persons unknown and carried out by person or persons currently unknown.

Although Sussex Police will take what steps it can to minimize the risk, the Police cannot protect you from this threat on a day-by-day, hour-by-hour basis.

I also stress that the passing of this information by me in no way authorizes you to take any action which would place you in contravention of the law (e.g. carrying weapons for defence, assault on others, breaches of public order) and should you be found to be so committing you will be dealt with accordingly.

I therefore suggest that you take such action as you see fit to increase your own safety measures (e.g. house burglar alarms, change of daily routines etc.). It may even be that you decide that it is more appropriate for you to leave the area for the foreseeable future. That is a matter for you to decide.

If you wish to provide me with full details of the address at which you will be resident I will ensure that the necessary surveys can be undertaken by police staff to advise you regarding the above safety measures.

I would also ask that you contact the Police regarding any suspicious incidents associated with this threat.

Signed   Detective Superintendent Roy Grace

Time/Date   5.35 p.m. Wednesday 5 May

_____

I ……………… acknowledge that at …… hrs on ………… 20 …

the above notice was read out to me by ……………………………

of Sussex Police

Signed ……………………………………………………………………

_____

Signed by Officer reading notice to ....

Time/Date ....

Signed by Officer witnessing reading ....

Time/Date ....

Carly read it through. When she had finished she looked up at the two officers.

'Let me understand something. Are you saying that if I don't agree to move, that's it, I'm on my own?'

Bella Moy shook her head. 'No, Carly. As DS Branson explained, we would provide you with a round-the-clock police guard for a period of time – two weeks. And we would put in CCTV surveillance for you. But we cannot guarantee your safety, Carly. We can just do our best.'

'You want me to sign?'

Bella nodded.

'This isn't for me, is it, this signature? It's to protect your backsides. If I get killed, you can show you did your best – is that about the size of it?'

'Look, you're an intelligent person,' Glenn Branson said. 'All of us at Sussex Police will do what we can to protect you. But if you don't want to move away, and I can understand that, and I imagine you don't want to be locked away in a secure panic room, then what we can do is limited. We'll have to try to work together.' He placed his card in front of Carly on a coffee table. 'Detective Sergeant Moy will be your immediate contact, but feel free to call me twenty-four-seven.'

Carly picked up her pen. 'Great,' she said, as she signed it, sick with fear, trying hard to think straight.

71

Roy Grace lay in bed beside Cleo, tossing and turning, wide awake, totally wired. He'd been at the mortuary until 2 a.m., when the post-mortem on the lorry driver was finally completed. At least he'd managed to persuade Cleo to go home early, so she'd left shortly before midnight. He now lived in constant fear that Cleo would have another bleed at any moment. Potentially a life-threatening one, for herself and for their baby.

Nadiuska De Sancha had been unavailable and they'd been saddled with the pedantic Home Office pathologist Dr Frazer Theobald for the post-mortem. But although slow, Theobald was thorough, and he had provided some good, immediate information regarding the unfortunate victim's death.

The bright blue dial on the clock radio, inches from Grace's eyes, flicked from 3.58 a.m. to 3.59 a.m., then after what seemed an interminable time to 4.00 a.m.

Shit.

He faced a long, hard day in front of him, during which he would need to be on peak form to manage his expanding inquiry team, to cope with the inevitable quizzing from Peter Rigg and to make important decisions on a revised press strategy. But most importantly of all, the absolute number one priority, he had to safeguard a woman who could be in imminent life-threatening danger.

He looked at the clock radio again: 4.01.

The first streaks of dawn were breaking over the city. But there was a deepening darkness inside him. How the hell could you fully protect someone, short of locking them away in a cell, or walling them up in a panic room? She wasn't willing to leave her home, which would have been the best option, and he could understand her reasons. But the buck stopped with him to make sure she was safe.

He thought again about the sight of Ewan Preece in the van. And the grisly spectre of Stuart Ferguson on the hook. But it was those cameras he was thinking about most. Particularly the second one.

The transmission range was only a few hundred yards. Which meant that the killer had to have been waiting nearby with a receiving device – almost certainly in a vehicle. Grace could understand it would have been difficult to retrieve the camera in the van, but surely he could have gone back for the second one? The two cameras, waterproof and with night vision, were worth a good thousand pounds each. A lot of money to throw away.

Who was this killer? He was clever, cunning and organized. In all of his career, Grace had never come across anything quite like this.

The filming reminded him of a case he had worked on the previous summer, involving a sick, snuff-movie ring, and it had crossed his mind he could be in the same terrain here, but he doubted it. This was about revenge for Tony Revere's death. The driver with his lorryload of frozen seafood being executed in the smokery left little room for doubt.

The pathologist estimated that Ferguson would have been dead in under two hours in the cold store and probably less than that. If the killer had been waiting nearby and picking up the transmission, and presumably waiting until the lorry driver was dead, why had he not retrieved the camera?

Because he hadn't wanted to take the risk? Had he been disturbed by someone arriving there? Or a passing police patrol car perhaps? Or was it to leave a message – a sign – for someone? Just a cynical message for the next victim? *This is what is going to happen to you and money is no object . . .*

Had the killer sat in his car, watching the transmitted images of Ferguson wriggling, shivering and steadily freezing to death for two hours? Frazer Theobald said that the man's skin was partially burned and he had smoke inhalation in his lungs, but not sufficient to have asphyxiated him. The hook through his jaw and out beneath his eye would have been agonizing but not life-threatening. His death in the cold store would have been excruciating.

What might this sadist be planning for Carly Chase?

Detective Investigator Lanigan's team were interviewing the Revere family, as well as Fernanda Revere's brother, who had assumed the position as official head of this crime family following his father's incarceration, but Lanigan was not optimistic about getting anywhere with them.

Grace sipped some water, then as gently as he could turned his pillows over, trying to freshen them up.

Cleo was not sleeping well either, finding it hard lying on her left, with a pillow tucked under her arm, as she had been instructed, as well as needing to go to the loo almost every hour. She was asleep now, breathing heavily. He wondered if reading for a few minutes might calm him down enough to get to sleep. On the floor, a short distance from the bed, their puppy, Humphrey, a Labrador and Border Collie cross, was snoring intermittently.

Moving slowly, trying not to disturb Cleo, he switched on the dimmest setting of his reading light and peered at the small pile of books on his bedside table, half of them bought on his colleague Nick Nicholl's recommendation.

Fatherhood. From Lad to Dad. The New Contented Little Baby Book. Secrets of the Baby Whisperer.

He picked up the top one, *Fatherhood*, and continued reading from the place he'd marked. But after a few pages, instead of calming down, he became increasingly concerned about the burden of responsibility of fatherhood. There was so much to take on board. And all that on top of his police workload.

From the moment Cleo had first given him the news that she was pregnant, he had determined that he would be an involved and committed parent. But now, reading through these books, the time and responsibilities required of him seemed daunting. He wanted to commit that time and he wanted those responsibilities, but how was it all going to be possible?

At 5.30 he finally quit trying to sleep, slipped out of bed, went into the bathroom and splashed some cold water on his face. His eyes felt like he'd been rubbing them with sandpaper. He wondered whether a short run would perk him up, but he felt just too tired. Instead, pulling on his tracksuit, he decided on a walk around the block, focusing his thoughts on the day ahead, and taking Humphrey, who had insisted on joining him, on his lead. Then he dosed himself up on coffee, showered and dressed, and drove to the office.

He arrived there just before 7 a.m., drank a Red Bull and made a phone call to the senior officer of the Close Protection Team that was concealed outside Carly Chase's house. To his relief, all had been quiet.

For this past night, at any rate.

72

'I want you all to know,' said Roy Grace at the start of the 8.30 a.m. briefing in MIR-1, 'that I am not a happy sodding bunny.'

Everyone in the room was already up to speed on the murder of the lorry driver. Major developments in an inquiry of this scale were passed around instantly.

Taking a sip of his coffee and looking down at his notes, he went on, 'Item One on my agenda is the ongoing series of leaks coming from someone to our friend Kevin Spinella at the *Argus*. OK?'

He looked up at thirty-five solemn faces. Yesterday afternoon's horrific discovery had shaken even the most hardened of this bunch. 'I'm not accusing any of you, but someone has leaked to him about Preece's hands being superglued to the steering wheel of his van. It is either a member of this inquiry team, or the Specialist Search Unit, or an employee at Shoreham Harbour, or one of the team in the mortuary. At some point I'm going to find that person and, when I do, I'm going to hang them out to dry on something even more painful than a meat hook. Do I make myself clear?'

Everyone nodded. All those who worked with Roy Grace knew him to be even-tempered and placid, someone who rarely lost his head. It startled them to see him in a temper.

He took another sip of his coffee. 'Our media strategy could be vitally important. We believe a professional contract killer is here in Brighton, in all probability hired by the Revere family in New York to avenge their son's death. We need to manage the media extremely carefully, both to try to get assistance from the public in finding this killer before he strikes again and to avoid any possible impact on the community.'

'Sir,' said DC Stacey Horobin, a bright-looking young woman in her early thirties, with fashionable straggly brown hair, who had been newly drafted into the inquiry team, 'what exactly are your concerns on community impact?'

Nick Nicholl's phone rang. Under Grace's withering glare, he hastily silenced it. There was a brief moment when Grace looked as if he would explode, but his response was calm. 'I think we can assure the public, if it comes to it, that there is no general risk to them,' he replied. 'But I do not want our force to appear incapable of protecting an innocent member of the public.'

'Was the Osman served on Mrs Chase, chief?' asked Duncan Crocker.

'Yes,' Glenn Branson replied on Grace's behalf. 'Bella and I served it yesterday evening just after 6 p.m. Mrs Chase was offered the opportunity to be moved away, out of the area, but she refused for family and business reasons. Frankly, I think she's unwise. DS Moy spent the night in her house, pending the installation of CCTV equipment this morning, and a Close Protection Team unit have been in place outside her residence since 9 p.m. last night. So far without incident.'

'Is there any protection on her commute to work?' asked Norman Potting. 'And while she's in her workplace?'

'I've spoken to Inspector Hazzard at the Hove Neighbourhood Policing Team,' Grace said. 'Today and tomorrow, and for the first part of next week, she will be driven to and from work in a marked police car. And I'm putting a PCSO in reception at her office. I want to send a clear signal to this killer, if he's out there and targeting this woman, that we are on to him.'

'What about Revere's family in New York, chief?' said Nick Nicholl. 'Is anyone speaking to them?'

'I updated our NYPD contact on the situation and they're on the case. He told me that the killings sound similar to the style of a former Mafia hitman, a charmer called Richard Kuklinski who was known as the Iceman. He used cold stores, and one of his specialities was tying up victims and putting them in a cave, then leaving a camera in there to record them steadily being eaten alive by rats.'

Bella, who had been about to pluck a Malteser from the box in front of her, withdrew her hand, wrinkling her face in disgust.

'He sounds our man, chief!' Norman Potting said animatedly.

'He does, Norman,' Grace replied. 'There's just one problem with Kuklinski.'

Potting waited apprehensively.

'He died in prison four years ago.'

'Yes, well, I suppose that might rather tend to eliminate him,' Potting retorted. He looked around with a grin, but no one smiled back. 'Fishy business, this cold store, yesterday,' he added, and again looked around, without success, for any smiles. All he got was a withering glare from Bella Moy.

'Thank you Norman,' Grace said curtly. 'Detective Investigator Lanigan was going to go and see Mr and Mrs Revere last night and report back to me. But frankly I'm not expecting anything from them. And one thing Lanigan told me, which is not good news for us, is that their intelligence on contract killers is very limited.'

'Chief, did this Kuklinski character paralyse his victims first?'

'Not from what I've learned so far from the post-mortem, Nick, no. Our man didn't paralyse Preece – only Ferguson.'

'Why do you think he did that?'

Grace shrugged. 'Maybe sadism. Or perhaps to make him easier to handle. Hopefully,' he said, raising his eyebrows, 'we'll get the chance to ask him that.'

'Boss, what information are you releasing to the press about the death of the lorry driver?' DC Emma-Jane Boutwood asked.

'For now, no more than a man was found dead in a cold store at Springs Smoked Salmon,' Grace said. 'I don't want speculation. Let people think for the moment that it might have been an industrial accident.'

He glanced down at his mobile phone, which was lying next to his printed notes on the work surface in front of him, as if waiting for the inevitable call from Spinella. But it remained, for the moment, silent. 'I haven't yet decided what we should release beyond that. But I've no doubt someone will make that decision for me.'

He gave a challenging stare to his team, without looking at any specific individual. Then he glanced down at his notes again. 'OK, according to his employers, Stuart Ferguson left the depot in the fridge-box lorry shortly after 2 p.m. on Tuesday. We need to find this lorry.' He looked at DC Horobin. 'Stacey, I'm giving you an action which is to try to plot the lorry's route and sightings from the time it left the depot in Aberdeen to wherever it currently is. We need to find it. You should be able to plot much of its journey fairly easily from an ANPR search.'

Automatic Number Plate Recognition cameras were positioned along many of the UK's motorways and key arterial roads. They filmed the registration plates of all passing vehicles and fed them into a database.

'Yes, sir,' she said.

Grace then read out a summary of the post-mortem findings so far. After he dealt with several questions on that, he drained the last of his coffee and moved on to the next item on his list.

'OK, an update on lines of enquiry. The murder of Preece's friend Warren Tulley at Ford Prison is still ongoing.' He looked at DS Crocker. 'Duncan, do you have anything there for us?'

'Nothing new, chief. Still the same wall of silence from the other inmates. The interviewing team is talking to each of the prisoners, but so far we have no breakthrough.'

Grace thanked him, then turned to DC Nick Nicholl. 'The superglue on Ewan Preece's hands. Nick, anything to report?'

'The Outside Inquiry Team are continuing to visit every retail outlet in the Brighton and Hove area that sells superglue. It's a massive task, chief, and we're really understaffed for it. Every news-agent, every DIY and hardware shop, every supermarket.'

'Keep them on it,' Grace said. Then he turned to Norman Potting. 'Anything to report with the camera?'

'We've covered every retailer that sells this equipment, chief, including the Cash Converters stores that sell 'em second-hand. One of them was good enough to check the serial number on the one in the van. He reckons it's not a model sold in the UK – it can only be bought in the USA. I haven't had a chance to start checking the one found in the cold store at Springs yet, but it looks identical.'

As the meeting ended, Glenn Branson received a call on his radio. It was from one of the security officers, Duncan Steele, on the front desk.

He thanked him, then turned to Roy Grace. 'Mrs Chase is down-stairs.'

Grace frowned. 'Here, in this building?'

'Yep. She says she needs to see me urgently.'

'Maybe she's come to her senses.'

73

Tooth sat at the desk in his room at the Premier Inn, with his laptop open in front of him. Through the window he kept an eye on the parking area. He could see the North Terminal building of Gatwick Airport in the distance beyond it and the blue sky above it. It would not be long before he was on an airplane in that blue sky, heading home, to the almost constant blue sky of the Turks and Caicos. He liked heat. Liked it when he had been in the military in hot places. From his experience of English weather, it rained most of the time.

He didn't do rain.

A Lucky Strike dangled between his lips. He stared at the screen, doing some blue-sky thinking, clicking through the images. Photographs of Hove Park Avenue, where Carly Chase lived. Photographs of the front, back and sides of her house.

Early in the morning after he had finished at Springs smokery he had driven down this street, memorizing the cars. Then he'd paid a brief visit to her property. A dog had started barking inside the house and an upstairs interior light came on as he was leaving. Last night he'd taken another drive down there and had spotted the parked dark-coloured Audi, with a shadowy figure behind the wheel. The Audi had not been there previously.

The police weren't stupid. He'd learned over the years never to underestimate the enemy. You stayed alive that way. Out of jail that way. In the US, police surveillance operated in teams of eight, on eight-hour shifts, twenty-four officers covering a twenty-four-hour watch. He had little doubt there were others out there in that area he hadn't spotted. Some on foot, probably in the back garden or down the sides of the house.

He had already listened to the conversation inside the house that the minute directional microphones he had concealed in her garden, pointed at her windows, had picked up when the police had visited her yesterday evening. When she had told them she did not want to leave.

He looked down at his notes. The kid had been picked up in his school uniform at 8.25 a.m. today by a woman in a black Range Rover, with two other kids in it. At 8.35 Carly Chase had left home in the back of a marked police car.

At 9.05 he made a phone call to her office, masquerading as a client, saying he needed to speak to her urgently. He was told she had not yet arrived. A second phone call told him she had still not arrived at 9.30.

Where was she?

74

Carly Chase sat down beside Glenn Branson at the small round conference table in Roy Grace's office. Grace joined them.

'Nice to meet you, Mrs Chase,' he said, sitting down. 'I'm sorry it's not under better circumstances. Would you like something to drink?'

She felt too sick with fear to swallow anything. 'I'm – I'm OK, thank you.'

She was conscious of her right foot jigging and she couldn't stop it. Both the policemen were staring at her intently and that was making her even more nervous.

'I wanted to talk to you,' she stammered, glancing at Glenn Branson, then looking back at the Detective Superintendent. 'Detective Sergeant Branson and his colleague explained the situation to me yesterday evening. I've been thinking about it overnight. I'm not sure if you know, but I'm a solicitor specializing in divorce.'

Grace nodded. 'I know a fair bit about you.'

She wrung her hands, then swallowed to try to stop her ears popping. Her eyes darted from a collection of old cigarette lighters on a shelf to framed certificates on the wall, then to a stuffed trout in a display case and back to Grace.

'I'm a great believer in compromise rather than confrontation,' she said. 'I try to save marriages, rather than destroy them – that's always been my philosophy.'

Grace nodded again. 'A very noble sentiment.'

She gave him a sideways look, unsure if he was taking the mickey, then realized she knew nothing about his own private life.

'In my experience, dialogue is so often missing,' she said, and shrugged, her foot jigging even harder.

Grace stared at her. He had no idea what point she was leading up to.

'I lost my husband five years ago in a skiing accident. He was buried in an avalanche in Canada. My first reaction was that I wanted to get on a plane to Canada, find the guide who had taken him on that mountain – and who survived – and kill him with my bare hands. OK?'

Grace glanced at Branson, who gave him a helpless shrug back. 'Everyone has to deal with grief in their own way,' he replied.

'Exactly,' Carly replied. 'That's why I'm here.' She turned to Glenn Branson. 'You told me last night that my life is in danger from a revenge killing arranged by the parents of the poor boy who died on his bike. But I wasn't a guilty part of that. OK, I know I've been prosecuted for drink driving, but it wouldn't have made a damned bit of difference if I'd been stone cold sober – your traffic police have confirmed that. It wasn't the van driver's fault either, even if he did do a hit-and-run, and it sure as hell wasn't the lorry driver's fault. The whole thing was caused by the poor kid himself, cycling on the wrong side of the road!'

Branson was about to reply, but Grace cut in on him. 'Mrs Chase, we're aware of that. But, as my colleague has explained, we are not dealing with normal, rational people. The Reveres, from what we understand, come from a culture where differences are settled not in court, but by physical brutality. They have been informed that you did not collide with their son, and it may be that they've now finished with their terrible revenge – if that's what these two killings are about. But I'm responsible for your safety and I have a duty of care to you.'

'I can't live my life in fear, Mr Grace – sorry – Detective Superintendent. There's always a way through a problem and I think I have found a way through this one.'

Both police officers looked hard at her.

'You do?' Glenn Branson said.

'Yes. I – I didn't sleep a wink last night, trying to figure out what to do. I've decided I'm going to go and see them. I'm going to New York to talk woman to woman to Mrs Revere. She's lost her son. I lost my husband. Both of us would like to try to blame other people to try to find some sense in our losses. I think constantly about that stupid ski guide who should never have taken my husband on that slope in those weather conditions. But nothing vengeful is going to bring Kes back or ease the pain of my loss. I have to find ways to move forward in life. She and her husband are going to have to do the same.'

'I know a little bit about loss too,' Roy Grace said gently. 'I've been there. I have a sense of where you are coming from. But from what I know about this family, I don't think going to see them is a good idea – and it's certainly not something Sussex Police could sanction.'

'Why not?' She glared at Grace with a sudden ferocity that startled him.

'Because we're responsible for your safety. I can protect you here in Brighton, but I couldn't look after you in New York.'

She turned to Glenn Branson. 'You told me last night that you could only guard me for a fortnight. Right?'

Branson nodded, then said, 'Well, we would review the situation before the end of that period.'

'But you can't protect me for the rest of my life. And that's what I would be scared of. I can't spend the next fifty years looking over my shoulder. I have to deal with this now.' She was silent for a moment, then she spoke again. 'Are you saying you'd stop me from going?'

Grace opened his arms expansively. 'I have no powers to stop you. But I cannot guarantee your safety if you go. I could send an officer with you, but frankly he wouldn't be able to do a lot out of his jurisdiction—'

'I'm going alone,' she said determinedly. 'I can look after myself. I can deal with it. I deal with difficult people all the time.'

Glenn Branson admired her determination, secretly wishing he'd hired this terrified but feisty woman to act for him in his divorce, instead of the rather wishy-washy solicitor he had.

'Mrs Chase,' Roy Grace said, 'we have some intelligence on the Revere family. Do you want to hear it before you make your final decision?'

'Anything you can tell me would be helpful.'

'OK. Until recently they owned a club in Brooklyn called the Concubine. They would invite their enemies there for a drink and when they arrived, as special guests of honour, these unfortunates would be invited downstairs to the VIP lounge. When they entered they would be greeted by three men, one of whom was a tall American-Italian charmer nicknamed Dracula, because he looked like Bella Lugosi. A fourth man, whom they would never see, would shoot them in the back of the head with a silenced handgun. Dracula would drain their blood into a bathtub. Another guy, who had started out as a butcher, would dismember their cadavers into six pieces. The fourth guy would package up each limb, the torso and the head, and dispose of them in various waste dumps around New York and in the Hudson River. It is estimated they murdered over one hundred people. Sal Giordino, Tony Revere's grandfather, is currently serving eleven consecutive life sentences for this, with a minimum of eighty-seven years in jail. Do you understand the people you would be dealing with?'

'I've been Googling them,' she said. 'There's a lot of stuff about Sal Giordino, but I've not found anything about his daughter. But from what you've told me about their world, isn't this all the more reason for me to go there and try to talk reason to them?' she said.

'These people don't reason,' Grace said.

'At least give me the chance to try. Do you have their address? The home address?'

'What about emailing or phoning Mrs Revere first, to see what reaction you get?' Grace asked her.

'No, it's got to be face to face, mother to mother,' Carly replied.

The two detectives looked at each other.

'I can find the address out for you on one condition,' Roy Grace said.

'Which is?'

'You allow us to arrange an escort for you in New York.'

After a long silence she said, 'Could – could I make that decision?'

'No,' he answered.

75

At 10.17 an alert pinged on Tooth's laptop. A voice file was recording. Which meant someone was speaking inside Carly Chase's house.

He clicked and listened in. She was on the phone to a woman called Claire, asking about flights to New York today and confirming she had a valid visa waiver, from a trip last year. It sounded like Claire was a travel agent. She reeled off a list of flight times. After some moments of checking availability, she booked Carly Chase on a 14.55 British Airways flight from London to Kennedy Airport, New York, this afternoon. Then they discussed hotels. The travel agent made a reservation for her at the Sheraton at Kennedy Airport.

Tooth glanced at his watch, double-checking the time and smiling. She was making this very easy for him. She had no idea!

Next he heard Carly Chase speak to a taxi company called Streamline. She booked a car to Terminal 5 at Heathrow Airport, to collect her at 11.30 a.m. – just over an hour's time. Then she made a further call.

It was to someone called Sarah. The woman sounded like a friend. Carly Chase explained to her that Tyler had a dental appointment at 11.30 a.m. the following morning to have an adjustment made to his tooth brace, which was hurting him. Ordinarily his gran could have taken him, but her doctor had booked her in for a scan on something he wasn't happy about in her tummy and Carly did not want her to miss that. She explained she had been planning to take Tyler herself, but something urgent had come up – would it be possible for Sarah to take him?

Sarah could not, because of her father, whose wrist was indeed broken, but she said that Justin had taken the week off to do some work on their new house and she was sure he could pick Tyler up. She said she would call back in a few minutes.

Tooth made himself another coffee and smoked another cigarette. Then his laptop pinged again and he listened to Sarah telling Carly Chase that everything was fine. Justin, who was presumably her husband, would pick Tyler up from school at 11.15 tomorrow. Carly Chase gave her the address and thanked her.

Tooth stared down at his notepad, on which he had written Carly Chase's flight details. She'd only booked one way, on an open ticket. He speculated about where she was going, and had a good idea. He wondered what she was like at ten-pin bowling.

Except he did not think she would get as far as the Reveres' bowling alley.

He just hoped they wouldn't kill her, because that would spoil all his plans.

76

'We can't let her do this,' Roy Grace said, placing his hands on the workstation top in MIR-1 and leaning over towards Glenn Branson.

'We don't have any legal power to stop her,' Branson replied. 'And she's terrified out of her wits.'

'I know. I could see that. I would be, too, in her situation.'

It was an hour since Carly Chase had left his office. Grace had a ton of urgent stuff to deal with, one of the most important of which was organizing a press conference. A lesson he had learned a long time back was that you got much better cooperation from the media by telling them about a murder, rather than waiting for them to tell you. Particularly in the case of Kevin Spinella.

But he hadn't been able to focus on any of that. He was desperately worried for this woman's safety. It was 5.30 a.m. in New York and Detective Inspector Pat Lanigan's phone went straight to voicemail. It was probably switched off. Sensible man, Grace thought. And lucky. Since he became Head of Major Crime he no longer had the luxury of being able to turn his phone off at night.

Branson's mobile phone was ringing. The DS raised a hand to his boss, answered it, then said curtly, 'Can't speak now. Bell you back.' He killed the call. Then, looking down at the phone, said, 'Bitch.' He shook his head. 'I don't get it. Why does she hate me so much? I could understand if I'd had an affair, but I didn't, ever. I never looked at another woman. Ari encouraged me to better myself, then it's like – like she resented it. Said I put my career before her and my family.' He shrugged. 'Did you ever figure out what goes on inside a woman's head?'

'I'd like to figure out what's going on inside this mad woman's head,' Grace replied.

'That's easy. I can tell you that, without a two hundred and fifty quid per hour bill from a shrink. Fear. All right, old-timer? She's sodding terrified. And I don't blame her. I would be, too.'

Grace nodded. Then his phone rang. It was one of his colleagues asking him if he would be joining their regular Thursday poker game tonight. For the second week running Grace apologized, but no, he wouldn't be. The game had been going for years and fortunately they were all police officers, so they understood about work commitments.

'Got to be a shit situation when someone feels we can't protect them. Right?' Branson said, as Grace hung up.

'We *can* protect them – but only if they want to be protected,' the Detective Superintendent replied. 'If they're willing to move and change their identity, we can make them reasonably safe. But I can understand where she's coming from. I wouldn't want to leave my home, my job and take my kid out of school. But people do it all the time – they up sticks and move – and not just because they're being hunted.'

'We're just going to let her go to New York alone? Shouldn't we send someone with her? Bella?'

'Aside from the cost, we don't have any jurisdiction there. Our best hope for her safety is to get the New York police guarding her. We'll keep a watch on her house – with her mother and her son on their own in it – and as a precaution, we should put a tail on the school run. Our contact in New York, Detective Investigator Lanigan, sounds a good guy. He'll know what to do far better than anyone we can send over.' Then Grace grimaced at his friend. 'So, no change with Ari?'

'Oh, she's changed all right. She's grown fucking horns out of the sides of her head.'

77

Carly stood in a long, snaking queue in the crowded Immigration Hall at Kennedy airport. Every few minutes she looked anxiously at her watch, which she had set back five hours to New York time, then she checked and rechecked the white Customs form she had filled in on the plane.

Her nerves were jangling. She'd never felt less sure of herself in her life.

The flight had been almost two hours delayed and she hoped the limousine she had ordered online was waiting. It was 10.30 p.m. in England, which meant it was 5.30 p.m. here. But it seemed like the middle of the night. Maybe that Bloody Mary, followed by a couple of glasses of Chardonnay on the plane, had not been such a good idea. She'd thought they might calm her and help her to sleep for a few hours, but now she had a blinding headache and a parched mouth, and was feeling decidedly spaced out.

It was strange, she thought. She'd brought Tyler to New York as a pre-Xmas treat last December. They'd both felt so excited in this queue then.

She dialled home, anxious to check on him. But just as her mother answered an angry-looking man in a uniform was in her face, pointing at a sign banning the use of mobile phones. Apologetically, Carly hung up.

Finally, after another twenty minutes, she reached a yellow line and was next. The immigration officer, a cheery-looking plump black woman, chatted interminably with the spindly man carrying a backpack who was in front of her. Then he moved on and Carly was summoned forward. She handed over her passport. She was asked to look into a camera lens. Then she was told to press her fingers on the electronic pad.

The woman might have smiled and joked with the previous person, but she was in no laughing mood now.

'Press harder,' she dictated.

Carly pressed harder.

'I'm not getting any reading.'

Carly pressed harder still and finally the red lights changed to green.

'Now your right thumb.'

As she pressed down hard with her right thumb, the woman frowned at her screen.

'Left thumb.'

Carly obeyed.

Then the woman suddenly said, 'OK, I need you to come with me.'

Bewildered, Carly followed her behind the line of immigration desks and through a door at the far end of the room. She saw several armed immigration officers standing chatting and several weary-looking people, from a mix of ethnic backgrounds, seated around the room, most of them staring vacantly ahead.

'Mrs Carly Chase from the United Kingdom,' the woman announced loudly, seemingly to no one in particular.

A tall man in a checked sports jacket, plain white shirt and brown tie, ambled over to her. He spoke with a Brooklyn accent.

'Mrs Chase?'

'Yes.'

'I'm Detective Investigator Lanigan from the Brooklyn District Attorney's Office. I've been asked by your police department in Sussex, England, to take care of you while you're over here.'

She stared back at him. In his fifties, she guessed, he had a powerful physique, a pockmarked face beneath a greying brush-cut and a concerned but friendly expression.

'I understand you have the home address of Mr and Mrs Revere for me?' she said.

'Yes. I'm going to take you there.'

She shook her head. 'I have a car booked. I need to go alone.'

'I can't allow you to do that, Mrs Chase. That's not going to happen.'

The firm way he spoke made her realize that the decision had been taken and was not going to be reversed.

Carly thought hard for a moment. 'Look, OK, follow me to their place, but at least let me go in alone. I can handle myself. Can I please do that?'

He stared at her for some moments.

'It's about a two-and-a-half-hour drive from here. We'll go in convoy. I'll wait outside, but here's what we're going to do. You're going to text me every fifteen minutes so I know you're OK. If I don't get a text I'm coming in. Understand what I'm saying?'

'Do I have any option?'

'Sure, you do. I can have Immigration put you on the first available flight back to London.'

'Thanks,' she said.

'You're welcome, lady.'

78

In the back of the Lincoln Town Car it was dark and silent. Carly sat immersed in her thoughts, occasionally sipping water from one of the small bottles in the rack in the central armrest. Maybe she should have said yes to the New York detective and let Immigration put her on a flight back to England. She felt a lump in her throat and a chill of fear running through her, worsened by the cold air-conditioning in the car.

The black leather seats and blacked-out windows made the interior feel as gloomy as her mood. The driver seemed in a bad mood, too, and had barely said two words to her since leaving the airport. Every few minutes his phone rang. He would gabble a few angry words in a language she didn't know and hang up.

Each time it irritated her more. She needed silence. Needed to think. She'd phoned home again as soon as she'd got into the car and her mother told her all was fine. She reminded her about Tyler's dental appointment in the morning and wished her good luck with the scan.

Her grandmother had died of colon cancer and now there was something in her mother's tummy her doctor did not like the look of. Since Kes had died, her mother had been the total and utter rock in her life. And if anything happened to Carly, her mother would become Tyler's rock too. The thought that she could get sick and die was too much for Carly to bear at this moment. She just fervently hoped and prayed the scan wouldn't show anything.

Then she turned her thoughts back to what she was going to say when she arrived at the Revere family's front door. If they even let her in.

From time to time she turned her head and looked out of the rear window. The dark grey sedan which Detective Investigator Lanigan was driving remained steadily on their tail. She felt inhibited by his presence and her instinct was that she had to be seen to be alone if she was going to have any chance with Fernanda Revere.

Most of the time she stared out at a dull landscape of seemingly endless straight road, bordered by green verge and low trees. The sun was setting behind them and dusk was falling rapidly. In another hour it would be dark. In her mind, the meeting with the Reveres was going to have taken place in daylight. She looked at her watch. It was 7.30. She asked the driver what time he expected to arrive.

The surly reply came back, 'Nine or thereabouts. Lucky this isn't summer. Be 'bout eleven then. Traffic no good in summer.'

Her headache was worsening by the minute. As were her doubts. All the confidence she'd had earlier today was deserting her. She felt a growing slick of fear inside her. She tried in her mind to reverse the roles. How would she feel in this woman's situation?

She simply did not know. She felt tempted, suddenly, to ask the driver to turn around and go to the hotel she had booked and forget all about this.

But what then?

Maybe nothing. Maybe those two killings had been coincidental? Maybe they'd been all the revenge the family wanted? But then, thinking more lucidly, she wondered how she would ever know that. How would she stop living in fear?

And she knew that she could not, ever, without resolving this.

Her determination became even stronger. She had the truth on her side. All she had to do was tell the woman the truth.

Suddenly, it seemed only minutes later, they were arriving in a town.

'East Hampton,' the driver said in a more friendly tone, as if he'd woken up to the fact that he was close to blowing his chances of a tip.

Carly looked at her watch. It was 8.55 p.m., which meant it was 1.55 a.m. in the UK. Her stomach tightened. Her nerves were in tatters.

Her fear deepened as the car made a right turn in front of a Mobil Oil garage and headed down a leafy lane with a double yellow line in the middle. All her clear thinking suddenly turned into a fog of panic. She was breathing deeper, perspiring, close to hyperventilating. She turned and through the rear window she saw the headlights of Detective Investigator Lanigan's car following, and now, instead of feeling irritated, she was comforted by his presence.

She felt a lump in her throat and a tightening knot in her stomach. Her hands were shaking. She took a few deep breaths to calm down. She tried to organize her thoughts, to rehearse that crucial way she would introduce herself. The driver's phone rang again, but as if sensing her mood he killed the call without answering it.

The double yellow line ended and the lane narrowed to single track. In the glare of the headlights Carly saw trim hedges on both sides of them.

The car slowed, then halted. Directly in front of them were tall, closed gates, painted grey, with spikes along the top. There was a speaker panel and a warning sign beside that which said ARMED RESPONSE.

'Want me to ring?' the driver asked.

She turned and peered through the rear window and saw that the detective was getting out of his car. Carly climbed out too.

'Good luck, lady,' Lanigan said. 'Let's see if they let you in. If they do, I'll be waiting here. I'll be waiting for that first text in fifteen minutes' time. You don't forget that, right?'

She tried to reply, but nothing came out. Her mouth was parched and it felt like there was an iron band around her throat. She nodded.

He entered his number on Carly's phone and tapped in 'OK'. 'That's what you're gonna text me, every fifteen minutes.'

The air was still and mild. Carly had dressed casually but conservatively, wearing a lightweight beige mackintosh over a dark grey jacket, plain white blouse, black jeans and black leather boots. Every shred of her confidence seemed to have deserted her and, despite the adrenalin pumping, she felt even more spaced out now. She tried to block from her mind the fact it was past 2 a.m., body time.

She pressed the square metal button. Instantly a light shone in her face. Above it she could see a CCTV camera pointing down at her.

A voice speaking in broken English crackled. 'Yes, who is this?'

Carly stared straight back at the camera and forced a smile. 'I've come from England to see Mr and Mrs Revere. My name is Carly Chase.'

'They expect you?'

'No. I think they know who I am. I was in the accident involving their son, Tony.'

'You wait, please.'

The light went off. Carly waited, clutching her iPhone, her finger on the *Send* button. She turned and saw Detective Investigator Lanigan leaning against his car, smoking a cigar. He gave her a good-luck shrug. She caught a whiff of the rich smoke and it reminded her for an instant of Kes.

A minute later, the gates began to swing open, in almost total oiled silence. There was just a faint electric whirr. Feeling sick with fear, she climbed back into the car.

79

Carly stepped out into the silence of the night. Above her loomed the façade of a huge modern mansion. It looked dark and unwelcoming, with barely any lights showing. She turned back to look at the limousine, having second thoughts. It was parked a few yards away on the woodchip-covered drive, close to a Porsche Cayenne sports utility vehicle. Floodlights printed stark shadows of shrubs and trees across an immaculate lawn. Her nerves shorting out, she sensed faces peering from the darkened windows down at her. She swallowed, then swallowed again, and stared at the front door, which was set beneath an imposing portico with square, modern pilasters.

Christ, am I up to this?

The silence was pressing in all around her. She heard the faint, distant, restless sound of the sea. She breathed in tangy, salty air and the scent of freshly mown grass. The normality of that scared her. These people, their life going on as normal. Their son was dead, but they still mowed the lawn. Something about that spooked her. She had not mown the lawn after Kes died. She'd let the garden go wild and the house turn into a tip around her. It was only for Tyler's sake she eventually pulled herself together.

Before she had a chance to change her mind, the front door opened and a woman emerged, unsteadily, dressed in a turquoise tracksuit and sparkly trainers. She had short, blonde hair, an attractive but hard face, and held a martini glass tilted at an angle in one hand and a cigarette in the other. Her whole demeanour was hostile.

Carly took a few, faltering steps towards her. 'Mrs Revere?' She tried to put on the smile she had been practising, but it didn't feel like it was working. 'Fernanda Revere?'

The woman stared at her with eyes as cold and hard as ice. Carly felt as if she was staring right through her soul.

'You got fucking balls coming here.' The words were slightly slurred and bitter. 'You're not welcome in my home. Get back in your car.'

The woman scared her, but Carly stood her ground. She had been preparing herself for a whole range of different responses and this was one of them, although she had not factored in that Fernanda Revere might be smashed.

'I've flown from England to talk to you,' she said. 'I just want a few minutes of your time. I'm not going to begin to pretend I understand what you must be going through – but you and I have something in common.'

'We do? We're alive, that's about all I can see we have in common. I don't believe we have much else.'

Carly had known all along this was not going to be easy. But she had nurtured the hope that perhaps she could get a dialogue going with this woman and find some common ground.

'May I come in? I'll leave the moment you want me to. But please let's talk for a few minutes.'

Fernanda Revere drew on her cigarette, snorted out smoke through her mouth and nose, then tossed the butt away with a contemptuous flick of her jewelled hand. It landed on the drive in a shower of sparks. With her drink slopping over the rim of her glass, she tottered back and gestured for Carly to enter, glowering hatred, only faintly diluted with curiosity, at her.

Carly hesitated. This woman looked dangerously unpredictable and she had no idea how her husband was going to react. Glad now that Detective Investigator Lanigan was sitting outside the gates in his car, she surreptitiously glanced at her watch. Thirteen minutes left before her first text.

She entered a grand hallway with a flagstone floor and a circular staircase, and followed the woman, who bumped against the wall several times, along a corridor furnished with antiques. Then they entered a palatial drawing room, with a minstrel's gallery. It had oak beams and tapestries hanging from the walls, alongside fine-looking oil paintings. Almost all of the furniture was antique, except for one item.

Seated, with his legs up in an incongruously modern leather recliner armchair, was a man in his fifties, with slicked-back grey hair and dense black eyebrows, watching a ball game on television. He held a can of beer in one hand and a large cigar in the other.

The woman walked towards him, picked up the TV remote from the antique wooden table beside him, peered at it for some moments as if she had never seen one of these before in her life, then muted the sound and dropped the remote back down with a clatter.

'Hey, what the—' the man protested.

'We have a visitor, Lou.' Fernanda pointed at Carly. 'She's come all the way from England. How nice is that?' she said icily.

Lou Revere gave Carly a weak smile and an abstracted wave of his hand. Then, keeping his eyes on the silent players on the screen, he turned to his wife and reached out for the remote.

'This is kind of an important moment in the game.'

'Yeah, right,' Fernanda said. 'Well, this is kind of an important moment, too.' She reached down, picked up a pack of Marlboro Lights and shook out a cigarette. Then she gave Carly a crushing glare.

Carly stood awkwardly, eyes darting between the two of them, thinking, trying desperately to remember her script.

'Know who this bitch is?' Fernanda said to her husband.

Lou Revere grabbed the remote and unmuted the sound.

'No. Listen, I need some quiet here.' Then he added, 'Get this lady a drink.' He glanced disinterestedly at Carly. 'You wanna drink?'

Carly felt in desperate need of a drink. And the sweet rich smell of the smoke was tantalizing. She craved a cigarette.

'I'll die before I give this fucking bitch anything,' Fernanda Revere said, staggering over to an antique drinks cabinet, the doors of which were already open, and clumsily refilling her glass from a silver cocktail shaker, slopping the contents over the side. Then she drank some, put the glass down, tottered back over to her husband, grabbed the remote and switched the television completely off.

'Hey!' he said.

She dropped the remote on to the rug and stamped hard on it. There was the sound of splintering plastic.

Carly's fear deepened. This woman was crazy and totally unpredictable. She looked at the man again, then back at the woman, before sneaking a glance at her watch. Three minutes had passed. What the hell was the woman going to do next? Somehow she had to bring her out of her anger.

'Jesus Christ!' Her husband put down his beer and ejected himself from his chair. Turning to his wife, he said, 'Do you know how important this goddamn game is? Do you? Do you care?'

He strode towards the door. Grabbing him by the arm and dropping her glass, which broke on the floor, Fernanda screamed at him, 'Do you fucking know or care who this bitch is?'

'Right now, I care about the New York Yankees winning this game. You know how bad it would be if they even just tied?'

'And you fucking think they care that you're watching? You want to just focus a second? This is the bitch who killed our son. You hear what I'm saying?'

Carly watched him, her eyes swinging between them. She was trying to keep calm, but her nerves were in meltdown. The man stopped in his tracks and turned towards her. He glanced for a moment back at his wife and said, 'What do you mean, hon?' Then he turned back to Carly, his whole demeanour changing.

'This is the bitch who was arrested at the scene for drunk driving. She killed our son, now she's fucking standing here in front of us.'

Fernanda Revere made her way over to the bar, taking measured steps across the floor as if it were an obstacle course. There was sudden menace in Lou Revere's voice as he spoke now. Gone was the mildly angry guy of a few seconds ago.

'Just what the hell do you think you are doing? Turning up at our home like this? Not satisfied you've caused us enough pain, is that what it is?'

'It's not that at all, Mr Revere,' Carly replied, her voice quavering. 'I'd just appreciate the opportunity to talk to you and Mrs Revere and explain what happened.'

'We know what happened,' he said.

'You were drunk and our son died,' his wife added bitterly. Then she staggered back over towards them, slopping more of her drink over the rim of her fresh glass.

Carly drew on all her reserves. 'I'm desperately sorry for you both. I'm desperately sorry for your loss. But there are things about this accident that you need to know, that I would want to know if it was my child. Could we please sit down, the three of us, and talk this through? I'll leave when you want me to, but please let me tell you how it actually happened.'

'We know how it happened,' Fernanda Revere said. Then she turned to her husband. 'Get rid of this bitch. She's killed Tony and now she's polluting our home.'

'Hon, let's just hear her out,' he said, without taking his glare off Carly.

'I can't believe I married someone who fell out of a fucking tree!' she shouted. 'If you don't tell her to go, I'm leaving. I'm not staying in this building with her. So tell her!'

'Hon, let's talk to her.'

'GET HER THE FUCK OUT OF HERE!'

With that Fernanda stormed out of the room and some moments later a door slammed.

Carly found herself facing Lou Revere, feeling very awkward. 'Mr Revere, maybe I should go . . . I'll come back . . . I can come back in the morning if that's—'

He jabbed a finger at her. 'You came to talk, so talk.'

Carly stared at him in silence, trying to think of the best way to calm him down.

'What's the matter? You gone dumb or something?' he said.

'No, I . . . look, I – I can't begin to understand how you must be feeling.'

'Can't you?' he said, with a bitterness that startled her.

'I have a young son,' she replied.

'*Have?*' he replied. 'Well you're a lucky lady, then, aren't you? My wife and I *had* a young son, too, before a drunk driver killed him.'

'It didn't happen like that.'

Outside, through the window, Carly heard a faint clunk, like a car door.

'Oh, it didn't happen like that?' Lou Revere looked, at this moment, as if he was about to strangle her with his bare hands. He raised them in the air, clenching and then opening them.

And suddenly Carly realized what it was that the two detectives in Brighton had meant when they'd tried to explain the nature of these people to her. That they were different. Their whole culture was different. She wavered for an instant about hitting the *Send* button on her phone, but she had to stand her ground. Had to find a way through to this man.

He was, she realized, her only chance.

80

Pat Lanigan, standing by his car and smoking his cigar, heard an automobile engine fire up, then saw the gates opening. Was the crazy English woman coming out already? She'd only been there five minutes. He glanced at his watch again, double-checking.

It was a positive, he thought, that at least she *was* coming out. Although if she had only lasted in there for five minutes, then for sure it had not gone well. Maybe she'd had some sense knocked into her reckless little head.

Then, to his surprise, instead of seeing the limousine, he saw a Porsche Cayenne, with the silhouette of a woman at the wheel, come at a reckless speed through the gates, then accelerate past him like a bat out of hell.

He turned, clocked the licence plate and watched the tail lights disappear round a bend in the lane. This did not feel good. He glanced down at the display of his phone. There was no text, no missed call. He didn't like this at all.

He flicked through his stored numbers and dialled the Suffolk County Police duty office, explained who he was and asked them to put an alert out for the Cayenne. He wanted to know where it was headed.

*

Fernanda Revere braked to a halt at the T-junction by the gas station, pulled a cigarette pack out of her purse, shook out a Marlboro Light and jammed it between her lips. Then she stabbed the cigar lighter, made a left and accelerated down the highway. Everything was a blur in her drunken fury. She overtook a slow-moving cab, her speed increasing: 70 . . . 80 . . . 90. She flashed past a whole line of tail lights, lit her cigarette and tried to replace the lighter, but it fell into the footwell.

She was shaking with rage. The road snaked away into the distance. Steering with one hand, smoke from the cigarette curling into her eyes, she rummaged in her purse and pulled out her diamanté-encrusted Vertu phone, then squinted through the smoke at the display. It was a blur. She brought it closer to her face, scrolled to her brother's number and hit the dial button.

She overtook a tractor-trailer, still steering with one hand. Had to get away. Just had to get away from the bitch polluting her home. After six rings, it went to voicemail.

'Where the fuck are you, Ricky?' she shouted. 'What the fuck's going on? The English bitch came to the house. She's there now. Do you hear me? The bitch who killed Tony is in my house. Why isn't she dead? I paid you this money, so why isn't she dead? What's going on here? You gotta deal with this, Ricky. Call me. Goddamn call me!'

She ended the call and tossed the phone down beside her on the passenger seat. She did not know where she was heading. Just away from the house and into the rushing darkness. The further the better. Lou could get rid of the bitch. She'd go back when Lou phoned her, when he told her the bitch was gone, out of their home, out of their lives.

She overtook another car. The night was hurtling past. Oncoming lights were a brief, blurred flash, then gone.

Tony was gone. Dead. He'd nearly died as a baby. That first year of his life he'd been in hospital on a ventilator for most of the time. Much of it inside a perspex isolation dome. She'd sat there day and night, while Lou had been working or kissing her father's ass or out on the golf course. Tony'd come through that, but he was always a sickly child, too, a chronic asthmatic. At the age of eight he'd spent the best part of a year bedridden with a lung virus. She'd spoonfed him. Mopped his brow. Got him through it. Nurtured him until slowly he'd grown stronger. By the time he reached his teens he was just like any other kid. Then, last year, he'd fallen for that stupid English girl.

She'd begged Lou to stop him going, but had he? Never. All he'd done was give her a whole bunch of crap about letting kids live their own lives. Maybe some kids would be fine in a foreign land. But Tony had been dependent on her. He needed her. And this proved it.

Three scumbags had taken his life away. Some asshole in a van. Some asshole in a truck. And this drunken bitch who had the nerve to come to their home with her whiny little voice. *I'd just appreciate the opportunity to talk to you and Mrs Revere and explain what happened.*

Yeah, well, I'll tell you what happened, Mrs Whining Bitch. You got drunk and you killed my son, that's what happened. Any part of that you don't understand?

The speedometer needle was hovering on 110mph. Or maybe it was 120, she could barely see it. A light began flashing on the passenger seat. Her phone was ringing, she realized. She grabbed it and held it up in front of her. The name was blurry but she could just about read it. Her brother.

She answered it, hurtling past another car, still steering with one hand into a tight left curve. The cigarette between her lips was burned right down to the butt and tears were streaming from her eyes and on to her cheeks.

'Ricky, I thought you were dealing with this?' she said. 'How do you let this stupid bitch come to the house? How?'

'Listen, it's all cool!'

'Cool? She came to my house – that's cool? You wanna tell me what's cool about that?'

'We have a plan!'

She steered the car through the curve, then there was another curve to the right, even sharper. She was going into it too fast, she realized. She stamped on the brake pedal and suddenly the car began snaking left, then right, then even more violently left again.

'Shit.'

She dropped the phone. The cigarette butt fell between her legs. There were bright lights coming in the opposite direction, getting brighter and more dazzling by the second. She heard the blare of a horn. She jerked the wheel. The Cayenne began a lumbering pirouette. The steering wheel suddenly turned with such force it tore free of her hands, spinning like it had taken on a mind of its own.

The lights got brighter. The horn was blaring, deafening her. The lights were straight at her eye level. Blinding her. She was spinning too now, like the wheel. Backwards for a second. Then sideways again. Sucking those blinding lights towards her as if she were a magnet.

Closer.

The horn even louder, shaking her eardrums.

Lights burning into her retinas.

Then a jarring impact. A clanging metallic boom like two giant oil drums swinging into each other.

In the silence that followed, Ricky's voice came through her phone. 'Hey, babe? Fernanda? Sis? Babe? Listen, you OK? Babe? Babe? Listen, we're cool. Listen, babe!'

But she could no longer hear him.

81

'You've really upset my wife,' Lou Revere said. 'She's pretty distressed already and so am I. I don't know what you thought you'd achieve by coming, but we don't want you here. You're not welcome in our house.' He stabbed his cigar at her. 'I'm gonna show you out.'

'Please just give me a chance,' Carly said, her desperation making her sound on the verge of tears.

'You had your chance, lady, when you were deciding whether to get into your automobile drunk or not. That's more chance than my son had.'

'It wasn't like that, Mr Revere. Please believe me. It wasn't like that.'

He stopped and for a moment Carly thought he was going to relent. Then he stabbed his cigar in even greater fury. 'Sure it wasn't like that, lady. We've had the toxicology report on our son from your police. He had nothing in him. Not one drop of alcohol, not one trace of any drug.' He lowered his head like a bull about to charge. 'How was your toxicology report? Huh? You wanna tell me how your toxicology report read? Tell me. I'm listening. You got my full attention.'

They faced each other in silence. Carly was trying desperately to find a way through to him. But he scared her. It was as if beneath his skin there was something venomous and feral. Outwardly he might be playing the role of a grieving father, but there was something truly chilling about him. She had met difficult people in her time, she'd had to deal with deep dislike, but she had never encountered anyone like Lou Revere. It felt as if she was in the presence of total, inhuman evil.

'I'm listening,' he repeated. 'I'm not hearing anything, but I'm listening.'

'I think maybe I should come back tomorrow,' she replied. 'Can I do that?'

He took another step towards her, quivering. 'You come back,' he said. 'You come back – if you dare come within one hundred miles of my home, I'll tear you apart with these.' He held up his trembling hands. 'You understand what I'm saying?'

Carly nodded, her mouth dry.

He pointed. 'That's the way out.'

Moments after she stepped out into the night, the front door slammed behind her.

82

It seemed only moments after he had fallen asleep that Roy Grace was woken by the sound of his phone ringing and vibrating.

He rolled over, reaching out for the flashing display in the darkness. The clock beside it said 1.37 a.m.

'It's OK. I'm awake,' said Cleo, a tad grumpily.

He switched on his bedside light, grabbed the phone and hit the green button. 'Yurrr?'

It was Duncan Crocker. 'You awake, boss?'

It was a dumb question, Grace thought. Did Detective Sergeant Crocker know many people who were capable of answering a phone in their sleep? He slid out of bed and tripped over Humphrey, who responded with a startled yelp. He dropped the phone and grabbed the side of the bed, just managing to stop himself falling flat on his face on the floor. He retrieved the phone.

'Hang on, Duncan.'

Wearing only the T-shirt he'd been sleeping in, he padded out of the room, accompanied by the dog, which jumped up excitedly, its sharp claws digging painfully into his leg.

'Down, boy!' he hissed, closing the door behind him.

Humphrey raced down the staircase, barking, then ran back up and launched himself at Grace's crotch.

Crocking the phone under his ear and protecting himself with his hands, he said, 'Be with you in a sec, Duncan. Down! Humphrey, off, off!'

He went downstairs, followed by a madly barking Humphrey, switched the lights on, moved a copy of *Sussex Life* that was open at the property pages – Cleo had suddenly gone into house-hunting mode – and sat on a sofa. Humphrey jumped on to the cushion beside him. Stroking him, trying to keep the dog quiet, Grace said, 'Sorry about that. What's up?'

'You asked me to let you know as soon as we found the lorry, boss.'

'You've found it? You're still at work?'

'Yes.'

'Thanks for staying so late. So, tell me?'

'Just had a call from Thames Valley Road Policing Unit. It's in a parking area at Newport Pagnell Services on the M1.'

'How did they find it?' Grace was doing his best to think clearly through his tiredness.

'It was logged by an ANPR camera as it entered Bucks on the M1 on Tuesday night, boss. There were no further logs, so we asked the local police to check likely pull-ins.'

'Good stuff. What CCTV do they have at the service station?'

'They've got cameras on the private vehicle and truckers' entrances.'

'OK, we need those, to see if Ferguson went inside. How long are you planning on staying up?'

'As long as you need me.'

'Ask them for copies of the videos from the time the ANPR clocked him to now and get them down to us as quickly as possible. If it helps them, we can send someone up there.'

'Will do.'

Grace stroked the dog again. He knew he wasn't thinking as clearly as he needed to at this moment.

'Sorry, one other important thing – Ferguson's lorry. I want it protected as a crime scene. Get on to Thames Valley Police to secure it. They need to cordon off a good twenty-foot radius around it. If the driver was attacked, it's likely to have happened close to the vehicle. We need a search team on to it at first light. What's the weather up there at the moment?'

'Dry, light wind – it's been the same since Tuesday night. Forecast the same for the morning.'

That was a relief to Grace. Rain could wash away forensic evidence very rapidly.

'I'll sort out the search team, Duncan. If you deal with the CCTV, please. Then go home and get some sleep. You've done well.'

'Thanks, boss.'

Grace let Humphrey out on to the patio and watched him pee. Then he went into the kitchen and put the kettle on. Upstairs he heard the sound of the loo flushing and wondered, for a moment, if Cleo was going to come down and join him. But instead he heard the bedroom door slam – a little too loudly.

Sandy used to slam the bedroom door when she was angry about a late-night phone call that had disturbed her. Cleo was a lot more tolerant, but he could sense her pregnancy getting to her. It was getting to both of them. Most of the time it was a shared joy, or a shared anxiety, but just occasionally it seemed like a growing wedge between them and she had been in a really grumpy mood last night.

He made a phone call, apologetically waking Crime Scene Manager Tracy Stocker and bringing her up to speed. He asked her to send a SOCO team up to Newport Pagnell – about a two-and-a-half-hour drive from Brighton – to be there ready to start at dawn. At the same time, in light of the latest development, he discussed the joint strategy she would need with the POLSA – the Police Search Advisor – and search team.

Then he spooned instant coffee into a mug, poured boiling water on to it, stirred it and carried it out into the living room. He felt chilly, but he could not be bothered to put on any more clothes.

He sat down on the sofa with his laptop, bleary-eyed, stirring the coffee again and staring at the laptop as it powered up. Humphrey found a chew and started a life or death tussle with it on the floor. Grace smiled at him, envying him his uncomplicated life. Maybe if he got the chance to choose, when he died he'd come back as a dog. So long as he got to pick his owners.

He Googled *Newport Pagnell Services. M*oments later he had a full listing of what was there, but that did not help him. He opened Google Earth and again he entered *Newport Pagnell Services.*

When the globe appeared, he zoomed in. Within moments he saw a close-up of the M1 motorway and the surrounding area. He stared at it, sipping his hot coffee and thinking hard.

Ferguson must have continued on down to Sussex in another vehicle. His assailant's? So how had he met his assailant?

Was it someone he knew and had arranged to rendezvous with

in the car park? Possible, he thought. But to his mind, it was more probable that the assailant had been following him, looking for a suitable opportunity. And if this assumption was right, it meant that the assailant could not have been more than a few vehicles behind Ferguson's lorry.

He put his coffee down and started suddenly, pacing around the room. Humphrey jumped up at him again, wanting to play.

'Down!' he hissed, and then he dialled MIR-1, relieved when DS Crocker answered almost immediately. 'Sorry, another task for you, Duncan. We need the indexes of the vehicles either side of Ferguson's lorry on the motorway immediately before Newport Pagnell Services,' he said. 'Get everything up to five vehicles in front and twenty back. I want to know every one of the vehicles that went into the services at the same time as him and where they went when they left afterwards. It's very likely that Ferguson was in one of those. Willingly or otherwise. I think it is highly likely to be a rental car, so we're looking, primarily, for late-model small to medium saloons.'

'I'll get what I can, but it may take me a while to check out every vehicle. Is the morning briefing meeting soon enough?'

No, it wasn't soon enough, Grace thought. But he needed to be realistic and Crocker sounded exhausted.

'Yes, that's fine. Do what you can, then get some sleep.'

Deciding to follow his own advice, he climbed back upstairs, followed by Humphrey, and went back to bed, trying not to disturb Cleo. At midday he was holding a press conference to announce that the police were treating the death of Stuart Ferguson as murder now. But although he had discussed it at length with ACC Rigg and the whole of the Sussex Police media team, he had not decided on the way he wanted to slant the conference. He wanted to make it clear that the police knew the two murders were linked, and the direction in which they were looking, but above all he needed witnesses to come forward. However, if he played up the Mafia link and the hit-man hypothesis, that might, he worried, actually do more harm than good, by scaring people into silence.

The only small positive was that Spinella seemed to have been as duped as the rest of the press into believing, to date, that

Ferguson's death was an industrial accident. That gave him some small satisfaction.

Finally, he fell into a troubled sleep, to be woken an hour later by Cleo going to the loo.

83

Carly sat in the back of the limousine as they drove through the gates of the Revere home. A few yards on she could see Detective Investigator Lanigan standing by his car and told her driver to stop.

'So?' he asked with an inquisitive but sympathetic stare.

'You were right,' she said, and gave a helpless shrug. She was still in shock from the way Lou Revere had spoken to her.

'It didn't go like you planned it?'

'No.'

'What's with Mrs Revere driving off like that? She was pissed at you?'

Carly fumbled in her handbag, pulled out a pack of cigarettes and lit one, inhaling deeply.

'She was drunk. She wasn't in a rational state of mind. I have to try again,' she said. 'Maybe I could come back in the morning when she's sobered up.'

He dragged on his cigar and blew the smoke out pensively. 'Lady, you've got guts, I'll give you that.' He smiled. 'You look like you could use a drink.'

Carly nodded. Then she said, 'What's your advice? What do you think I should do – you know – how can I deal with these people? There must some way – there always is.'

'Let's get you to your hotel. We'll have a drink and you can talk me through what happened in there. Before we leave, is there any point in me trying to speak to Mr Revere?'

'I don't think so,' she said. 'Not tonight. No.'

'OK. Your driver knows where to go?'

'The Sheraton JFK Airport Hotel.'

'I'll follow you. I'll be right behind.'

She took two more rapid drags on her cigarette, crushed it, then got back into the limousine and gave the driver her instructions.

She sat perched on the edge of her seat, replaying the events of the past ten minutes in her mind, as they drove away down the lane, then made a left turn, heading away from the town. Inside she was jangling, with nerves and tiredness. The bad dream just seemed to keep getting worse.

She closed her eyes and prayed, a short silent prayer. She asked the God she had not spoken to in years to give her some strength and a clear mind. Then she rummaged in her bag for her handkerchief and dabbed away the tears that were streaming down her cheeks.

Darkness slid by on either side of the car. For several minutes it did not occur to her that it was strange that no headlights were coming in the opposite direction. She looked at her watch: 9.25 p.m. New York time, 2.25 a.m. in England. Too late to call Detective Sergeant Branson and give him an update. She would do that in the morning. Hopefully after she had made a revised plan with Detective Investigator Lanigan later this evening.

She yawned. Ahead, through the windscreen, she saw red flashing lights and the bright tail lights of traffic braking and backing up. Moments later the limousine slowed, braking increasingly sharply, and they came to a halt behind a line of stationary vehicles.

The driver ended yet another of the constant calls he was on and turned his head towards her. 'Looks like an accident up ahead.'

She nodded silently. Then she heard a rap on her window and saw Detective Investigator Lanigan standing there. She pressed the button and lowered the window.

'You want to come with me? Sounds like Mrs Revere's involved in a wreck up ahead. They've closed the road.'

'An accident? Fernanda Revere?'

'Yup,' he said grimly, and opened the door for her.

The words flooded her with dread. She climbed out shakily and the night air suddenly seemed a lot chillier than ten minutes ago. She pulled her mackintosh tightly around her as she followed the detective past a line of cars towards a stationary police car that was angled across the road, its roof spinners hurling shards of red light in every direction. A row of traffic cones was spread across the road behind it.

An accident. The woman would be blaming her. Everyone would be blaming her.

A cacophony of sirens was closing in on them. Just beyond the patrol car now, she could see the mangled wreckage of a car partially embedded in the front of a halted white truck. Carly stopped. This wasn't just a minor bump, this was major. Massive. Horrific. She turned away, towards Lanigan.

'Is she OK?' Carly asked. 'Have you heard if she's OK? Is she injured?'

The sirens got louder.

He strode on, through the cones, saying nothing. Carly hurried after him, feeling like a thousand different knots were being tightened inside her all at the same time. She tried to look away from the accident, but at the same time she was mesmerized by it, kept looking, looking, staring.

A cop was standing in their way, blocking their path. A young plump man wearing glasses and a cap that was too big for him. He looked about eighteen years old and waiting to grow into his uniform.

'Stay back, please, folks.'

Lanigan held up his police shield.

'Ah, right. OK. OK, sir.' Then he pointed questioningly at Carly.

'She's with me,' the Detective Investigator said.

He waved them past, then turned in confusion as an ambulance and fire tender screamed to a halt.

Over to her right, Carly saw a man in a boiler suit walking around unsteadily, as if he were disoriented. He was in shock, she realized. Ahead of her, Lanigan had pulled out a torch and switched it on. In the beam she saw what might have been a grim tableau in a museum of modern art.

The front wheels of the truck had been pushed back several feet by the impact, so that they were right underneath the cab. The side of the gold Porsche facing them had been so badly buckled that the front and rear of the car were almost at right angles to each other. The destroyed vehicle resembled a crudely sculpted artistic impression of a snow plough, as if it was actually part of the front of the truck.

PETER JAMES

Carly smelled the stench of vomit, then heard a retching sound. There was a smell of petrol, too, and of oil, but another deeply unpleasant, coppery smell mixed in.

'Jesus!' Lanigan exclaimed. 'Oh shit!'

He stepped back and put out an arm to prevent Carly from seeing the same sight. But he was too late.

In the torch beam Carly saw a pair of legs, covered from the knees down by turquoise tracksuit bottoms, but the top part was naked. A mess of crimson, black, dark red and bright red was splayed out around the crotch. Out of the middle of it rose, for about eighteen inches, what looked like a giant white fish bone.

Part of the woman's spine, she realized, clutching the detective's arm involuntarily, her stomach rising up into her throat. Fernanda Revere had been cut in two.

Carly turned away, quaking in horror and shock. She staggered a few yards, then fell to her knees and threw up, her eyes blinded by tears.

84

A large whiskey at the hotel bar, followed by two glasses of Pinot Noir, helped calm Carly down a little, but she was still in shock. Detective Investigator Lanigan drank a small beer. He looked fine – as if he saw stuff like that accident all the time and was immune to it. Yet he seemed such a caring man. She wondered how anyone could ever get used to something as horrific as that.

Despite the woman's rudeness to her, she felt a desperate sadness for Fernanda Revere. Lanigan told her she didn't need to feel any pity, because this was a woman with blood on her hands, and from a brutal family living high off the spoils of violence. But Carly could not help it. Whatever her background had been, Fernanda Revere was still a human being. A mother capable of intense love for her son. No one deserved to end up the way she had.

And Carly had caused it.

The Detective Investigator told her she should not think that way. Fernanda Revere had no business getting into a vehicle in the state she was in. She didn't have to drive away, that was her choice. She could, and should, have simply told Carly to leave. Driving away – and doing so drunk – was not a rational act.

But Carly still blamed herself. She could not help thinking, over and over, that she had caused it. That if she had not gone to the house, Fernanda Revere would still be alive. Part of her wanted to drive straight back out to the Hamptons and try to apologize to Lou Revere. Pat Lanigan nixed that one fast and hard.

They stood outside for a long time while he smoked another cigar and she smoked her way through half a pack of cigarettes. The question neither of them could answer was *What happens next*?

She felt utterly bewildered. How was Fernanda Revere's husband going to react? The other members of the woman's family? When she had boarded the plane to come here, she knew she had a difficult task ahead of her. But she had never, remotely, thought of a consequence like this. She lit another cigarette with a trembling hand.

'I think now, Carly, you're going to have to think pretty seriously and quickly about entering a witness protection scheme,' Pat Lanigan said. 'I'm going to see that you have someone guarding you all the time you're here, but people like the Reveres have long memories and a long reach.'

'Do you really think I'd ever be truly safe in a witness protection scheme?'

'You can never say one hundred per cent, but it would give you your best chance.'

'You know what it means? To move to another part of the country, just you and your child, and never see any of your family or friends again, ever. How would you like to do that?'

He shrugged. 'I wouldn't like it too much. But if I figured I didn't have any option, then I guess it would be better than the alternative.'

'What – what alternative?'

He gave Carly a hard stare. 'Exactly.'

85

The air-conditioning was too cold and too loud, but nothing Carly did to the controls in her hotel bedroom seemed to make any difference. She couldn't find any extra bedding either, so had ended up almost fully clothed, under the sheets, tossing and turning, a tsunami of dark thoughts crashing through her mind.

Shortly after 6 a.m. and wide awake, she slipped out of bed, walked across to the window and opened the blinds. Light flooded in from a cloudless dark blue sky. She watched a jet plane climb into it, then dropped her gaze on to a sprawling mess of industrial buildings and a busy road, thirty floors below.

Her head was pounding. She felt queasy and very afraid. God, how she desperately wished Kes was here now, more than ever. Just to talk this through with him. He was bigger than any shit the world could throw at him. Except that damned white stuff that had encased and suffocated him.

Shit happens, he was fond of saying. He was right. His death was shit. Her accident was shit. Fernanda Revere's death was shit. Everything was shit.

But most of all, the idea of walking away from her life and going into hiding, forever, was total and utter shit. It wasn't going to happen. There had to be a better solution.

Had to be.

Suddenly her mobile phone rang. She hurried across and picked it off her bedside table, staring at the display. It simply said, *International.*

'Hello?' she answered.

'Hi, Carly?' It was Justin Ellis and his voice was sounding strange.

'Yes. You all right?' Carly replied, conscious her voice was strained. She needed paracetamol and a cup of tea, badly.

'Well – not really,' Justin replied. 'I think there's been some mix-up over Tyler.'

'How do you mean? His dentist appointment? Have I screwed up?' She looked at the clock radio, doing a mental calculation. She always got the time differences wrong. England was five hours ahead. Coming up to 11.15 a.m. there. Tyler's appointment was for 11.30, wasn't it?

'What's the problem, Justin?'

'Well, you asked me to take him to the dentist. I'm at the school now to collect him, but they're telling me you arranged a taxi to take him there.'

Carly sat down on the side of the bed. 'A taxi? I didn't arrange any—'

A terrible, dark dread began to seep through her.

'A taxi collected him half an hour ago,' Justin said, sounding a little pissed off. 'Did you forget?'

'Oh, God,' Carly said. 'Justin! Oh, my God. Tell me it's not true?'

'What do you mean?'

'This can't have happened. They must have made a mistake. Tyler has to be in the school somewhere. Have they checked? Have they looked everywhere?' Her voice was trembling with rising panic. 'Please get them to check. Tell them to check. Tell them they *have* to check.'

'Carly, what's the matter? What is it?'

'Please let him be there. Please, Justin, you have to find him. Please go in there and find him. Please! Oh, my God, please.' She stood up, hyperventilating now, walking around the room blindly. 'Please, Justin!'

'I don't understand, Carly. I spoke to Mrs Rich. She walked him to the gate and watched until he was safely in the taxi.'

'It's not possible! It's not possible, Justin. Please don't tell me he's not there.' She was sobbing and shouting in her desperation. 'Please tell me he's still there!'

There was a brief moment of silence, then Justin said, 'What's the matter, Carly. Calm down! Tell me – what's the matter?'

'Justin, call the police. I did not order a taxi.'

86

The traffic jam along the seafront was irritating Tooth. This had not been part of his plan. On his schedule he'd allowed a maximum of ten minutes for this section of the journey, but it had already taken twenty-two. And they were still barely moving in stop-start traffic that was being coned into a single lane by roadworks ahead.

The noise behind him was irritating him too, but it was keeping the kid distracted while he drove, so that was a good thing. He watched him in the mirror. The boy, in his red school blazer and wire-framed glasses, was concentrating hard on some electronic game.

Click. Beeehhh . . . gleeep . . . uhuhuhurrr . . . gleep . . . grawww-wwp . . . biff, heh, heh, heh-warrrup, haha . . .

Suddenly the kid looked up. 'Where are we going? I thought we were going to the Drive? This isn't the right way.'

Tooth spoke in his English accent. 'I had a message that the address got changed. Your dentist is working at his other clinic today in a different part of the city, over in Regency Square.'

'OK.'

Click. Beeehhh . . . gleeep . . . uhuhuhurrr . . . gleep . . . grawww-wwp . . . biff, heh, heh, heh-warrrup, haha . . .

The taxi's radio crackled, then a voice said, 'Pick up for Withdean Crescent. Anyone close to Withdean Crescent?'

From behind Tooth came, *Twang . . . heh, heh, heh, graww-wwpppp . . .*

They were getting closer now. In a few moments he would make a left turn.

Twang . . . eeeeeekkkk . . . greeeep . . . heh, heh, heh . . .

'What game are you playing?' Tooth asked, wanting the kid to feel OK, relaxed, normal, at least for the next couple of minutes.

'It's called Angry Birds. It's ace. Have you played it?'

Concentrating now, Tooth did not reply. The Skoda taxi made a sharp left turn off the seafront into Regency Square. As it did so, Tooth sneezed, loudly, then sneezed again.

'Bless you,' Tyler said politely.

Tooth grunted. He drove up the square of terraced Regency houses, all painted white and in different stages of dilapidation, some divided into apartments and some converted into hotels. At the top he made a right, following the road around the grassy park in the middle of the square and then back down towards the seafront. He swung right into the entrance to the underground car park and partway down the ramp, had another fit of sneezing. He halted the car, sneezing again and pulling a handkerchief out of his pocket. He sneezed once more into it.

'Bless you,' Tyler said again.

The driver turned. Tyler thought the man was going to thank him, but instead he saw something black in the man's hand that looked like the trigger of a gun, but without the rest of the weapon. Then he felt a hard jet of air on his face, accompanied by a sharp hiss. Suddenly he found it hard to breathe, and he took a deep gulp, while the air still jetted at him from the capsule.

Tooth watched the boy's eyes closing, then turned and continued down the ramp, lowering his window, then removing the handkerchief from his face. He carried on winding down to the car park's lowest level, which was deserted apart from one vehicle. His rental Toyota, with new licence plates.

He reversed into the bay alongside it.

87

At 11.25 a.m. Roy Grace was seated at his desk, making some last-minute adjustments to his press statement, which he was due to read out at midday.

So far nothing seemed to be going his way in this investigation, and to make matters even more complicated, the trial of snuff-movie merchant Carl Venner was starting in just over two weeks' time. But for now he had no time to think about anything other than *Operation Violin*.

There had been no progress reported on any of the lines of enquiry at this morning's briefing meeting. The Outside Inquiry Team had not found anyone who had sold the cameras that had filmed Preece's and Ferguson's demise. No one so far had witnessed anything unusual outside Evie Preece's house. The West Area Major Crime Branch Team had had no breakthrough yet in their investigation into Warren Tulley's murder in Ford Prison.

So many people had bought tubes of superglue in shops around the city during the past week that it made any follow-up a resourcing nightmare. Despite that, the team members had collected all available CCTV footage from inside and outside each of the premises that was covered by it. If – and when – they were able to put a face to the suspect, then they'd begin a trawl through these hundreds of hours of video.

His phone rang. It was his Crime Scene Manager, Tracy Stocker, calling from Newport Pagnell Services.

'Roy, we've found one item of possible interest so far. The stub of a Lucky Strike cigarette. I can't tell you if it is significant, but it's a relatively unusual brand for the UK.'

As a smoker, albeit an occasional one, Grace knew a bit about cigarette brands. Lucky Strikes were American. If, as he surmised, the killings of Preece and Ferguson were the work of a professional, it was a distinct possibility that a hit man known to the Reveres and trusted by them had been employed. He could be an American, sent over here. He felt a beat of excitement, as if this small item did have the potential to be interesting – although he knew, equally, its presence could have a totally innocent explanation.

'Did you manage to get a print from it, Tracy?' he asked.

Getting fingerprints from cigarette butts was difficult and depended to some extent on how they had been held.

'No. We can send it for chemical analysis, but we may have more luck with DNA. Do you want me to fast-track it?'

Grace thought for a moment. Fast-tracking could produce a result within one to two days. Otherwise it would take a working week or longer. The process was expensive, at a time when they were meant to be keeping costs down, but money was less of an issue on murder inquiries.

'Yes, fast-track definitely,' he said. 'Good work, Tracy. Well done.'

'I'll ping you the photos of it,' she said.

'Any luck with shoe prints or tyre prints?'

'Not so far. Unfortunately the ground's dry. But if there is anything, we'll find it.'

He smiled, because he knew that if anyone could, she would. He asked her to keep him updated. Then, as he hung up, his phone rang again. It was Duncan Crocker, sounding as if he had been up all night.

'Boss, we've had two possible hits on cars at Newport Pagnell that arrived at the same time as Stuart Ferguson. One is a Vauxhall Astra and the other is a Toyota Yaris – both of them common rental vehicles,' the Detective Sergeant said. 'We've eliminated the Astra, which was being driven by a sales rep for a screen-printing company. But the Yaris is more interesting.'

'Yes?'

'You were right, sir. It's a rental car – from Avis at Gatwick Airport. I put a marker on it and it pinged an ANPR camera on the M11 near Brentwood at 8 a.m. this morning. A local traffic unit stopped it. It was a twenty-seven-year-old female driver who lives in Brentwood, on her way to work.'

Grace frowned. Was Crocker being dim?

'It doesn't sound like you got either of the right vehicles, Duncan.'

'I think it may do when you hear this, sir. When the young lady got out of the car, she realized it wasn't her licence plates on the car. Someone had taken hers and replaced them with these.'

'While she was in the Newport Pagnell Services?'

'She can't swear that, sir – she can't remember the last time she noticed her number plates. To be honest, a lot of us probably don't.'

Grace thought for a moment.

'So it may be that our suspect has switched plates with hers. Have you put a marker out on her plates?'

'I have, sir, yes. So far nothing.'

'Good work. Let me know the instant anyone sees that car.'

'Of course, sir.'

'Have you sent someone down to Avis at Gatwick?'

'I've sent Sara Papesch and Emma-Jane Boutwood.'

Grace frowned. 'Who's Sara Papesch?'

'She's just joined the team. Bright girl – a Kiwi detective, over here on a secondment.'

'OK, good.'

Grace liked to know everyone on his team personally. It worried him when an inquiry started getting so big that his team members began taking on new members without his sanction. He was feeling, for one of the rare moments in his career, that things were getting on top of him. He needed to calm down, take things steady.

He looked at the round wooden clock on his wall. It had been a prop in the fictitious police station in the TV police series *The Bill*. Sandy had bought it for his twenty-sixth birthday. Beneath it was a stuffed seven pound, six ounce brown trout Sandy had also bought him, from an antiques stall in Portobello Road, early in their marriage. He kept it beneath the clock to give him a joke he could crack to detectives working under him, about patience and big fish.

It was also there as a reminder to himself. To always be patient. Every murder investigation was a puzzle. A gazillion tiny pieces to find and fit together. Your bosses and the local media were always breathing down your neck, but you had to remain calm, somehow. Panic would get you nowhere, other than leading you to make wrong, uninformed decisions.

His door opened and Glenn Branson came in, looking as he did most of the time these days, as if he was carrying the weight of the world on his shoulders. Grace waited for him to begin regaling him with the latest saga in his marriage break-up, but instead the DS placed his massive hands on the back of one of the two chairs in front of his desk and leaned forward. 'We have a development, old-timer, and it's not a good one. I've just had a call from Carly Chase in New York.'

Now he had Grace's full attention. 'Her mission isn't going well, as predicted, right?'

'You could say that, boss. Tony Revere's mother was killed in a car smash last night.'

Grace stared at him in stunned silence. He could feel the blood draining from every artery in his body.

'Killed?'

'Yes.'

For some moments, the Detective Superintendent was too shell-shocked to even think straight. Then he asked, 'What information do you have? How? I mean, what happened?'

'I'll come back to it – that's the least of our problems. We have a much bigger one. Carly Chase's twelve-year-old son has gone missing.'

'Missing? What do you mean?'

'It sounds like he's been abducted.'

Grace stared into Branson's big, round eyes. He felt as if a bolus of cold water had been injected into his stomach. 'When – when did this happen?'

'A friend of Carly, called Justin Ellis, should have picked her son up from St Christopher's School at 11.15 a.m. to take him to a dental appointment – he was having a brace adjusted. Ellis got there at ten past, to discover the boy had been collected twenty minutes earlier by a taxi. But Carly Chase is absolutely adamant she didn't order a taxi.'

Grace stared at him, absorbing the information, trying to square it with the news he had just had about the licence plates from Duncan Crocker.

'She seemed in a pretty ramped-up state yesterday. Are you sure she didn't forget she'd ordered one?'

'I just came off the phone to her. She didn't order it, she's one hundred per cent sure.'

Branson sat down in front of him, folded his arms and went on, 'One of his teachers at the school got a call that the taxi was outside. She knew he was being picked up, because his mum had already told them that was going to happen. She didn't think to query it.'

'Did she see the driver?'

'Not really, no. He was wearing a baseball cap. But she wasn't really focused on him. Her concern was that Tyler got into the car safely – and she watched him do that from the school gates.'

'So they just let their pupils get into taxis without checking with anyone?' Grace quizzed.

'They have strict procedures,' Branson replied. 'The parents have to have given prior sanction, which Carly Chase had, on a blanket basis. Apparently Tyler was regularly dropped off and picked up by taxis, so no one had any reason to question it today.'

Grace sat in silence for some moments, thinking hard and fast. He looked at his watch. 'The appointment is for 11.30 a.m.?'

'Yes.'

'Has anyone checked with the dentist to see if he's turned up?'

'Someone's on that now. He hadn't as of a couple of minutes ago.'

'Where's the dentist?'

'In Wilbury Road.'

'St Christopher's is a private school, right? On New Church Road?'

Branson nodded.

'That's a five-minute drive. Ten, max. He was picked up just before 11 a.m.?'

'That's right.'

'Are you on to the taxi companies?'

'All of them. I've got Norman Potting, Nick Nicholl, Bella Moy and Stacey Horobin making calls right now.'

Grace thumped his desk in anger and frustration. 'Shit, shit, shit! Why wasn't I told about this dental appointment?'

Branson gave him a helpless look. 'We guarded her house with the boy and her mother – the boys' gran – in it all night. And we had a friend of Carly Chase, who was doing the school run, tailed – to make sure he got there safely. We were going to do the same this afternoon when he came out of school. No one said anything about him having an appointment.'

Grace shook his head. 'She was vulnerable. That meant anyone close to her was vulnerable, too. We should have had someone at the school today.'

'Hindsight's easy. Most people wouldn't get out of bed in the morning if they knew what was going to happen.'

Grace stared at him bleakly. 'Knowing what was going to happen would make this job a damned sight easier.' He picked up a pen and began making notes on his pad, his brain going into overdrive. 'OK, do we have a photograph of this boy?'

'No. I have a description of him. He's five foot tall, looks a little like a young Harry Potter – floppy brown hair, oval wire-framed glasses, wearing a school uniform of red blazer, white shirt, red and grey tie, and grey trousers.'

'Good, that's fairly distinctive,' Grace said. 'We need a photo PDQ.'

'We're on to that.'

'Has anyone spoken to the gran?'

'She's at a doctor's appointment at the Sussex County. I have someone on their way there.'

'Do we have the make of the taxi? Was it a saloon or an estate car or a people carrier?'

'I don't have that yet.'

'Why not?'

'Because I haven't had time. I wanted you to know right away.'

Grace looked up at a map of East and West Sussex on his wall, then at his bookshelf, where he could see a copy of the official *Kidnap Manual*, which contained all the procedures and protocols for kidnap and abduction. He knew a lot of them by heart, but he would check carefully through it. Before that he had some urgent fast-time actions to carry out. He grabbed the phone off his desk and, as he dialled, he said, 'Glenn, we need to plot an arc around the school – how far away someone could be in any direction now and in thirty minutes' time. We've got to get the make of vehicle. Is someone going to see the teacher?'

'Two officers from the Outside Inquiry Team should be at the school now.'

'We need more officers down at that school immediately, talking to everyone around it, in houses, walking their dogs, cats, goldfish.'

Grace dialled the number for Ops-1 – the Duty Inspector in the Force Control Room, Becky Newman. He gave her a quick summary and asked her who the Force Gold was today. The Gold Commander was normally a Superintendent or Chief Superintendent who would take control of any Critical Incident that happened on his watch.

He was pleased to hear it was Chief Superintendent Graham Barrington, the current Commander of Brighton and Hove, an exceptionally able and intelligent officer. Moments later he was on the line. Grace quickly brought him up to speed. Barrington said he wanted a Detective as Silver and suggested Chief Inspector Trevor Barnes. He quickly reeled off the Bronzes to complete his command team: one a POLSA for searches, then one for Intelligence, one for Investigations and one for Media. In all child abductions or kidnaps, the way the media was handled was crucial.

'I think because of the gravity we should have an ACC handle the media. ACC Rigg is on call today.'

Grace smirked. He liked the idea of the very slightly arrogant Peter Rigg being given a role down the pecking order, beneath the Chief Superintendent.

'I think we should make your deputy SIO the Investigations Bronze, as he'll be up to speed. Who is that?"

'Glenn Branson.'

'He's a DS?'

'Yes, but he's good,' Grace said, turning to his colleague and winking.

'OK.'

'I think our very first priority, Graham, is road checks.'

'Yes, we'll get them on all major routes. What do you think? Forty-five minutes' or one hour's drive away?'

Grace looked at his watch, doing a calculation. It would take time to get cars in place.

'An hour's drive, to be safe. Can we scramble Hotel 900.'

Hotel 900 was the call sign for the police helicopter.

'Right away. Get me a description of the taxi as quickly as possible to give to them. What about utilizing *Child Rescue Alert*?'

'Yes, definitely. I'm about to do that,' Grace said, although he was aware of the deluge of calls his team would receive from this, most of which would be false alarms.

Child Rescue Alert was a recent police initiative, modelled on the US's *Amber Alert*, for getting descriptions of missing or abducted children circulated fast, nationwide. It included mobile messaging, social-networking sites, news bulletins and posting descriptions on motorway signs. Its use always generated thousands of responses, each of which would have to be checked out. But it was a valuable resource and ideal for this current situation.

'We need an all-ports alert out, too,' Grace said. 'No one's leaving this country with a young boy until we've cleared them. We need to throw everything we have at this. We need to find this bastard and we're going to have to find him fast, before he has a chance to hurt the kid.'

Grace hung up, leaving the Chief Superintendent to get started, and turned back to Branson.

'OK, you're Investigations Bronze. Chief Superintendent Barrington will brief you shortly, but there are three urgent things you need to do.'

'Yes?'

'The first is to get the boy's computer – I assume he must have one – down to the High-Tech Crime Unit for analysis. Find out who he's been talking to and engaging with on Facebook, chat lines, email.'

Branson nodded. 'I'll access that via his gran.'

'The second is to get every inch of his house and garden

searched, and his immediate neighbours', and the homes of all his friends. You may be able to draft in some locals as volunteers to help search his entire home area.'

'Yep.'

'The third is to keep checking with the dentist and the school. I don't want egg all over my face if this kid turns up safe and sound because his mum forgot to tell you something.'

'Understood, but that's not going to happen. Not from what she's told me.'

'It had better not.' Then Grace shrugged. 'Although I wish it would, if you know what I mean.'

Branson nodded, getting up to leave. He knew exactly what Roy meant.

As the door closed, Grace grabbed the *Kidnap Manual* off the shelf and laid it on his desk, but before he opened it he scribbled down several more actions on his pad as they came into his head, then sat in silence for some moments, thinking. His phone rang. It was his MSA, Eleanor Hodgson, asking if he had the amended draft of his press statement ready for retyping.

In the panic of the last few minutes he'd forgotten all about it, he realized. He told her he was going to have to rewrite it totally because of the latest development and that the press conference might need to be delayed by half an hour.

He felt very afraid for this young boy. This man who had killed Preece and Ferguson was a cruel sadist. There was no telling what he had in mind for Tyler Chase, and all Grace's focus now was on how to get the boy safely out of his clutches. Thirty minutes had elapsed so far. They could be in a lot of different places in thirty minutes. But a taxi was distinctive. A man and a young boy were distinctive – particularly if Tyler was still in his school uniform.

He felt a deep, dark dread inside him. This was not his fault, but he still had overall responsibility for providing the protection Carly and her family needed, and he was angry with himself for letting this happen.

At least the timing of the press conference could hardly be better. Within the next hour, combining *Child Rescue Alert*, the press and the media, he could have nationwide blanket coverage on the missing boy.

Then he picked up his phone and made the call that he was not looking forward to.

Assistant Chief Constable Peter Rigg answered on the first ring.

88

Carly walked around her hotel room in a black vortex of terror, tears streaming down her face, desperately wanting to get back to England. Her brain was jumping around all over the place and she was feeling physically sick.

How could she have been so damned stupid leaving him at home, unprotected like this? Why, oh why, hadn't she thought everything through more carefully before making this dumb decision to come here?

Was she forgetting something? A simple explanation for the taxi? Was there something she had overlooked in the chaos of the past weeks? She regularly ordered taxis to take him places when she was tied up at work. Had she double-booked Tyler for another appointment somewhere else? With whom? Had she perhaps ordered this taxi weeks ago for that and forgotten all about it? Perhaps the taxi had picked up the wrong boy? That could be it, a mix-up at the school!

She felt a fleeting moment of relief.

Clutching at straws, she knew.

She tried to shut the images of Fernanda Revere in the wreckage of her car from her mind. Some of them were intertwined, horrifically, with Tyler's face. She shivered and thought about getting into a hot shower, but she did not want to risk missing a call. She had to get home. Someone helpful down at the front desk was looking into flights to England for her. She had to get back today, somehow had to, had to. She looked at her watch but could hardly read the dial. Her eyes felt as if they weren't working properly. Everything she looked at seemed out of focus.

She had to think straight. Had to think clearly. But the only thing that came to her mind was the image of Tyler getting into a taxi.

Driven by a monster.

She walked over to the window and looked out again. It had

been a blue sky a few minutes ago. Now it was grey. The landscape was all washed out. She watched a man on a dumper truck. *Has your son been kidnapped?* She saw a woman get out of a small car. Starting her day. Just a day like any other, for her. *Has your son been kidnapped?*

She went into the bathroom to brush her teeth, but her hands were shaking so much the toothpaste fell into the sink each time she tried to squeeze some on to her brush. A coiled spring felt as if it was being wound tighter and tighter inside her. She filled the kettle, but then could not find the switch on the damned thing. All the time she kept her phone beside her, willing Tyler to ring. Desperately praying he would ring.

And suddenly it began ringing. The display said, BLOCKED.

'Yes-hi-hello,' she blurted.

'Carly? It's DS Branson.'

'Yes?' she said, trying to mask her disappointment. But maybe he had news? *Please, please have news.*

'I need to ask you some questions, Carly.'

Her heart sinking, she rushed on, 'I was thinking – I don't know – is it possible there was a mix-up at the school and the taxi was for another boy? Have they checked he's not somewhere at the school. He likes science, history, stuff like that. He often just goes into the labs and works on his own. He can be a loner. Did they check? Did they?'

'They're searching the school now. The taxi was definitely there to collect your son, Tyler.'

'Did he turn up at the dentist? Do you have any news at all?'

'So far not, but we'll find him, don't worry. But I need your help.'

'DON'T WORRY? YOU'RE TELLING ME NOT TO WORRY?' she shouted.

'We're doing everything we possibly can, Carly.'

'I'm going to get the first flight home. Maybe I can get a daytime one and be home this evening.'

'I think you should get back as fast as you can. Let me know your flight details when you can and we'll meet you at the airport. We've heard about Mrs Revere.'

'This is just a nightmare,' she said. 'Please help me. Please find my son. Oh, God, please help me.'

'One thing that could be significant. Can you tell me who might have known about Tyler's dental appointment?'

'Who? Only – only his school – and my friends, Sarah and Justin Ellis. He – Justin – was going to take him. I – I can't think of anyone else.'

'Our High-Tech Unit's done some searches. Tyler's on a number of social networking sites, which I presume you know,' Branson said.

'Well – some.'

'Did he Tweet it? He had put that he was going to the dentist up on Facebook, making a joke of it. Did he talk to you about any of the responses he had?'

'No,' she said. 'These past two weeks since my accident he's been in a really strange mood. I – I—' She was fighting off tears. 'Tyler's a – he's a very special child. He's incredibly resourceful. He wouldn't get into a car with a stranger. You may wonder how I know that for sure, but I do, I can promise you. He's streetwise. Have you checked he didn't go home?'

'We're keeping a round-the-clock watch on your home. There doesn't appear to be anyone in. But he definitely went off from his school in a taxi.'

'Please find him,' she said. 'Please find him.'

'We are going to find him, I promise you. The whole nation's looking for him.'

Tears were stinging her eyes and everything was a blur. The detective's kind voice was making her weepy.

'The Revere family,' she sobbed. 'They can do anything they want to me. I don't care. Tell them that. Tell them they can kill me. Tell them to give me my son back and then kill me.'

He promised to call her back the moment he had any news. As she hung up, she crossed back over to the window and stared out at the drab landscape. Christ, the world was a big place. How could you find someone? Where did you start looking? Way down below her on the ground she watched a man walking along, phone to his ear. And suddenly she had a thought.

Wiping away tears, she stared down at the screen of her iPhone, fingered through the apps, sliding them across, until she reached the one she was looking for. Then she tapped it hard.

Moments later she felt a sudden flicker of hope. She stared at it harder, brought it closer to her face.

'Oh yes! Oh, you good boy, Tyler! Oh, you clever boy!'

89

Grace came out of the press conference at 12.50 p.m., pleased with the solid performance ACC Rigg had delivered, and very relieved. He found all press conferences to be minefields. One wrong answer and you could be made to look a total idiot. Rigg had been sensible, keeping it tight and focused, and brief.

He was tailed by Kevin Spinella, as ever wanting one more question answered. But the Detective Superintendent was in no mood to talk to him. As he reached the security door at the start of the corridor, he turned to face the reporter.

'I don't have anything to add. If you want more information you need to speak to ACC Rigg, who is now responsible for press liaison on *Operation Violin*.'

'I know you're still angry with me over writing about the reward,' Spinella said. 'But you seem to forget sometimes, Detective Superintendent, that you and I both have a job to do and it's not the same job. You solve crimes, I have to help sell newspapers. You need to understand that.'

Grace stared at him incredulously. A child's life was at stake, he was right in the middle of the fast-time stage of one of the most serious critical incidents of his career, and this young reporter had decided now was the moment to start lecturing him about the newspaper business.

'What part of that do you think I don't understand, Kevin?' Grace said, turning back to the door and holding up his security card to the pad.

'You have to realize that I'm not your puppet. I want to help you, but my first loyalty will always be to my editor.'

'Why don't you save your breath right now, hurry back to your office and file a story that might help save Tyler Chase's life?'

'Coz I don't need to. I can use this,' Spinella said. Then he fished out his BlackBerry and held it up, with a smug grin.

Grace slammed the door behind him. He was about to call the Gold Commander for an update, when his phone rang. It was Glenn Branson.

'You out of the conference, boss?'

'Yes.'

'We're cooking with gas! We have a development with Tyler.'

'Where are you?'

'MIR-1.'

'I'll be right there.'

Grace threw himself down a few steps, sprinted along the corridor and entered the packed Incident Room. In contrast to the corridor, which had a permanent smell of fresh paint, MIR-1 at lunchtime always smelled like a canteen. Today an aroma of hot soup and microwaved Veg Pots was mixed with a tinge of curry.

There was that quiet buzz of energy in here that Grace loved so much. A sense of purpose. Some members of the team at their workstations – on the phone or reading or typing – and some standing, making adjustments to the family tree or photograph displays on the whiteboards. There was a constant muted ringing of landline phones, plus the louder cacophony of mobile phones and the rattle of keyboards.

Some of the team were eating as they worked. Norman Potting was hunched over a printout, munching a huge Cornish pasty, oblivious to the crumbs falling like sleet down his tie and bulging shirt.

Glenn Branson was seated in the far corner of the room, close to a water dispenser. Grace hurried across to him, ignoring Nick Nicholl and David Howes, who both tried to get his attention. He glanced at his watch, then at the clock on the wall, as if to double-check. It was something he often did and could not help. Every second of every minute in this current situation was crucial.

'Boss, have you used an iPhone?'

'No. Why?' Grace frowned.

'There's an app called Friend Mapper. It operates on GPS, just like a satnav. You and someone you know with an iPhone can both be permanently logged on to it. So, for instance, if you and I are logged on to it, provided you've got the app running, I'd be able to see where you are, anywhere in the world, and ditto you'd be able to see me, to within about fifty yards.'

Grace suddenly had a feeling he knew where this was going.

'Carly Chase and her son?'

'Yes!'

'And? Tell me.'

'That apparently was the deal when Carly Chase got her son an iPhone, that he had to keep Friend Mapper on all the time he was out of her sight.'

'And it's on now?'

We had a call from her twenty minutes ago. 'It's not moving, but there was a signal coming from Regency Square. We don't know whether it's been switched off or the battery's dead – or he could, as I suspect, just be in a bad reception area.'

'How old is this signal?'

'She can't tell, because she's only just checked. But she doesn't understand why it's where it is. Regency Square's a couple of miles east of the school and nowhere near where his dental appointment is. She says Tyler would not have had any reason to be there. She's magnified the map as much as she can. She says it looks like it's very near the entrance to the underground car park.'

Grace suddenly felt himself sharing Branson's excitement. 'If he's in the car park that could explain the lack of a signal!'

Branson smiled. 'Gold's got every unit in Brighton down there now. They're ring-fencing it, covering every exit, searching the place and any vehicle that leaves.'

'Let's go!' Grace said.

90

With his memory of Glenn Branson's driving still too close for comfort, Grace took the wheel. As they blitzed through Brighton's lunchtime traffic, the Detective Sergeant said, 'Carly Chase is booked on a BA flight that leaves at 8.40 a.m. New York time – 1.40 p.m. UK time – less than an hour. She'll get back to Heathrow at 8.35 p.m.'

'OK.'

Grace's phone rang. 'Could you answer it, Glenn?'

Branson took the call while Grace overtook a line of traffic waiting at a red light at the junction of Dyke Road and the Old Shoreham Road, blazing down the wrong side of the road. He checked that everyone had seen him, changed the tone of his siren, then accelerated over the junction.

When Branson ended the call he turned to Grace. 'That was E-J, reporting back from Avis. That Toyota Yaris was rented Monday morning of last week to a man called James John Robertson, according to his licence. The address he had given was fictitious and the information received back from the High-Tech Crime Unit was that the Visa credit card he had paid with was a sophisticated clone. Avis gave a description of the renter, but it wasn't much to go on. A short, thin man with an English accent, wearing a baseball cap and dark glasses. He'd been offered an upgrade which he had declined.'

'Interesting to decline an upgrade,' Grace said. 'Wonder why?'

Branson nodded. 'You know, it would be brilliant if we could take Carly Chase's son to the airport to greet her,' he said.

'It would.'

'And with a bit of luck, that's going to happen.'

Roy Grace shared his friend's hope, but not his optimism. After enough years in this job, your optimism gradually got eroded by experience. So much so that if you weren't careful, one day you'd wake up the cynical bastard you'd always promised yourself you would never become.

Driving normally, the journey to Regency Square from Sussex House would have taken around twenty minutes. Grace did it in eight. He turned off the seafront, ignoring the No Entry sign, and pulled up behind two marked cars and two police transit vans that were halted either side of the car park entry ramp. They were both out of the Ford almost before the wheels had stopped turning.

The entire historic, but in parts dilapidated, square was teeming with uniformed police officers, and the statuesque figure of the Brighton and Hove Duty Inspector, Sue Carpenter, was heading over to greet them. In her early forties, she stood a good six feet tall and the hat riding high on her head, with her long dark hair pushed up inside it, made her look even taller. Grace remembered her from some years back, when she was a sergeant, and had been impressed by her competence.

'Good afternoon, sir,' she said, greeting him with nervous formality, and then giving Glenn Branson a quick smile.

'How are you doing?' Grace asked.

'We've just found a taxi parked on the third level – the lowest. The vehicle is locked, sir. It's a bit unusual to find a taxi in a city multi-storey car park. We've radioed Streamline, which it's registered with, to see if we can get any information.'

'Let's take a look,' Grace said.

As a precaution, never knowing when he might need them, he took out a pair of blue gloves from his go-bag in the boot of the car, and a couple of small, plastic evidence bags. Then he glanced quickly around the grassy centre of the square. Across the far side, where the exit was, he saw a halted Jaguar surrounded by police, with its boot open.

'Presumably there's CCTV on the entrance and exit?'

'There are cameras, sir, and some inside. Every single one of them was vandalized last night.'

'All of them?'

'Yes, they're being replaced later today, but that doesn't help us, I'm afraid.'

'Shit, shit, shit,' he said, banging his knuckles together. He shook his head. 'Seems a little coincidental, the timing.'

'This car park is quite a hot spot for trouble, sir – in fact this whole area is,' she reminded him, and pointed across the road at the ruin of the West Pier – one of Brighton's biggest landmarks, which had been burned down some years before in one of the city's biggest ever acts of vandalism.

Grace and Branson followed Inspector Carpenter past a PCSO who was guarding the entrance and down a smelly concrete stairwell. Then they walked along the bottom level of the car park, which was almost deserted and smelled of dry dust and engine oil. The old, tired-looking concrete floor, white stanchions and red piping stretched away into the distance, gridded by parking-bay markings.

Over to the right, partially obscured by a concrete abutment, he saw a Skoda saloon taxi that had been reversed into a bay and backed up tight against the rear wall. Two young officers stood beside it.

As they approached, Grace noticed a few fragments of black plastic on the ground close to the car. He fished the gloves from his pocket and snapped them on. Then he knelt, picked the fragments up and put them in an evidence bag, just in case.

At that moment a controller's voice came through Inspector Carpenter's radio. Grace and Branson could both hear it clearly. Apparently the Streamline operator was concerned, as she'd not been able to get a response from the driver since just after midnight last night.

'Do we have a name?' Carpenter asked.

'Mike Howard,' the voice crackled back.

'Ask if she has a mobile phone number for him,' Grace said.

He peered into the front, then the rear of the car before trying each of the doors in turn, but they were all locked.

Sue Carpenter radioed the request. A few moments later the operator came back with the number. Grace scribbled it down on his notebook, then immediately dialled it.

A few moments later they heard a muted ringtone from inside the rear of the taxi. Grace ended the call, turned to one of the PCs and asked him for his baton. Looking apprehensive, the young officer produced it and handed it to him.

'Stand back!' Grace said, as he swung the baton hard at the driver's door window.

It cracked, with a loud bang, but remained intact. He hit it again, harder, and this time the glass broke. He smashed away some of the jagged edges with the baton, then slipped his arm in, found the handle and tugged it. He pulled the door open, leaned in and released the handbrake.

'Give me a hand,' he said to the officers, and began trying to push the car.

For an instant it resisted, then slowly, silently, it inched forward. Grace kept going until it was a few feet out from the wall, then jerked the brake back on. He leaned in, staring at the unfamiliar controls, saw the driver's ID on the windscreen, which showed a photograph of a burly-looking man in his forties with thinning brown hair and a startled expression. The name *Mike Howard* was printed beneath. Grace looked around hard, wondering if there was an internal boot release. Moments later he found it and the boot lid popped open.

Glenn Branson reached the rear of the car first.

Then, as he stared in, his face dropped.

'Oh shit,' he said.

91

Carly, seated in the busy waiting area by boarding gate 47, looked at her watch. Then she stared for a moment at the two British Airways women standing and chatting behind the desk. Occasionally there was a *bong*, then a brief announcement. Final call for boarding for some other flight. She looked at her watch again. Twenty-two minutes past eight. The flight was due to depart in less than twenty minutes and they hadn't even started boarding yet. What was going on?

She gripped her handbag and kept her holdall right in front of her. No checked luggage, she did not want any risk of delay at the other end. Her legs kept knocking together. She badly needed a cup of tea and something to eat, but she did not feel able to swallow anything.

She called her mother. She was almost in a worse state than Carly was, blaming herself for having her medical appointment and not picking Tyler up. Then Carly just sat, shaking, raw-eyed, staring around the room at her fellow passengers, and occasionally looking through the emails that were pouring into her iPhone. Mostly work stuff. Questions or information she had requested from clients. Emails from her colleagues. Jokes from a couple of friends who hadn't yet heard about Tyler. She did not read any of them. All she was interested in was looking to see if, by chance, an email had come in from her son.

Two middle-aged couples sat near her, Americans in a jovial mood, heading to the UK for a golfing holiday. They were talking about golf courses. Hotels. Restaurants. The normality was irritating her. These people were in earnest discussion. Her son had been kidnapped and they were chatting away about long carries and fast greens and some water hazard they'd all had a problem with on their visit last year.

She stood up and moved away, walked up to the desk and asked

338

if the flight was going to be leaving on time. She was told they would be starting boarding in a couple of minutes.

That gave her some small relief. But not much.

She checked Friend Mapper on her phone for the hundredth time since leaving the hotel. But Tyler's purple dot remained stubbornly in that same place, close to the entrance to Regency Square car park.

Why there? Why are you there?

The screen blurred with her tears. It had been over an hour since she'd spoken to DS Branson. She wondered if she should call him one more time before she got on the plane.

But he had already promised to call the moment he had any news and she was sure he would; he seemed a good communicator. But what if he had been calling and was unable to get through? The flight was about seven hours long. How the hell was she going to be able to sit there for seven hours without news?

She dialled to check her messages, but there were no new ones. Nothing from DS Branson. So she called his mobile number and, to her relief, he answered almost immediately.

'It's Carly,' she said. 'I'm at Kennedy Airport, about to board. Just thought I'd check in with you.'

'Right, yeah. You OK?'

'Just about.'

'We've got your flight times and one of us will be at the gate to meet you when you land.'

His voice sounded strange, as if he was hiding something from her. And he sounded in a hurry.

'So – no – no news?'

'Not yet, but we hope to have some for you later. We have just about every police officer in the county looking for Tyler. We're going to find him.'

'I had a thought – if there is – you know – any news while I'm up in the air, can you get a message to me via the pilot?'

'Yes, we can. We can get you an ACARS text message via the cockpit, and most long-haul planes have satellite phones in the cockpit. The moment there's any news I'll get it relayed straight to you. OK?'

She thanked him and hung up. As she did so, she heard the boarding announcement. She towed her overnight bag over towards the rear of the rapidly lengthening queue, her insides a solid knot that was getting tighter by the second.

Seven hours.

Seven hours of waiting.

Carly handed over her passport and boarding card for inspection, then walked on in a silent haze, more alone and scared than she'd ever felt in her life.

Suddenly, as she stood in the crush in the aisle of the plane, her phone pinged with an incoming text. Her heart flipped with sudden hope and she looked down eagerly. But to her disappointment it was from the phone company, O2, warning her she was close to her 50 MB overseas data limit.

She deleted it, then found her seat. Or at least the part of it which wasn't already occupied by the damp, overflowing girth of a perspiring bald man who looked like he weighed uncomfortably north of 500 pounds.

If her day wasn't already bad enough, the journey from hell had now got even worse. She sat, squashed, her elbows tucked uncomfortably in against her chest, her whole body trembling with fear.

Fear that she might never see her son alive again.

92

In the total darkness, Tyler's head hurt. He couldn't see anything, couldn't move his arms or legs. He was frightened and confused and knew this was not a game, that something bad was happening.

They were travelling, he could sense that. Motion. There were strong smells of carpet and plastic, new-car smells. He'd been in a friend's mother's brand-new Hyundai recently and it had smelled like this. He thought he could detect rubber, too. Could hear a hum. He must be in the boot of a car, he reckoned. The taxi? Braking and accelerating. All he could move were his knees – he could bend and flex them just a little. He tried to wedge them against something solid, to get a grip, but moments later he was thrown away backwards and felt himself rolling over, until he hit something hard.

He tried to shout to the driver, to ask him who he was, where they were going, but he could not move his mouth and his voice sounded all muffled.

After the two police officers had come to their house and his friends had left, his mum had sat down in his bedroom and told him there were bad things happening. Bad people. They had to be careful. They needed to keep a watch for strangers near the house. He must call the police if he saw anyone.

Was this one of the bad people driving him now?

At least he had his iPhone in his jacket and it was switched on. Friend Mapper would be logging him and his mum would know that. She'd know exactly where he was and she would tell the police. He didn't really need to be afraid. They would find him.

He just hoped they would find him soon, because he had an IT class this afternoon that he really did not want to miss. And because he did not like this darkness, and not being able to move, and his arms were hurting, too.

But it was going to be all right.

93

Grace dashed around to the rear of the taxi, just as Glenn Branson leaned into the boot.

The man inside looked terrified and there was a sour reek of urine. His fleshy face was pale and clammy. Duct tape was wound around his arms, legs and mouth, the same kind of tape that Evie Preece had been bound with, Grace clocked, as he fished out his warrant card and held it up to give the man reassurance.

'Police,' he said. 'Don't worry, you're safe. We'll get you out of there.'

He turned to Branson and to Inspector Sue Carpenter, who had joined them.

'Let's get the tape off his mouth first. Sue, call for a paramedic and POLSA and a search team, and get someone to bring some water, or tea if you can. And I want this level of the car park closed, as well as all the stairwells, in case they left by foot.'

'Yes, sir.'

Then he leaned in and, as gently as he could, got his fingertips in the join in the tape. It would have been easier without his gloves, he knew, but he kept them on and finally managed to start peeling it off, mindful that although it would be extremely painful for the man, at the same time he needed to preserve it as best he could for forensic analysis.

As he peeled it away from his mouth, the man shouted out in pain.

'Sorry,' Grace murmured.

The tape went all the way around the back of the man's head and he didn't want to hurt him any more.

'Mike Howard?' he asked.

'Yes! Jesus, that hurt,' the man said, then smiled.

Grace folded the tape back on itself. 'I'm sorry. We're going to lift you out. Are you injured? In pain?'

He shook his head. 'Just get me out.'

Mike Howard was a big, heavy man. With considerable difficulty, between himself and Glenn Branson they managed to manoeuvre him forward to the edge of the boot. They freed his arms and legs, and tried as best they could to remove the rest of the tape around his head. Then they stood him up and walked him around a little, supporting him until the circulation was back in his legs and he was steadier. But he was wheezing, close to hyperventilating, so they sat him down on the Skoda's rear bumper.

'Can you tell us what happened?' Grace asked him gently.

'I'm sorry,' he said. 'I pissed. I couldn't help it. I couldn't keep it in any more.'

'It's OK, don't worry. Are you able to tell me what happened?'

'What time is it?'

'Half past one,' Glenn Branson said.

'What day?'

'Friday.'

The man frowned. 'Friday? Friday morning?'

'It's afternoon, lunchtime.'

'Holy shit.'

'How long have you been there?' Grace asked.

Mike Howard took several deep breaths. 'I was working nights. I was just heading home – about 1 a.m. – and this man hailed me along the seafront.'

'Where exactly?'

'Just near the Peace Statue. He got in the back and told me to take him to Shoreham Airport – said he was working a night shift there. I remember turning into the perimeter road – and that's the last thing.'

Grace knew that road. It had no street lighting.

'The last thing you remember?'

'I woke up being shaken about. I could smell diesel and fumes. I figured out I was in the boot of my cab. I was terrified. I didn't know what was going to happen.'

'Can you remember what this guy looked like?' Grace asked.

'He was wearing a baseball cap pulled low. I tried to get a look at his face – you always do in this game when you pick someone up late at night off the street. But I couldn't see it.'

Grace was relieved that the taxi driver seemed to be cheering up a little.

'What about his accent?'

'He didn't say much. Sounded English to me. Do you have any water?'

'There's some on its way. Do you need anything to eat?'

'Sugar. I'm diabetic.'

'An ambulance will be here any minute – they'll have something for you. Will you be all right for a few minutes?'

Mike Howard nodded.

Grace continued his questioning. 'We think the man who did this to you has kidnapped a child and we need to find him urgently. I know you've had a horrendous ordeal, but anything you can tell us, anything at all that you can remember, would be valuable.'

Mike Howard eased himself forward and stood up. 'Agggghhh,' he said. 'I've got the most terrible cramp.' He stamped his foot, then stamped it again. 'I'm trying to think. He was short. A short, thin little fellow, like a weasel. Promise me something?'

'What?' Grace asked.

'If you find him, can I get him to pay me what he owes me, then thump him one, really hard, where it hurts?'

For the first time in what felt a long while, Grace smiled. 'You'll have to beat me to it,' he said.

'I will, mate, don't you worry.'

Glenn Branson then said to the driver, 'Is there someone you'd like us to contact and tell that you're safe?'

Grace looked at his watch pensively. Almost two and a half hours since Tyler Chase had been picked up. Why was he brought here? His assumption was that the abductor had a car parked here, with luck the rental Toyota Yaris, choosing this as a good location to attack and disable the boy, then switch vehicles. Even more ideal with its CCTV cameras out of action. Inspector Carpenter might think it was scummy Brighton vandals, but he didn't. He had a feeling he was starting to recognize the killer's handwriting.

He did a calculation in his head. There were roadworks along the seafront clogging up the traffic, badly. The journey from the school would have been in the region of fifteen to twenty minutes, assuming they came straight here. The pervert seemed to like to film his victims dying. Grace was able to make another assumption, that he had not done that here. From the image he was building of the man, this wasn't his style of location. He was going to take the boy somewhere he could film him dying. And he sensed it would be somewhere dramatic. But where?

Where in this whole damned city – or beyond?

He studied his watch again. If he'd brought the boy in here around 11.20 a.m., it was likely he'd not hung around. He would have left again within a few minutes. Certainly within half an hour.

Two paramedics, accompanied by a uniformed officer, were running towards them. Grace edged Glenn Branson to one side to make way for them, then he said the DS, 'We're out of here.'

'Where to?'

'I'll tell you in the car.'

94

Tooth, keeping rigidly to the 30mph speed limit, drove the Toyota west along the main road above Shoreham Harbour. He was looking at the flat water of the basin, down to his left, where Ewan Preece had taken his last drive, and almost did not notice a roadworks traffic light turning red in front of him.

He braked hard. Behind him in the boot of the car he heard a thud and further back a scream of locked tyres. For an anxious moment he thought the car behind was going to rear-end him.

Then the sudden wail of a siren gave him a new concern. Moments later, blue lights flashing, a police car tore past from the opposite direction. He kept a careful watch in his mirrors, but it kept on going, either not noticing or not interested in him. Relieved, he drove on for some distance, passing a number of industrial buildings to his left, until he saw his landmark, the blue low-rise office block of the Shoreham Port Authority building.

He turned right into a narrow street opposite it, passing a modern kitchen appliances showroom on the corner. He drove a short way up the street, which rapidly became shabbier and went under a railway bridge up ahead. But before then he turned off it into a messy area that was part industrial estate and part low-rent apartment blocks. He remembered it all well and it seemed un-changed.

He passed a massive, grimy printing works on his left and various cars, some of which were parked on the road, while others had been left haphazardly in front of and around different buildings. It was the kind of area where no one would notice you, or take any interest in you if they did.

He turned right again, into the place he had discovered six years ago. He drove along the side of a shabby ten-storey apartment block, passing cars and vans parked outside, and came into a wide, half-empty parking area at the rear of the building, bounded by a crumbling wall on two sides, a wooden fence on a third and the rear of the apartment block.

He reversed the car in, backing it tight up against the wall, then sat and ate the chicken sandwich he had bought earlier at a petrol station, drank a cranberry juice, got out and locked up. With his cap pulled down low and his sunglasses on, he peered up at the grimy windows for any sign of an inquisitive face, but all he saw was laundry flapping from a couple of balconies. He stood by the car, pretending to be checking a rear tyre, listening to make sure that his passenger was silent.

He heard a thud.

Angrily he opened the boot and saw the boy's frightened eyes behind his glasses. It didn't matter how tightly he bound him, there was nothing to anchor him to in here. He wondered if it would be wisest to break his back and paralyse him – but that would mean lifting him out first and he didn't want to take that risk.

Instead he said, 'Make another sound and you're dead. Understand what I'm saying?'

The boy nodded, looking even more frightened.

Tooth slammed down the lid.

95

Tyler was terrified by the man in the black baseball cap and the dark glasses, but he was angry, too. His wrists were hurting from the bindings and he had cramp in his right foot. He listened, hard, could hear footsteps crunching, getting fainter.

He'd felt the car move when the man got out, but it hadn't moved again, which meant he hadn't got back in. He must have gone somewhere.

Tyler tried to work out what time it was, or where he might be. He'd just seen daylight when the boot lid rose up. And the wall of a building, a crummy-looking wall, and a couple of windows, but it could have been anywhere in the city, anywhere he had ever been to. But the fresh air that had come in, momentarily, smelled familiar. A tang of salt, but mixed with timber and burnt gas and other industrial smells. They were close to a harbour, he thought. Almost certainly Shoreham Harbour. He'd been kayaking here with his school, several times.

The daylight wasn't bright, but it didn't feel like it was evening, more just overcast as if it was going to rain.

They would find him soon. His mother would know where he was from Friend Mapper. She might even ring him – not that he would be able to answer it.

Defiantly, he threw himself against the side of the car, kicking out as hard as he could. Then again. And again.

He kicked until he had tired himself out. It didn't sound as if anyone had heard him.

But surely they would find him soon?

96

Grace, followed by Branson, sprinted up three floors at Brighton's John Street Police Station, hurried along a corridor and went into the CCTV Control Room, which was manned around the clock.

It was a large space, with blue carpet and dark blue chairs, and three separate workstations, each comprising a bank of CCTV monitors on which was a kaleidoscope of moving images of parts of the city of Brighton and Hove and other Sussex locations, keyboards, computer terminals and telephones. Every police CCTV camera in the county could be viewed from here.

Two of the workstations were currently occupied by controllers, both hunched over them with headsets on. One of them looked busy, engaged in a police operation, but the other turned as they came in and nodded a greeting. He was a fresh-faced man in his late thirties with neat brown hair, wearing a lightweight black jacket. His badge gave his name as Jon Pumfrey. Moments later they were joined in the room by Chief Superintendent Graham Barrington, the Gold Commander.

Barrington, in his mid-forties, was a tall, slim man with short, fair hair, and the athletic air of a regular marathon runner. He wore a short-sleeved white uniform shirt with epaulettes, black trousers and shoes, held a radio in his hand and had a phone clipped to his belt.

'Jon,' the Chief Superintendent said, 'which are the nearest cameras to the Regency Square car park?'

'There's a police one right opposite boss,' Pumfrey said, 'but it's hopeless – there's some constant interference with it.'

He tapped the keyboard and a moment later they saw successive waves rippling up and down one of the screens directly in front of him.

'How long's it been like that?' Roy Grace asked suspiciously.

'At least a year. I keep asking them to do something about it.'

He shrugged. 'There are also cameras to the east and west – which direction do you want?'

'We've just done a quick recce,' Grace said. 'If you exit in a vehicle from the Regency Square car park, you have to turn left on the seafront, on Kings Road – unless you go around up to Western Road, but that's complicated.'

Part of that road was buses and taxis only. Grace did not think the abductor would take the risk of getting stopped there.

'I've set some parameters,' he said. 'What we need to see is the video footage showing all vehicles in motion close to the car park, travelling east or west on King's Road between 11.15 a.m. and 11.45 a.m. today. We're looking particularly for a dark-coloured Toyota Yaris saloon, with a single male driving, either accompanied by a twelve-year-old boy or solo.'

Graham Barrington said, 'All right, you guys, I'll leave you to it. Anything you want, just shout.'

Grace thanked him, and the two detectives then stood behind Pumfrey and began to watch intently.

'The Yaris is a popular car, sir,' Pumfrey said. 'Must be thousands on the roads. We're likely to see a few.'

'We'll put markers on the first five we see, to start with,' Grace said. 'If they're turning left, they're heading east, but that might be only for a short distance, before they make a U-turn and head west. Let's check east first.'

Almost as he spoke they saw a dark-coloured Yaris heading east, past the bottom of West Street. The camera was on the south side of the road.

'Freeze that!' Branson said. 'Can you zoom in?'

Jon Pumfrey tapped the keyboard and the camera zoomed in, jerkily but quickly, on the driver's door and window. It was a grainy zoom, but they could see clearly enough that it was two elderly ladies.

'Let's move on,' Grace said.

They watched the fast-forwarding images, cars darting by in flickering movements.

Then Grace called out, 'Stop! Go back.'

They watched the tape rewind.

'OK! That one.' They were looking at a dark grey Yaris with what appeared to be a single occupant, a male, driving. The time said 11.38.

'Now zoom in, please.'

The image was again grainy, but this time it looked like a male, most of his face obscured by a baseball cap and dark glasses.

'It's not that bright out there. Why's he wearing dark glasses?' Pumfrey queried.

Grace turned to Branson. 'That was the description by the school teacher – the taxi driver was wearing a baseball cap. And so was the man who rented the car from Avis!' Suddenly he felt his adrenalin pumping. Turning back to Pumfrey, he asked, 'Is that the best image you can get?'

'I can send it for enhancement, but that would take a while.'

'OK, run forward. Can we get the registration?'

Pumfrey inched the car forward frame by frame.

'Golf Victor Zero Eight Whisky Delta X-Ray,' Branson read out, as Grace wrote it down.

'Right. Can you run an ANPR check from here?' he asked Pumfrey.

'Yes, sir.'

They continued watching. Then, to Grace's excitement, the car reappeared, this time travelling west.

'It's gone round the roundabout at the Palace Pier, doing a U-turn!' he said. 'Where's the next camera?'

'Other than the dud one opposite the Regency Square car park, the next is a mile to the west, on Brunswick Lawns.'

'Let's look at that one,' Grace said.

Five minutes later, which indicated the vehicle was sticking rigidly to the speed limit, and allowing for a couple of traffic-light stops and the roadworks delay, the car appeared, still travelling west.

'Where's the next?' Grace asked.

'That's the last of the city's CCTV cameras in this direction, sir,' Pumfrey said.

'OK. Now let's see if this vehicle has triggered any ANPR camera since 11.15 a.m. What's the first one west of this position?'

Pumfrey turned to a different computer and entered the data.

Grace noticed his partially eaten lunch on the wooden table beside him. An empty plastic lunchbox, a coil of orange peel and an unopened yoghurt. Healthy, he thought, depending of course on what had been in the sandwich.

'Here we are: 11.54 a.m. This is the ANPR camera at the bottom of Boundary Road, Hove, at the junction with the end of the Kingsway.'

Suddenly a photograph of the front of a dark grey Yaris appeared on the screen, its number plate clearly visible, but the occupant hard to make out through an almost opaque screen. By looking very closely it was possible to distinguish what might have been someone in a baseball cap and dark glasses, but without any certainty.

'Can't we get a better image of the face?' Branson asked.

'Depends how the light hits the windscreen,' Pumfrey replied. 'These particular cameras are designed to read number plates, I'm afraid, not faces. I can send it for enhancement if you want?'

'Yes, both of those images, please,' Grace said. 'Is that the only ANPR it's triggered?'

'The only one showing today.'

Grace did a mental calculation. If the driver avoided breaking the law, and with a kidnapped child on board he would not want to risk getting stopped . . . The exit from the car park on to King's Road was a left turn only . . . That meant he would have driven east to the end of King's Road and then gone round the roundabout, by the Palace Pier, and then come back on himself. Allowing for the distance and hold-ups at traffic lights, that would put the car there at the right time from its sighting on King's Road. Excitement was growing inside him.

The car's location was alongside Shoreham Harbour, close to Southwick. He was certain that the sadist knew this area. A lot of villains perpetrated their crimes in the places they knew, their comfort zones. He made a note of a new line of enquiry, to have Duncan Crocker do a search on all previous violent crimes in this area. But first, still staring at the frozen image of the front of the Yaris and the faint silhouette of its driver, on the monitor, he called for a PNC check on the car.

The information came back almost immediately that the owner

was a male, Barry Simons, who lived in Worthing, West Sussex, some fifteen miles to the west of Brighton. Grace's excitement waned at this news. That fitted with the car's occupant and position, heading in the direction where he lived. The only thing that kept him hopeful was the fact that the Yaris appeared to have stopped somewhere in Shoreham or Southwick. He was about to call Gold to ask him to get the helicopter over there and block off the area when his phone rang.

It was Duncan Crocker. 'Roy, we've found a car, a Toyota Yaris, driving on those switched plates taken from the service station at Newport Pagnell – the plates from the woman's car – that twenty-seven-year-old who was stopped on the M11 near Brentwood. It's just pinged an ANPR camera, heading north from Brighton on the A23.'

97

Tyler tried kicking again. He could hear the hollow metallic *boom-boom-boom* echo around him.

What if the man did not come back?

There was a story he had read – he was trying to remember the book – in which someone was locked in the boot of a car and nearly suffocated. How long could you stay in one? How long had he already been here? Was there any sharp edge he could rub against? He tried rolling over, exploring the space as best he could, but it was tiny and seemed to be completely carpeted.

His watch was luminous but he couldn't see the face. He had lost all track of time. He didn't know how long the man had been gone, whether it was still day out there or if night had fallen. If the man did not come back, how long would it be, he wondered, before someone wondered about a strange car?

Then he had a sudden panic about Friend Mapper. Had his mother remembered to log on? She made him keep it on all the time, but she often forgot herself. And she was crap with technology.

Maybe he should keep kicking, in case someone passed by and heard him. But he was scared. If the man came back and heard him he might get really angry. He had just made the decision to wait a little longer when he heard footsteps approaching – quick, sharp crunches. Then he felt the car tilt slightly.

Someone had got in.

98

In the CCTV room, Grace stared at the frontal photograph of a dark grey Toyota Yaris on a familiar stretch of the A23, just north of Brighton. But to his dismay the windscreen was even more opaque than the car by Shoreham Harbour in the previous photograph. He could see nothing at all inside, no shadows or silhouettes, no clue as to how many people might be in it.

Branson immediately informed Gold, then listened intently to his radio.

Grace ordered Jon Pumfrey to put out a *high-act* nationwide marker on the car. He did not intend to take any risks. Then he sat for a moment, clenching his fists. Maybe, finally, this was it.

'What CCTV units do you have on the A23?' he asked the controller.

'The only fixed ones are ANPRs on the motorway. The next one, if he keeps heading north, is Gatwick.'

Grace was feeling excitement but, at the same time, frustration. He would have liked to be out there, on the road, present when they stopped the car. Pumfrey pulled up a road map on to one of the monitors, showing the position of the two ANPR cameras. There were plenty of opportunities for the suspect to turn off the motorway. But with luck the helicopter would have him in sight imminently.

He turned back to the bank of monitors and looked at the car that had been photographed heading east along the seafront, owned, according to its registration document, by Barry Simons. Just as a precaution, he phoned the Incident Room. Nick Nicholl answered. Grace tasked him with finding Barry Simons and establishing for certain that he had been driving his car along Brighton seafront this morning.

From the suspect's current position on the A23, it would take him about twenty-five minutes, Grace estimated, to ping that next

ANPR camera at Gatwick. On the radio he could follow the developments. This was a true fast-time operation. The helicopter, which was also fitted with ANPR, would be over the M23 in ninety seconds. One unmarked car was already on the motorway, approximately two miles behind the target, and two more were only minutes away. It was policy in kidnap pursuits to use unmarked cars wherever possible. That way, the perpetrator would not panic as he might at the sight of a marked car passing him, with the risk of involving his victim in a high-speed chase. If they could get unmarked cars in front of and behind the suspect, a minimum of three vehicles, and preferably four, they could box him in – TPAC him – before he realized what was happening.

'I need to get back to Sussex House,' Glenn said.

'Me too.'

'I can patch any images you want through to you in the Incident Room,' Pumfrey said.

Grace thanked him and the two detectives left. As they walked out of the rear of the building into the car park, Grace's phone rang. It was Inspector Sue Carpenter at the Regency Square car park.

'Sir,' she said, 'I don't know if this is significant, but I understand that the Regency Square car park was identified by an application on the missing boy's iPhone.'

'Yes,' Grace replied, his hopes rising. 'An application called Friend Mapper. We're hoping he keeps it on – that it could lead us to him if we can't find him before.'

'I'm afraid, sir, one of the search team has found a smashed iPhone in a bin in the car park – close to the taxi.'

99

As he climbed into his car, Grace instructed Sue Carpenter to get the phone checked immediately for finger- and footprints, then get it straight to the High-Tech Crime Unit. He told her he wanted it in their hands, having been dusted for prints, within the next thirty minutes. Getting the contents of the phone analysed was more important to him at this stage than getting forensic evidence from it.

Then, as he drove out and turned left down the steep hill, he said to Branson, who was listening to the Ops-1 instructions on his radio, 'I'm still struggling to get my head around the motive here. Did the perp take this boy as a substitute because his mother was unavailable?'

'Because she'd unexpectedly gone to New York, so the boy was the next best thing? Is that what you're saying?'

'Yes,' Grace replied. 'Or was taking the boy his plan all along?'

'What's your sense?'

'I think he plans everything. He's not someone who takes chance opportunities. My view is that probably, by going to the States, Carly Chase made seizing the boy a little easier for him.'

Branson nodded and looked at his watch. 'Just over six hours until she lands.'

'Maybe we'll be able to greet her with good news.'

'I promised I'd get a message to her on the plane as soon as we have any.'

'With a bit of luck, that could be any minute now.'

Grace gave Branson a wistful smile, then glanced at the car clock. It was half past two. He should eat something, he knew, but he didn't have any appetite, and he didn't want to waste valuable time stopping anywhere. He fished in his suit jacket pocket and produced a Mars bar in a very crumpled wrapper that had been there for some days.

'Haven't had any lunch. You hungry?' he said to Branson. 'Want to share this?'

'Boy, you know how to give someone a good time!' Branson said, peeling off the wrapper. 'A slap-up, no-expenses-spared lunch with Roy Grace. Half an old Mars bar. This been in your pocket since you were at school?'

'Sod off!'

Branson tore the chocolate bar in two and held out the slightly larger portion to Grace, who popped it in his mouth. 'You ever see that film about—'

Grace's phone rang. As he wasn't driving at high speed, he stuck it into the hands-free cradle and answered. Both of them heard the voice of Chief Inspector Trevor Barnes, the newly appointed Silver Commander. An experienced and methodical Senior Investigating Officer, Barnes, like Roy Grace, had handled many major crime investigations.

'Roy,' he said, 'we've just stopped the Toyota Yaris on the M23, four miles south of the Crawley interchange.'

Grace, his mouth full of chewy chocolate and toffee, thumped the steering wheel with glee.

'Brilliant!' Branson replied.

'That you, Glenn?' Barnes asked.

'Yeah, we're in the car. What's the situation?'

'Well,' Barnes said, his voice somewhat lacking in enthusiasm, although he always spoke in a considered, deadpan tone, 'I'm not sure that we have the right person.'

'What description can you give us, Trevor?' Grace asked, the Silver's words now making him uneasy.

He halted the car at a traffic light.

'Well, I'm assuming your hit man is not eighty-four years old.'

'What do you mean?' Grace had a sinking feeling.

'Toyota Yaris, index Yankee Delta Five Eight Victor Juliet Kilo? Is that the correct one?'

Grace pulled out his notebook and flipped to the right page. 'Yes. Those are the plates that were taken from a car at Newport Pagnell that we believe our suspect is using.'

'The driver of this Yaris is eighty-four years old and has his wife who is eighty-three with him. It's their car, but it's not their registration number.'

'Not their registration?' Grace echoed.

The lights changed and he drove on.

'The licence plates on the car aren't theirs, Roy. The driver may be old, but he has all his marbles, I'm told. Knew his registration number off by heart. Sounds like someone's nicked his plates and replaced them with different ones.'

'Where's he come from?' Grace asked, but he had a feeling he already knew the answer.

'They've been in Brighton. They enjoy the sea air, apparently. Like to take their dog for a walk between the piers. It's their regular constitutional. They have fish and chips at some place on the front.'

'Yep, and let me guess where they parked. The Regency Square car park?'

'Very good, Roy. Ever thought of going on *Mastermind*?'

'Once, when I had a brain that worked. So, give us their index that's been stolen.'

Branson wrote it down.

Grace drove in silence for some moments, thinking about the killer with grudging admiration. *Whoever you are, you are a smart bastard. What's more, you clearly have a sense of humour. And just in case you don't know, right at this moment I have a major sense-of-humour failure.*

His phone rang again. This time it was Nick Nicholl in MIR-1, sounding perplexed.

'Chief, I'm coming back to you on the vehicle owner check you asked me to do, on Barry Simons.'

'Thanks. What do you have, Nick?'

'I've just spoken to him. I sent someone round to his house and they asked a neighbour who knew where he worked – and I got his mobile phone number from his company.'

'Well done.'

The Detective Constable sounded hesitant. 'You asked me to check if it was him driving his car first east on King's Road, then west past the junction between Kingsway and Boundary Road this morning? Index Golf Victor Zero Eight Whisky Delta X-Ray?'

'Yes.'

'Well, he's a bit baffled, chief. He and his wife are lying on a beach in Limassol in Cyprus at the moment. They've been there for nearly two weeks.'

'Could anyone they know be driving this car while they're away?'

'No,' Nick Nicholl said. 'They left it at the long-term car park at Gatwick Airport.'

Grace pulled over to the side of the road and stopped sharply.

'Nick, put a high-act marker on that index. Get on to the Divisional Intelligence Unit – I want to know every ANPR sighting from the day Barry Simons's car arrived at Gatwick to now.'

'To double-check, chief, index Golf Victor Zero Eight Whisky Delta X-Ray.'

'Correct.'

Grace switched on the car's lights and siren, then turned to Glenn Branson.

'We're taking a ride to Shoreham.'

'Want me to drive?' Branson asked.

Grace shook his head. 'Thanks for the offer, but I think I'll be of more help to Tyler Chase alive.'

100

Tooth sat in the Yaris in the parking lot behind the apartment block. The same cars were still here that had been here when he left to do his reconnaissance an hour ago. It was still the middle of the afternoon and maybe the lot would fill up when people came back from work. But it hadn't filled up last time, six years ago. The windows of the apartment block didn't look like they had been cleaned since then either. Maybe it was full of old people. Maybe they were all dead.

He stared at the text that had come in and which had prompted his early return to the car. It said just one word: **call.**

He removed the SIM card and, as he always did, burned it with his lighter until it was melted. He would throw it away later. Then he took one of the phones he had not yet used from his bag and dialled the number.

Ricky Giordino answered on the first ring. 'Yeah?'

'You texted me to call.'

'What the fuck took you so long, Mr Tooth?'

Tooth did not reply.

'You still there? Hello, Mr Tooth?'

'Yes.'

'Listen to me. We've had another tragedy in our family and that woman, Mrs Chase, she's the cause of it. My sister's dead. I'm your client now, understand me? You're doing this for me now. I want that woman's pain to be so bad. I want pain she's never going to forget, you with me?'

'I'm doing what I can,' Tooth replied.

'Listen up, I didn't pay you a million bucks to do what you can do. Understand? I paid you that money to do something more than that. Something different, right? Creative. Give me a big surprise. Blow me away. Show me you got balls!'

'Balls,' Tooth commented.

'Yeah, you heard, balls. You're going to bring those videos to me, right? Soon as you're done?'

'Tomorrow,' Tooth said.

He ended the call, again burned the SIM card, then lit a cigarette. He did not like this man.

He didn't do rudeness.

101

Roy Grace turned the siren and lights off as they passed Hove Lagoon, two shallow man-made recreational lakes beside a children's playground. Up on the promenade beyond there was a long row of beach huts facing the beach and the sea.

The Lagoon ended at Aldrington Basin, the eastern extremity of Shoreham Harbour, and from this point onwards, until Shoreham town, a few miles further on, the buildings and landscape along this road became mostly industrial and docklands. He slowed as they approached the junction with Boundary Road and pointed up through the windscreen.

'There's the ANPR camera that Barry Simons pinged this morning.'

Then Nick Nicholl radioed through. 'Chief, I've got the information you requested on the Toyota Yaris index Golf Victor Zero Eight Whisky Delta X-Ray. It's rather strange, so I went back an extra two weeks and I now have all sightings for the past month. For the first two weeks it pinged cameras during weekdays that are consistent with a regular morning and evening commute from Worthing to central Brighton and back. Then on Sunday morning, just under two weeks ago, it travelled from Worthing to Gatwick.'

'Consistent with what Simons told you,' Branson said, butting in, 'that they drove to Gatwick Airport long-term parking before their flight to Cyprus.'

'Yes,' Nicholl said. 'Now here's the bit that doesn't make sense. The next sighting was the one this morning, when it pinged the CCTV camera on the seafront at the bottom of West Street, travelling east. There's nothing to show how the car got from Gatwick Airport down to Kingsway. Even if it drove directly from the airport down to Brighton, with the marker on the vehicle it should have been picked up by the A23 camera at Gatwick, and by another on the approach to Brighton, and I would have thought by others in Brighton.'

'Unless it commenced its journey from the Regency Square car park,' Grace said thoughtfully. 'Then it would have exited the car park on King's Road and had to make a left turn along the seafront, which would explain why it passed the CCTV camera at the bottom of West Street twice – first going east and then, a few minutes later, west. Followed by the one on Brunswick Lawns, a mile further west, and then this one.'

'You've lost me, sir,' Nicholl said. 'That doesn't explain how the car got from Gatwick Airport to that car park in the first place.'

'It didn't, Nick,' Grace said. 'Our suspect has already demonstrated he is rather cute with number plates. We believe he rented this Toyota from Avis at Gatwick. I'm prepared to put money on Mr and Mrs Simons returning from their Cyprus holiday to find their number plates are missing. Good work. What about subsequent sightings since Boundary Road?'

'None, sir.'

Which would indicate, Grace thought, that either the car was parked up somewhere or the killer had changed number plates yet again.

He ended the conversation and immediately called Graham Barrington to update him.

'My hunch is that he's in the Shoreham area,' Grace said. 'But we can't rely on that. I think you need to get every dark-coloured Toyota Yaris within a three-hour drive of Brighton stopped and searched.'

'That's already happening.'

'And we need to throw everything we have at Shoreham Harbour and its immediate vicinity.'

'The problem is, Roy, it's a massive area.'

'I know. We also need to search every ship leaving and every plane at Shoreham Airport. We need to check the tides. The harbour has a shallow entrance, so there's a lot of shipping can't come in or leave for a period of time either side of low water, from what I remember as a sailor.'

'I'll get that information. Where are you now?'

'At the bottom of Boundary Road with DS Branson – the position of the last sighting of our suspect. I think we should set an initial search parameter of a half-mile radius west of this camera.'

'Harbour and inland?'

'Yes. We need house-to-house, all outbuildings, garages, sheds, industrial estates, ships, boats. We're beyond the range of the Brighton and Hove CCTV network, so we need to focus on commercial premises that have CCTV. A car doesn't disappear into thin air. Someone's seen it. Some camera's picked it up.'

'Just to be clear, Roy, the last sighting of the vehicle is at the bottom of Boundary Road, the junction with Kingsway, and it was heading west?'

'Correct, Graham.'

'Leave it with me.'

Grace knew that the Gold Commander, who happened, fortunately, to be one of the officers he most respected in the entire force, would leave no stone unturned. He should let Barrington get on with it and return to Sussex House, first to MIR-1 to show support to his team, and then prepare for this evening's briefing. With the Chief Constable, Tom Martinson, and the Assistant Chief Constable, Peter Rigg, both due to attend, it was vital he was well prepared. But he was reluctant to leave the chase.

The killer was in Shoreham somewhere, he was certain of it. If anyone had asked him why, his only answer would have been a shrug of his shoulders and the lame response, *copper's nose.* But Glenn Branson understood. That was why, one day, his mate would get to the very top of their profession, so long as he was able to survive his marriage wreckage.

Grace made a call to the Incident Room and Nick Nicholl answered.

'Nick, I want you to get everyone in MIR-1 to stop doing what they're doing for two minutes and have a hard think about this, right? If you'd abducted a child, where in Shoreham might be a good place to hide him? Somewhere no one goes. Maybe somewhere no one even knows about. This whole city is riddled with secret passages going back to smuggling days. Have a quick brainstorm with the team, OK?'

'Yes, chief, right away.'

'We're dealing with someone smart and cunning. He'll choose a smart place.'

'I'm on to it now.'

Grace thanked him and drove on, turning right at the next opportunity. He drove slowly through a network of streets, a mixture of terraced houses and industrial buildings. Looking for a needle in a haystack, he knew. And remembering, as a mantra, the words that his father, who had been a policeman too, had once told him. *No one ever made a greater mistake than the man who did nothing because he could only do a little.*

102

Tyler felt the car rock suddenly. Then he heard a loud boom, like a door slamming. Followed by scrunching footsteps.

He waited until he could not hear them any more, then he threw himself around again, kicking as hard as he could, drumming with his feet and with his right shoulder and his head, breaking out into a sweat, drumming and drumming until he had exhausted himself.

Then he lay still again, thinking.

Why hadn't they found him yet?

Come on, Mum, Mapper! Remember Mapper!

Where was his phone? It had to be in here somewhere. If he could somehow get whatever was covering his mouth off, then he could shout. He rolled himself over on to his stomach, moved his face around, but all he could feel was the fuzz of carpet. There had to be a sharp edge somewhere in here. He wormed forward, raised his head up. Soft new carpet, like rubbing against a brush.

What would his heroes have done? What would Harry Potter have done? Or Alex Rider? Or Amy and Dan Cahill in *The 39 Clues*? They all got out of difficult situations. They'd have known. So what was he missing?

Suddenly he heard a scrunching sound. A vehicle! He started kicking out wildly, as hard as he could again. *Here! In here! In here!*

He heard doors slam. More footsteps.

Fading away.

103

Carly did not hear a word from Sussex Police throughout the flight. Every time a member of the cabin crew walked down the aisle in her direction, she hoped it would be with a message. It was now 8.45 p.m., UK time. Tyler had been missing for almost ten hours.

Feeling sicker by the minute, she had eaten nothing, just sipped a little water, that was all, on the flight-from-hell, squashed in the tiny part of her seat that the sweating fat man next to her, who stank of BO and drank non-stop vodka and Cokes, hadn't overflowed into.

She replayed her decision to go to New York over and over. If she had not gone, she'd have collected Tyler herself from school and he would be safe. He'd be up in his room now, on his computer, alone or with a friend, or doing something with his fossil collection, or practising his cornet.

Fernanda Revere, who could have stopped all this, was dead.

Lou Revere scared her. There was something feral and evil about him. Woman to woman, she might have had a chance with Fernanda Revere, when she was sober. But not with the husband. No chance. Especially not now.

The plane came to a halt. There was a *bing-bong*, followed by the sound of seat belts being unclipped and overhead lockers popping open. People were standing up and she joined them, relieved to get away from the stinking fat blob. She pulled her bag and coat down, then quickly called her mother to say they had landed, and in the hope she had some news. But there was none.

A couple of minutes later she nodded to the two cabin crew standing by the exit, then followed the passengers in front of her out through the plane's door and on to the covered bridge. Instantly she saw, waiting for her, the tall figure of Glenn Branson, accompanied by a younger male officer in uniform, whom she did not recognize, and DS Bella Moy.

'Do you have any news?' Carly blurted.

Branson took her bag for her and steered her to one side, away from the crush of emerging passengers. She looked at him, then at DS Moy, then at the stranger who was in uniform, desperate to read something positive in their eyes, but she could see nothing.

'I'm afraid not yet, Carly,' Bella Moy said. 'Presumably you've heard nothing?'

'I rang all his friends – the parents – before I got on the plane. No one's seen him.'

'They're certain he's not anywhere in their house or their garden or garage?'

'They've all searched thoroughly,' she said forlornly.

'How was the flight?' Glenn Branson asked.

'Horrendous.'

'One positive thing, Carly,' Branson went on, 'is we are fairly sure that Tyler is still within the Brighton and Hove area. We believe he may be in Shoreham or Southwick or Portslade. Do you have any friends or relatives over there that he might go to if he runs away?'

'From his captor, you mean?'

'Yes.'

'I have some friends on Shoreham Beach,' she said. 'But I don't think Tyler knows where they live.'

'We'll get you home as quickly as we can,' Bella said, 'and we'll keep you constantly updated.' Then she gestured to the uniformed officer. 'This is PC Jackson from the Metropolitan Police – we're in his jurisdiction here at Heathrow. He's very kindly going to fast-track you through the Immigration process.'

Carly thanked him.

Fifteen minutes later she was in the back of a police car, heading through the airport tunnel. Glenn Branson drove and Bella Moy sat in the front passenger seat. Moy turned to face her.

'We have a number of questions we need to ask you about Tyler, Carly. Are you happy to talk in the car or would you rather wait until we get you home?'

'Please, now,' Carly said. 'Anything I can give you that might be helpful.'

'You've already given us the names and addresses of his friends. We're looking to see who he's been in contact with, outside of his immediate circle, on his computer and iPhone. They're being examined by the High-Tech Crime Unit.'

'His iPhone?' Carly said. 'You have his phone?'

DS Moy's face froze. She glanced at Branson, then awkwardly back at Carly. 'I'm sorry – didn't anyone tell you?'

'Tell me what?' Carly began shivering and perspiring at the same time. She leaned forward. 'Tell me what?' she said again. 'What do you mean?'

'His iPhone was found in that underground car park – the one you alerted us to on his Friend Mapper.'

'Found? How do you mean *found*?'

Bella Moy hesitated, unsure how much to tell the woman. But she had a right to know the truth.

'There were broken fragments on the ground – then it was discovered in a waste bin in the car park.'

'No,' Carly said, her voice quavering. 'No. Please, no.'

'He may have dropped it, Carly,' Glenn Branson said, trying to put a positive slant on the situation, trying to give her some cause for optimism – to give them all some cause for optimism. 'He might have dropped it while running away. That's our best hope at the moment, that he's hiding somewhere.'

In utter desperation, and shaking with terror, Carly said, 'Please don't tell me you found his phone. Tyler's bright. I thought he was going to keep Friend Mapper on. I thought that would take us to him. I really, really felt that was our best hope.'

She began to sob uncontrollably.

104

By 9.30 p.m. it was dark, the wind had risen and rain was falling. Tooth returned to Shoreham in a Toyota Camry he had rented from Sixt in Boundary Road, Brighton, just a short distance away, using a different ID. He drove around the side of the apartment block and into the pitch-dark parking area at the rear. The space next to the Toyota Yaris was free. He reversed into it, then switched off the engine and lights.

He was in a bad mood. No matter how well you planned things, shit happened. There was always something you hadn't accounted for. On this particular job now, it was tides. It just had not occurred to him. Now in the rucksack he had bought, lying beside him on the passenger seat, he had a tide chart which he'd printed out at an Internet café half an hour ago. He'd study it carefully in a few minutes and get his head around it. Meanwhile he was anxious to move the boy on. The area was crawling with police and it looked as if a massive systematic search was in progress. A quarter of a mile further up the road there was a roadblock, but the only vehicles they seemed interested in were Toyota Yaris saloons.

Too much heat on those vehicles. Too much danger of his being found. The search line still had a while to go before they reached this locality, he worked out, an hour and a half, maybe two hours. He would make sure they didn't find anything.

He climbed out of the car, popped open the boot, then swiftly walked across to the rear of the Yaris.

*

Tyler, clenched up, fighting an urgent need to pee that was getting worse and worse, and craving water for his parched mouth and throat, had heard the sound of a car moving close by, then stopping. He was about to start kicking again when suddenly there was a sharp, metallic *clunk* and the boot opened. He felt a blast of fresh, damp air, but could not see any daylight now, just darkness with an orange streetlighting tinge to it.

Then he saw the dazzling beam of a torch and the shadowy shape of a baseball cap and dark glasses beyond. He was truly scared. If he could just speak, maybe the man would get him some water and something to eat?

Suddenly he felt himself being lifted. He was swung through the air, feeling spots of rain on his face, then dropped, painfully, inside another space that smelled similar, but different. Maybe even newer?

There was a thud and he was entombed once more in pitch darkness. He listened for footsteps but instead heard the car starting up. From the bumping motion, he could tell they were moving.

The car accelerated harshly, sending him rolling backwards and cracking his head painfully on something sharp. He let out a muffled cry of pain. Then the car braked sharply and he tumbled forward a couple of feet.

Whatever he had hit had definitely been sharp. He wormed his way back, as the car accelerated again, then felt with his face, rubbing his nose up against what he thought must be the rear of the boot. Then he found something that was protruding. He didn't know what it was – perhaps the back of one of the rear light housings. He tried to press his mouth up against it and rub, but the car was swaying too much and he was finding it hard to keep steady.

Then he felt the car brake sharply and turn, and keep on turning. He was rolled, helplessly, on his side. There was a massive bump and he cracked his head again on the boot lid, then the car halted, throwing him forward.

*

Tooth looked carefully as he pulled off the side of the road above the harbour, bumping over the kerb and on to the grass, driving far enough away so that the car was almost invisible from the road. The lights of traffic flashed past above him and he could see the glow from the houses across the road, most of them with curtains or blinds drawn.

He halted beside a small, derelict-looking building, the size of a bus shelter, directly opposite the massive edifice of Shoreham Power

Station, across the black water of the harbour. The little building was constructed in brick, with a tiled roof, and had a rusting metal door with a large, rusted padlock on it. It was the padlock he had put on last time he was here, six years ago. Clearly no one had been in, which was good. Not that anyone had any reason to go in there. The place was condemned, highly dangerous, toxic and in imminent danger of collapsing. A large yellow and black sign on the wall displayed an electricity symbol and the words KEEP OUT – DANGER OF DEATH.

In the distance he could hear a helicopter. It had been flying around, on and off, for most of the afternoon and evening. From his rucksack, with his gloved hands, he pulled out a head-mounted flashlight, strapped it around his baseball cap and removed the bolt cutters he had acquired in a hardware store. He switched on the flashlight, then snapped the padlock on the door of the brick building and switched the light off again. He checked the windows of the houses once more before lifting the boy out of the car and carrying him inside the building, along with his rucksack. He pulled the door closed with an echoing clang.

Then he switched on his flashlight once more. Directly in front of him was a short, narrow flight of concrete steps going down, between two brick walls. A pair of tiny red eyes appeared momentarily in the darkness at the bottom of the steps, then darted away.

Tooth put the boy down on his feet, still holding him to stop him falling over.

'You need to take a piss, kid?'

The boy nodded. Tooth helped him and zipped him back up. Then he carried the boy down the steps, brushing past several spider webs. At the bottom was a gridded metal platform, with a handrail, and a whole cluster of pipes, some overhead, some on the walls, most of them bare, exposed metal, rusting badly and covered in what looked like fraying asbestos. It was as silent as a tomb in here.

On the other side of the handrail was a shaft, with a steel ladder, that dropped 190 feet. Tooth looked at the boy, ignoring the pleading in his eyes, then tilted him over the handrail and, shining his flashlight beam down, to enable the boy to see the vertical drop. The boy's eyes bulged in terror.

Tooth pulled a length of blue, high-tensile rope from his rucksack and tied it carefully around the boy's ankles. Then he lowered the boy, who was struggling now, thrashing in terror and making a whining, yammering sound through the duct tape across his mouth, a short distance down the shaft and tied the rope around the guard rail.

'I'll be back in a while, kid,' Tooth said. 'Don't struggle too much. You wouldn't want your ankles coming loose.'

105

Tyler's glasses were falling up his nose. He was scared that at any moment they would drop into the void below. But worse, he could feel the rope slipping, especially down his left ankle. He was swaying and starting to feel giddy and totally disoriented.

Something tiny was crawling over his nose. A cold draught blew on his face, the air dank, musty and carrying the fainter, noxious odour of something rotting.

The rope slipped a little more.

Was the man going to come back?

Where was his phone? Was it in the car? How would anyone find him here without Mapper?

He began to panic, then felt the rope slip further. His glasses fell further, too. He froze, stiffening his legs and feet, pushing them against the bindings to keep them as tight as he could. The creature was climbing over his lips now, tickling his nose. He could feel the rush of blood in his head. Suddenly, something touched his right shoulder.

He screamed, the sound trapped inside him.

Then he realized he had just swung into the side of the shaft.

The walls had looked rough, he thought, in the brief moment he had seen them in the beam of the torch. The edges of the ladder would be rough, or at least sharp. As gently as he could, he tried to swing himself around, swaying, bumping into the shaft again, and again, then painfully against the ladder.

Yes!

If he could rub the bindings around his arms up and down against the rough edge, maybe he could saw through them.

His glasses moved further up his forehead. The insect was now crawling over his eyelid.

The rope slipped further down his ankles.

106

This place had worked well for him last week, Tooth reasoned. It was dark, no one overlooked it and there were no cameras. Aside from the power station, there were only timber warehouses, closed and dark for the night, on the far wharf. And the water was deep.

Someone had replaced the padlock on the chain-link fence. He cut through it with his bolt cutters and pushed the gates open. The southerly wind, which seemed to be rising by the minute and was coming straight off the choppy water of the harbour basin ahead, instantly pushed one gate shut. He opened it again and hauled an old oil drum, lying on its side nearby, in front of it.

Then he jumped into the Yaris and drove it forward on to the quay, passing the skip crammed with rubbish that had been there last week and the old fork-lift truck that had been conveniently left for his use. Not that he would need it now.

He got out of the car and took a careful look around. He could hear the lapping of water, the distant *clack-clack-clack* of yacht rigging in the wind. He could also, in the distance, hear the clatter of a helicopter again. Then, with the aid of his flashlight, he did a final check on the interior of the vehicle, pulling out the ashtray, taking the contents to the water's edge and throwing the butts and melted SIM cards into the dark, choppy water. Satisfied he had left nothing else in the car, he prepared himself by taking several deep breaths.

Then he backed the car up a short distance, opened all the windows and doors and popped the boot lid. He slid back behind the steering wheel and, keeping the driver's door open, he put the car into gear and accelerated hard at the edge of the quay. At the very last minute, he threw himself sideways and rolled as he hit the hard surface. Beyond him he heard a deep splash.

Tooth scrambled to his feet and saw the car floating, submerged up to its sills, pitch-poling backwards and forwards in the chop. He was about to snap on his flashlight, to get a better view, when to his dismay he heard an engine. It sounded as if it was approaching. A boat coming down the basin.

He froze.

Bubbles rose all around the car, making a steady *bloop-bloop-bloop* sound. The car was sinking. The engine compartment was almost underwater. The sound of the engine was getting louder.

Sink. Sink, damn you. Sink!

He could see a light, faint but getting brighter, approaching from the right.

Sink!

Water lapped and bubbled, up to the windshield now.

Sink!

The engine sound was louder now. Powerful twin diesels. The light was getting rapidly brighter.

Sink!

The roof was going under now. It was sinking. The rear window was disappearing. Now the boot.

It was gone.

Moments later, navigation lights on and search lights blazing, a Port Authority launch came into view, with two police officers standing on the deck.

Tooth ducked down behind the skip. The boat carried on past. For an instant, above the throb of its engines and the thrash of its bow wave, he heard the crackle of a two-way radio. But the sound of the vessel was already fading, its lights getting dimmer again.

He breathed out.

107

Tyler heard a loud, metallic *clang*. Then a sound like footsteps. For an instant his hopes rose.

Footsteps getting nearer. Then the smell of cigarette smoke. He heard a familiar voice.

'Enjoying the view, kid?'

*

Tooth switched on the flashlight, untied the rope from the balcony and began lowering the boy further, carefully paying the rope through his gloved hands. He could feel the boy bumping into the sides, then the rope went slack.

Good. The boy had landed on the first of the three rest platforms, spaced at fifty-foot intervals.

With his rucksack on his back and the light on, Tooth began to descend the ladder, using just one hand and taking up the slack of the rope as he went with the other. When he reached the platform, he repeated the procedure, then again, until the boy landed face down on the floor of the shaft. Tooth clambered down the last flight and joined him, then pulled a small lamp from his rucksack, switched it on and set it down.

Ahead was a tunnel that went beneath the harbour. Tooth had discovered it from an archive search during the planning for his previous visit. Before it had been replaced because of its dangerous condition, this tunnel carried the electricity lines from the old power station. The tunnel had been replaced, and decommissioned, at the same time as the new power station had been built and a new tunnel bored.

It was like looking along the insides of a rusted, never-ending steel barrel that faded away into darkness. The tunnel was lined on both sides with large metal asbestos-covered pipes, containing the old cables. The flooring was a rotted-looking wooden walkway, with pools of water along it. Massive livid blotches of rust coated the insides of the riveted plates, and all along were spiky cream-coloured stalactites and stalagmites, like partially melted candles.

But it was something else entirely that Tooth was staring at. The human skull, a short distance along the tunnel, greeting him with its rictus grin. Tooth stared back at it with some satisfaction. The twelve rats he had bought from pet shops around Sussex, then starved for five days, had done a good job.

The Estonian Merchant Navy captain's uniform and his peaked, braided cap had gone, along with all of his flesh and almost all of the sinews and his hair. They'd even had a go at his sea boots. Most of his bones had fallen in on each other, or on to the floor, except for one set of arm bones and an intact skeletal hand, which hung from a metal pipe above him, held in place by a padlocked chain. Tooth hadn't wanted to risk the rats eating through his bindings and allowing the man to escape.

Tooth turned and helped the boy to sit upright, with his back propped against the wall, and a view ahead of him along the tunnel and of the bones and the skull. The boy was blinking and something looked different about him. Then Tooth realized what that was. His glasses were missing. He shone his flashlight around, saw them and replaced them on the boy's face.

The boy stared at him. Then flinched at the skeletal remains, his eyes registering horror and deepening fear as Tooth held the beam on it.

Tooth knelt and ripped the duct tape from the boy's mouth.

'You all right, kid?'

'Not really. Actually, no. I want to go home. I want my mum. I'm so thirsty. Who are you? What do you want?'

'You're very demanding,' Tooth said.

Tyler looked at the sight.

'He doesn't look too healthy to me. What do you think, kid?'

'Male, between fifty and sixty years old. Eastern European.'

Tooth frowned. 'You want to tell me how you know that?'

'I study archaeology and anthropology. Can I have some water now please – and I'm hungry.'

'You're a goddamn smartass, right?'

'I'm just thirsty,' Tyler said. 'Why have you brought me here? Who are you?'

'That guy,' Tooth said, pointing at the skeleton, 'he's been here for six years. No one knows about this place. No one's been here in six years. How would you feel about spending six years down here?'

'I wouldn't feel good about that,' Tyler said.

'I bet you wouldn't. I mean, who would, right?'

Tyler nodded in agreement. This guy seemed a little crazy, he thought. Crazy but maybe OK. Not a lot crazier than some of his teachers.

'What had that man done?'

'He ripped someone off,' Tooth said. 'OK?'

Tyler shrugged. 'OK,' he said, his voice coming out as a parched, frightened croak.

'I'll get you sorted, kid. You have to hang on. You and me, we have a big problem. It's to do with the tides, right?'

Tyler stared at him. Then he stared at the remains, shaking. Was this going to be him in six years?

'Tides?' he said.

The man pulled a folded sheet of printout from his rucksack, then opened it up.

'You understand these things, kid?'

He held the paper in front of Tyler's face, keeping his flashlight trained on it. The boy looked at it, then shot a glance at the man's wristwatch.

'Big ships can't come into this harbour two hours either side of low tide,' Tooth said.

He stared at the boxes, each of which had a time written inside it, below the letters LW or HW. Alongside was written *Predicted heights are in metres above Chart Datum.*

'This is not easy to figure out. Seems like low tide was 11.31 p.m. here, but I'm not sure I've got that right. That would mean ships start coming in and out again after 1.31 a.m.'

'You're not looking at today's date,' Tyler said. 'Today it will be 2.06 a.m. Are you taking me on a boat?'

Tooth did not reply.

108

The phones in MIR-1 had been ringing off the hook ever since the *Child Rescue Alert* had been triggered, and the abduction of Tyler Chase was front-page news in most of the papers, as well as headline news on radio and television. It was coming up to 12.30 a.m. During the nearly fourteen hours since his abduction just about everyone in the nation who didn't live under a rock knew his name and a good many of them had seen his photograph.

The room was as busy now as it was in the middle of the day and the air was thick with the continuous ringing of landline and mobile phones. Roy Grace sat, jacket off, sleeves rolled up, tie slackened, reading through a list that had been emailed over by Detective Investigator Lanigan of the methods of operation of all known currently active contract killers. Not wanting to restrict their search to the US, police forces around Europe had also been contacted and their information was starting to come in.

But nothing matching their man so far.

Or his car.

In view of the frequency with which the suspect appeared to go about changing number plates, Grace had sent out requests to every police force in the UK to stop and search every dark-coloured Yaris, regardless of whether it was grey or not. He wanted to eliminate any possible risk of the suspect slipping through the net, including a mistake being made by someone who might be colour blind.

It was possible the boy was already abroad, despite the watch that had been put on all airports, seaports and the Channel Tunnel. There were private aircraft and private boats that could easily have slipped the net. But he was fairly certain that the Toyota Yaris belonging to Barry Simons was the one Tyler Chase had been driven in from the Regency Square car park. And if that was the case, Grace did not think he had left the Shoreham area.

Checks had been carried out with the Harbour Master, the Port

Authority and the Coast Guard. All vessels that had sailed from Shoreham Harbour today had been accounted for. No cargo ship had passed through the lock after eight o'clock this evening. A few fishing boats had gone out, but that was all.

Suddenly Stacey Horobin came over to him and said, 'Sir, I have a Lynn Sebbage on the phone, from a firm of chartered surveyors called BLB. She's asking to speak to Norman Potting – said she's tried his mobile but he's not picking up. She says she's been working through the night to look for the information he asked her for, urgently, and she thinks she's found it.'

Grace frowned. 'Chartered surveyors?'

'Yes, called BLB.'

'You mean chartered surveyors as in *structural engineers*?'

Horobin nodded. 'Yes, sir, that area.'

'What do they want at this hour of the morning?'

'I don't know.'

'Where is DS Potting?'

'DS Moy says she thinks he may have gone out to get something to eat, sir.'

'OK, let me speak to the woman. Did you say Sebbage?'

'Lynn Sebbage.'

He picked up the phone and moments later she was put through. 'Detective Superintendent Grace,' he said. 'Can I help you?'

'Yes,' she said. She sounded as fresh as if it was the middle of her normal working day. 'I'm a partner in BLB. We're very old-established chartered surveyors in Brighton. We had a visit from Detective Sergeant Potting late this afternoon, regarding the little boy who's been abducted, saying he was looking for places around Shoreham Harbour where someone might be concealed. The Chief Engineer told him that he knew my firm, BLB, has done a lot of work at the harbour over the past century, particularly in the construction of the original coal-fired power station. He said he thought there was a tunnel bored then that's been disused for decades.'

'What kind of a tunnel?' Grace asked.

'Well, I've been hunting through our archives all night – they go back over a hundred years – and I think I've found what he was referring to. It's a tunnel that was built for the old power station, Shoreham B, about seventy years ago, to carry the electricity cables under the harbour, and it was decommissioned when the new power station was built twenty years ago.'

'How would someone other than a harbour worker know about it?'

'Anyone studying the history of the area could find it easily. It's probably on Google if people look hard enough.'

She then explained where the access to it was.

A couple of minutes later, just as he thanked her and hung up, Glenn Branson walked in carrying two steaming mugs.

'Brought you a coffee.'

'Thanks. Want to come and take a ride? We could both do with a quick change of scenery.'

'Where to?'

'Somewhere in Brighton you and I have never been before.'

'Thanks for the offer, boss man, but being a tourist at 1 a.m. doesn't float my boat.'

'Don't worry. We're not going boating – we're going to go underwater.'

'Terrific. This is getting better every second. Scuba-diving?'

'No. Tunnelling.'

'Tunnelling? Now? At this hour? You're not serious?'

Grace stood up. 'Get your coat and a torch.'

'I'm claustrophobic.'

'So am I. We can hold hands.'

109

'What do you think the chances are?' Glenn Branson said, as Grace drove slowly along the road, peering to the left, looking for the building Lynn Sebbage had described. A strong wind buffeted the car and big spots of rain spattered on the windscreen.

'One in a million? One in a billion? One in a trillion that he's in this tunnel?'

'You're not trying to think like the perpetrator,' Grace said.

'Yeah, and that's just as well, coz I'd be hanging you on a meat hook and filming you right now if I did.'

Grace smiled. 'I don't think so. You'd be trying to outsmart us. How many times has he changed number plates? Those cameras he left behind, like giving us two fingers. This is a very smart guy.'

'You sound like you admire him.'

'I do admire him – for his professionalism. Everything else about him I loathe beyond words, but I admire his cunning. If he's holed up anywhere with that kid, it's not going to be some garden shed full of mushrooms. It's going to be somewhere he knows that we haven't thought of. So I don't think we're looking at one in a million. I think we're looking at very good odds and we need to eliminate this place.'

'You could have sent a couple of uniforms along,' Branson said grumpily. 'Or Norman Potting.'

'And spoiled our fun?' Grace said, pulling over on the kerb. 'This looks like it.'

Moments later, in the beam of his torch, Grace saw the broken padlock lying on the ground. He knelt and peered at it closely.

'It's been cut through,' he said.

Then he pulled the door open and led the way down the concrete steps. At the bottom they stepped on to a gridded metal platform with a handrail. A network of old metal pipes spread out all around them.

Branson sniffed. 'Someone's managed to use this place as a toilet,' he said.

Grace peered over the handrail, then shone his torch beam down the vertical shaft.

'Shit,' he said under his breath. It looked a long, long way down. Then he shouted, as loudly as he could, 'POLICE! Is anyone down there?'

His voice echoed. Then he repeated his question again.

Only the echo, falling into silence, came back at them.

The two officers looked at each other.

'Someone's been here,' Glenn Branson said.

'And might still be here,' Grace replied, peering down the shaft again, and then looking at the ladder. 'And I'm sodding terrified of heights.'

'Me too,' Branson said.

'Heights and claustrophobia? Anything you're not scared of?' Grace quizzed him with a grin.

'Not much.'

'Shine the torch for me. I can see a rest platform about fifty feet down. I'll wait for you there.'

'What about Health and Safety?' Branson asked.

Grace tapped his chest. 'You're looking at him. You fall, I'll catch you.'

He climbed over the safety rail, decided he was not going to look down, gripped both sides of the rail, found the first rung and slowly, carefully, began to descend.

It took them several minutes to get to the bottom.

'That was seriously not fun,' Glenn Branson said, and flashed his torch around. The beam struck the tunnel. 'Holy fucking shit!' He was staring at the skeletal remains.

Both men took a few steps towards them.

'Looks like a new cold case to add to your workload, boss,' Branson said.

But Grace wasn't looking at the skull and bones any more. He was looking at a screwed-up ball of paper on the ground. He pulled on a pair of gloves, knelt, picked it up and opened it out. Then he frowned.

'What is it?' Branson said.

Grace held it up. 'A tide chart.'

'Shit! How long do you reckon that's been down here?'

'Not long,' Grace replied. 'It's current. This week's – seven days' tides for Shoreham, starting yesterday.'

'Why would someone want a tide chart?'

'The entrance to the harbour mouth is only six feet deep at low tide. There's not enough draught for big ships two hours either side of low water.'

'You think this is connected with Tyler?'

Grace almost failed to spot the tiny object lying beneath a section of rusted piping. He knelt again and picked it up, carefully, between his gloved forefinger and thumb, then held it up.

'I do now, for sure,' he said. 'A Lucky Strike cigarette.' He pressed the burnt end to his check. 'You know what? That's still warm.'

Pulling on gloves himself, Glenn Branson took the tide chart and studied it for a moment. Then he checked his watch.

'The harbour mouth opens, if that's what they call it, at 2.06 a.m. That's fifty-six minutes' time. Shit! We have to stop any ship from leaving.'

This time, all his fear of heights forgotten, the Detective Sergeant threw himself up the first rungs of the ladder, with Grace inches behind.

110

Tyler, utterly terrified, was whimpering with fear and quaking, yet at the same time he did not dare struggle too much. Choppy, ink-black water splashed at him like some wild, angry creature just inches below his feet. Rain lashed down on him. He was hung by his arms, which were agonizingly outstretched like in a crucifixion.

He had thought he was being thrown into the water but then he had been jerked tight just above it. He kept trying to cry out, but there was tape over his mouth again and all his cries just echoed around and around inside his skull.

He was crying, sobbing, pleading for his mother.

There was a strong stench of seaweed. The blindfold the man had put around his head after he had climbed back up from the tunnel had been taken off only at the last minute before he had been dropped.

Above the sound of the water he heard the *chop-chop-chop* of a helicopter approaching. A dazzling beam of light passed over him, briefly, then darkness again.

Come over here! Come over here! I'm here! Come over here!
Please help me. Please help me. Mum, please help me, please.

111

It wasn't until they reached the top of the ladder that Grace and Branson were able to get any radio or phone signal. Grace immediately called Trevor Barnes, the Silver Commander, who was at his desk in Sussex House.

The two detectives sprinted up the stone steps and out into the fresh wind and rain, sweating profusely, grateful for the cooling air. Above them they heard the clatter of the helicopter swooping low over the harbour basin, the dazzling bright pool of its searchlight illuminating a wide radius of the choppy water.

Moments later Barnes radioed back that he'd checked with the Harbour Master and the only vessel scheduled to leave the harbour, via the large lock, was the dredger the *Arco Dee*. It had already left its berth and was heading along the canal towards the lock.

'I've been on that ship,' Grace shouted at Branson, above the noise of the helicopter and the howling of the wind. 'There's any number of ways he could kill that kid on it.' Then he radioed to the Silver Commander. 'Trevor, get it boarded and searched while it's in the lock.'

For some moments Grace stood still, following the beam of light as it crossed the massive superstructure of Shoreham Power Station. The building had a dog-leg construction, with the first section, which had a flat roof, about sixty feet high, and then the main section about 100 feet high. At the western end was the solitary chimney stack, rising 200 feet into the sky. Suddenly, as the beam traversed it, he thought he saw something move on the flat roof.

Instantly he radioed the Controller. 'Patch me through to Hotel 900.'

Moments later, through a crackling connection, he was speaking to the helicopter spotter. 'Go back round. Light up the power station roof again,' he shouted.

Both detectives waited as the helicopter turned in a wide arc.

The beam struck the chimney first and the ladder that went all the way up it. Then the flat roof of the first section. They could see a figure scurrying across it, then ducking down behind a vent.

'Keep circling,' he instructed. 'There's someone up there!' He turned to Branson. 'I know the quick way there!'

They ran over to the car and jumped in. Grace switched on the blues and twos and raced out into the road.

'Call Silver,' he said. 'Get all available units to the power station.'

A quarter of a mile on he braked hard and swung left, in front of the Port Authority building, then sped down the slip road beside it, until they reached a barrier of tall steel spikes. The sign ahead of them, fixed to the spikes, read:

SHOREHAM PORT AUTHORITY

NO UNAUTHORIZED ACCESS

PUBLIC ROUTE ACROSS LOCKS

Abandoning the car, they ran along the walkway, which was bounded on each side by a high railing. Grace flashed his torch beam ahead of them. To their right now he could see, brightly illuminated by a bank of floodlights on a tower, the harbour's two locks, a small one for fishing boats and yachts, the other, much larger, for tankers, dredgers and container ships.

A long quay separated the locks, in the middle of which was a substantial building housing the control room. On its wall, beneath the windows, was a vertical traffic light, with three red signals showing.

He briefly clocked a warning sign on the entrance gate to this quay, forbidding unauthorized people to enter. The gate had no lock on it, he observed, but his focus was to his left, to the massive superstructure of the power station, partially lit by the helicopter's beam. He ran on, followed by a puffing Branson, stepping over metal slats and then past more red warning lights at the start of the curved walkway over the main lock gates. A sign cautioned against entering when the red lights were flashing and the siren was sounding.

When he reached the join in the middle, between the two halves of the ancient, massive wooden lock gates, he turned and looked at the power station again. What the hell was he doing up there, if it was the suspect? For sure it would be a terrific vantage point, but for what? Did he have the boy up there with him?

They ran on, around the curve of the other half of the lock gates and on to the quay, then sprinted towards the power station. Ahead Grace saw a stack of pallets against the tall spikes of the power station's perimeter fence.

'Wait here,' he said to Branson, then scrambled up the pallets.

Having clambered over the top of the spikes, he dropped down ten feet or so to the other side. He landed with a painful jolt and allowed himself to fall forward, trying to roll to break his fall, but instead hit the ground chest first and lay there winded.

Above, the helicopter clattered, the beam passing momentarily over him, illuminating the steel ladder up the side of the power station superstructure.

He ran to it and began to clamber up, as fast as he could, the wind pulling at him as he climbed higher and higher. This is sodding crazy, he thought. But he climbed on, gripping each rung tightly, clinging to it, the rain lashing him while the wind pulled at him harder and harder, as if it was on a mission to dislodge him. Suddenly he heard a terrible, pitiful crying sound, like a woman in distress, and a huge black shape swooped out of the darkness at him.

He turned his head instinctively and saw the lights of the harbour, and the city beyond, miles beneath him. The wind ripped at him even harder. The black creature was swooping, flapping, crying again. The peregrine falcons, he suddenly remembered, that were in a nesting box on the power station wall – some damned ecological deal that had been made when the place was built.

The bird swooped again.

Great! I've survived twenty years as a copper and now I'm going to be killed by a sodding protected bird.

He clung to the rung, vertigo suddenly hitting him.

Don't let go. Hang on. Hang on. Remember rule one of ladders. Always keep three limbs on and you can't fall off.

With his fourth limb, his right arm, he swiped at the air, not caring at this moment how much damage he did to a protected bird of prey. Then he climbed on, the wind stronger still.

The bird seemed to have taken the hint and vanished back into the night.

Finally, he was at the top. He hauled himself over, on to the asphalt roof, and crawled forward on his knees until he was safely away from the edge. He then stopped and crouched down, trying to get his breath back. His heart felt like it was about to explode as he looked around in the darkness. Moments later he heard the sound of the helicopter and the beam momentarily turned the entire roof, and the wall of the next stage of the superstructure, into daylight.

Then he saw the camera.

It was directly in front of him, on a squat metal tripod, the telephoto lens aimed down.

He looked beyond it, for a brief instant, for the figure he had seen earlier, but there was no sign of the man. As the helicopter beam moved away, he ran to the camera, a complex-looking affair, found the viewfinder and squinted through it.

Oh shit. Oh no. Oh no.

In eerie green night vision, in a tight close-up, he could see Tyler Chase. The boy was suspended across the middle of the lock gates, several feet below the top, his feet inches above the surface of the water. His arms were outstretched, his hands strapped to the left and right gates. A tiny flashing light indicated the camera was running in recording or transmitting mode.

And now to his horror he realized what that tide chart had been all about.

He tried to raise Glenn on his radio but the channel was busy. Frustrated, he tried again. At the third attempt, with the helicopter right overhead, he heard his colleague's voice.

'Glenn!' he shouted. 'Stop the lock gates from opening! For Christ's sake stop them! They're going to kill the boy! They're going to tear him in half!'

The din of the helicopter and wind and the rain, which was now pelting down, was deafening.

'Say that again?' Branson said. 'Can't hear you, boss.'

'STOP THE FUCKING LOCK GATES FROM OPENING!' Grace screamed.

Then a blow on the back of his head sent him crashing to the ground.

He dimly heard a crackle, then a voice from his radio saying, 'Did you say stop the lock gates?'

He tried to stand up, and fell over, sideways. He lay there, feeling like he was going to throw up. Ahead, he saw a figure scramble over the lip of the roof and disappear. In the light beam of the helicopter hovering overhead again, he stared at the camera. In fury he rolled over towards it, into the base of the tripod, and sent it crashing over. He tried to stand again, but his legs gave way. In desperation he hauled himself on to his hands and knees, looking around for his radio, but it had vanished.

He tried to stand again, but this time the wind blew him over. *No, no, no.* He got up again, virtually oblivious to the splitting pain in his head, and staggered across the roof. He grabbed the top rung of the ladder, then made the mistake of looking down.

The whole world spun 360 degrees.

He had to do it. Had to. Had to. Gripping the top ladder posts, he swung his legs over the roof. The wind tried to push him over, backwards.

Don't look down.

He thought for an instant of Cleo. Of their unborn child. Of their life ahead. And of how, in the next few moments, he might plunge to his death. Was this worth it?

Then he thought of the image of the boy, suspended by his arms from the lock gates. Anything that might save his life was worth it.

Half climbing, half sliding, he descended as fast as he could. Looking ahead all the time, never down. He still had his gloves on, he realized, and they protected his hands for a few seconds until the ladder cut through them, burning into his hands as he slid.

Then his feet hit the bottom and he tumbled over on to his back. He scrambled to his feet. Over to his right he could see the light on the bow of the *Arco Dee* dredger slipping steadily past the end of the power station. He saw red lights on the lock ahead, starting to flash.

No. No. No.

He ran to the steel fence and realized, to his frustration, that he was trapped in here. It had been OK coming in, over the pallets, but it wasn't so easy to get back again. There was nothing to give him a leg-up now.

'Glenn!' he screamed, having no idea where his friend might be at this moment. 'Glenn!'

'I'm here, boss!' he shouted back, from – to Grace's immense relief – the other side of the fence.

'Give me a hand out of here!'

Moments later, Glenn was leaning over the top of the fence. Grace grabbed his strong hand and was hoisted up. He scrambled over the top and on to the tarpaulin over the first pallet. As he jumped down on the ground, the front of the dredger was drawing level with them.

'Is anyone at the lock gate?' Grace yelled.

Branson shook his head.

'We have to stop it opening!'

Grace broke into a sprint, with Branson alongside him. As they ran, Grace could hear a cacophony of police sirens approaching. They raced down the quay and reached the entrance to the gate. Red lights were flashing and a klaxon was sounding loudly. As Grace stepped on to the lock walkway, he felt it vibrating. He continued running, the gate juddering harder and harder beneath him. Then he reached the join.

Suddenly the vibration stopped. The gates had paused. He looked down and saw the boy beneath him. The helicopter was right overhead, Tyler clearly illuminated like some grotesque crucifixion figurine, water swirling wildly beneath him. He was about to be torn in half at any second.

'Stop the fucking gates!' Grace screamed at Branson, as he clambered over the top of the gate. He could see one end of the rope, tied around a wooden peg just below the top and frantically pulled at it.

A wild froth of water was building up beneath him. The gates juddered, the gap widening, inch by inch.

*

393

Branson ran on, over to the far side, the gate juddering more and more. He threw himself over the metal plates, pushed open the unlocked gate and then ran towards the control room. As he did so, he suddenly felt something wrap around his legs and he hurtled, face down, to the ground.

*

Roy Grace tugged again at the rope, which was getting tighter by the second. He could hear, above the roar of the helicopter and the wind and the rain and the klaxon, a muffled crying sound. Suddenly, an instant before the gates opened wider, the rope fell free.

The boy dropped down into the water and disappeared with a splash, as the gates parted, one of them swinging steadily away, out of sight to the left.

Grace dived into the mad, thrashing cold water. Bubbles exploded all around him. It was ten times colder than he had imagined. He burst back up to the surface, gulping air. In front of him, towering above him like a skyscraper, he saw the bow of the dredger, less than a couple of hundred yards away. He tried to swim, but the undertow dragged him back down. When he surfaced again, he was choking on vile oily water. He spat it out, then, despite the weight of his clothes, he swam with all his strength across the width of the lock, to the far side, where he saw a rope hanging straight down into the water from the gate.

He grabbed it and pulled, pulled as hard as he could, and after a few moments a deadweight surfaced. He cradled the boy's head in his arms, trying with his wet, slippery hands to pull the tape free from his mouth.

They both went under, then came back up again, Grace coughing and spluttering.

'You're OK! You're OK!' he tried to reassure Tyler.

Then they went under again.

They surfaced again. The dredger seemed to have stopped. They were bathed in a pool of light from the helicopter. The boy was thrashing, in wild panic. Grace struggled, kicking with his feet, trying to get a purchase on the weeds and at the same time hold the boy. He was shivering. He gripped a handful of weed and it held. The boy's head went under. He brought it back up again, then he clung on to the boy and the weed as hard as he could, his hand almost numb with cold.

*

Glenn Branson rolled over and saw a small man running towards the door of the control room. He scrambled to his feet, lunged after him and grabbed him just at he was pulling the door open.

The man turned and punched him in the face, then ran off down the dock.

The wrong way, Branson realized, dazed, but not so badly he couldn't think straight. He stumbled after him, then blocked his path as the man tried to zigzag back past him, forcing him close to the edge of the quay. The man tried a feint, to dodge round him, but Branson grabbed him. The man aimed a punch at his face. Branson, who had trained in self-defence in his former life as a nightclub bouncer, dodged the blow and swung his leg round in a classic kick-boxing manoeuvre, deadening the man's right leg. As he fell, Branson slammed a punch into the man's left kidney. He hadn't realized they were so close to the edge of the dock. The man plunged backwards, over the edge, and vanished under the surface of the maelstrom of water.

The helicopter beam momentarily swept over them. The man had disappeared.

Then he heard a voice shouting, 'Hey! Someone! Glenn! Where the hell are you? Someone get us out of here! Come on! It's sodding freezing!'

112

It was the first really warm day of the year, with the thermometer in Brighton hitting seventy-five degrees, and the beaches of the city, along with its bars and cafés, were crowded. Roy Grace and Cleo returned home after a short walk with Humphrey, mindful of the instructions of the consultant gynaecologist that Cleo was not to do too much exercise.

Then they sat on the roof terrace of her house, Grace drinking a glass of rosé, Cleo with an elderflower cordial and Humphrey gnawing on a chew.

'So what happens next with Carly Chase? Your suspect is presumed drowned in Shoreham Harbour and Tony Revere's mother is dead, right?'

'They're diving and dragging the harbour. But it's pretty murky down there. You can't see anything with underwater lights, so you have to do it all by sonar and feel. And there are some pretty strong currents. A body could get pulled out to sea very quickly.'

'I thought they floated to the surface after a few days?'

'Takes about a week for the internal gases to build up. But if they do surface, say at night, with the tide and wind in the wrong direction, they'll go on out to sea. Then eventually they'll sink again, and when they do, they'll get picked clean by fish and crabs and lobsters.'

'What about Tony Revere's father?'

'I've spoken to Detective Investigator Lanigan in New York. The guy who could be the problem going forward is his wife's brother – the dead boy's uncle, Ricky Giordino. With his father, Sal, locked up in jail for the rest of his life, realistically, it sounds like this guy is the one to watch. Lanigan thinks he's the man who probably hired the killer in the first place. We're going to continue with protection on Carly Chase and her family for a while, but I personally don't think the threat is as severe now.'

Cleo placed Roy's hand on her swollen abdomen and said, 'Bump's busy today.'

He could feel their child moving around.

'Probably because you just ate a chocolate ice cream, right? You said he always becomes energetic when you eat chocolate – and that he's probably going to become a chocaholic.'

'*He?*' she said quizzically.

Grace grinned. 'You're the one who keeps going on about all these old wives' tales, that if your baby's high up, or sticking out a lot, it's going to be a boy.'

She shrugged. 'We could easily find out.'

'Do you want to?' he asked.

'No. Do you? You didn't last time we discussed it.'

'I will love our child just as much whether it is a boy or a girl. I'll love it because it is *our* child.'

'Are you sure, Roy? You wouldn't want it to be a boy, so he could be an action man like my hero, Roy Grace? The claustrophobic who goes down a deep tunnel. The man who's scared of heights who climbs power stations? The crap swimmer who dives into a harbour and saves a boy's life?'

Grace shrugged. 'I'm a copper. Sometimes in my job you can't make choices based on what you're afraid of or not. The day you do is the day you wake up and know you're in the wrong career.'

'You love it, don't you?'

'I didn't love climbing down that ladder into the tunnel. And I was shit scared climbing up on to the power station roof. But at least young Tyler's going to be OK. And to see his mother's face when we took her to him at the Sussex County, where he was being checked over – that was something else. That's why I do this job. I can't think of any other job in the world where you could make a difference like that.'

'I can,' Cleo said, and kissed him on the forehead. 'It doesn't matter what job you do, you'd always make a difference. You're that kind of person. That's why I love you.'

He gave her a sideways look. 'Do you?'

'Yup.' She shrugged and sipped her drink. 'You know, sometimes I wonder about you and Sandy.'

'In what sense?'

'You told me that you tried for several years to have a child, without success, right?'

He nodded.

'If you had succeeded, what would have happened? Would you and I – you know – be together?'

'I've no idea. But I can tell you one thing, I'm glad we are. You're the best thing that ever happened to me in my life. You're my rock.'

'You're mine too.'

She squeezed his hand. 'Let me ask you something. Did Sandy ever call you her *rock*?'

Roy Grace hugged her. After some minutes he said, 'You know what they say about the past being another country?'

Cleo nodded.

'So let's not go there.'

He kissed her.

'Good plan,' she agreed.

113

'The time is 8.30 a.m., Wednesday 12 May,' Roy Grace read from his notes to his team in MIR-1. 'This is an update on *Operation Violin*. To bring you up to speed on the latest regarding the unknown suspect, missing, presumed drowned, this is the start of the fifth day of the search of Shoreham Harbour by the Specialist Search Unit. One development yesterday was the recovery of a Toyota Yaris car from thirty feet of water at Aldrington Basin, close to the location where Ewan Preece was discovered in the white van. The vehicle bears the last known licence plates of the suspect. It is now undergoing intensive forensic examination.'

Duncan Crocker raised a hand. 'Chief, we haven't heard anything from Ford Prison regarding the death of Warren Tulley. Has there been any progress in that enquiry that could shed any light on our suspect?'

Grace turned to Potting. 'Norman, do you have anything for us?'

'I spoke to prison officer Lisa Setterington this afternoon, guv, and to the West Area Major Crime Branch Team, who are investigating. They are preparing to charge their original suspect, Tulley's fellow inmate Lee Rogan.'

Grace thanked him, then went on, 'We are continuing to maintain protection on Carly Chase and her family for the time being. I'm waiting for intelligence from the US which may help us to decide how long this should go on and in what form.'

*

This intelligence came sooner than Grace expected. As he left the briefing, his phone beeped, telling him he had a missed call and voicemail. It was from Detective Investigator Lanigan.

As soon as he got to his office, Grace called him back, mindful that it was the middle of the night in New York.

Lanigan, as ever sounding like he had a mouth full of marbles, answered immediately, seeming wide awake.

'Something strange going on here, Roy,' he said. 'Might be significant to you.'

'What's happened?'

'Well, it's not like I'm shedding any tears, you know. Fernanda Revere's brother, Ricky Giordino – son of Sal Giordino, right?'

'The Mafia capo who's doing a bunch of life sentences?'

'You got him. Well, I think I told you, Ricky's the guy we reckon would have hired the guy who's been causing all your problems, right?'

'You did.'

'Well, I thought you should know, Ricky Giordino was found dead in his apartment a couple of hours ago. Pretty gruesome. Sounds like some kind of a hit. You know – wise guys on wise guys kind of thing. Strapped to his bed with his dick cut off – looks like he bled to death from that. Had it jammed in his mouth and held in place with duct tape. Also looks like whoever did it cut his balls off and took them with him.'

'Before or after he was dead?' Grace asked.

Lanigan laughed. 'Well, with a guy like that, I'd want the best for him, know what I'm saying?'

'Absolutely!'

'So let's hope it was before. Oh – and there's one other thing – this is why I thought you might be interested. The perp left a video camera running at the scene.'

114

Yossarian lay in his usual place, shaded from the midday sun, just inside the permanently open patio doors, dozing. Once a day he got interrupted by the woman who brought him food and changed the water in his bowl. He would eat the food, drink some of the water and then return to his dozing.

He missed his associate. Missed the runs up in the hills and the days out on the boat, when he got to gulp down endless quantities of fresh fish.

But today felt different.

There was a vibe. He felt excited. Every few minutes, after he woke from his doze, he'd pad around the inside of his home, then go outside for a few moments into the hot sunlight, then back to the shade.

He was just dozing off once more when he heard the sound of the front door opening.

It was a different sound from the one the woman made. This was a sound he recognized. His tail began to wag. Then he jumped to his feet and ran to the door, barking excitedly.

His associate was home.

His associate stroked him and made some nice sounds.

'Hey, good to see you, boy. How've you been?'

His associate put his case down and opened it, then took out a small white plastic bag. He walked over to the empty food bowl on the floor, in the shade, near the patio door.

'Bought you a treat!' he said. 'A special delicacy, all the way from New York. How about that?'

Yossarian stared at his associate expectantly. Then he looked down at his bowl. Two small oval shapes dropped into it with a soft *thud, thud*. He wolfed them down, then stared at his associate again, wanting more.

Tooth shook his head. He didn't do quantity.

He did quality.

115

The office of the Yacht-Club Rheindelta was a small white wooden building on the edge of the vast Bodensee. They were taking a week's vacation and she thought it would be fun if they did a dinghy-sailing course together. He had been really keen when she had mooted the idea.

The fit-looking young German manager behind the counter was pleasant and helpful.

'So, do you have any sailing experience?'

She nodded. 'Yes, my – my ex-husband was very keen. We used to sail a bit in England – off the south coast around Brighton. And we did a flotilla sailing holiday in small yachts in Greece once.'

'Good.' He smiled, and started to fill in a form on a clipboard. 'So, first the young man. He is how old, please?'

'He'll be ten, next birthday.'

'Which is when?'

'March, next year.'

The German manager smiled at the boy. 'So you have your father's sailing genes, perhaps?'

'Oh, he has a lot of his father's genes, don't you?' she said, looking at her son.

He shrugged. 'Maybe. I don't know. I've never met him.'

The smile momentarily changed to a frown on the manager's face, then he said, 'OK. So if I may have the young man's full name, please.'

She wrote down *Bruno Lohmann* and handed him the form back.

'Sorry, I need the full name. Does Bruno have a second name, perhaps?'

Sandy smiled apologetically. 'Yes, I'm sorry.'

She turned the form back around and in the space provided in the middle she wrote, *Roy*.

ACKNOWLEDGEMENTS

I try hard to get my facts right in every book. Most of the places named here are real, but just occasionally I've needed to make a street or a house number fictitious. The glorious house in the Hamptons is real, too, and it does have a bowling alley in the basement! But I should point out it is not owned by a crime family, but by the very delightful Jack and June Rivkin, who graciously allowed it to be the model for the Reveres' home in my story.

I owe huge thanks to very many people who so kindly and patiently put up with my endless questions and give me so much of their time. Most of all I owe an incalculable debt to Sussex Police. My first thank-you is to the Chief Constable, Martin Richards, QPM, not just for his kind sanction, but for the very active interest he has taken in my Roy Grace novels and the numerous helpful observations and suggestions he has made.

Roy Grace is inspired by a real-life character, former Detective Chief Superintendent David Gaylor of Sussex CID, my close friend and tireless fountain of wisdom, who helps me to ensure that Roy Grace thinks the way a sharp detective would, and to shape my books in so many ways.

Chief Superintendent Graham Bartlett, Commander of Brighton and Hove Police, has also been immensely helpful on this book, even taking my calls and responding with great creative suggestions while out on training runs for the Brighton Marathon! Chief Inspector Steve Curry and Inspector Jason Tingley have both been hugely helpful in so many ways, too. As have Detective Superintendent Andy Griffiths; DCI Nick Sloan; DCI Trevor Bowles; Senior Support Officer Tony Case; Inspector Gary Medland of Gatwick Police; DI William Warner; Sgt Phil Taylor; Ray Packham and Dave Reed of the High-Tech Crime Unit; Inspector James Biggs; Sgt Mel Doyle; Sgt Paul Wood; PC Tony Omo-toso; PC Ian Upperton and PC Dan Pattenden of the Road Policing Unit; Sgt Lorna Dennison-Wilkins and the team at the Specialist Search

Unit – especially Critch, for his amazing bacon butties! – Chris Heaver; Martin Bloomfield; Sue Heard, Press and PR Officer; and Neil (Nobby) Hall, former Assistant Commissioner of Police for the Turks and Caicos.

Exceptional thanks are due to Colin O'Neill of the Road Collision Unit for helping so much with the details of the tragic fatal accident in the story.

Very special thanks also to the NYPD, to Detective Investigator Patrick Lanigan, Special Investigations Unit, Officer of the District Attorney, and to retired Detective Investigator Dennis Bootle, for their exceptional help and generosity of spirit.

A huge and very special thank-you to Ashley Carter for being the role model for Tyler Chase, and for so enthusiastically helping me on so many aspects of his character, and to his mum, Helene, for allowing me to roam their home.

And as always I owe massive thanks to Sean Didcott at Brighton and Hove Mortuary. Also to Dr Nigel Kirkham, consultant pathologist, Newcastle; Crime Scene Manager Tracy Stocker and Scene of Crime Officer James Gartrell; fingerprint analyst Sam Kennor; forensic archaeologist Lucy Sibun and forensic pathologist Dr Benjamin Swift; Michele Websdale of the UK Border Agency; Sharon Williams, Governor of Ford Prison; and Deputy Governors Lisa Setterington and Jackie Jefcut. And thanks to my terrific researchers, Tracey Connolly and Tara Lester, as well as Nicky Mitchell, and Sian and Richard Laurie for sharing the world and perspectives of pregnancy with me.

Thanks also to Juliet Smith, Chief Magistrate of Brighton and Hove; Michael Beard, Editor, the *Argus*; BA captain Wayne Schofield; Judith Richards and the staff of St Christopher's School; Dave Phillips and Vicky Seal from the South East Coast Ambulance Service; Consultant Obstetrician Des Holden; Les Jones; Rob Kempson; Sheila Catt at Brighton District Probate Registry; Mar Dixon; Danielle Newson; Hans Jürgen Stockerl; Sam Brennan; Mark Tuckwell; and David Crouch of the Press Office Toyota (GB) plc.

Shoreham Harbour, one of my favourite parts of the city, features prominently through the book and I'm immensely grateful to Rodney Lunn, CEO, Chief Engineer Tony Parker and Deputy Chief Engineer Keith Wadey. As someone who, like Roy Grace, is both scared of heights and claustrophobic, I'm also indebted to David Seel, James

Seel and Barry Wade of Rescue and Emergency Medical Services for coaxing me all the way down that 200-foot sheer descent into the tunnel beneath the harbour, and to Keith Carter and Colin Dobson of Scottish Power for giving me such a great tour and information about Shoreham Power Station.

Thanks as ever to Chris Webb of MacService, who has unlimited patience, for ensuring my Mac knows who is the boss . . .

Very big and special thanks to Anna-Lisa Lindeblad, who has again been my tireless and wonderful 'unofficial' editor and commentator throughout the Roy Grace series; to Martin and Jane Diplock, incisive new members of this team; and to Sue Ansell, whose sharp eye for detail has saved me many an embarrassment.

Professionally I have my publishing dream team to thank: the wonderful Carole Blake representing me; my awesome publicists, Tony Mulliken, Sophie Ransom and Claire Richman of Midas PR; and there is simply not enough space to say a proper thank you to everyone in Macmillan, but I must mention my superstar publishing director, Wayne Brookes, and editor, Susan Opie. And massive thanks are due to my wonderful PA, Linda Buckley.

Helen has as ever been tirelessly supportive, and my canine friends continue to keep me sane. The ever-cheerful Coco, lovely Phoebe and totally laid-back Oscar never let me put in too many hours without reminding me it's time for yet another walk . . .

Lastly, thank you, my readers, for the wonderfully enthusiastic support you give me. Keep those emails, tweets and blog posts coming!

Peter James
Sussex, England
scary@pavilion.co.uk
www.peterjames.com
Find and follow me on
http://twitter.com/peterjamesuk